STUDY GUIDE to accompany

Foundations of MODERN BIOLOGY and CHEMISTRY

Compiled and with contributions by

A. Cherif • L. Michel • D. Jedlicka • R. Aron • S. Jenkins • F. Movahedzadeh • J. Siuda

Taken from:

Study Guide with Selected Solutions for Chemistry: An Introduction to General, Organic, and Biological Chemistry, Ninth Edition
by Karen C. Timberlake

Study Guide for Essential Biology, Third Edition
by Neil A. Campbell and Edward J. Zalisko

Study Guide to accompany Biology, Seventh Edition
by Martha R. Taylor

Study Guide to accompany Chemistry for Changing Times, Eleventh Edition
by John W. Hill and Richard Jones

Practice Book for Conceptual Integrated Science
by Paul G. Hewitt, Suzanne Lyons, John Suchocki, and Jennifer Yeh

Study Guide for Microbiology: Alternate Edition with Diseases by Body System
by Robert W. Bauman, Elizabeth Machunis-Masuoka, and Laura Bonazzoli

Student Study Companion, Second Edition
by Colleen Belk

Essential Biology, Third Edition
by Neil A. Campbell, Jane B. Reece, and Eric J. Simon

Custom Publishing

New York Boston San Francisco
London Toronto Sydney Tokyo Singapore Madrid
Mexico City Munich Paris Cape Town Hong Kong Montreal

Cover Art: Courtesy of PhotoDisc/Getty Images

Excerpts taken from:

Study Guide with Selected Solutions for Chemistry: An Introduction to General, Organic, and Biological Chemistry, Ninth Edition
by Karen C. Timberlake
Copyright © 2006 by Pearson Education, Inc.
Published by Prentice Hall
Upper Saddle River, New Jersey 07458

Study Guide to accompany Chemistry for Changing Times, Eleventh Edition
by John W. Hill and Richard Jones
Copyright © 2007 by Pearson Education, Inc.
Published by Prentice Hall

Practice Book for Conceptual Integrated Science
by Paul G. Hewitt, Suzanne Lyons, John Suchocki, and Jennifer Yeh
Copyright © 2007 by Pearson Education, Inc.
Published by Addison-Wesley
Boston, Massachusetts 02116

Study Guide for Microbiology: Alternate Edition with Diseases by Body System
by Robert W. Bauman, Elizabeth Machunis-Masuoka, and Laura Bonazzoli
Copyright © 2006X by Pearson Education, Inc.
Published by Benjamin Cummings

Study Guide for Essential Biology, Third Edition
by Neil A. Campbell and Edward J. Zalisko
Copyright © 2007 by Pearson Education, Inc.
Published by Benjamin Cummings
San Francisco, California 94111

Study Guide to accompany Biology, Seventh Edition
by Martha R. Taylor
Copyright © 2005 by Pearson Education, Inc.
Published by Benjamin Cummings

Student Study Companion, Second Edition
by Colleen Belk
Copyright © 2007 by Pearson Education, Inc.
Published by Benjamin Cummings

Essential Biology, Third Edition
by Neil A. Campbell, Jane B. Reece, and Eric J. Simon
Copyright © 2007 by Pearson Education, Inc.
Published by Benjamin Cummings

Printed in the United States of America

10 9 8 7 6 5 4 3 2 1

2008460132

KW

Pearson Custom Publishing
is a division of

www.pearsonhighered.com

ISBN 10: 0-558-06500-7
ISBN 13: 978-0-558-06500-3

Brief Contents

Preface

Welcome to the ***study guide*** that accompanies your textbook, ***Foundation of Modern Biology and Chemistry***. The text, which integrates biology and chemistry, is designed to help you develop the strong foundation in biology and chemistry required to prepare you for a professional career and to become an informed and scientifically literate citizen. Your study guide is designed to help you successfully learn and master the materials in your textbook and to demonstrate your understanding of those materials by applying your knowledge in various situations.

Your study guide includes **Ten Tips for Studying Chemistry and Biology**, prepared by professor Edward J. Zalisko from Blackburn College. These tips for successfully mastering chemistry and biology are based on Zalisko's years of observing his own students and also on related study skills literature. We strongly urge you to carefully read these tips and integrate them into your study practices; they will help you to successfully study and master both the contents of this course and other courses that you take by helping you learn what to study, when and how to study, how to know what you already know, and how to know when you have really completed the study process.

First, let's take a look at Zalisko's Ten Tips. Once we have done that, we will look at your study guide's components and discuss how they can help improve your mastery of the material covered in this course.

Ten Tips for Studying Chemistry and Biology*

There are many subjects and many ways to study. These are tips that have proven successful for many biology students. Try them, refine them, and tailor them to your specific needs.

1. Read your textbook assignments before listening to lectures on the same material.

Your comprehension of the material and the quality of your notes are greatly improved if you read ahead. Think about it—if you have read ahead, the lecture material will seem familiar, your notes will make more sense, and you will need to take fewer notes because you know what is included in the textbook. Research reveals that reading ahead is one of the most important ways to improve a student's comprehension and course grades.

**Zalisko, Edward J. (2007). Study Guide for Campbell • Reece • Simon's Essential Biology (3th). San Francisco: Pearson – Benjamin Cummings.*

2. Study on a regular schedule.

Waiting until the last minute to study usually produces disappointing results. One bad grade can really pull down an average of many good grades. Students who play sports, play an instrument, or have participated in a play all know about the need for regular practice. We all know that daily practice is required to perform well. The same is true in the classroom.

- Start studying when the course begins. Don't wait until a week before an exam.
- Establish good study habits early. Don't wait until you've received poor grades.
- Know that a little bit of studying over a long period of time is much better than the same amount of studying over a short period of time. An hour a day for 15 days is many times better than 15 hours at one time (cramming).
- You can spend less time than cramming and get better grades!

3. **Take frequent and short study breaks.**

Many times when we study, our minds drift as we listen to someone in the hallway, a sound outside, or get distracted by people around us. There are two main methods to address this problem.

- First, study in short bursts of 20–30 minutes each. Then take a 5–10 minute break to rest your mind. After the break, settle back in and focus intensely on your work. Repeat as necessary!
- Second, try to study in ways that are more interactive. The additional tips below describe a highly successful interactive way to study.

4. **Identify all of the material that is addressed by the exam. Know what you need to know.**

- After the first day of class, start identifying material for the first exam.
- Use your course syllabus to help you determine this material.
- If you are still unclear, talk to your instructor.

5. **Try to write many questions that address all of the information for the exam.**

- Write questions that can be answered with short answers, 5–20 words or so.
- Many students like to use 3 × 5 cards, with a question on the front and the answer on the back.
- Consider using some of the questions from the study guide.
- Begin with definitions and short lists from the material you need to study.
- Write these questions after every lecture, keeping up with the material.
- Writing the questions checks your understanding of the material. Use this opportunity to clear up confusion.

6. **Quiz yourself every day or so on all of the questions you have created.**

- As you try to answer the questions, create a pile of cards with questions you got correct and a pile for those questions that you missed.
- After quizzing yourself over all the questions, return to the pile of questions that you missed.
- As you quiz yourself over the questions you missed, again create a pile of those you got correct and those questions you have now missed twice.
- Look at the questions that you have missed twice. Use the Web/CD activities and your textbook to review this material again. Try to figure out ways to remember this difficult information.
- With every new lecture, add new questions to the list of questions you have already created.

7. **Stop studying when you have correctly answered every question.**

- Finally, a way to study that builds confidence, takes less time, and has a clear end!
- As you continue to quiz yourself, the questions will seem easier and you should feel more confident.
- Remember to keep up with your writing and quizzing. This process doesn't work well unless done regularly.

8. **Use short 10–30 minute periods of your day to quiz yourself.**

- Students that manage their time well will use the short periods before, between, and after classes to review.
- The result is more free time.

9. **Study during the times of the day when you are most alert.**

- Many students study in the evenings, when their mind and/or body is tired.
- Find times in your day when you are most alert and make these your study times.
- Use times when you tend to get sleepy for other activities (for many of us, this is early afternoon).

10. Use the night before a test to quickly review. Then get plenty of sleep.

- These techniques build confidence in your knowledge of the course material.
- Many students need only a quick review of their stack of note cards the night before the test. This might take an hour or so.
- Then get plenty of sleep. A well-rested mind always functions better.
- Review the questions that you missed on the exam and see if the information was in your note cards. Try to improve your study methods based upon the reasons for missing these questions.

**Zalisko, Edward J. (2007). Study Guide for Campbell • Reece • Simon's Essential Biology (3th). San Francisco: Pearson – Benjamin Cummings.*

Using Your Study Guide

The purpose of your study guide is to help you organize, review, and test your understanding of the information presented in ***Foundation of Modern Biology and Chemistry***.

Each study guide chapter corresponds to a text chapter of the same number, and most of the study guide chapters include common components, described below in the sequence that they typically appear. However, from chapter to chapter you will find that there is some variation in both the components and their sequence, depending on what we thought would best help you master the material in the chapter.

Please take a few minutes to review how the various study guide components can help you master the textbook information.

Study Goals

Study Goals are the outcomes you should master by the time you finish a given chapter.

Chapter Review

The chapter review is a quick overview of the key chapter concepts and content.

Concept Map

Most of the chapters in this study guide include a well developed concept map which diagrams the relationships among various concepts. The concept maps enhance meaningful learning by harnessing the power of your sight to view and understand complex information at-a-glance. They are intended to help you visualize the relationships among different ideas and concepts and show how they are organized and related to each other.

Chapter Concept Review

The Chapter review section provides a very brief summary, covering concepts you have learned. It is a reinforcement tool and is intended to help you remember key points.

Think About It and Learning Exercise

The "Think About It and Learning Exercise" includes short essay questions and other types of questions to help you reinforce your learning.

Chapter Check List and Practice Test

Chapter Check Lists help you to make sure that you have accomplished the learning goals for that chapter. In essence, they help you get ready to take the chapter practice test.

The Chapter Practice Test is designed to comprehensively test your understanding of a chapter's learning materials. This component is included in every chemistry chapter.

Organizing Tables*

These tables provide the framework for organizing complex information presented in the textbook. They help you organize the information for easier review.

Content Quiz

This is the largest section of each chapter. Some students use these questions to develop their note card questions. Others prefer to use it in its existing format. The answers to the content quiz are located in the back of the study guide. The content quiz includes the following types of questions:

- *Matching*—Most chapters have at least one set of matching questions, which include long lists of terms or names.
- *Multiple Choice*—These are generally short questions with one correct answer. Consider using the correct statements in these questions for note card questions.
- *Correctable True/False*—These true/false statements have underlined words that are to be corrected if the statement is false. These corrected statements also make good material for note card questions.

- *Fill-in-the-Blank*—These questions check your knowledge of definitions. They also make excellent note card questions.
- *Figure Quiz*—These questions address the information presented in the textbook figures. You will need to refer to the figures in your textbook to answer them.
- *Analogy Questions*—These questions ask you to identify relationships that are analogous to something in biology. For example, the shape of a DNA molecule is most like the shape of a spiral staircase.

Word Roots*

Present in selected chapters, the Word Root lists present the meaning of word roots that exist in and form many key terms. If you Learn the meaning of word roots, it helps you guess the meaning of new terms. For example, you might know that "milli" means one thousandth and "centi" means one hundredth because you know that a millimeter is one thousandth of a meter and a centimeter is one hundredth of a meter. Therefore, you might guess that a millipede has more legs than a centipede!

Key Terms

These lists take two forms: (1) in some chapters they include all the boldfaced terms and phrases; and (2) in other chapters, they are a matching exercises that require you to match terms with the correct statements.

Crossword Puzzle*

Crossword puzzle consists of the key terms and key phrases from the chapter. This is a fun way to review your knowledge of these definitions. The crossword answers are also listed at the back of the study guide.

Answers for Selected Questions in Your Textbook

Answers to selected questions from your textbook are available in your study guide—you will find them at the end of the study guide in the study guide answer appendix. The answers are organized by chapter along with the study guide answers and are the final item in each chapter's answers.

My Chemistry & Biology Portal

My Chemistry & Biology Portal

Your textbook *Foundation of Modern Biology and Chemistry is supported by a website that features in-depth resources* that complement the content of the course. My Chemistry & Biology Portal is a very rich Web-support system that contains numerous animations and other interactive multimedia tools that help explain chemistry's and biology's toughest topics. We have referenced *My Chemistry & Biology Portal in your text and at appropriate locations throughout your study guide. My Chemistry & Biology Portal can be accessed at http://www.pearsoncustom.com/devry/mycbp*

In Conclusion

We designed this study guide to help you master the content in your textbook, ***Foundation of Modern Biology and Chemistry***. We hope you find it helpful and wish you every success in the course. In addition, we urge you to again take a few minutes to study the ***Ten Tips for Studying Chemistry and Biology***, prepared by Professor Edward J. Zalisko to learn how those tips can also help you improve your performance and master the content in ***Foundations of Biology and Chemistry***.

Prepared and Edited by

Abour H. Cherif, Ph.D.
Robert D. Aron, Ph.D.

January 2009

Unit 1

Science as a Way of Knowing

Chapter 1: Can Science Cure the Common Cold? Introduction to the Scientific Method

1 Can Science Cure the Common Cold? Introduction to the Scientific Method

Another cold! What can I do?

LOOKING AHEAD

The application of reason that we call science can only be effective when directed toward objective observations (that do not change from one observer to another). As George H Kieffer, (1985) has argued, for a proposal to be called "scientific": 1) it must involve natural occurrences; 2) it must be testable, by agreed upon standards, so that it can be conclusively proven *WRONG* (!); and 3) it must be subject to revision or dimissal based on the outcomes of such tests, or the acquisition of new, objective observations.

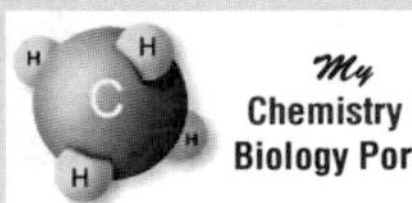

http://www.pearsoncustom.com/devry/mycbp

Study Goals

The Process of Science
- Describe the characteristics of a scientific hypothesis.

The Logic of Hypothesis Testing
- Describe the process of deductive reasoning and the role of prediction in hypothesis testing.
- Explain why a hypothesis test that does not falsify a hypothesis also does not prove that hypothesis.

The Experimental Method
- Know that some scientific hypotheses can be tested via experiments and others are tested via observations of the natural world.

Controlled Experiments
- Explain the role of controls in experiments.
- Be able to design a simple controlled experiment when provided with a testable hypothesis.
- Describe how random assignment of individuals to experimental and control groups and how placebos help to eliminate alternative hypotheses for an experimental result.

Minimizing Bias in Experimental Design
- Define "double-blind" when applied to experimental design and explain how double-blind experiments minimize the effects of bias on experimental results.

Using Correlation to Test Hypotheses
- Be able to interpret a graph that describes a correlation between two factors.
- Understand the limitations of hypotheses tests that rely on correlations.

Understanding Statistics
What Statistics Can Tell Us
Statistical Significance
Factors Influencing Statistical Significance
What Statistical Tests Cannot Tell Us
- Describe how sampling error can affect experimental results and the role of statistical tests in identifying these effects on any study.
- Illustrate the effect of sample size and treatment effect on the likelihood of statistical significance.
- Give two reasons why a statistically significant experimental result does not represent the "last word" on the status of any hypothesis.

Evaluating Science Information
- Distinguish between primary and secondary sources.

Information from Anecdotes
- Explain why anecdotes and testimonials are not at all equivalent to hypothesis tests.

Science in the News
- Be able to critically evaluate a news story about science or health.

Understanding Science from Secondary Sources
- Explain how to assess the objectivity of news reports about scientific research.

Chapter Review

Dr. Ross & the Scientific Method of Inquiry

1.1 The Process of Science
The Logic of Hypothesis Testing
The Experimental Method
Controlled Experiments
Minimizing Bias in Experimental Design
Using Correlation to Test Hypotheses
Understanding Statistics

1.2 Evaluating Scientific Information
Information from Anecdotes
Science in the News
Understanding Science from Secondary Sources

1.3 Is There a Cure for the Common Cold?

1.4 Science as a Way of Knowing: Chemistry and Biology

Summary

Section 1.1 The Process of Science

- Science is a process of testing **hypotheses**, which are ideas about how the natural world works. Scientific hypotheses must be **testable** and **falsifiable (Figure 1.1)**.
- Hypotheses are often generated as a result of **inductive reasoning**, in which scientists infer a general principle from the observation of a number of specific events. They are tested via the process of **deductive reasoning**, which allows researchers to make **predictions** about the outcomes of a test or action **(Figure 1.2)**.
- It is not possible to prove hypotheses to be absolutely true. However, well-designed scientific experiments can allow researchers to strongly infer that their hypothesis is correct.
- A **scientific theory** is an explanation for a set of related **observations** based on well-supported hypotheses from a number of different, independent, lines of research.
- Controlled **experiments** to test a hypothesis about the effect of experimental treatments are performed by comparing an experimental group with a control group, both of which are composed of **randomly assigned** individuals **(Figure 1.5). Controls** are individuals who are treated identically to the experimental group except that they receive a **placebo** in place of the experimental treatment.
- **Bias** in scientific results can be minimized with **double-blind** experiments that keep subjects and data collectors unaware of which individuals belong in the control or experimental group **(Figure 1.6)**.
- In situations where performing controlled experiments on humans is considered unethical, scientists sometimes employ **model organisms** such as other mammals **(Figure 1.7)**.
- Some hypotheses can be tested by using a correlational approach, which looks for associations between two factors **(Figure 1.8)**. However, although a **correlation** can show a relationship between two factors, it does not eliminate all **alternative hypotheses (Figure 1.9)**.
- Statistics help scientists evaluate the results of their experiments, which are called **data**, by determining if those results appear to reflect the true effect of an experimental treatment on a sample of a population. Statistics can then be used to extend the results from the **sample** to the entire population.
- A **statistically significant** result is one that is very unlikely to be due to chance differences between the experimental and control group **(Figure 1.11)**. A **statistical test** indicates the role that chance plays in the experimental results; this is called **sampling error**.
- Even when an experimental result is highly significant, hypotheses are tested multiple times before scientists come to a consensus on the true effect of a treatment.

Section 1.2 Evaluating Scientific Information

- **Primary sources** of information are experimental results that are reviewed by other scientists before being published in professional journals (**Figure 1.12**).
- Most people get their scientific information from **secondary sources** such as the news media. Being able to evaluate science from these sources is an important skill (**Table 1.1**).
- **Anecdotal evidence** is an unreliable means of evaluating information, and media sources are of variable quality-distinguishing between news stories and advertisements is important when evaluating the reliability of information. The Internet is a rich source of information, but users should look for clues to gauge a particular web site's credibility.
- Stories about science should be carefully evaluated for information about the actual study performed, the universality of the claims made by the researchers, and other studies on the same subject. Conflicting or confusing stories about scientific information are sometimes a reflection of controversy within the scientific field itself.

Section 1.3 Is There a Cure for the Common Cold?

- The common cold afflicts billions of people each year in the United States alone, and much effort has been focused on finding effective protection against the viruses that cause it (**Figure 1.3**).
- Studies have shown that good personal hygiene, and in particular, effective hand-washing procedures, are the best way to prevent a cold.
- Other studies have shown a correlation between psychological stress and cold susceptibility. Vitamin C intake, exercise, and exposure to cold temperatures appear to have no effect on cold susceptibility, although vitamin C, echinacea, and zinc lozenges may help reduce symptoms once infection has occurred.

Section 1.4 Science as a Way of Knowing: Chemistry and Biology

The Antarctic research team headed by James McClintock, professor of biology at the University of Alabama at Birmingham, and Bill Baker, professor of chemistry at the University of South Florida, was studying the toxic chemicals Antarctic marine organisms secrete to defend themselves against predators. McClintock and Baker observed an unusual relationship between two animal species, a sea butterfly and an amphipod—an observation that led to a question, a scientific hypothesis, a prediction, tests concerning the chemicals involved in the relationship, and finally, a conclusion. The research generally proceeded according to the steps of the classic scientific method.

Practice Test for Chapter 1

Section 1.1 The Process of Science

1. Which of the following hypotheses is NOT testable?
A. Men who belong to fraternities have more dates than men who do not belong to fraternities.
B. Allergies are an overreaction of the immune system to foreign chemicals.
C. People who wear copper bracelets have greater relief from arthritis than people who do not wear copper bracelets.
D. Drinking excess amounts of alcohol impairs learning ability.
E. Evolution is a result of the intervention of God in the development of organisms.

2. Susan observes that vegetarians in her dorm experience fewer colds than nonvegetarians. Which of the following statements would be the best prediction for a test of this hypothesis?
A. If vegetarians eat meat, then they will become ill.
B. If a person is a vegetarian, then he or she will experience fewer colds than a nonvegetarian.
C. Eating meat causes colds.
D. People who have fewer colds are most likely vegetarians.
E. If college students take vitamin C, then they will avoid colds.

3. Which of the following hypotheses would NOT be directly testable using experiments?
   A. Artificial sweeteners can cause bladder cancer.
   B. Vitamin E supplements can extend life span.
   C. Athletes are more aggressive than non-athletes.
   D. Mammals appeared in the living world before the dinosaurs became extinct.

4. Li is studying the effects of a potential anticancer drug on cancer cells. The drug is designed to kill cancerous cells after a day of treatment. What would be the best control to use in her experiments?
   A. Normal cells exposed to the same solution in which the drug is dissolved, minus the drug itself
   B. Cancer cells exposed to the same solution in which the drug is dissolved, minus the drug itself
   C. Normal cells exposed to the anticancer drug for a day
   D. Cancer cells treated with the anticancer drug but exposed for a shorter time than the experimental group of cells
   E. Cancer cells not treated with anything

5. Dr. Patel wants to test his hypothesis that consumption of glucosamine sulfate reduces joint pain. How can he reduce the likelihood than an alternative hypothesis can explain his experimental result?
   A. He asks for volunteers among the hospital staff and chooses the control group by asking every-one to draw from a deck of numbered cards.
   B. He solicits ten volunteers from the hospital staff and asks which individuals want to be in the control group.
   C. He emails his colleagues in the hospital and chooses the first 15 volunteers for his experimental group.
   D. He selects older individuals from the pool of volunteers since they experience more joint pain.
   E. The women who volunteer to participate in the study are assigned to the control group, and the men who volunteer are placed in the experimental group.

6. Which of the following situations could bias the results of an experiment?
   A. Carol takes a pill each day as part of a drug study; she has no idea what the pill contains or what it is expected to do.
   B. Julie is a lab technician hired to conduct surveys for her supervisor; she is not told what the studies are designed to test.
   C. Ann agrees to participate in a psychology study for her class, but has no prior knowledge of what she will be asked in the provided survey.
   D. George is a statistician who collects information from researchers' surveys and compiles the data. Each survey is coded so he doesn't know what the survey is testing.
   E. Fred knows that he is participating in a weight loss study and guesses that he is in the control group.

7. In a study of random volunteers who answered a newspaper ad for a cold remedy study, there was a correlation between the use of the remedy and a reduction in the duration of a cold. Why would this result alone not be enough to demonstrate that the cold remedy is effective?
   A. The study should include members of different ethnicities, age, and gender to ensure uniform results.
   B. Statistics cannot be used in correlation studies, so the results have no significance.
   C. Only double-blind, controlled experiments can provide supportive data for scientific hypotheses.
   D. Correlation studies use controlled experiments that may not apply to all people.
   E. There might be differences among the volunteers that provide alternative hypotheses explaining the duration of their colds.

8. What experimental result would lead a scientist to reject the hypothesis that a certain nutritional supplement can increase a person's mental activity level?
   A. There will be a significant change in the experimental group compared to the control group.
   B. The control group will have a significantly lower response to the nutritional supplement compared to the experimental group.

C. There will be no statistically significant change in the control group's response to the nutritional supplement.
D. There will be no significant difference between the group that takes the nutritional supplement and those who take a placebo.

9. A biotech company publishes results that indicate a large difference in recovery time from cancer in patients that take its new drug. The studies were conducted on a small group of cancer patients. Assuming the hypothesis is true, what would be the most likely conclusion someone would draw from this report?
A. The results are very unlikely to be statistically significant.
B. The results are very likely to be statistically significant.
C. The results are likely to be statistically significant.
D. The results are unlikely to be statistically significant.

10. True or false. The statement "Acid rain causes declines in Adirondack fish populations" is an example of a scientific hypothesis.

11. Statistics are an important tool in scientific research because they:
A. help scientists distinguish between results that are not consistent with their hypothesis and those that deviate just by chance.
B. allow scientists to use math to prove their hypotheses are correct.
C. help scientists choose between scientific theories that are correct and those that are incorrect.
D. help scientists differentiate between a hypothesis and a theory.

12. Which of the following statements best describes a double-blind experiment?
A. The researcher does not tell the subjects whether they are in the control or experimental groups.
B. The researcher does not know if the subjects are in the control or experimental groups.
C. Neither the research subjects nor the researchers know who is in the control and experimental groups.
D. The research subjects do not know who is performing the measurements for their experiment.

13. True or false. George determines that long-distance runners appear to have fewer colds, and this observation proves his hypothesis that running prevents colds.

14. True or false. In an experiment to test the hypothesis that Ginkgo biloba pills improve memory skills, the control group would take no pills, while the experimental group would take Ginkgo biloba pills.

15. True or false. Dr. Giorno tries to reduce the possibility of alternative hypotheses for the results of his study by picking the volunteers for the two experimental groups alphabetically by first name.

16. True or false. Correlational studies that limit the volunteer pool to one age group, gender, or occupation can reduce the possibility of alternative hypotheses.

17. True or false. Statistical tests allow scientists to determine if uncontrolled variables influence experimental results.

18. True or false. A large sample size decreases the likelihood that an experimental result will be significant.

19. True or false. If a drug is tested for harmful side effects and the results show no statistically significant side effects in the study, then it is definitely safe to use this drug.

Section 1.2 Evaluating Scientific Information

20. Which of the following situations is NOT equivalent to a hypothesis test?
A. Jeanne drinks an herbal tea that her brother insists can cure her of allergies because it worked for him.
B. Patty treats similar species of fish in one aquarium with normal water and in another aquarium with slightly saltier water to see how the fish survive under different conditions.

C. Henry feeds niger seeds to the control birds and corn kernels to the experimental birds to determine their food preference.
D. Justin rubs ointment A on his left hand and ointment B on his right hand to determine if either treatment will help his chapped hands.

21. Which of the following examples would be considered a primary scientific source?
A. The news of new gene therapy clinical trials is posted on a company's Web site.
B. Students in Dr. Parker's lab publish their research results in the college newsletter.
C. Yvonne publishes part of her master's thesis research in a major scientific journal after two months of peer review and revision.
D. A scientist who develops a new vaccine for influenza appears on television to discuss her work.
E. A talk show host interviews a famous cancer physician about his latest findings on chemotherapy for colon cancer.

22. True or false. Any scientific information that appears in a written format is considered a primary source.

23. A celebrity promotes a product by saying, "It worked for me." This information is an example of a(n):
A. anecdote
B. primary source
C. unbiased source of information
D. peer-reviewed claim

24. Which of the following news stories from a media source contains scientific findings with the least credibility?
A. A worldwide consortium of academic scientists funded by several governments publishes the sequence of the human genome.
B. A large number of scientists, including the majority of living Nobel laureates, publishes a statement calling for action on global warming, citing concerns about the Earth's future environment.
C. A biotech company publishes its findings on the beneficial effects of a cholesterol-lowering drug in the Journal of the American Medical Association.
D. A biologist promotes a prescription drug that is produced by a company of which he is an employee.

Section 1.4 Science as a Way of Knowing: Chemistry and Biology

25. We each need a knowledge filter to tell the difference between what is true and what only pretends to be true. The best knowledge filter ever invented for explaining the physical world is:
A. Philosophy.
B. Science.
C. Religion.
D. All of the above.
E. None of the above.

26. An interdisciplinary scientific research project, called the Chemical Ecology of Antarctic Marine Organisms, demonstrates how scientists from a wide variety of backgrounds can work together on a science project and how the scientific method works. The project was initiated in 1988 by:
A. James McClintock.
B. Bill Baker.
C. Peter Agre.
D. Eric Lander.

27. True or False. McClintock and Baker observed an unusual relationship between two animal species, a sea butterfly and an amphipod—a relationship that led to a question, a scientific hypothesis, a prediction, tests concerning the chemicals involved in the relationship, and finally, a conclusion. The research generally proceeded according to the classic steps of the scientific method.

28. True or False. The amphipod, Hyperiella dilatata, is a brightly-colored shell-less snail with wing like extensions used in swimming; and the sea butterfly, Clione Antarctica, resembles a small shrimp.

29. McClintock and Baker observed a large percentage of amphipods carrying sea butterflies on their backs, with the sea butterflies held tightly by the legs of the amphipods. Any amphipod that lost its sea butterfly would quickly:
A. Seek another—the amphipods were actively abducting the sea butterflies!
B. Die—the amphipods cannot live without the butterflies!
C. Change its life style—the amphipods have considerable ability to adapt to new environments.

30. True or False. McClintock and Baker noted that amphipods carrying butterflies were slowed considerably, making the amphipods more vulnerable to predators and less adept at catching prey. They therefore asked, "Why did amphipods abduct sea butterflies?"

31. True or False. Given their experience with the chemical defense systems of various sea organisms, the research team hypothesized that amphipods carry sea butterflies because they produce a chemical that deters the amphipod's predator or predators.

32. All scientific tests need to minimize the number of possible conclusions. Often this is done by running an experimental test along with a control test. Ideally, the experimental test and the control test should differ by _______________. Any differences in results can then be attributed to how the experimental test differed from the control test.
A. Several variables
B. Only one variable
C. The length of the time of the tests
D. All of the above

33. True or False. To confirm that the deterrent was chemical and not physical, the researchers made one set of food pellets containing both fish meal and sea butterfly extract (the experimental pellets). For their control test, they made a physically identical set containing only fish meal (the control pellets). The predator fish readily ate the control pellets, but not the experimental ones. These results strongly supported the chemical hypothesis.

34. True or False. Only after obtaining consistent results can a scientist draw a conclusion. In this case, McClintock and Baker were able to conclude that amphipods abduct sea butterflies in order to use the sea butterflies' secretion of pteroenone as a defense against predator fish.

35. True or False. Pteroenone is a molecule produced by sea butterflies as a chemical deterrent against predators. Its name is derived from *ptero-*, which means "winged" (for the sea butterfly), and *-enone*, which describes information about the chemical structure.

36. True or False. The graceful shrimp-like amphipod is a species of snail that does not have a shell. The Antarctic sea butterfly attaches a sea butterfly to its back even though doing so limits the amphipod's mobility.

Key Terms

alternative hypotheses Factors other than the tested hypothesis that may explain observations.
anecdotal evidence Information based on one person's personal experience.
bias Influence of research participants' opinions on experimental results.
control Subject for an experiment who is similar to experimental subject except is not exposed to the experimental treatment. Used as baseline values for comparison.
correlations Describes a relationship between two factors.
data Information collected by scientists during hypothesis testing.
deductive reasoning Making a prediction about the outcome of a test; "if ... then" statements.
double blind Experimental design protocol when both research subjects and scientists performing the measurements are unaware of either the experimental hypothesis or who is in the control or experimental group.
experiments Contrived situations designed to test specific hypotheses.
falsifiable Able to be proved false.
hypotheses Tentative explanation for an observation that requires testing to validate.
inductive reasoning A logical process that argues from specific instances to a general conclusion.
model organisms Nonhuman organisms used in the Human Genome Project that are easy to manipulate in genetic studies and help scientists understand human genes because they share genes with humans.
objective Without bias.
observations Measurements of nature.
placebos Sham treatments in experiments.
prediction Result expected from a particular test of a hypothesis in the hypothesis were true.
primary sources Articles written by researchers and reviewed by the scientific community.
random assignment Placing individuals into experimental and control groups randomly to eliminate systematic differences between the groups.
sample Small subgroup of a population used in an experimental test.
sampling error Effect of chance on experimental results.
scientific theory Body of scientifically accepted general principles that explain natural phenomena.
secondary sources Books, news media, and advertisements as sources of scientific information.
statistical tests Tests that help scientists evaluate whether the results of a single experiment demonstrate the effect of treatment.
statistically significant Low probability that experimental groups differ simply by chance.
statistics Specialized branch of mathematics used in the evaluation of experimental data.
strong inference A strong statement about the truth of a given hypothesis possible when an experimental protocol greatly minimizes the number of alternative hypotheses that can explain a result.
testable Possible to evaluate through observations of the measurable universe.
theory of evolution Theory that all organisms on earth today are descendants of a single ancestor that arose in the distant past.

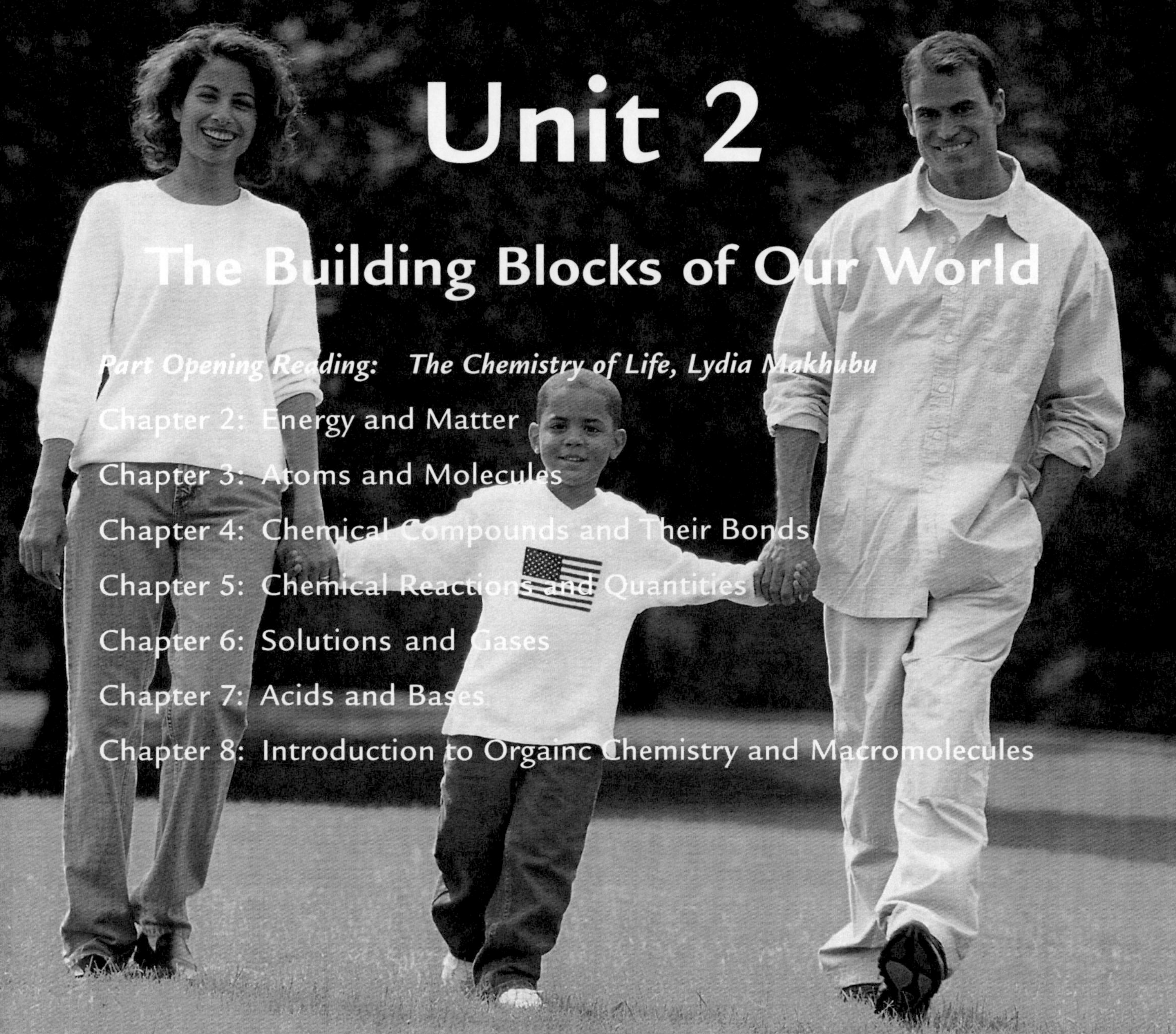

Unit 2

The Building Blocks of Our World

Like everyone and everything, we are made of atoms. Our atoms are energized by the food we eat, and they are constantly moving, coming together in clusters called *molecules*, then breaking apart again. This energetic dance of my atoms underlies much about us, including how we grow. It's amazing that chemistry can reveal so much about the complicated and invisible dance of atoms, giving us the power to understand, care for, and improve the material world!

2 Energy and Matter

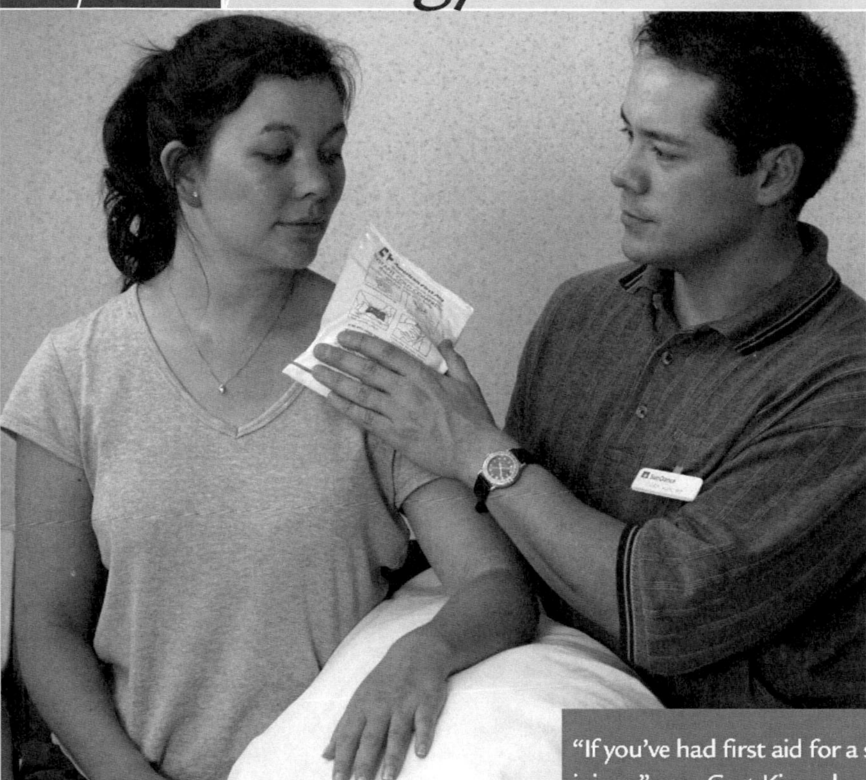

LOOKING AHEAD

"If you've had first aid for a sports injury," says Cort Kim, physical therapist at the Sunrise Sports Medicine Clinic, "you've likely been treated with a cold pack or hot pack. We use them for several kinds of injury. Here, I'm showing how I can use a cold pack to reduce swelling in my patient's shoulder."

A hot or cold pack is just a packaged chemical reaction. When you hit or open the pack to activate it, your action mixes chemicals together and thus initiates the reaction. In a cold pack, the reaction is one that absorbs heat energy, chills the pack, and draws heat from the injury. Hot packs use reactions that release energy, thus warming the pack. In both cases, the reaction proceeds at a moderate pace, so that the pack stays active for a long time and doesn't get too cold or hot.

http://www.pearsoncustom.com/devry/mycb

Study Goals

- Describe potential and kinetic energy.
- Determine the kilocalories for food samples.
- Calculate temperature values in degrees Celsius and kelvins.
- Calculate the calories lost or gained by a specific amount of a substance for a specific temperature change.
- Determine the energy lost or gained during a change of state at the melting or boiling point.
- Identify the states of matter and changes of state on a heating or cooling curve.

Chapter Review

Concept Map

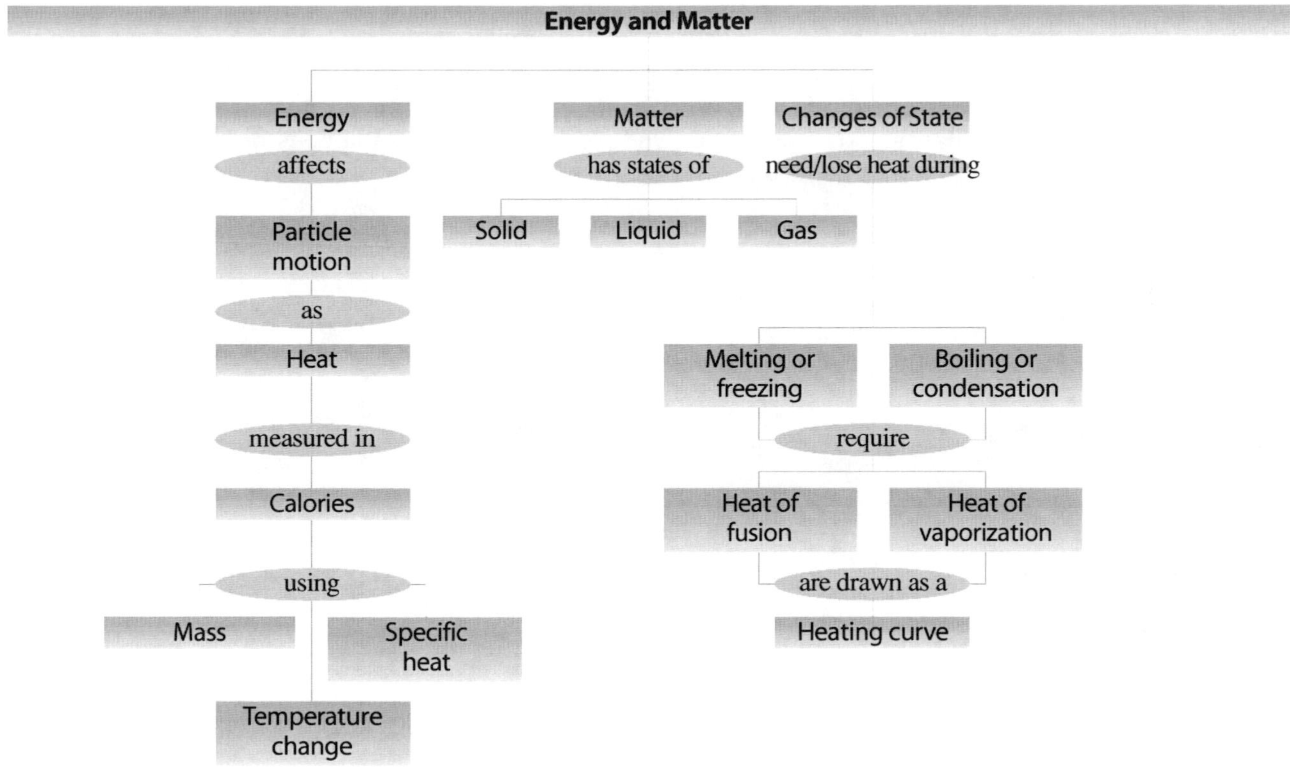

Chapter Concept Review

2.1 Energy

Energy is the ability to do work. Potential energy is stored energy; kinetic energy is the energy of motion. Heat, a common form of energy, is measured in calories or joules. One cal is equal to 4.184 J.

2.2 Energy and Nutrition

The nutritional Calorie is the same amount of energy as 1 kcal or 1000 calories. The caloric content of a food is the sum of kilocalories from carbohydrate, fat, and protein.

2.3 Temperature Conversions

On the Celsius scale, there are 100 units between the freezing point of water (0°C) and the boiling point (100°C). On the Fahrenheit scale, there are 180 units between the freezing point of water (32°F) and the boiling point (212°F). A Fahrenheit temperature is related to its Celsius temperature by the equation $T_F = 1.8\ T_C + 32°$.

2.4 Specific Heat
Specific heat is the amount of energy required to raise the temperature of exactly 1 g of a substance by exactly 1°C. The heat lost or gained by a substance is determined by multiplying its mass (g), the temperature change (ΔT), and its specific heat (cal/g °C).

2.5 States of Matter
Matter is anything that has mass and occupies space. The three states of matter are solid, liquid, and gas.

2.6 Gases
In a gas, particles are so far apart and moving so fast that their attractions are unimportant. A gas is described by the physical properties of pressure (P), volume (V), temperature (T), and amount in moles (n).

2.7 Changes of State
Melting occurs when the particles in a solid absorb enough energy to break apart and form a liquid. The amount of energy required to convert exactly 1 g of solid to liquid is called the heat of fusion. Boiling is the vaporization of a liquid at its boiling point. The heat of vaporization is the amount of heat needed to convert exactly 1 g of liquid to vapor. A heating or cooling curve illustrates the changes in temperature and state as heat is added to or removed from a substance. Plateaus on the graph indicate changes of state with no change in temperature.

Think About It

1. What kinds of activities did you do today that used *kinetic* energy?
2. What are some of the forms of energy you use in your home?
3. Why is the energy in your breakfast cereal *potential* energy?
4. Why is the high specific heat of water important to our survival?
5. How does perspiring during a workout help to keep you cool?
6. During a rain or snowfall, temperature rises. Why?
7. Why is a steam burn much more damaging to skin than a hot water burn?

Key Terms

Match the following terms with the statements below:

a. change of state **b.** kinetic energy **c.** potential energy
d. calorie **e.** Kelvin

1. _____ The amount of heat needed to raise the temperature of 1 g of water by 1°C.
2. _____ Water boiling at 100°C.
3. _____ The energy of motion.
4. _____ Stored energy.
5. _____ SI unit of temperature.

2.1 Energy

- Energy is the ability to do work.
- Potential energy is stored energy; kinetic energy is the energy of motion.
- Some forms of energy include heat, mechanical, radiant, solar, electrical, chemical, and nuclear.

◆ Learning Exercise 2.1A

Match the words in column A with the descriptions in column B.

	A		B
1. _____	kinetic energy	a.	Inactive or stored energy
2. _____	potential energy	b.	The ability to do work
3. _____	chemical energy	c.	The energy of motion
4. _____	energy	d.	The energy available in the bonds of chemical compounds

◆ Learning Exercise 2.1B

State whether the following statements describe potential (P) or kinetic (K) energy:

1. _____ A potted plant sitting on a ledge
2. _____ Your breakfast cereal
3. _____ Logs sitting in a fireplace
4. _____ A piece of candy
5. _____ An arrow shot from a bow
6. _____ A ski jumper at the top of the ski jump
7. _____ A jogger running
8. _____ A sky diver waiting to jump
9. _____ Water flowing down a stream
10. _____ A bowling ball striking the pins

◆ Learning Exercise 2.1C

Match the words in column A with the descriptions in column B.

	A		B
1. _____	calorie	a.	1000 calories
2. _____	specific heat	b.	The heat needed to raise 1 g of water by 1°C
3. _____	kilocalorie	c.	A measure of the ability of a substance to absorb heat

2.2 Energy and Nutrition

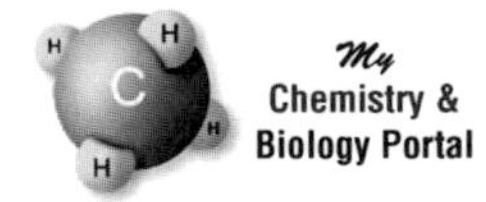

CASE STUDY:
Calories from Hidden Sugar

- A nutritional Calorie is the same amount of energy as 1 kcal or 1000 calories.
- When a substance is burned in a calorimeter, the water that surrounds the reaction chamber absorbs the heat given off. The calories absorbed by the water are calculated and the caloric value (energy per gram) is determined for the substance.

◆ Learning Exercise 2.2A

State the caloric value in kcal/g associated with the following:

a. amino acid _______________
b. protein _______________
c. sugar _______________
d. sucrose _______________
e. oil _______________
f. fat _______________
g. starch _______________
h. lipid _______________
i. glucose _______________
j. lard _______________

◆ Learning Exercise 2.2B

Study Note

The caloric content of a food is the sum of calories from carbohydrate, fat, and protein. It is calculated by using their number of grams in a food and the caloric values of 4 kcal/g for carbohydrate and protein, and 9 kcal/g for fat.

Calculate the kcal for the following foods using the following data:

Food	Carbohydrate	Fat	Protein	kcal
a. Peas, green, cooked	19 g	1 g	9 g	______
b. Potato chips, 10 chips	10 g	8 g	1 g	______
c. Cream cheese, 8 oz	5 g	86 g	18 g	______
d. Hamburger, lean, 3 oz	0	10 g	23 g	______
e. Salmon, canned	0	5 g	17 g	______
f. Snap beans, 1 cup	7 g	2 g	30 g	______
g. Banana, 1	26 g	0	1 g	______

◆ Learning Exercise 2.2C

Using caloric values, give answers with two significant figures for each of the following problems:

1. How many kcal are in a single serving of pudding that contains 4 g protein, 31 g of carbohydrate, and 5 g of fat?

2. A can of tuna has a caloric value of 200 kcal. If there are 2 g of fat and no carbohydrate, how many grams of protein are contained in the can of tuna?

3. A serving of breakfast cereal provides 220 kcal. In this serving, there are 8 g of protein and 6 g of fat. How many grams of carbohydrate are in the cereal?

4. Complete the following table listing ingredients for a peanut butter sandwich.

	Protein	Carbohydrate	Fat	kcal
2 slices bread	4 g	30 g	0	______
2 Tbsp peanut butter	8 g	6 g	______	170 kcal
2 tsp jelly	0	______	0	40 kcal
1 tsp margarine	0	0	5 g	______
			Total kcal in sandwich	______

2.3 Temperature Conversions

- A nutritional Calorie is the same amount of energy as 1 kcal or 1000 calories.
- In the sciences, temperature is measured in Celsius units, °C, or kelvin, K. In the United States, the Fahrenheit scale, °F, is still in use.
- The equation $°F = 1.8°C + 32$ is used to convert a Celsius temperature to a Fahrenheit temperature. When rearranged for °C, the equation is used to convert from °F to °C.

$$°C = \frac{(°F - 32)}{1.8}$$

- The temperature on the Celsius scale is related to the Kelvin scale: $K = °C + 273$.

◆ Learning Exercise 2.3

Calculate the temperatures in the following problems:

a. To prepare yogurt, milk is warmed to 68°C. What Fahrenheit temperature is needed to prepare the yogurt?

b. On a cold day in Alaska, the temperature drops to −12°C. What is that temperature on a Fahrenheit thermometer?

c. A patient has a temperature of 39.5°C. What is that temperature in °F?

d. On a hot summer day, the temperature is 95°F. What is the temperature on the Celsius scale?

e. A pizza is cooked at a temperature of 425°F. What is the °C temperature?

f. A research experiment requires the use of liquid nitrogen to cool the reaction flask to −45°C. What temperature will this be on the Kelvin scale?

2.4 Specific Heat

- Specific heat is the amount of energy required to raise the temperature of 1 g of a substance by 1°C.
- The specific heat for liquid water is 1.00 calorie/g°C or 4.184 joules/g°C.

◆ Learning Exercise 2.4

Study Note

The heat lost or gained by a substance is calculated from the mass, temperature change, and specific heat of the substance.

Heat (calories) = **mass** (g) × **temperature change** (ΔT) × **specific heat** (cal/g°C)

There are 4.184 joules in one calorie.

Number of calories × 4.184 = number of joules

Calculate the calories (cal) gained or released during the following:

1. Heating 20. g of water from 22°C to 77°C

2. Heating 10. g of water from 12°C to 97°C

3. Cooling 4.00 kg of water from 80.0°C to 35.0°C

4. Cooling 125 g of water from 45.0°C to 72.0°C

2.5 States of Matter

- Matter is anything that has mass and occupies space.
- The three states of matter are solid, liquid, and gas.
- Physical properties such as shape, state, or color can change without affecting the identity of a substance.

◆ Learning Exercise 2.5

State whether the following statements describe a gas (G), a liquid (L), or a solid (S).

1. _____ There are no attractions among the molecules.
2. _____ Particles are held close together in a definite pattern.
3. _____ The substance has a definite volume, but no definite shape.
4. _____ The particles are moving extremely fast.
5. _____ This substance has no definite shape and no definite volume.
6. _____ The particles are very far apart.
7. _____ This material has its own volume, but takes the shape of its container.
8. _____ The particles of this material bombard the sides of the container with great force.
9. _____ The particles in this substance are moving very, very slowly.
10. _____ This substance has a definite volume and a definite shape.

2.6 Gases

- In a gas, particles are so far apart and moving so fast that they are not attracted to each other.
- A gas is described by the physical properties of pressure (P), volume (V), temperature (T), and amount in moles (n).

◆ Learning Exercise 2.6

True or false:

a. _____ Gases are composed of small particles.

b. _____ Gas molecules are usually close together.

c. _____ Gas molecules move rapidly because they are strongly attracted.

d. _____ The distances between gas molecules are great.

e. _____ Gas molecules travel in straight lines until they collide.

2.7 Changes of State

- A substance undergoes a physical change when its shape, size, or state changes, but not the type of substance itself.
- A substance melts and freezes at its melting (freezing) point.
- As long as a substance is changing state during boiling, or condensation, the temperature remains constant.
- The *heat of fusion* is the heat energy required to change 1 g of solid to liquid. For water to freeze at 0°C, the heat of fusion is 80. calories. This is also the amount of heat lost when 1 gram of water freezes at 0°C.
- Sublimation is the change of state from a solid directly to a gas.
- When water boils at 100°C, 540 calories (the heat of vaporization) is required to change 1 g of liquid to gas (steam); it is also the amount of heat released when 1 g of water vapor condenses at 100°C.
- A heating or cooling curve illustrates the changes in temperature and states as heat is added to or removed from a substance.

◆ Learning Exercise 2.7A

Identify each of the following as

1. melting **2.** freezing **3.** sublimation.

a. _____ A liquid changes to a solid.

b. _____ Ice forms on the surface of a lake in winter.

c. _____ Dry ice in an ice cream cart changes to a gas.

d. _____ Butter in a hot pan turns to liquid.

◆ Learning Exercise 2.7B

Study Note

The amount of heat needed or released during melting or freezing can be calculated using the heat of fusion:

$$\text{Heat (cal)} = \text{mass (g)} \times \text{heat of fusion}$$

Calculate the energy required or released when the following substances melt or freeze:

a. How many calories are needed to melt 15 g ice at 0°C?

b. How much heat in kilocalories is released when 325 g of water freezes at 0°C?

c. How many grams of ice would melt when 4000 calories of heat were absorbed?

◆ Learning Exercise 2.7C

Calculate the energy required or released for the following substances undergoing boiling or condensation:

a. How many calories are needed to completely change 10. g of water to vapor at 100°C?

b. How many kilocalories are released when 515 grams of steam at 100°C condense to form liquid water at 100°C?

c. How many grams of water can be converted to steam at 100°C when 272 kcal of energy are absorbed?

◆ Learning Exercise 2.7D

On each heating or cooling curve, indicate the portion that corresponds to a solid, liquid, gas, and the changes in state.

1. Draw a heating curve for water that begins at −20°C and ends at 120°C. Water has a melting point of 0°C and a boiling point of 100°C.

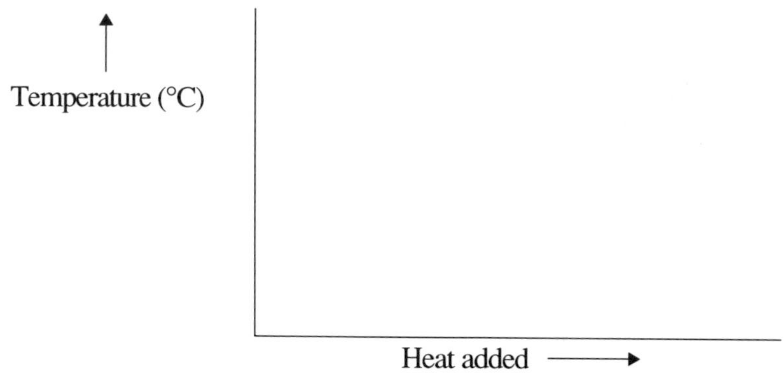

2. Draw a heating curve for bromine from −25° to 75°C. Bromine has a melting point of −7°C and a boiling point of 59°C.

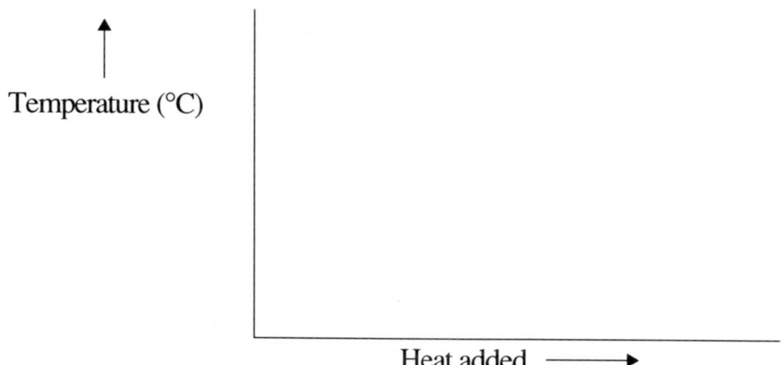

3. Draw a cooling curve for sodium from 1000°C to 0°C. Sodium has a freezing point of 98°C and a boiling (condensation) point of 883°C.

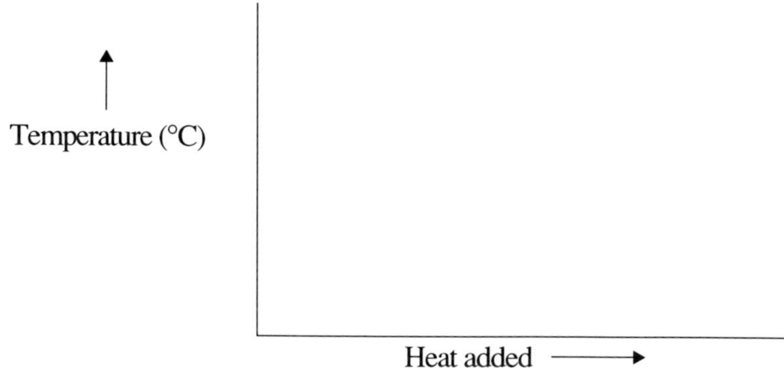

Check List for Chapter 2

You are ready to take the practice test for Chapter 2. Be sure that you have accomplished the following learning goals for this chapter. If you are not sure, review the section listed at the end of the goal. Then apply your new skills and understanding to the practice test.
After studying Chapter 2, I can successfully:

_____ Describe some forms of energy (2.1).

_____ Calculate the energy of a food sample (2.2).

_____ Given a temperature, calculate a corresponding temperature on another scale (2.3).

_____ Given the mass of a sample, specific heat, and the temperature change, calculate the heat lost or gained (2.4).

_____ Identify the physical state of a substance as a solid, liquid, or gas (2.5).

_____ Calculate the heat change for the boiling and condensation of a specific amount of a substance (2.7).

_____ Draw heating and cooling curves using the melting and boiling points of a substance (2.7).

Practice Test for Chapter 2

1. Which of the following would be described as potential energy?
A. A car going around a racetrack **B.** A rabbit hopping
C. Oil in an oil well **D.** A moving merry-go-round
E. A bouncing ball

2. Which of the following would be described as kinetic energy?
A. A car battery **B.** A can of tennis balls
C. Gasoline in a car fuel tank **D.** A box of matches
E. A tennis ball crossing over the net

3. The number of calories needed to raise the temperature of 5.0 g water from 25°C to 55°C is
A. 5 cal **B.** 30 cal **C.** 50 cal **D.** 80 cal **E.** 150 cal

4. The number of calories (kcal) released when 150 g of water cools from 58°C to 22°C is
A. 1.1 kcal **B.** 4.2 kcal **C.** 5.4 kcal **D.** 6.9 kcal **E.** 8.7 kcal

For questions 5 through 8, consider a cup of milk with a caloric value of 165 kcal. In the cup of milk, there are 9 g of fat, 12 g of carbohydrate, and some protein.

5. The number of kcal provided by the carbohydrate is
A. 4 kcal **B.** 9 kcal **C.** 36 kcal **D.** 48 kcal **E.** 81 kcal

6. The number of kcal provided by the fat is
A. 4 kcal **B.** 9 kcal **C.** 36 kcal **D.** 48 kcal **E.** 81 kcal

7. The number of kcal provided by the protein is
A. 4 kcal **B.** 9 kcal **C.** 36 kcal **D.** 48 kcal **E.** 81 kcal

8. Which of the following describes a liquid?
A. A substance that has no definite shape and no definite volume
B. A substance with particles that are far apart
C. A substance with a definite shape and a definite volume
D. A substance containing particles that are moving very fast
E. A substance that has a definite volume, but takes the shape of its container

Identify the statements in questions 9 through 12 as

A. evaporation
B. heat of fusion
C. heat of vaporization
D. boiling

9. _____ The energy required to convert a gram of solid to liquid

10. _____ The heat needed to boil a liquid

11. _____ The conversion of liquid molecules to gas at the surface of a liquid

12. _____ The formation of a gas within the liquid as well as on the surface

13. Ice cools down a drink because
   A. the ice is colder than the drink and heat flows into the ice cubes.
   B. heat is absorbed from the drink to melt the ice cubes.
   C. the heat of fusion of the ice is higher than the heat of fusion for water.
   D. Both A and B
   E. None of the above

14. The number of kilocalories needed to convert 400 g of ice to liquid at 0°C is
   A. 400 kcal B. 320 kcal C. 80 kcal D. 40 kcal E. 32 kcal

For questions 15 through 18, consider the heating curve below for *p*-toluidine. Answer the following questions when heat is added to *p*-toluidine at 20°C where toluidine is below its melting point.

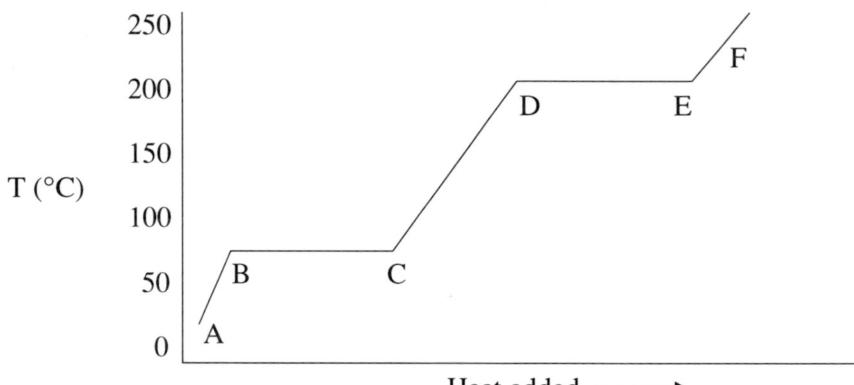

15. On the heating curve, segment BC indicates
   A. solid B. melting C. liquid D. boiling E. gas

16. On the heating curve, segment CD shows toluidine as
   A. solid B. melting C. liquid D. boiling E. gas

17. The boiling point of toluidine would be
   A. 20°C B. 45°C C. 100°C D. 200°C E. 250°C

18. On the heating curve, segment EF shows toluidine as
   A. solid B. melting C. a liquid D. boiling E. a gas

19. 105°F = _____ °C
   A. 73°C B. 41°C C. 58°C D. 90°C E. 189°C

20. The melting point of gold is 1064°C. The Fahrenheit temperature needed to melt gold would be
   A. 129°C B. 623°F C. 1031°F D. 1913°F E. 1947°F

21. The average daytime temperature on the planet Mercury is 683 K. What is this temperature on the Celsius scale?
   A. 956°C B. 715°C C. 680°C D. 410°C E. 303°C

Key Terms

boiling The formation of bubbles of gas throughout a liquid.

boiling point (bp) The temperature at which a liquid changes to gas (boils) and gas changes to liquid (condenses).

caloric value The kilocalories obtained per gram of the food types: carbohydrate, fat, and protein.

calorie (cal) The amount of heat energy that raises the temperature of exactly 1 g of water exactly 1°C.

Calorie (Cal) The dietary unit of energy, equal to 1000 cal, or 1 kcal.

change of state The transformation of one state of matter to another; for example, solid to liquid, liquid to solid, liquid to gas.

condensation The change of state of a gas to a liquid.

cooling curve A diagram that illustrates temperature changes and changes of states for a substance as heat is removed.

energy The ability to do work.

evaporation The formation of a gas (vapor) by the escape of high-energy molecules from the surface of a liquid.

freezing A change of state from liquid to solid.

freezing point (fp) The temperature at which a liquid changes to a solid (freezes), a solid changes to a liquid (melts).

gas A state of matter characterized by no definite shape or volume. Particles in a gas move rapidly.

heat The energy associated with the motion of particles in a substance.

heat of fusion The energy required to melt exactly 1 g of a substance at its melting point. For water, 80. cal are needed to melt 1 g of ice; 80. cal are released when 1 g of water freezes.

heat of vaporization The energy required to vaporize 1 g of a substance at its boiling point. For water, 540 calories are needed to vaporize exactly 1 g of liquid; 1 g of steam gives off 540 cal when it condenses.

heating curve A diagram that shows the temperature changes and changes of state of a substance as it is heated.

joule (J) The SI unit of heat energy; 4.184 J = 1 cal.

kinetic energy The energy of moving particles.

kilocalorie (kcal) An amount of heat energy equal to 1000 calories.

liquid A state of matter that takes the shape of its container but has a definite volume.

matter Anything that has mass and occupies space.

melting The conversion of a solid to a liquid.

melting point (mp) The temperature at which a solid becomes a liquid (melts). It is the same temperature as the freezing point.

potential energy An inactive type of energy that is stored for future use.

solid A state of matter that has its own shape and volume.

specific heat A quantity of heat that changes the temperature of exactly 1 g of a substance by exactly 1°C.

sublimation The change of state in which a solid is transformed directly to a gas without forming a liquid first.

work An activity that requires energy.

3 Atoms and Molecules

"Many of my patients have diabetes, ulcers, hypertension, and cardiovascular problems," says Sylvia Lau, registered dietitian. "If a patient has diabetes, I discuss foods that raise blood sugar such as fruit, milk, and starches. I talk about how dietary fat contributes to weight gain and complications from diabetes. For stroke patients, I suggest diets low in fat and cholesterol because high blood pressure increases the risk of another stroke."

If a lab test shows low levels of iron, zinc, iodine, magnesium, or calcium, a dietitian discusses foods that provide those essential elements. For instance, she may recommend more beef for an iron deficiency, whole grain for zinc, leafy green vegetables for magnesium, dairy products for calcium, and iodized table salt and seafood for iodine.

LOOKING AHEAD

http://www.pearsoncustom.com/devry/mycb

Study Goals

- Write the name of an element from its symbol or its period and group number.
- Classify an element as a metal or nonmetal.
- Describe the three important particles in the atom, their location, charges, and relative masses.
- Describe Rutherford's gold-foil experiment and how it led to the current model of the atom.
- Use atomic number and mass number of an atom to determine the number of protons, neutrons, and electrons in the atom.
- Understand the relationship of isotopes to the atomic mass of an element on the periodic table.
- Write the electron level arrangements for elements 1–18 in the periodic table.
- Describe orbitals in the energy levels of atoms.
- Explain the relationship between electron arrangement, group number, and periodic law.
- Use the electron arrangement to explain periodic trends of the elements.

Chapter Review

Concept Map

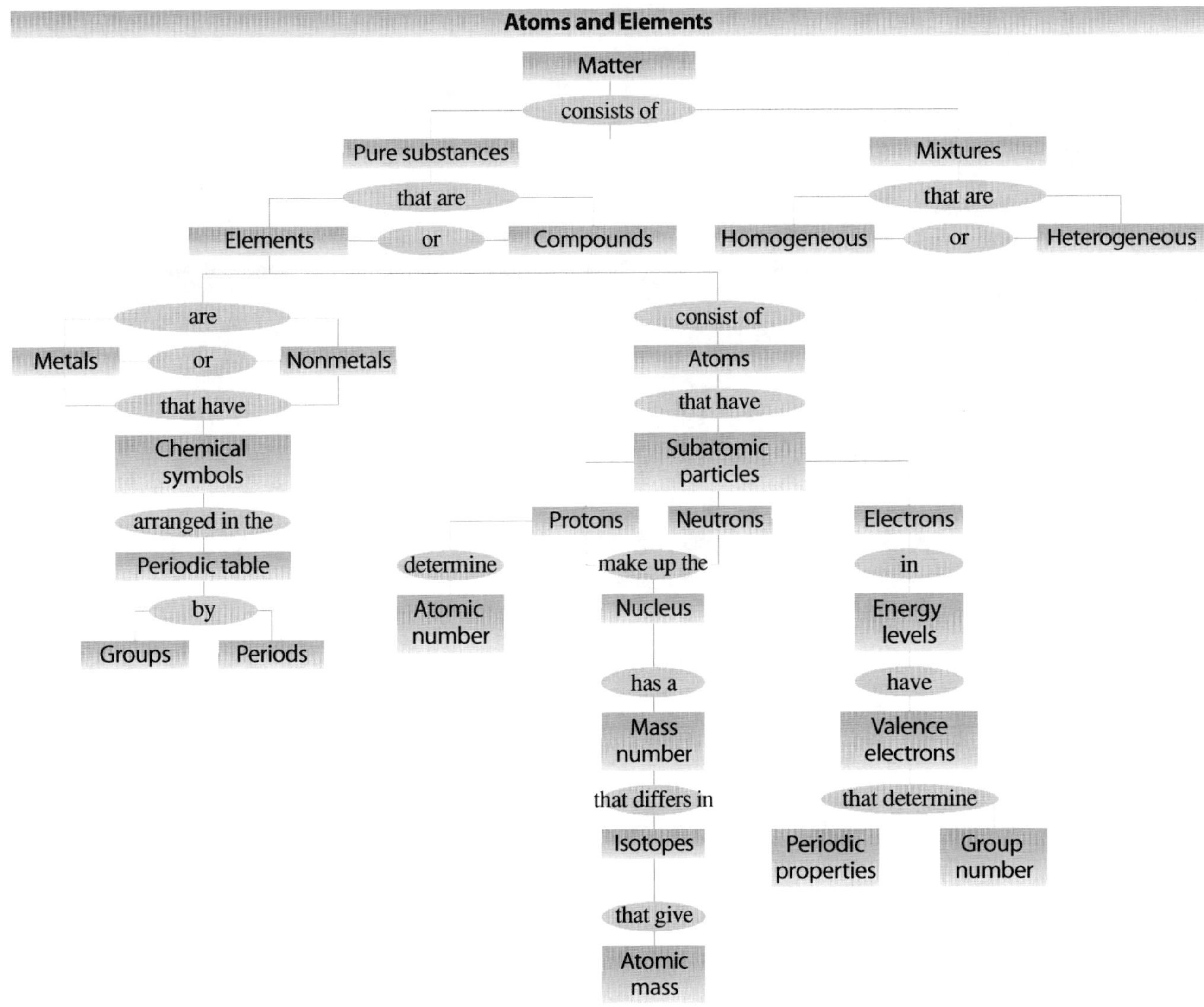

Chapter Concept Review

3.1 Classification of Matter
Matter is everything that occupies space and has mass. Matter is classified as pure substances or mixtures. Pure substances, which are elements or compounds, have fixed compositions, and mixtures have variable compositions. The substances in mixtures can be separated using physical methods.

3.2 Elements and Symbols
Elements are the primary substances of matter. Chemical symbols are one- or two-letter abbreviations of the names of the elements.

3.3 The Periodic Table
The periodic table is an arrangement of the elements by increasing atomic number. A vertical column on the periodic table containing elements with similar properties is called a group. A horizontal row is called a period. Elements in Group 1A (1) are called the alkali metals; Group 2A (2), alkaline earth metals; Group 7A (17), the halogens; and Group 8A (18), the noble gases. On the periodic table, metals are located on the left of the heavy zigzag line, and nonmetals are to the right of the heavy zigzag line. Elements located on the heavy line are called metalloids.

3.4 The Atom
An atom is the smallest particle that retains the characteristics of an element. Atoms are composed of three subatomic particles. Protons have a positive charge (+), electrons carry a negative charge (−), and neutrons are electrically neutral. The protons and neutrons are found in the tiny, dense nucleus. Electrons are located outside the nucleus.

3.5 Atomic Number and Mass Number
The atomic number gives the number of protons in all the atoms of the same element. In a neutral atom, there is an equal number of protons and electrons. The mass number is the total number of protons and neutrons in an atom.

3.6 Isotopes and Atomic Mass
Atoms that have the same number of protons but different numbers of neutrons are called isotopes. The atomic mass of an element is the weighted average mass of all the isotopes in a naturally occurring sample of that element.

3.7 Electron Energy Levels
Every electron has a specific amount of energy. In an atom, the electrons of similar energy are grouped in specific energy levels. The first level nearest the nucleus can hold 2 electrons, the second level can hold 8 electrons, the third level will take up to 18 electrons. Each level consists of orbitals, which represent the space where electrons of that energy are likely to be found. An *s* orbital has a spherical shape. A *p* orbital has two lobes like a dumbbell and there are three *p* orbitals in each level from $n = 2$.

3.8 Periodic Trends
The properties of elements are related to the valence electrons of the atoms. The electron arrangement is written by placing the number of electrons in that atom in order from the lowest energy levels and filling to higher levels. The similarity of behavior for the elements in a group is related to having the same number of electrons in their outermost, valence, level. The group number for an element gives the number of electrons in its outer most energy level. With only a few minor exceptions, each group of elements has the same arrangement of valence electrons differing only in the energy level. The radius of an atom increases going down a group and decreases going across a period. The energy required to remove a valence electron is the ionization energy, which generally decreases going down a group and generally increases going across a period.

TABLE 3.1
Classification of Matter

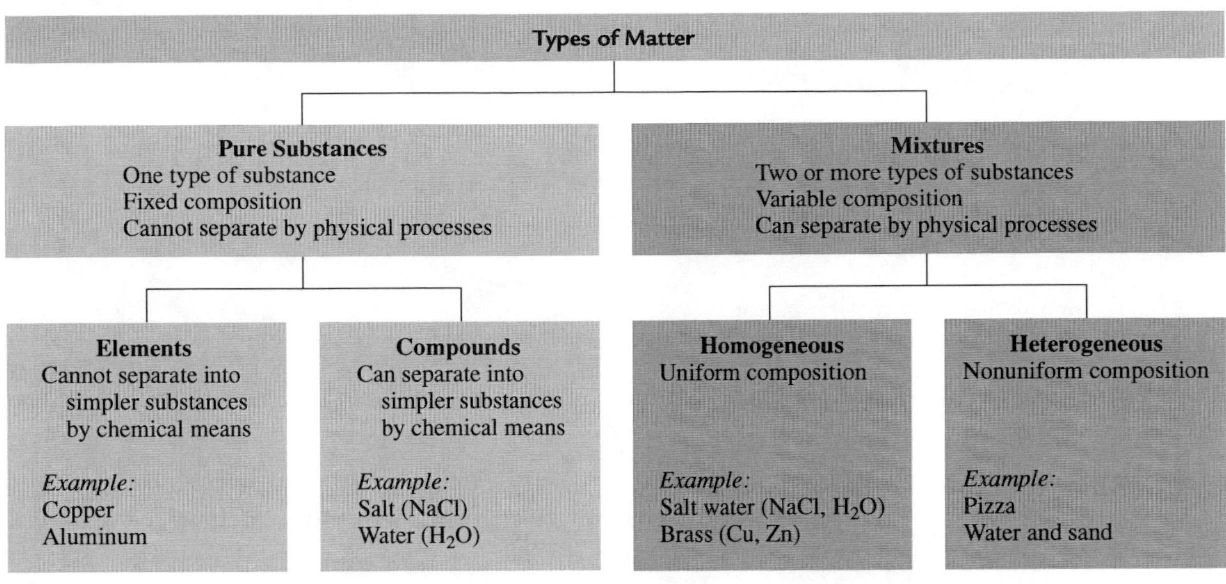

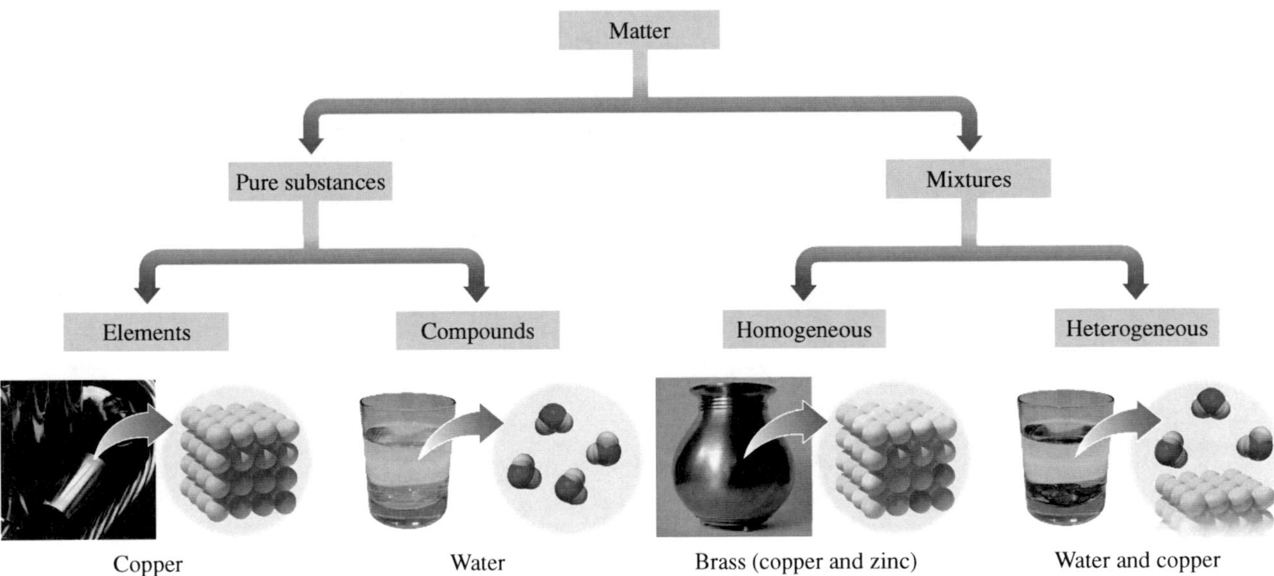

FIGURE 3.1
Matter is organized by its components: elements, compounds, and mixtures. An element or a compound has a fixed composition, whereas a mixture has a variable composition. A homogeneous mixture has a uniform composition, but a heteroge neous mixture does not.

Think About It

1. Name some of the elements you have seen today.
2. How are the symbols of the elements related to their names?
3. What are some elements that are part of your vitamins?

Key Terms

Match each of the following key terms with the correct definition.

a. element **b.** atom **c.** atomic number **d.** mass number **e.** isotope

1. _____ The number of protons and neutrons in the nucleus of an atom

2. _____ The smallest particle of an element

3. _____ A primary substance that cannot be broken down into simpler substances

4. _____ An atom of an element that has a different number of neutrons than another atom of the same element

5. _____ The number of protons in an atom

3.1 Classification of Matter

- A pure substance, element or compound, has a definite composition.
- Elements are the simplest type of matter; compounds consist of a combination of two or more elements.
- Mixtures contain two or more substances that are physically, not chemically, combined.
- Mixtures are classified as homogeneous or heterogeneous.

◆ Learning Exercise 3.1A

Identify each of the following as an element (E) or compound (C):

1. _____ carbon

2. _____ carbon dioxide

3. _____ potassium iodide

4. _____ silver

5. _____ aluminum

6. _____ table salt (sodium chloride)

◆ Learning Exercise 3.1B

Identify each of the following as a pure substance (P) or mixture (M):

1. _____ bananas and milk

2. _____ sulfur

3. _____ gold

4. _____ a bag of raisins and nuts

5. _____ water

6. _____ sand and water

◆ Learning Exercise 3.1C

Identify each of the following mixtures as homogeneous (HO) or heterogeneous (HE):

1. _____ chocolate milk

2. _____ sand and water

3. _____ lemon soda

4. _____ a bag of raisins and nuts

5. _____ air

6. _____ vinegar

3.2 Elements and Symbols

- Elements are the primary substances of matter.
- Chemical symbols are one- or two-letter abbreviations for the names of the elements.
- The physical properties of an element are those characteristics such as color, density, and melting and boiling points that we can observe or measure without changing the identity of the element.

Study Note

Now is the time to learn the names of the elements and their symbols. Practice saying and writing the names of the elements in the periodic table with atomic number 1–54 and Cs, Ba, Hg, Au, and Pb. Cover the symbols in the list of elements and practice writing the symbols for the elemental names.

◆ Learning Exercise 3.2A

Write the symbols for each of the following elements:

1. carbon ____	**6.** nitrogen ____	**11.** calcium ____
2. iron ____	**7.** iodine ____	**12.** gold ____
3. sodium ____	**8.** sulfur ____	**13.** copper ____
4. phosphorus ____	**9.** potassium ____	**14.** neon ____
5. oxygen ____	**10.** lead ____	**15.** chlorine ____

◆ Learning Exercise 3.2B

Write the names of the elements represented by each of the following symbols:

1. Mg ____________	**7.** Ag ____________
2. K ____________	**8.** Br ____________
3. Au ____________	**9.** Zn ____________
4. F ____________	**10.** Al ____________
5. Cu ____________	**11.** Ba ____________
6. Be ____________	**12.** Li ____________

◆ Learning Exercise 3.2C

Gold (Au, *aurum,* atomic number 79) has been highly valued from ancient times. Gold, which has a density of 19.3 g/ML, melts at 1064°C and boils at 2857°C. It is found free in nature usually along with quartz or pyrite deposits. Gold is a beautiful metal with a yellow color. It is a soft metal that is also the most malleable metal, which accounts for its use in jewelry and gold leaf. Gold is also a good conductor of heat and electricity. List all the physical properties that describe gold.

3.3 The Periodic Table

- The periodic table is an arrangement of the elements by increasing atomic number.
- Each vertical column contains a *group* of elements, which have similar properties.
- A horizontal row of elements is called a *period.*
- On the periodic table, the *metals* are located on the left of the heavy zig-zag line, the nonmetals are to the right, and metalloids are next to the zig-zag line.

◆ Learning Exercise 3.3A

Study Note

1. The periodic table consists of horizontal rows called *periods* and vertical columns called *groups.*
2. Elements in Group 1A (1) are the *alkali metals.* Elements in Group 2A (2) are the *alkaline earth metals,* and Group 7A (17) contains the *halogens.* Elements in Group 8A (18) are the *noble gases.*

Indicate whether the following elements are in a group (G), period (P), or neither (N):

a. Li, C, and O ____________	**e.** Mg, Ca, and Ba ____________
b. Br, Cl, and F ____________	**f.** C, S, and Br ____________
c. Al, Si, and Cl ____________	**g.** Li, Na, and K ____________
d. C, N, and O ____________	**h.** K, Ca, and Br ____________

◆ Learning Exercise 3.3B

Complete the list of elements, group numbers, and period numbers in the following table:

Element and Symbol	Group Number	Period Number
	2A (2)	3
Silicon, Si		
	5A (15)	2
Aluminum, Al		
	4A (14)	5
	1A (1)	6

◆ Learning Exercise 3.3C

Identify each of the following elements as a metal (M), nonmetal (NM), or metalloid (ML):

1. Cl _____ **3.** Fe _____ **5.** Sb _____ **7.** Ca _____ **9.** Ag _____

2. N _____ **4.** K _____ **6.** C _____ **8.** Ge _____ **10.** Mg _____

◆ Learning Exercise 3.3D

Match the names of the chemical groups with the elements K, Cl, He, Fe, Mg, Ne, Li, Cu, and Br.

1. Halogens ______________________

2. Noble gases ______________________

3. Alkali metals ______________________

4. Alkaline earth metals ______________________

5. Transition metals ______________________

3.4 The Atom

My Chemistry & Biology Portal

WEB TUTORIAL
The Atom

- An atom is the smallest particle that retains the characteristics of an element.
- Atoms are composed of three subatomic particles. Protons have a positive charge (+), electrons carry a negative charge (−), and neutrons are electrically neutral.
- The protons and neutrons each with a mass of about 1 amu are found in the tiny, dense nucleus. The electrons are located outside the nucleus.

◆ Learning Exercise 3.4A

Indicate whether each of the following statements is consistent with atomic theory (true or false):

1. All matter is composed of atoms.

2. All atoms of an element are identical.

3. Atoms combine to form compounds.

4. Most of the mass of the atom is in the nucleus.

◆ Learning Exercise 3.4B

Match the following terms with the correct statements:

a. proton **b.** neutron **c.** electron **d.** nucleus

1. _____ Found in the nucleus of an atom

2. _____ Has a −1 charge

3. _____ Found outside the nucleus

4. _____ Has a mass of 1 amu

5. _____ The small, dense center of the atom

6. _____ Is neutral

3.5 Atomic Number and Mass Number

- The *atomic number* is the number of protons in every atom of an element. In neutral atoms, the number of electrons is equal to the number of protons.
- The *mass number* is the total number of protons and neutrons in an atom.

◆ Learning Exercise 3.5A

Give the number of protons in each of the following neutral atoms:

a. An atom of carbon _________

b. An atom of the element with atomic number 15 _________

c. An atom with a mass number of 40 and atomic number 19 _________

d. An atom with 9 neutrons and a mass number of 19 _________

e. A neutral atom that has 18 electrons _________

◆ Learning Exercise 3.5B

Study Note

1. The *atomic number* is the number of protons in every atom of an element. In neutral atoms, the number of electrons equals the number of protons.
2. The *mass number* is the total number of neutrons and protons in the nucleus of an atom.
3. The number of neutrons is *mass number* – *atomic number.*

Give the number of neutrons in each of the following atoms:

a. A mass number of 42 and atomic number 20 _________

b. A mass number of 10 and 5 protons _________

c. $^{30}_{14}Si$ _________

d. A mass number of 9 and atomic number 4 _________

e. A mass number of 22 and 10 protons _________

f. A zinc atom with a mass number of 66 _________

Study Note

In the atomic symbol for a particular atom, the mass number appears in the upper left corner and the atomic number in the lower left corner.

Mass number → Atomic number → $^{32}_{16}S$ $^{26}_{13}Al$

◆ Learning Exercise 3.5C

Complete the following table for neutral atoms.

Symbol	Atomic Number	Mass Number	Number of Protons	Number of Neutrons	Number of Electrons
	12			12	
			20	22	
		55		29	
	35			45	
		35	17		
$^{120}_{50}Sn$					

3.6 Isotopes and Atomic Mass

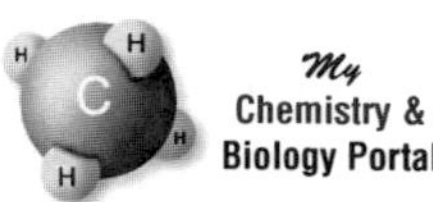

WEB TUTORIAL
Atoms and Isotopes

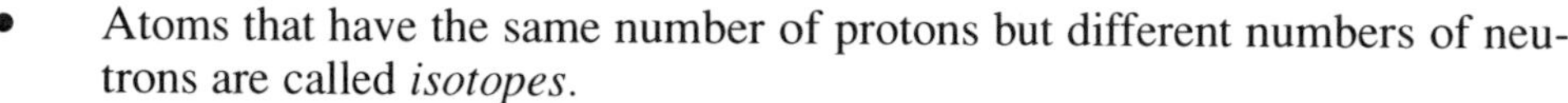

- Atoms that have the same number of protons but different numbers of neutrons are called *isotopes*.
- The atomic mass of an element is the average mass of all the isotopes in a naturally occurring sample of that element.

◆ Learning Exercise 3.6A

Identify the sets of atoms that are isotopes.

A. $^{20}_{10}X$ **B.** $^{20}_{11}X$ **C.** $^{21}_{11}X$ **D.** $^{19}_{10}X$ **E.** $^{19}_{9}X$

◆ Learning Exercise 3.6B

ESSAY: Copper has two naturally occurring isotopes, ^{63}Cu and ^{65}Cu. If that is the case, why is the atomic mass of copper listed as 63.55 on the periodic table?

3.7 Electron Energy Levels

WEB TUTORIAL
Bohr's Shell Model of the Atom

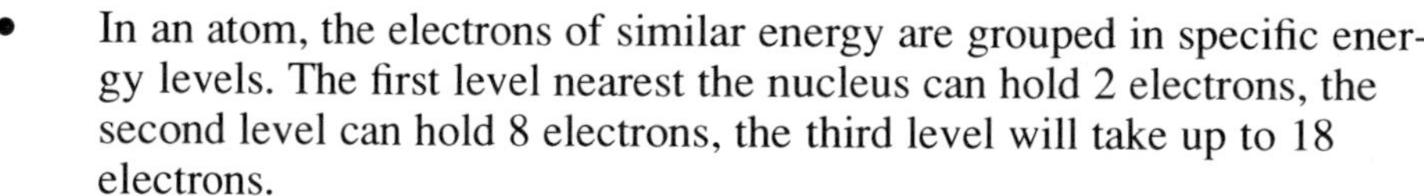

- In an atom, the electrons of similar energy are grouped in specific energy levels. The first level nearest the nucleus can hold 2 electrons, the second level can hold 8 electrons, the third level will take up to 18 electrons.
- The electron arrangement is the number of electrons in each energy level beginning with the lowest energy level.
- In an atom, an electron occupies a region in space around the nucleus called an orbital.
- Energy level 1 consists of one *s* orbital; energy level 2 has two orbitals (one *s* and three *p* orbitals); energy level 3 has three orbitals (one *s*, three *p*, and five *d* orbitals).

◆ Learning Exercise 3.7A

Write the electron level arrangements for the following elements:

Element	Electron Level 1 2 3 4	Element	Electron Level 1 2 3 4
a. beryllium	______________	**e.** phosphorus	______________
b. carbon	______________	**f.** nitrogen	______________
c. potassium	______________	**g.** chlorine	______________
d. sodium	______________	**h.** silicon	______________

◆ Learning Exercise 3.7B

State the maximum number of electrons for each of the following:

a. 3*s* orbital ____________

d. three 4*p* orbitals ____________

b. 2*p* orbital ____________

e. five 4*d* orbitals ____________

c. energy level 2 ____________

f. energy level 3 ____________

3.8 Periodic Trends

- The physical and chemical properties of elements change in a periodic manner going across each period and are repeated in each successive period.
- Representative elements in a group have similar behavior.
- The group number of an element gives the number of valence electrons.
- The electron dot symbol shows each valence electron as a dot placed around the atomic symbol.
- The atomic radius of representative elements generally increases going down a group and decreases going across a period.
- The ionization energy generally decreases going down a group and increases going across a period.

◆ Learning Exercise 3.8A

State the number of electrons in the outermost energy level, the group number of each element, and the electron dot symbol for the following elements:

Element	Valence Electrons	Group Number	Dot Symbol
a. sulfur			
b. oxygen			
c. magnesium			
d. hydrogen			
e. fluorine			
f. aluminum			

◆ Learning Exercise 3.8B

Indicate the element that has the larger atomic radius.

a. _____ Mg or Ca

b. _____ Si or Cl

c. _____ Sr or Rb

d. _____ Br or Cl

e. _____ Li or Cs

f. _____ Li or N

g. _____ N or P

h. _____ As or Ca

◆ Learning Exercise 3.8C

Indicate the element that has the lower ionization energy.

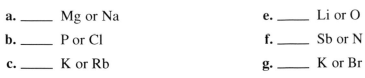

a. _____ Mg or Na

b. _____ P or Cl

c. _____ K or Rb

d. _____ Br or F

e. _____ Li or O

f. _____ Sb or N

g. _____ K or Br

h. _____ S or Na

Excercises in Investigating Matter

Melting Points of the Elements

There is a remarkable degree of organization in the periodic table. As discussed in your textbook, elements within the same atomic group (vertical column) share similar properties. Also, the chemical reactivity of an element can be deduced from its position in the periodic table. Two additional examples of the periodic table's organization are the melting points and densities of the elements.

The periodic table below shows the melting points of nearly all the elements. Note the melting points are not randomly oriented, but, with only a few exceptions, either gradually increase or decrease as you move in any particular direction. This can be clearly illustrated by color coding each element according to its melting point.

Use colored pencils to color in each element according to its melting point. Use the suggested color legend. Color lightly so that symbols and numbers are still visible.

Color	Temperature Range, °C	Color	Temperature Range, °C
Violet	-273 — -50	Yellow	1400 — 1900
Blue	-50 — 300	Orange	1900 — 2900
Cyan	300 — 700	Red	2900 — 3500
Green	700 — 1400		

Melting Points of the Elements (°C)

1	2	3	4	5	6	7	8	9	10	11	12	13	14	15	16	17	18
H -259																	He -272
Li 180	Be 1278											B 2079	C 3550	N -210	O -218	F -219	Ne -248
Na 97	Mg 648											Al 660	Si 1410	P 44	S 113	Cl -100	Ar -189
K 63	Ca 839	Sc 1541	Ti 1660	V 1890	Cr 1857	Mn 1244	Fe 1535	Co 1495	Ni 1453	Cu 1083	Zn 419	Ga 30	Ge 937	As 817	Se 217	Br -7	Kr -156
Rb 39	Sr 769	Y 1522	Zr 1852	Nb 2468	Mo 2617	Tc 2172	Ru 2310	Rh 1966	Pd 1554	Ag 961	Cd 320	In 156	Sn 231	Sb 630	Te 449	I 113	Xe -111
Cs 28	Ba 725	La 921	Hf 2227	Ta 2996	W 3410	Re 3180	Os 3045	Ir 2410	Pt 1772	Au 1064	Hg -38	Tl 303	Pb 327.	Bi 271	Po 254	At 302	Rn -71
Fr 27	Ra 700	Ac 1050	--	--	--	--	--	--									

Lanthanides:	Ce 799	Pr 931	Nd 1021	Pm 1168	Sm 1077	Eu 822	Gd 1313	Tb 1356	Dy 1412	Ho 1474	Er 1159	Tm 1545	Yb 819	Lu 1663
Actinides:	Th 1750	Pa 1600	U 1132	Np 640	Pu 641	Am 994	Cm 1340	Bk --	Cf --	Es --	Fm --	Md --	No --	Lr --

1. Which elements have the highest melting points?

____

2. Which elements have the lowest melting points?

____

3. Which atomic groups tend to go from higher to lower melting points reading from top to bottom? (Identify each group by its group number.)

____

4. Which atomic groups tend to go from lower to higher melting points reading from top to bottom?

____

Densities of the Elements

The periodic table below shows the densities of nearly all the elements. As with the melting points, the densities of the elements either gradually increase or decrease as you move in any particular direction. Use colored pencils to color in each element according to its density. Shown below is a suggested color legend. Color lightly so that symbols and numbers are still visible. (Note: All gaseous elements are marked with an asterisk and should be the same color. Their densities, which are given in units of g/L, are much less than the densities nongaseous elements, which are given in units of g/mL.)

Color	Density (g/mL)	Color	Density (g/mL)
Violet	gaseous elements	Yellow	16 — 12
Blue	5 — 0	Orange	20 — 16
Cyan	8 — 5	Red.	23 — 20
Green	12 — 8		

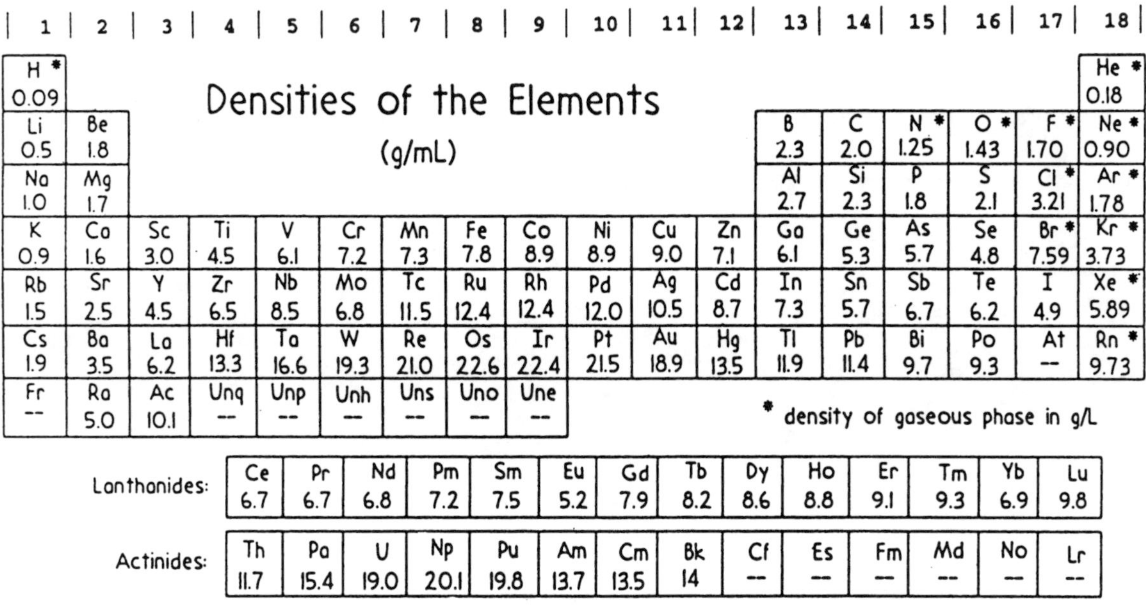

Densities of the Elements

(g/mL)

1	2	3	4	5	6	7	8	9	10	11	12	13	14	15	16	17	18
H * 0.09																	He * 0.18
Li 0.5	Be 1.8											B 2.3	C 2.0	N * 1.25	O * 1.43	F * 1.70	Ne * 0.90
Na 1.0	Mg 1.7											Al 2.7	Si 2.3	P 1.8	S 2.1	Cl * 3.21	Ar * 1.78
K 0.9	Ca 1.6	Sc 3.0	Ti 4.5	V 6.1	Cr 7.2	Mn 7.3	Fe 7.8	Co 8.9	Ni 8.9	Cu 9.0	Zn 7.1	Ga 6.1	Ge 5.3	As 5.7	Se 4.8	Br * 7.59	Kr * 3.73
Rb 1.5	Sr 2.5	Y 4.5	Zr 6.5	Nb 8.5	Mo 6.8	Tc 11.5	Ru 12.4	Rh 12.4	Pd 12.0	Ag 10.5	Cd 8.7	In 7.3	Sn 5.7	Sb 6.7	Te 6.2	I 4.9	Xe * 5.89
Cs 1.9	Ba 3.5	La 6.2	Hf 13.3	Ta 16.6	W 19.3	Re 21.0	Os 22.6	Ir 22.4	Pt 21.5	Au 18.9	Hg 13.5	Tl 11.9	Pb 11.4	Bi 9.7	Po 9.3	At --	Rn * 9.73
Fr --	Ra 5.0	Ac 10.1	Unq --	Unp --	Unh --	Uns --	Uno --	Une --									

* density of gaseous phase in g/L

Lanthanides:	Ce 6.7	Pr 6.7	Nd 6.8	Pm 7.2	Sm 7.5	Eu 5.2	Gd 7.9	Tb 8.2	Dy 8.6	Ho 8.8	Er 9.1	Tm 9.3	Yb 6.9	Lu 9.8
Actinides:	Th 11.7	Pa 15.4	U 19.0	Np 20.1	Pu 19.8	Am 13.7	Cm 13.5	Bk 14	Cf --	Es --	Fm --	Md --	No --	Lr --

1. Which elements are the most dense?

____

2. How variable are the densities of the lanthanides compared to the densities of the actinides?

____

3. Which atomic groups tend to go from higher to lower densities reading from top to bottom? (Identify each group by its group number).

____

4. Which atomic groups tend to go from lower to higher densities reading from top to bottom?

____

The Submicroscopic

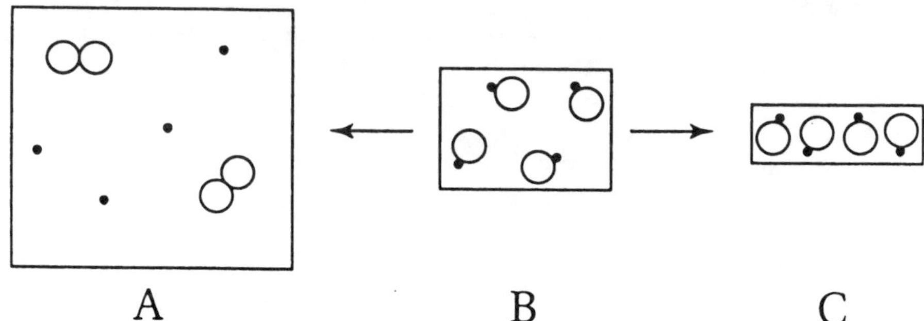

1. How many molecules are shown in A ______ B ______ C ______
2. How many atoms are shown in A ______ B ______ C ______
3. Which represents a physical change? B ⟶ A B ⟶ C (*circle one*)
4. Which represents a chemical change? B ⟶ A B ⟶ C (*circle one*)
5. Which box(es) represent(s) a mixture? A ______ B ______ C ______
6. Which box contains the most mass? A ______ B ______ C ______
7. Which box is coldest? A ______ B ______ C ______
8. Which box contains the most air between molecules? A ______ B ______ C ______

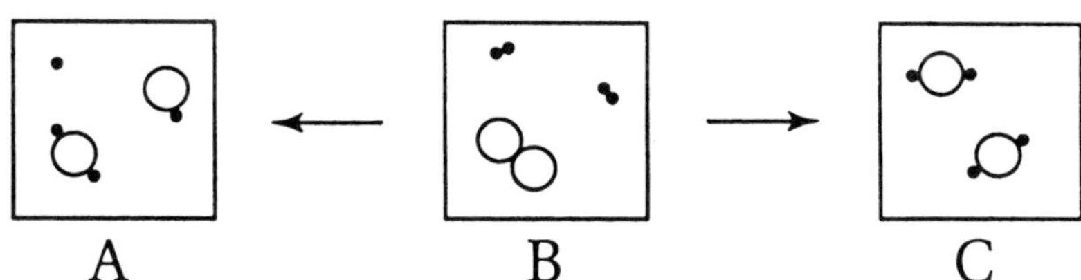

9. How many molecules are shown in A ______ B ______ C ______
10. How many atoms are shown in A ______ B ______ C ______
11. Which represents a physical change? B ⟶ A B ⟶ C (*circle one*)
12. Which represents a chemical change? B ⟶ A B ⟶ C (*circle one*)
13. Which box(es) represent(s) a mixture? A ______ B ______ C ______
14. Which box contains the most mass? A ______ B ______ C ______
15. Which should take longer? B ⟶ A B ⟶ C (*circle one*)
16. Which box most likely contains ions? A ______ B ______ C ______

Physical and Chemical Changes

1. What distinguishes a chemical change from a physical change?

2. Based upon observations alone, why is distinguishing a chemical change from a physical change not always so straight-forward?

Try your hand at categorizing the following processes as either chemical or physical changes. Some of these examples are debatable! Be sure to discuss your reasoning with fellow classmates or your instructor.

	(*circle one*)	
3. A cloud grows dark. ____________	chemical	physical
4. Leaves produce oxygen. ____________	chemical	physical
5. Food coloring is added to water. ____________	chemical	physical
6. Tropical coral reef dies. ____________	chemical	physical
7. Dead coral reef is pounded by waves into beach sand. ____________	chemical	physical
8. Oil and vinegar separate. ____________	chemical	physical
9. Soda drink goes flat. ____________	chemical	physical
10. Sick person develops a fever. ____________	chemical	physical
11. Compost pit turns into mulch. ____________	chemical	physical
12. A computer is turned on. ____________	chemical	physical
13. An electrical short melts a computer's integrated circuits. ____________	chemical	physical
14. A car battery runs down. ____________	chemical	physical
15. A pencil is sharpened. ____________	chemical	physical
16. Mascara is applied to eyelashes. ____________	chemical	physical
17. Sunbather gets tan lying in the sun. ____________	chemical	physical
18. Invisible ink turns visible upon heating. ____________	chemical	physical
19. A light bulb burns out. ____________	chemical	physical
20. Car engine consumes a tank of gasoline. ____________	chemical	physical
21. B vitamins turn urine yellow. ____________	chemical	physical

Check List for Chapter 3

You are ready to take the practice test for Chapter 3. Be sure that you have accomplished the following learning goals for this chapter. If you are not sure, review the section listed at the end of the goal. Then apply your new skills and understanding to the practice test.
After studying Chapter 3, I can successfully:

_____ Classify matter as a pure substance or a mixture (3.1).

_____ Write the correct symbol or name for an element (3.2).

_____ Use the periodic table to identify the group and period of an element, and describe it as a metal, nonmetal, or metalloid (3.3).

_____ State the electrical charge, mass, and location of the protons, neutrons, and electrons in an atom (3.4).

_____ Given the atomic number and mass number of an atom, state the number of protons, neutrons, and electrons (3.5).

_____ Identify an isotope and describe the atomic mass of an element (3.6).

_____ Write the electron energy level arrangements for elements with atomic number 1–18 (3.7).

_____ State the number of electrons in *s, p,* and *d* orbitals.

_____ Use the periodic table to predict periodic trends in atomic size and ionization energy (3.8).

Practice Test for Chapter 3

Write or select the correct answer for each of the following questions.
Write the correct symbol for each of the elements listed:

1. potassium _______________ **4.** carbon _______________

2. phosphorus _______________ **5.** sodium _______________

3. calcium _______________

Write the correct name for each of the symbols listed below:

6. Fe _______________ **9.** Pb _______________

7. Cu _______________ **10.** Ag _______________

8. Cl _______________

11. The elements C, N, and O are part of a
A. period **B.** family **C.** neither

12. The elements Li, Na, and K are part of a
A. period **B.** family **C.** neither

13. What is the classification of an atom with 15 protons and 17 neutrons?
A. metal **B.** nonmetal **C.** transition element **D.** noble gas **E.** halogen

14. What is the group number of the element with atomic number 3?
A. 1 **B.** 2 **C.** 3 **D.** 7 **E.** 8

For questions 15 through 18, consider an atom with 12 protons and 13 neutrons.

15. This atom has an atomic number of
A. 12 **B.** 13 **C.** 23 **D.** 24 **E.** 25

16. This atom has a mass number of
A. 12 **B.** 13 **C.** 23 **D.** 24 **E.** 25

17. This is an atom of
A. carbon **B.** sodium **C.** magnesium **D.** aluminum **E.** manganese

18. The number of electrons in this atom is
A. 12 **B.** 13 **C.** 23 **D.** 24 **E.** 25

For questions 19 through 22, consider an atom of calcium with a mass number of 42.

19. This atom of calcium has an atomic number of
A. 20 **B.** 22 **C.** 40 **D.** 41 **E.** 42

20. The number of protons in this atom of calcium is
A. 20 **B.** 22 **C.** 40 **D.** 41 **E.** 42

21. The number of neutrons in this atom of calcium is
A. 20 **B.** 22 **C.** 40 **D.** 41 **E.** 42

22. The number of electrons in this atom of calcium is
A. 20 **B.** 22 **C.** 40 **D.** 41 **E.** 42

23. Platinum, ^{195}Pt, has
A. 78 p^+, 78e^-, 78n **B.** 195 p^+, 195e^-, 195n **C.** 78p^+, 78e^-, 195n **D.** 78p^+, 78e^-, 117n
E. 78p^+, 117e^-, 117n

For questions 24 through 25, use the following list of atoms.

$^{14}_{7}V$ $^{16}_{8}W$ $^{19}_{9}X$ $^{16}_{7}Y$ $^{18}_{8}Z$

24. Which atoms(s) are isotopes of an atom with 8 protons and 9 neutrons?
A. W **B.** W, Z **C.** X, Y **D.** X **E.** Y

25. Which atom(s) are isotopes of an atom with 7 protons and 8 neutrons?
A. V **B.** W **C.** V, Y **D.** W, Z **E.** none

26. Which element would you expect to have properties most like oxygen?
A. nitrogen **B.** carbon **C.** chlorine **D.** argon **E.** sulfur

27. Which of the following is an isotope of nitrogen?
A. $^{14}_{8}N$ **B.** $^{7}_{3}N$ **C.** $^{10}_{5}N$ **D.** $^{4}_{2}N$ **E.** $^{15}_{7}N$

28. Except for helium, the number of electrons in the outer levels of the noble gases is
A. 3 **B.** 5 **C.** 7 **D.** 8 **E.** 12

29. The electron level arrangement for an oxygen atom is
A. 2,4 **B.** 2,8 **C.** 2,6 **D.** 2.4.2 **E.** 2,6,2

30. The electron level arrangement for aluminum is
A. 2,11 **B.** 2,8,5 **C.** 2,8,3 **D.** 2,10,1 **E.** 2,2,6,3

Key Terms

alkali metals Elements of Group 1A (1) except hydrogen; these are soft, shiny metals with one outer shell electron.

alkaline earth metals Group 2A (2) elements, which have 2 electrons in their outer shells.

atom The smallest particle of an element that retains the characteristics of the element.

atomic mass The weighted average mass of all the naturally occurring isotopes of an element.

atomic mass unit (amu) A small mass unit used to describe the mass of very small particles such as atoms and subatomic particles; 1 amu is equal to one-twelfth the mass of a ^{12}C atom.

atomic number A number that is equal to the number of protons in an atom.

atomic symbol An abbreviation used to indicate the mass number and atomic number of an isotope.

chemical symbol An abbreviation that represents the name of an element.

compound A pure substance consisting of two or more elements, with a definite composition, that can be broken down into simpler substances by chemical methods.

electron A negatively charged subatomic particle having a very small mass that is usually ignored in calculations; its symbol is e^-.

electron-dot symbol The representation of an atom that shows valence electrons as dots around the symbol of the element.

element A pure substance that cannot be separated into any simpler substances by chemical methods.

group A vertical column in the periodic table that contains elements having similar physical and chemical properties.

group number A number that appears at the top of each vertical column (group) in the periodic table and indicates the number of electrons in the outermost energy level.

halogen Group 7A (17) elements of fluorine, chlorine, bromine, iodine, and astatine.

heterogeneous mixture A mixture of two or more substances that are not mixed uniformly.

homogeneous mixture A mixture of two or more substances that are mixed uniformly.

ionization energy The energy needed to remove the least tightly bound electron from the outermost energy level of an atom.

isotope An atom that differs only in mass number from another atom of the same element. Isotopes have the same atomic number (number of protons) but different numbers of neutrons.

mass number The total number of neutrons and protons in the nucleus of an atom.

matter Anything that has mass and occupies space.

metal An element that is shiny, malleable, ductile, and a good conductor of heat and electricity. The metals are located to the left of the zigzag line in the periodic table.

metalloid Elements with properties of both metals and nonmetals located along the heavy zigzag line on the periodic table.

mixture The physical combination of two or more substances that does not change the identities of the mixed substances.

neutron A neutral subatomic particle having a mass of 1 amu and found in the nucleus of an atom; its symbol is n or n^0.

noble gas An element in Group 8A (18) of the periodic table, generally unreactive and seldom found in combination with other elements.

nonmetal An element with little or no luster that is a poor conductor of heat and electricity. The nonmetals are located to the right of the zigzag line in the periodic table.

nucleus The compact, very dense center of an atom, containing the protons and neutrons of the atom.

orbital The region around the nucleus where electrons of a certain energy are more likely to be found. The *s* orbitals are spherical; the *p* orbitals have two lobes.

period A horizontal row of elements in the periodic table.

periodic table An arrangement of elements by increasing atomic number such that elements having similar chemical behavior are grouped in vertical columns.

physical property A characteristic that can be observed or measured without affecting the identity of an element, including shape, color, odor, taste, density, hardness, melting point, and boiling point.

proton A positively charged subatomic particle having a mass of 1 amu and found in the nucleus of an atom; its symbol is p or p^+.

pure substance A type of matter with a fixed composition: elements and compounds.

subatomic particle A particle within an atom; protons, neutrons, and electrons are subatomic particles.

valence electrons Electrons in the outermost energy level of an atom.

4 Chemical Compounds and Their Bonds

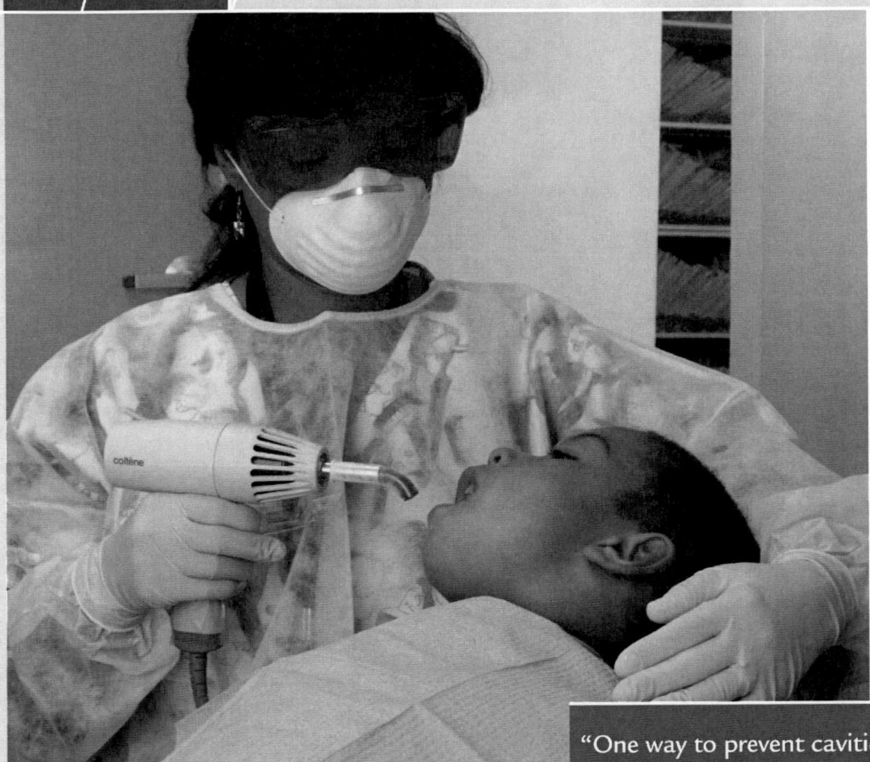

LOOKING AHEAD

"One way to prevent cavities in children is to apply a thin, plastic coating called a sealant to their teeth," says Dr. Pam Alston, a dentist in private practice. "We look for teeth with deep grooves and pits that trap food. We clean the teeth and apply an etching agent, which helps the sealant bind to the teeth. Then we apply the liquid sealant, which fills in the grooves and pits, and use ultraviolet light to solidify the coating."

The use of fluoride compounds, such as SnF_2 in toothpaste and NaF in water, and mouth rinses have greatly reduced tooth decay. The fluoride ion replaces the hydroxide ion to form $Ca_{10}(PO_4)_6F_2$, which strengthens the enamel and makes it less susceptible to decay. Other compounds used in dentistry are the anesthetic known as laughing gas, N_2O, and Novocaine, $C_{13}H_{20}N_2O_2$.

http://www.pearsoncustom.com/devry/mycbp

Study Goals

- Write an electron dot formula for an atom of a representative element.
- Use the octet rule to determine the ionic charge of ions for representative elements.
- Use charge balance to write an ionic formula.
- Draw the electron dot formula for covalent compounds.
- Write the correct names for ionic and covalent compounds.
- Write ionic formulas and names of compounds with polyatomic ions.
- Use electronegativity to determine the polarity of a bond.
- Use VSEPR theory to determine the shape and bond angles of a molecule.
- Identify a covalent compound as polar or nonpolar.

Chapter Review

Concept Map

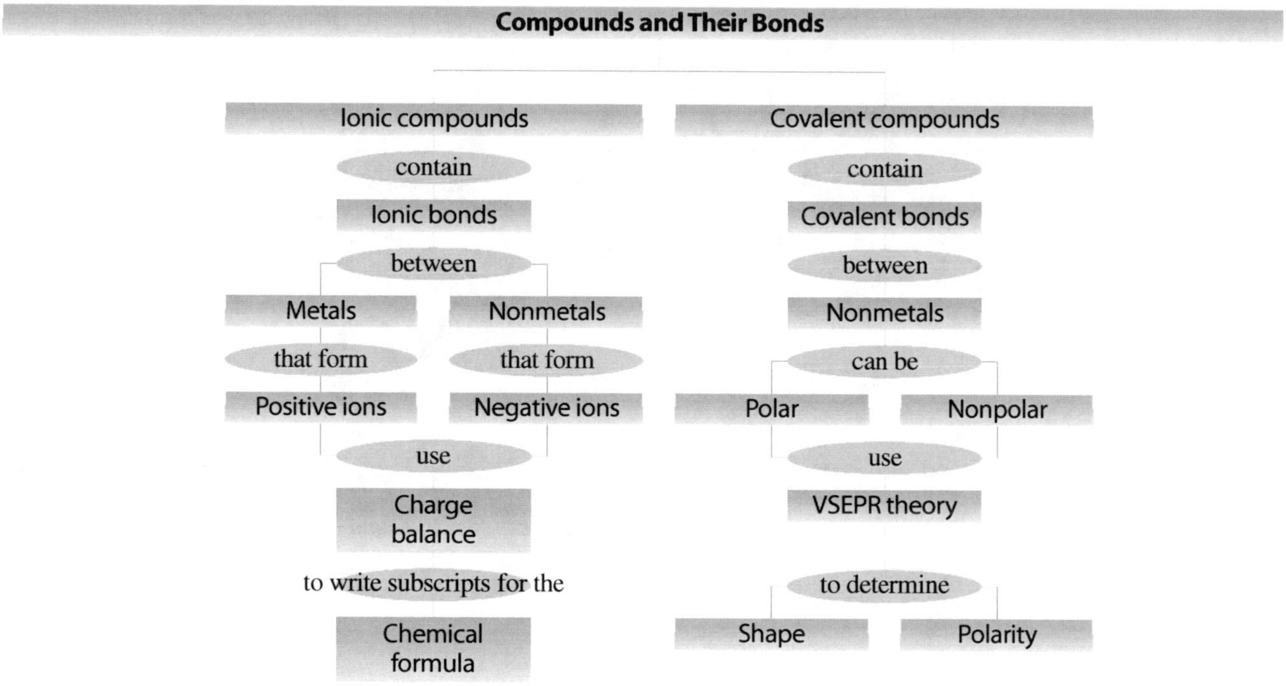

Compounds and Their Bonds

Ionic compounds
contain
Ionic bonds
between
Metals | Nonmetals
that form | that form
Positive ions | Negative ions
use
Charge balance
to write subscripts for the
Chemical formula

Covalent compounds
contain
Covalent bonds
between
Nonmetals
can be
Polar | Nonpolar
use
VSEPR theory
to determine
Shape | Polarity

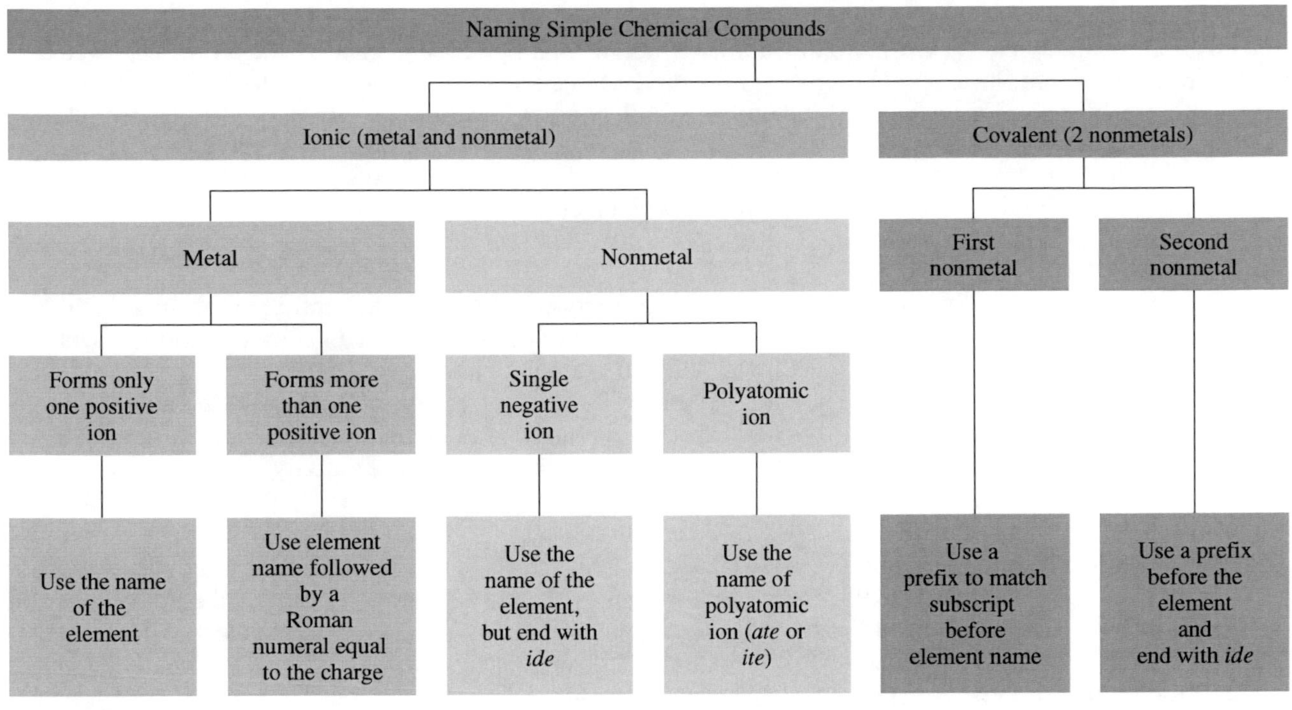

FIGURE 4.1

A flowchart of how ionic and covalent compounds are named.

Q Why are the names of some metal ions followed by a Roman numeral in the name of a compound?

Chapter Concept Review

4.1 Octet Rule and Ions

The nonreactivity of the noble gases is associated with the stable arrangement of 8 electrons, an octet, in their valence shells; helium needs 2 electrons for stability. Atoms of elements other than the noble gases achieve stability by losing, gaining, or sharing their valence electrons with other atoms in the formation of compounds. Metals of the representative elements form an octet by losing their valence electrons to form positively charged cations: Group 1A (1), 1+, Group 2A (2), 2+, and Group 3A (13), 3+. When they react with metals, nonmetals gain electrons to form octets in their valence shells. As anions, they have negative charges: Group 5A (15), 3−, Group 6A (16), 2−, Group 7A (17), 1−.

4.2 Ionic Compounds

The total positive and negative ionic charge must balance in the formula of an ionic compound. Charge balance in a formula is achieved by using subscripts after each symbol so that the overall charge is zero.

4.3 Naming and Writing Ionic Formulas

In naming ionic compounds, the positive ion is given first, followed by the name of the negative ion. Ionic compounds containing two elements end with *ide*. When the metal can form more than one positive ion, its ionic charge is determined from the total negative charge in the formula. Typically transition metals form cations with two or more ionic charges. The charge is given as a Roman numeral in the name, such as iron(II) and iron(III) for the cations of iron with 2+ and 3+ ionic charges.

4.4 Polyatomic Ions

A polyatomic ion is a group of nonmetal atoms that carries an electrical charge; for example, the carbonate ion has the formula CO_3^{2-}. Most polyatomic ions have names that end with *ate* or *ite*.

4.5 Covalent Compounds
In a covalent bond, electrons are shared by atoms of nonmetals. By sharing, each of the atoms achieves a noble gas arrangement. In a nonpolar covalent bond, electrons are shared equally by atoms. In a polar covalent bond, electrons are unequally shared because they are attracted by the more electronegative atom. In some covalent compounds, double or triple bonds are needed to provide an octet. Two nonmetals can form two or more different covalent compounds. In their names, prefixes are used to indicate the subscript in the formula. The ending of the second nonmetal is changed to *ide*.

4.6 Electronegativity and Bond Polarity
Electronegativity is the ability of an atom to attract the electrons it shares with another atom. In general, the electronegativities of metals are low, while nonmetals have high electronegativities. In a nonpolar covalent bond, atoms share the bonding pair of electrons equally. In a polar covalent bond, the bonding electrons are unequally shared because they are attracted to the more electronegative atom. As a result, the atom with the lower electronegativity is partially positive (δ^+) and the atom with the higher electronegativity is partially negative (δ^-). Atoms that form ionic bonds have large differences in electronegativity.

4.7 Shapes and Polarity of Molecules
The shape of a molecule is determined from the electron-dot formula and the number of bonded atoms and lone pairs. The electron arrangement of four electron groups around a central atom is tetrahedral. When all the electron groups are bonded to atoms, the shape has the same name as the electron arrangement. A central atom with two bonded atoms and two lone pairs has a bent shape. A central atom with three bonded atoms and one lone pair has a pyramidal shape.

A polar covalent bond is a covalent bond in which one end has a more electronegative atom than at the other end. Nonpolar molecules contain nonpolar covalent bonds or have an arrangement of bonded atoms that causes the dipoles to cancel out. In polar molecules, the dipoles do not cancel because there are non-identical bonded atoms or lone pairs.

Think About It

1. How does a compound differ from an element?

2. What are some compounds listed on the labels of your vitamins, toothpaste, and foods?

3. What makes salt an ionic compound?

4. Why are some covalent compounds polar and others nonpolar?

Key Terms

Match each the following key terms with the correct definition:

a. molecule **b.** ion **c.** ionic bond **d.** covalent bond **e.** octet

1. _____ A sharing of valence electrons by two atoms

2. _____ An arrangement of 8 electrons in the outer energy level

3. _____ The attraction between positively and negatively charged particles

4. _____ The smallest unit of two or more atoms held together by covalent bonds

5. _____ An atom or group of atoms with a positive or negative charge

4.1 Octet Rule and Ions

- The stability of the noble gases is associated with 8 electrons, an octet, in their valence energy levels. Helium is stable with 2 electrons in its valence energy level.

  He 2 Ar 2-8-8 Ne 2-8

  Atoms of elements other than the noble gases achieve stability by losing, gaining, or sharing their valence electrons with other atoms in the formation of compounds.
- A metal of the representative elements in Groups 1, 2, and 3 achieves a noble gas electron arrangement by losing its valence electrons to form a positively charged cation 1+, 2+, or 3+.
- When a nonmetal forms ions, electrons add to the valence energy level to give an octet, and form a negatively charged anion with a charge of 3−, 2−, or 1−.

◆ Learning Exercise 4.1A

Study Note

When an atom loses or gains electrons, it acquires the electron arrangement of its nearest noble gas. For example, sodium loses 1 electron, which gives the Na^{+} ion an arrangement like neon. Oxygen gains 2 electrons to give an oxide ion O^{2-} an arrangement like neon.

The following elements lose electrons when they form ions. Indicate the group number, the number of electrons lost, and the ion (symbol and charge) for each of the following:

Element	Group Number	Electrons Lost	Ion Formed
Magnesium			
Sodium			
Calcium			
Potassium			
Aluminum			

Study Note

The valence electrons are the electrons in the outermost energy level of an atom. For representative elements, you can determine the number of valence electrons by looking at the group number.

◆ Learning Exercise 4.1B

The following elements gain electrons when they form ions. Indicate the group number, the number of electrons gained, and the ion (symbol and charge) for each of the following:

Element	Group Number	Electrons Gained	Ion Formed
Chlorine			
Oxygen			
Nitrogen			
Fluorine			
Sulfur			

4.2 Ionic Compounds

- In the formulas of ionic compounds, the total positive charge is equal to the total negative charge. For example, the compound magnesium chloride, $MgCl_2$, contains Mg^{2+} and 2 Cl^-. The sum of the charges is zero: $(2+) + 2(1-) = 0$.
- When two or more ions are needed for charge balance, that number is indicated by subscripts in the formula.

◆ Learning Exercise 4.2A

For this exercise, you may want to cut pieces of paper that represent typical positive and negative ions as shown below. To determine an ionic formula, place the pieces together (positive ion first). Add more positive ions or negatives to complete a geometric shape. Write the number of positive ions and negative ions as the subscripts for the formula.

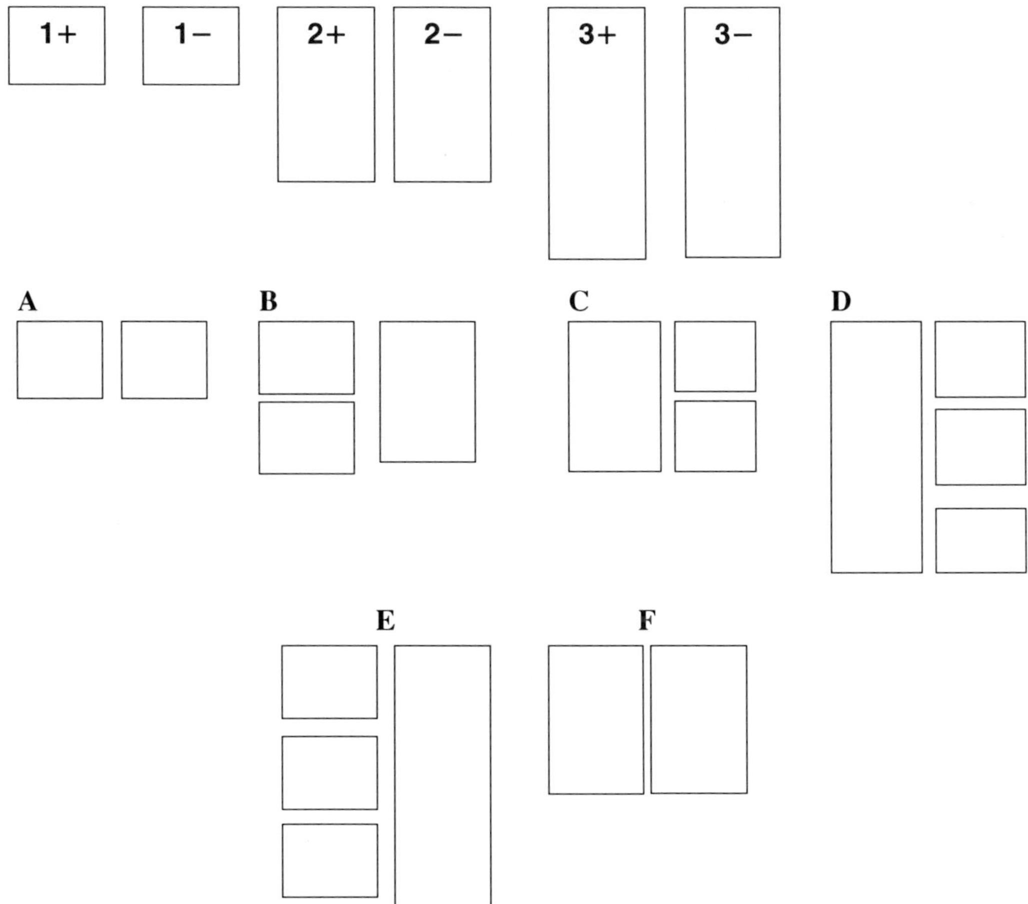

Give the letter (A, B, C, etc.) that matches the arrangement of ions in the following compounds:

	Compound	Combination		Compound	Combination
1.	$MgCl_2$	________	**5.**	K_3N	________
2.	Na_2S	________	**6.**	$AlBr_3$	________
3.	LiCl	________	**7.**	MgS	________
4.	CaO	________	**8.**	$BaCl_2$	________

◆ Learning Exercise 4.2B

Study Note

You can check that the formula you write is electrically neutral by multiplying each of the ionic charges by their subscripts. When added together, their sum should equal zero. For example, the formula Na_2O gives 2 (1+) + 1 (2−) = (2+) + (2−) = 0

Write the correct ionic formula for the compound formed from the following pairs of ions:

1. Na^+ and Cl^- ______________ **5.** Ca^{2+} and S^{2-} ______________

2. K^+ and S^{2-} ______________ **6.** Al^{3+} and Cl^- ______________

3. Al^{3+} and O^{2-} ______________ **7.** Li^+ and N^{3-} ______________

4. Mg^{2+} and Cl^- ______________ **8.** Ba^{2+} and P^{3-} ______________

4.3 Naming and Writing Ionic Compounds

- In naming ionic compounds, the positive ion is named first, followed by the name of the negative ion. The name of a representative metal ion (Group 1A (1), 2A (2), or 3A (13)) is the same as its elemental name. The name of a nonmetal ion is obtained by replacing the end of its element name with *ide.*
- Most transition metals form cations with two or more ionic charges. Then the ionic charge must be written as a Roman numeral after the name of the metal. For example, the cations of iron, Fe^{2+} and Fe^{3+}, are named iron(II) and iron(III). The ions of copper are Cu^+, copper(I), and Cu^{2+}, copper(II).
- The only transition elements with fixed charges are zinc, Zn^{2+}, silver, Ag^+, and cadmium, Cd^{2+}.

◆ Learning Exercise 4.3A

Many of the transition metals form two or more ions with positive charge. Complete the table:

	Name of ion	Symbol of ion		Name of ion	Symbol of ion
1.	iron(III)	______________	**2.**	____________	Cu^{2+}
3.	zinc	______________	**4.**	____________	Fe^{2+}
5.	copper(I)	______________	**6.**	____________	Ag^+

◆ Learning Exercise 4.3B

Write the ions and the correct ionic formula for the following ionic compounds:

Compound	Positive ion	Negative ion	Formula of compound
Aluminum sulfide			
Copper(II) chloride			
Magnesium oxide			
Iron(II) bromide			
Silver oxide			

◆ Learning Exercise 4.3C

Write the name of each of the following ions:

1. Cl^-	____________	7. S^{2-}	____________
2. Fe^{2+}	____________	8. Al^{3+}	____________
3. Cu^+	____________	9. Fe^{3+}	____________
4. Ag^+	____________	10. Ba^{2+}	____________
5. O^{2-}	____________	11. Cu^{2+}	____________
6. Ca^{2+}	____________	12. N^{3-}	____________

◆ Learning Exercise 4.3D

Study Note

The ionic charge of a metal that forms more than one positive ion is determined from the total negative charge in the formula. For example, in $FeCl_3$, the 3 Cl^- = 3(−). Therefore, the iron ion has an ionic charge of 3+ or Fe^{3+}, which is named iron(III).

Write the ions and a correct name for each of the following ionic compounds:

Formula	Ions		Name
1. $BaCl_2$	________	________	____________
2. $FeBr_3$	________	________	____________
3. Na_3P	________	________	____________
4. Al_2O_3	________	________	____________
5. CuO	________	________	____________
6. Mg_3N_2	________	________	____________

4.4 Polyatomic Ions

- A polyatomic ion is a group of nonmetal atoms that carries an electrical charge, usually negative, 1−, 2−, or 3−.
- Polyatomic ions cannot exist alone, but are combined with an ion of the opposite charge.
- Ionic compounds containing three elements (polyatomic ions) end with *-ate* or *-ite*.

Study Note

Learn the most common polyatomic ions: nitrate NO_3^-, carbonate CO_3^{2-}, sulfate SO_4^{2-}, and phosphate PO_4^{3-}. From these, you can derive the related polyatomic ions. For example, the nitrite ion, NO_2^-, has one oxygen atom less than the nitrate.

◆ Learning Exercise 4.4A

Write the polyatomic ion (symbol and charge) for each of the following:

1. sulfate ion ______________ **5.** ammonium ion ______________

2. hydroxide ion ______________ **6.** phosphate ion ______________

3. carbonate ion ______________ **7.** nitrate ion ______________

4. sulfite ion ______________ **8.** nitrite ion ______________

◆ Learning Exercise 4.4B

Write the formula of each ion or polyatomic ion, and the correct formula for the following compounds:

Compound	Positive ion	Negative ion	Formula
Sodium phosphate			
Iron(II) hydroxide			
Ammonium carbonate			
Silver bicarbonate			
Iron(III) sulfate			
Ferrous nitrate			
Potassium sulfite			
Barium phosphate			

4.5 Covalent Compounds

WEB TUTORIAL
Covalent Bonds

- In a covalent bond, atoms of nonmetals share electrons to achieve an octet. For example, oxygen with six valence electrons shares electrons with two hydrogen atoms to form the covalent compound water (H_2O).

$$\begin{array}{c} \mathrm{H}:\ddot{\underset{\cdot\cdot}{\mathrm{O}}}: \\ \mathrm{H} \end{array}$$

- In a double bond, two pairs of electrons are shared between the same two atoms. In a triple bond, three pairs of electrons are shared.
- Covalent compounds are composed of nonmetals bonded together to give discrete units called molecules.
- The formula of a covalent compound is written using the symbol of the nonmetals in the name following by subscripts given by the prefixes.

◆ Learning Exercise 4.5A

Write the electron dot formulas for the following covalent compounds (the central atom is underlined):

H_2 $\underline{N}Cl_3$ HCl

Cl_2 $H_2\underline{S}$ $\underline{C}Cl_4$

◆ Learning Exercise 4.5B

Study Note

Two nonmetals can form two or more different covalent compounds. In their names, prefixes are used to indicate the subscript in the formula. Some typical prefixes are mono (1), di (2), tri (3), tetra (4), and 5 (penta). The ending of the second nonmetal is changed to *-ide*.

Use the appropriate prefixes in naming the following covalent compounds:

1. CS_2 ____________ **4.** SO_2 ____________

2. CCl_4 ____________ **5.** N_2O_4 ____________

3. CO ____________ **6.** PCl_3 ____________

◆ Learning Exercise 4.5C

Write the formula of each of the following covalent compounds:

1. dinitrogen oxide ________ **4.** carbon dioxide ________

2. silicon tetrabromide________ **5.** sulfur hexafluoride ________

3. nitrogen trichloride ________ **6.** oxygen difluoride ________

Summary of Writing Formulas and Names

- In both ionic and covalent compounds containing *two* different elements, the name of the element written first is named as the element. The ending of the name of the second element is replaced by "ide." For example, $BaCl_2$ is named *barium chloride.* If the metal is variable and forms two or more positive ions, a Roman numeral is added to its name to indicate the ionic charge in the compound. For example, $FeCl_3$ is named *iron(III) chloride.*
- In naming covalent compounds, a prefix before the name of an element indicates the numerical value of a subscript. For example, N_2O_3 is named *dinitrogen trioxide.*
- In ionic compounds with three or more elements, a group of atoms is named as a polyatomic ion. The names of negative polyatomic ions end in "ate" or "ite," except for hydroxide. For example, Na_2SO_4 is named *sodium sulfate.*
- When a polyatomic ion occurs two or three times in a formula, its formula is placed inside parenthesis, and the number of ions are shown as a subscript after the parenthesis $Ca(NO_3)_2$.

◆ Learning Exercise 4.5D

Indicate the type of compound (ionic or covalent) formed from each pair of elements. If it is ionic, write the ions; if covalent, write the electron-dot formula of the molecule. Then give a formula and name for each.

Components	Ionic or covalent?	Ions or electron-dot formula of molecule	Formula	Name
Mg and Cl				
N and Cl				
K and SO_4				
Li and O				
C and Cl				
Na and PO_4				
H and S				
Ca and HCO_3				

◆ Learning Exercise 4.5 E

Write the formula of each ion or polyatomic ion, and the correct formula for each of the following compounds:

Compound	Positive ion	Negative ion	Formula
Sodium phosphate			
Iron(II) hydroxide			
Ammonium carbonate			
Sodium phosphate			
Silver bicarbonate			
Iron(III) sulfate			
Copper(II) nitrate			
Potassium sulfite			
Barium phosphate			

4.6 Electronegativity and Bond Polarity

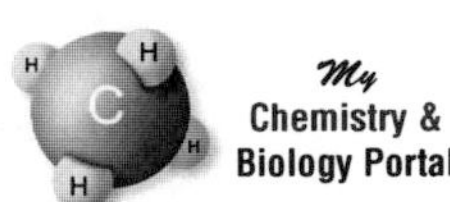

WEB TUTORIAL
Electronegativity

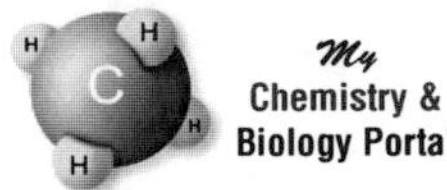

WEB TUTORIAL
Bonds and Bond Polarity

- Electronegativity indicates the ability of an atom to attract electrons. In general, metals have low electronegativity values and nonmetals have high values.
- When atoms sharing electrons have the same or similar electronegativity values, electrons are shared equally and the bond is *nonpolar covalent*.
- Electrons are shared unequally in *polar covalent* bonds because they are attracted to the more electronegative atom.
- An electronegativity difference of 0 to 0.4 indicates a nonpolar covalent bond, while a difference of 0.5 to 1.7 indicates a polar covalent bond.
- An electronegativity difference of 1.8 or greater indicates a bond that is ionic.

◆ Learning Exercise 4.6

Using the electronegativity values, determine the following:

1. the electronegativity difference for each pair
2. the type of bonding as (I) ionic, (PC) polar covalent, or (NC) nonpolar covalent

	Elements	Electronegativity difference	Bonding
a.	H and O	____________	____________
b.	N and S	____________	____________
c.	Al and O	____________	____________
d.	Li and F	____________	____________

	Elements	Electronegativity difference	Bonding
e.	H and Cl	____________	____________
f.	Cl and Cl	____________	____________
g.	S and F	____________	____________
h.	H and C	____________	____________

4.7 Shapes and Polarity of Molecules

WEB TUTORIAL
The Shape of Molecules

- Valence-shell electron-pair repulsion (VSEPR) theory predicts the geometry of a molecule by placing the electron pairs around a central atom as far apart as possible.
- A tetrahedral molecule has a central atom bonded to four atoms and no lone pairs. In a pyramidal molecule (109°), a central atom is bonded to three atoms and one lone pair. In a bent molecule at 109°, a central atom is bonded to two atoms and two lone pairs.
- A polar bond with its charge separation is called a dipole.
- Nonpolar molecules can have polar bonds when the dipoles are in a symmetrical arrangement.
- In polar molecules, the dipoles do not cancel each other.

Study Note

Guidelines for predicting the shaping of molecules:

1. Write the electron-dot formula.
2. Use VSEPR theory to predict the arrangement of the electron groups around the central atom.
3. Identify the shape of the molecule from the number of atoms bonded to the central atom.

◆ Learning Exercise 4.7A

Match the shape of a molecule with the following descriptions of the electron groups around the central atoms and the number of bonded atoms.

a. tetrahedral **b.** pyramidal **c.** bent (109°)

1. four electron groups with three bonded atoms _______
2. four electron groups with four bonded atoms _______
3. four electron groups with two bonded atoms _______

◆ Learning Exercise 4.7B

For each of the following, write the electron-dot formula, state the number of electron groups and bonded atoms, and predict the shape and angles of the molecule.

Molecule or ion	Electron-dot formula	Number of electron groups	Number of bonded atoms	Shape and angle
CH_4				
PCl_3				
H_2S				

◆ Learning Exercise 4.7C

Write the symbols δ^+ and δ^- over the atoms in polar bonds.

1. H—O **2.** N—N **3.** C—Cl

4. O—F **5.** N—F **6.** P—Cl

◆ Learning Exercise 4.7D

Indicate the dipoles in each of the following and determine whether the molecule is polar or nonpolar:

1. CF_4 **2.** HCl

3. NH_3 **4.** OF_2

Exercises in The Nature of Chemical Bonds

Losing Valence Electrons

The shell model can be used to explain a wide variety of properties of atoms. Using the shell model, for example, we can explain how atoms within the same group tend to lose (or gain) the same number of electrons. Let's consider the case of three group 1 elements: lithium, sodium, and potassium. Look to a periodic table and find the nuclear charge of each of these atoms:

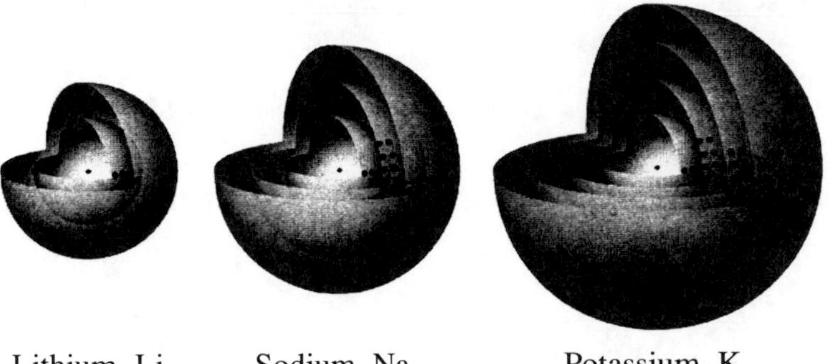

	Lithium, Li	Sodium, Na	Potassium, K
Nuclear charge:	________	________	________
Number of inner shell electrons:	________	________	________

How strongly the valence electron is held to the nucleus depends on the strength of the nuclear charge—the stronger the charge, the stronger the valence electron is held. There's more to it, however, because inner-shell electrons weaken the attraction outer-shell electrons have for the nucleus. The valence shell in lithium, for example, doesn't experience the full effect of three protons. Instead, it experiences a diminished nuclear charge of about +1. We get this by subtracting the number of inner-shell electrons from the actual nuclear charge. What do the valence electrons for sodium and potassium experience?

Diminished nuclear charge: ________ ________ ________

Question: Potassium has a nuclear charge many times greater than that of lithium. Why is it actually *easier* for a potassium atom to lose its valence electron than it is for a lithium atom to lose its valence electron?

Hint: Remember what happens to the electric force as distance is increased!

Drawing Shells

Atomic shells can be represented by a series of concentric circles as shown in your textbook. With a little effort, however, it's possible to show these shells in three dimensions. Grab a pencil and blank sheet of paper and follow the steps shown below. Practice makes perfect.

1. Lightly draw a diagonal guideline. Then, draw a series of seven semicircles. Note how the ends of the semicircles are not perpendicular to the guideline. Instead, they are parallel to the length of the page, as shown in Figure 1.

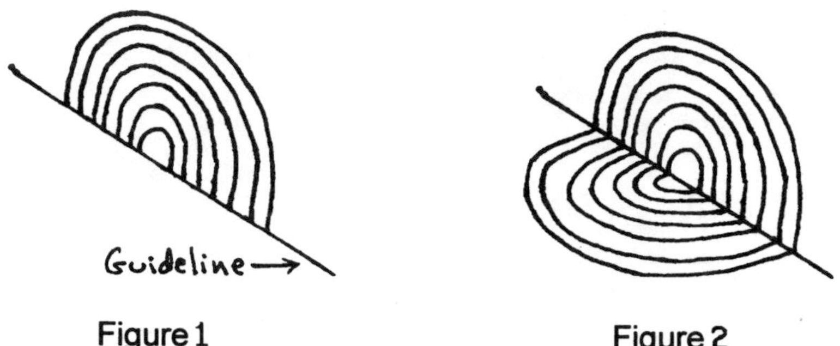

Figure 1 Figure 2

2. Connect the ends of each semicircle with another semicircle such that a series of concentric hearts is drawn. The ends of these new semicircles should be drawn perpendicular to the ends of the previously drawn semicircles, as shown in Figure 2.

3. Now the hard part. Draw a portion of a circle that connects the apex of the largest vertical and horizontal semicircles, as in Figure 3.

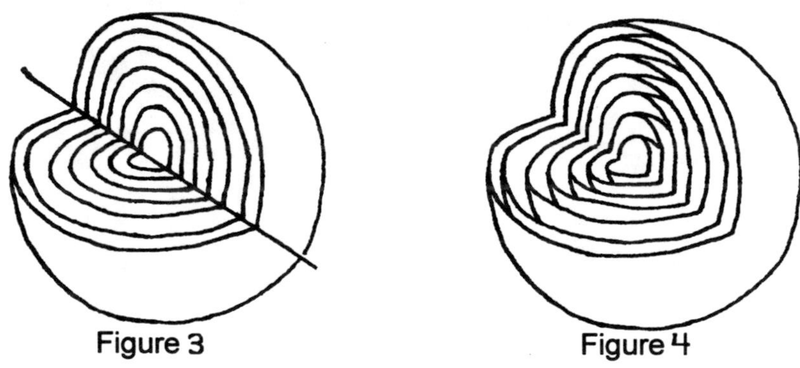

Figure 3 Figure 4

4. Now the fun part. Erase the pencil guideline drawn in Step 1, then add the internal lines, as shown in Figure 4, that create a series of concentric shells.

You need not draw all the shells for each atom. Oxygen, for example, is nicely represented drawing only the first two inner shells, which are the only ones that contain electrons. Remember that these shells are not to be taken literally. Rather, they are a highly simplified view of how electrons tend to organize themselves with an atom. You should know that each shell represents a set of atomic orbitals of similar energy levels as shown in your textbook.

Atomic Size

1. Complete the shells for the following atoms using arrows to represent electrons.

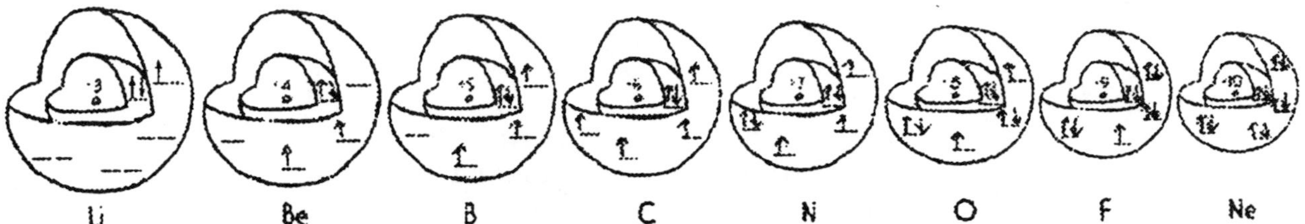

2. Neon, Ne, has many more electrons than lithium, Li, yet it is a much smaller atom. Why?

3. Draw the shell model for a sodium atom, Na (atomic number 11), adjacent to the neon atom in the box shown below. Use a pencil because you may need to erase.

   a. Which should be larger: neon's first shell or sodium's first shell. Why? Did you represent this accurately within your drawing?

   b. Which has a greater nuclear charge, Ne or Na?

   c. Which is a larger atom, Ne or Na?

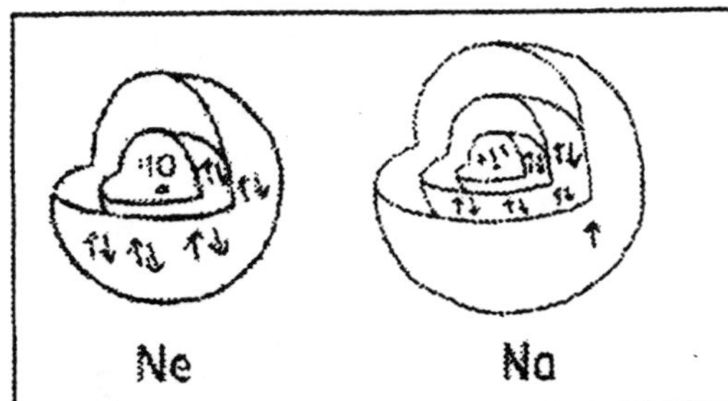

4. Moving from left to right across the periodic table, what happens to the nuclear charge within atoms? What happens to atomic size?

5. Moving from top to bottom down the periodic table, what happens to the number of occupied shells? What happens to atomic size?

6. Where in the periodic table are the smallest atoms found? Where are the largest atoms found?

Effective Nuclear Charge

The magnitude of the nuclear charge sensed by an orbiting electron depends upon several factors, including the number of positively–charged protons in the nucleus, the number of inner shell electrons shielding it from the nucleus, and its distance from the nucleus.

1. Place the proper number of electrons in each shell for carbon and silicon (use arrows to represent electrons).

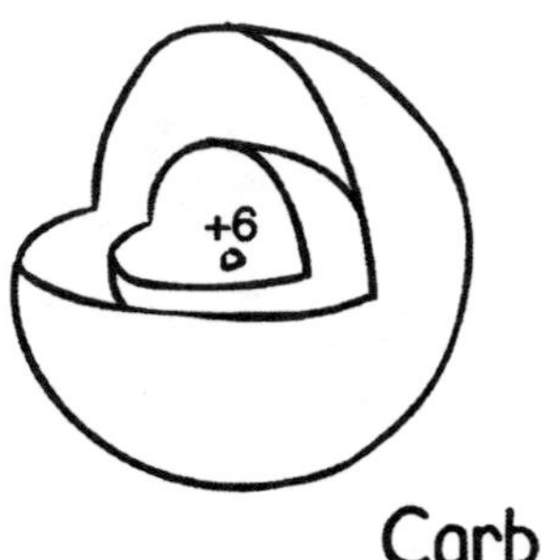
+6
Carbon

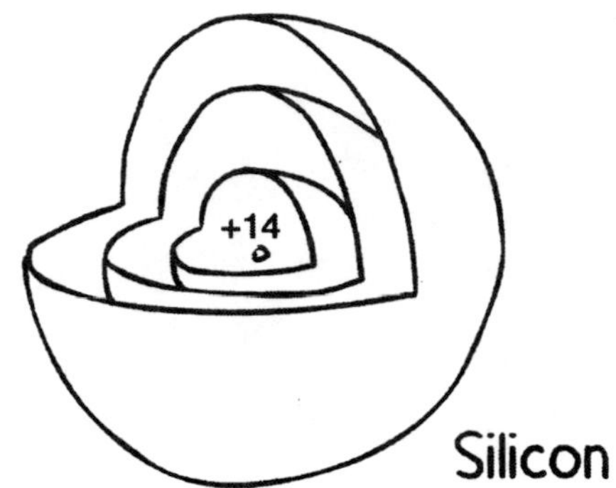
+14
Silicon

2. According to the shell model, which should experience the greater effective nuclear charge: an electron in
- **a.** carbon's 1st shell or silicon's 1st shell? (circle one)
- **b.** carbon's 2nd shell or silicon's 2nd shell? (circle one)
- **c.** carbon's 2nd shell or silicon's 3rd shell? (circle one)

3. List the shells of carbon and silicon in order of decreasing effective nuclear charge.

______________ > ______________ > ______________ > ______________ > ______________

4. Which should have the greater ionization energy, the carbon atom or the silicon atom? Defend your answer.

Periodic Table

5. How many additional electrons are able to fit in the outermost shell of carbon? _______silicon? _______

6. Which should be stronger, a C-H bond or an Si-H bond? Defend your answer.

7. Which should be larger in size, the ion C^{4+} or the ion Si^{4+}? Why?

Solutions

1. Use these terms to complete the following sentences. Some terms may be used more than once.

solution	**solvent**	**solute**
dissolve	**concentrated**	**dilute**
saturated	**concentration**	**mole**
molarity	**solubility**	**soluble**
insoluble	**precipitate**	

Sugar is _____________ in water for the two can be mixed homogeneously to form a _____________. The _____________ of sugar in water is so great that _____________ homogeneous mixtures are easily prepared. Sugar, however, is not infinitely _____________ in water for when too much of this _____________ is added to water, which behaves as the _____________, the solution becomes _____________. At this point any additional sugar is _____________ for it will not _____________. If the temperature of a saturated sugar solution is lowered, the _____________ of the sugar in water is also lowered. If some of the sugar comes out of solution, it is said to form a _____________. If, however, the sugar remains in solution despite the decrease in solubility, then the solution is said to be supersaturated. Adding only a small amount of sugar to water results in a _____________ solution. The _____________ of this solution or any solution can be measured in terms of _____________, which tells us the number of solute molecules per liter of solution. If there are 6.022×10^{23} molecules in 1 liter of solution, then the _____________ of the solution is 1 _____________ per liter.

2. Temperature has a variety of effects on the solubilities of various solutes. With some solutes, such as sugar, solubility increases with increasing temperature. With other solutes, such as sodium chloride (table salt), changing temperature has no significant effect. With some solutes, such as lithium sulfate, Li_2SO_4, the solubility actually decreases with increasing temperature.

   a. Describe how you would prepare a supersaturated solution of lithium sulfate.

   ____

   b. How might you cause a saturated solution of lithium sulfate to form a precipitate?

   ____

Pure Mathematics

Using a scientist's definition of *pure,* identify whether each of the following is 100% pure:

	100% pure?	
Freshly squeezed orange juice . .	Yes	No
Country air.	Yes	No
Ocean water	Yes	No
Fresh drinking water.	Yes	No
Skim milk	Yes	No
Stainless steel.	Yes	No
A single water molecule	Yes	No

A glass of water contains on the order of a trillion trillion (1×10^{24}) molecules. If the water in this were 99.9999% pure, you could calculate the percent of impurities by subtracting from 100.0000%.

$$\begin{array}{rl} & 100.0000\% \text{ water + impurity molecules} \\ - & 99.9999\% \text{ water molecules} \\ \hline & 0.0001\% \text{ impurity molecules} \end{array}$$

Pull out your calculator and calculate the number of impurity molecules in the glass of water. Do this by finding 0.0001% of 1×10^{24}, which is the same as multiplying 1×10^{24} by 0.000001.

$$(1 \times 10^{24})(0.000001) = \underline{\hspace{4cm}}$$

1. How many impurity molecules are there in a glass of water that's 99.9999% pure?
  a. 1000 (one thousand: 10^3)
  b. 1,000,000 (one million: 10^6)
  c. 1,000,000,000 (one billion: 10^9)
  d. 1,000,000,000,000,000,000 (one million trillion: 10^{18}).

2. How does your answer make you feel about drinking water that is 99.9999 percent free of some poison, such as pesticide?

____

3. For every one impurity molecule, how many water molecules are there? (Divide the number of water molecules by the number of impurity molecules.)

____

4. Would you describe these impurity molecules within water that's 99.9999% pure as "rare" or "common"?

____

5. A friend argues that he or she doesn't drink tap water because it contains thousands of molecules of some impurity in each glass. How would you respond in defense of the water's purity, if it indeed does contain thousands of molecules of some impurity per glass?

____

Chemical Bonds

1. Based upon their positions in the periodic table, predict whether each pair of elements will form an ionic bond, covalent bond, or neither (atomic number in parenthesis).
   - **a.** Gold (79) and platinum (78) ______
   - **b.** Rubidium (37) and iodine (53) ______
   - **c.** Sulfur (16) and chlorine (17) ______
   - **d.** Sulfur (16) and magnesium (12) ______
   - **e.** Calcium (20) and chlorine (17) ______
   - **f.** Germanium (32) and arsenic (33) ______
   - **g.** Iron (26) and chromium (24) ______
   - **h.** Chlorine (17) and iodine (53) ______
   - **i.** Carbon (6) and bromine (35) ______
   - **j.** Barium (56) and astatine (85) ______

2. The most common ions of lithium, magnesium, aluminum, chlorine, oxygen, and nitrogen and their respective charges are as follows:

Positively Charged Ions	Negatively Charged Ions
Lithium ion: Li^{1+}	Chloride ion: Cl^{1-}
Barium ion: Ba^{2+}	Oxide ion: O^{2-}
Aluminum ion: Al^{3+}	Nitride ion: N^{3-}

Use this information to predict the chemical formulas for the following ionic compounds:

- **a.** Lithium chloride:______
- **b.** Barium chloride:______
- **c.** Aluminum chloride:______
- **d.** Lithium oxide:______
- **e.** Barium oxide:______
- **f.** Aluminum oxide:______
- **g.** Lithium nitride:______
- **h.** Barium nitride:______
- **i.** Aluminum nitride:______
- **j.** How are elements that form positive ions grouped in the periodic table relative to elements that form negative ions?______________________________

3. Specify whether the following chemical structures are polar or nonpolar:

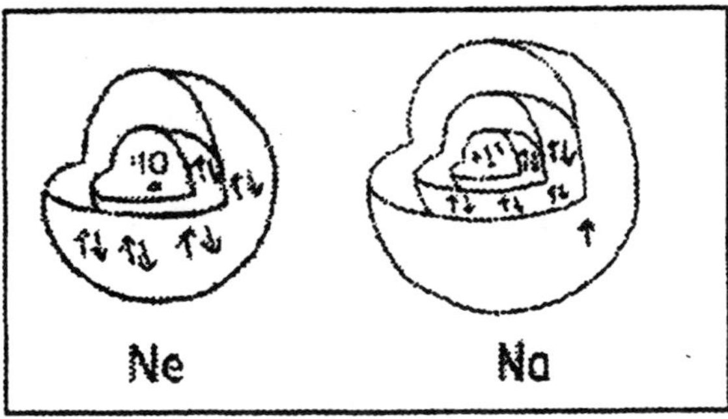

Shells and the Covalent Bond

When atoms bond covalently, their atomic shells overlap so that shared electrons can occupy both shells at the same time.

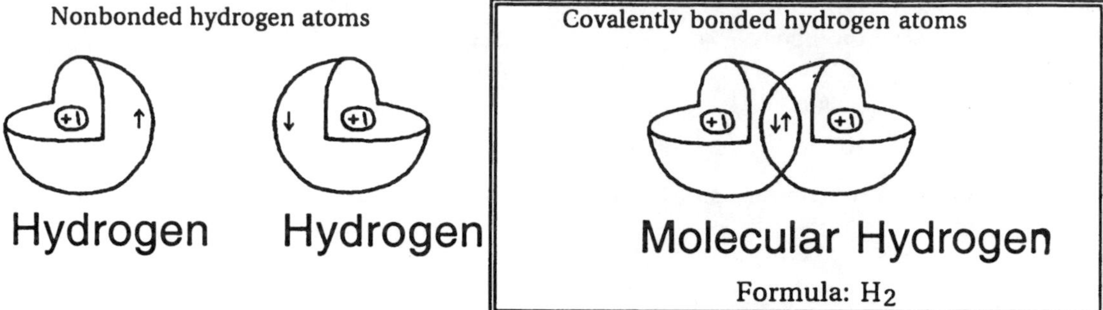

Fill each shell model shown below with enough electrons to make each atom electrically neutral. Use arrows to represent electrons. Within the box draw a sketch showing how the two atoms bond covalently. Draw hydrogen shells more than once when necessary so that no electrons remain unpaired. Write the name and chemical formula for each compound.

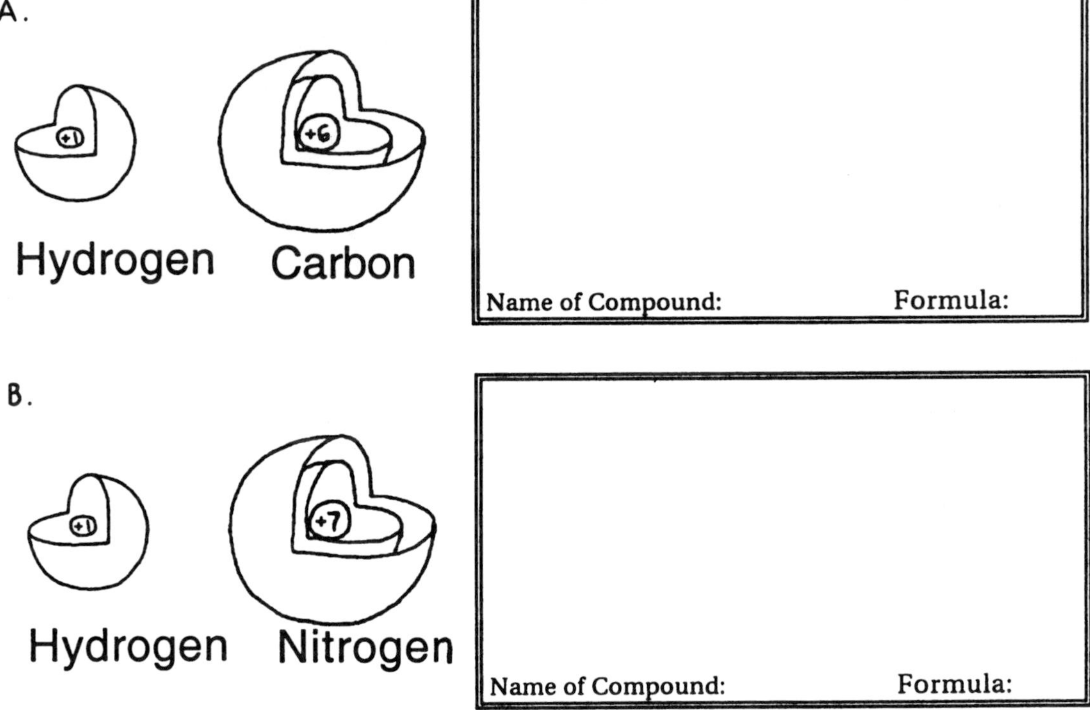

Shells and the Covalent Bond—*continued*

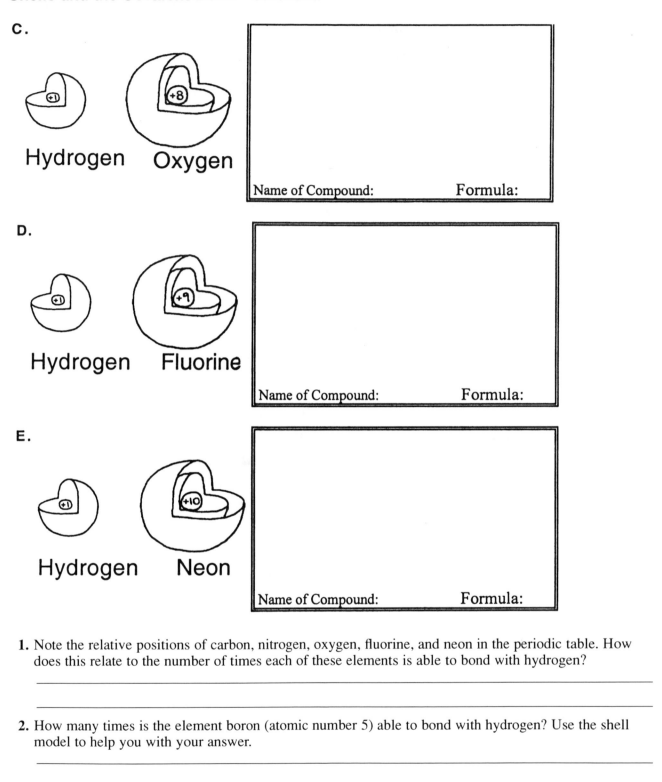

C.

Hydrogen Oxygen

Name of Compound: Formula:

D.

Hydrogen Fluorine

Name of Compound: Formula:

E.

Hydrogen Neon

Name of Compound: Formula:

1. Note the relative positions of carbon, nitrogen, oxygen, fluorine, and neon in the periodic table. How does this relate to the number of times each of these elements is able to bond with hydrogen?

2. How many times is the element boron (atomic number 5) able to bond with hydrogen? Use the shell model to help you with your answer.

Bond Polarity

solution	solvent	solute
dissolve	concentrated	dilute
saturated	concentration	mole
molarity	solubility	soluble
insoluble	precipitate	

1. Why are the nuclei of these atoms attracted to you?______________________
2. What type of chemical bonding is this?______________________________

You are held within hydrogen's 1st shell and at the same time within fluorine's 2nd shell. Draw a sketch using the shell models below to show how this is possible. Represent yourself and all other electrons using arrows. Note your particular location with a circle.

Hydrogen Fluorine

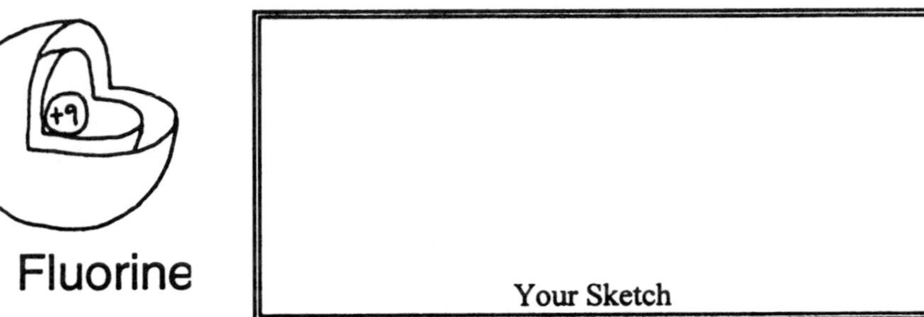

According to the laws of physics, if the nuclei are both attracted to you, then you are attracted to both of the nuclei.

3. You are pulled toward the hydrogen nucleus, which has a positive charge. How strong is this charge from your point of view—what is its *electronegativity?*______

4. You are also attracted to the fluorine nucleus. What is its electronegativity?______

You are being shared by the hydrogen and fluorine nuclei. But as a moving electron you have some choice as to your location.

5. Consider the electronegativities you experience from both nuclei. Which nucleus would you tend to be closest to? ______________

Bond Polarity—*continued*

Stop pretending you are an electron and observe the hydrogen-fluorine bond from outside the hydrogen fluoride molecule. Bonding electrons tend to congregate to one side because of the differences in effective nuclear charges. This makes one side slightly negative in character and the opposite side slightly positive. Indicate this on the following structure for hydrogen fluoride using the symbols δ- and δ+

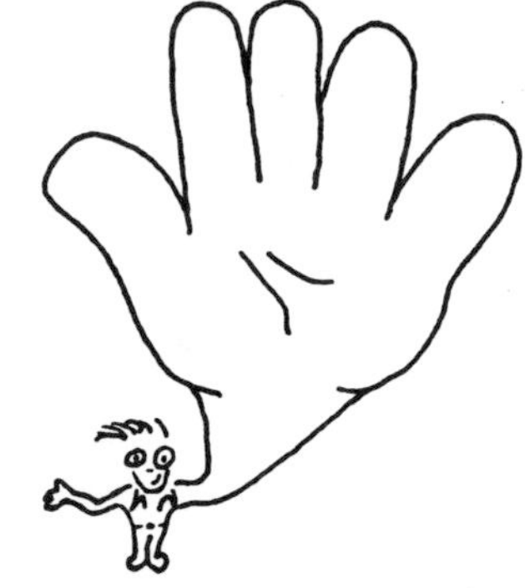

H : F

By convention, bonding electrons are not shown. Instead, a line is simply drawn connecting the two bonded atoms. Indicate the slightly negative and positive ends.

6. Would you describe hydrogen fluoride as a polar or nonpolar molecule?______

7. If two hydrogen fluoride molecules were thrown together, would they stick or repel? (Hint: What happens when you throw two small magnets together?)______

8. Place bonds between the hydrogen and fluorine atoms to show many hydrogen fluoride molecules grouped together. Each element should be bonded only once. Circle each molecule and indicate the slightly negative and slightly positive ends.

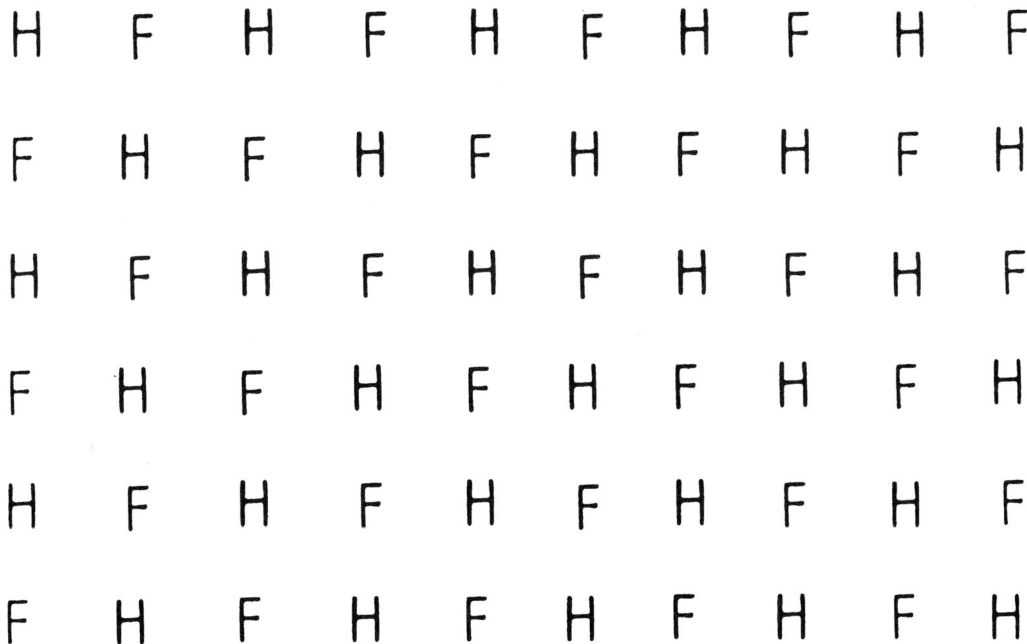

Atoms to Molecules

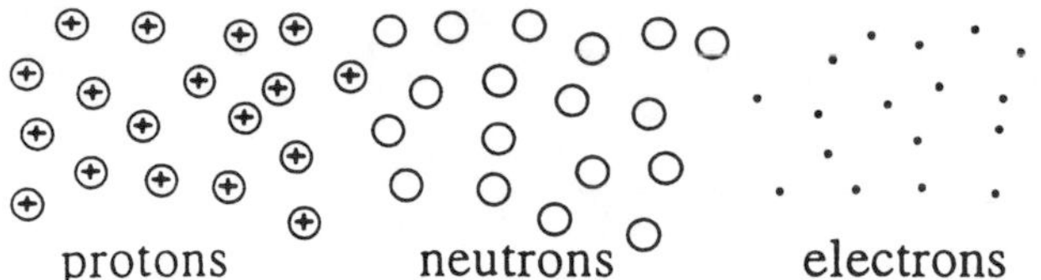

SUBATOMIC PARTICLES

Subatomic particles are the fundamental building blocks of all ______________.

hydrogen atom

hydrogen atom

oxygen atom

oxygen atom

hydrogen atom

hydrogen atom

ATOMS

An atom is a group of ______________ held tightly together. An oxygen atom is a group of 8 ______________, 8 ______________, and 8 ______________. A hydrogen atom is a group of only 1 ______________ and 1 ______________.

water molecule

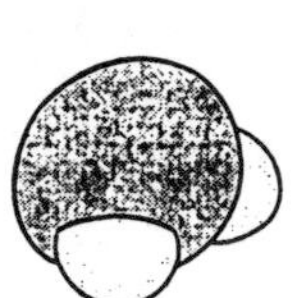

water molecule

MOLECULES

A ______________ is a group of atoms held tightly together. A water ______________ consists of 2 ______________ atoms and 1 ______________ atom.

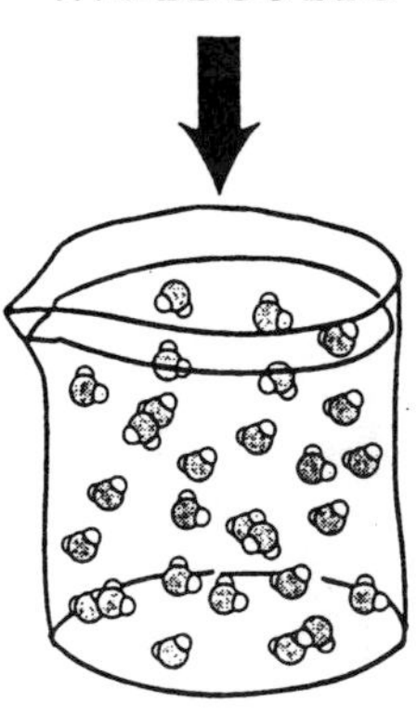

WATER

Water is a material made up of billions upon billions of water ______________. The physical properties of water are based upon how these water ______________ interact with one another.

Check List for Chapter 4

You are ready to take the self-test for Chapter 4. Be sure that you have accomplished the following learning goals for this chapter. If you are not sure, review the section listed at the end of the goal. Then apply your new skills and understanding to the practice test.
After studying Chapter 4, I can successfully:

_____ Illustrate the octet rule for the formation of ions (4.1).

_____ Write the formulas of compounds containing the ions of metals and nonmetals of representative elements (4.2).

_____ Use charge balance to write an ionic formula (4.2).

_____ Write the name of an ionic compound (4.3).

_____ Write the formula of a compound containing a polyatomic ion (4.4).

_____ Write the electron dot formula of a covalent compound (4.5).

_____ Write the name and formula of a covalent compound (4.5).

_____ Classify a bond as nonpolar covalent, polar covalent, or ionic (4.6).

_____ Use VSEPR theory to determine the shape of a molecule (4.7).

_____ Classify a molecule as a polar or nonpolar molecule (4.7).

Practice Test for Chapter 4

For questions 1 through 4, consider an atom of phosphorus.

1. It is in Group
A. 2A (2) **B.** 3A (13) **C.** 5A (15) **D.** 7A (17) **E.** 8A (18)

2. How many valence electrons does it have?
A. 2 **B.** 3 **C.** 5 **D.** 8 **E.** 15

3. To achieve an octet, the phosphorus atom will
A. lose 1 electron **B.** lose 2 electrons **C.** lose 5 electrons
D. gain 2 electrons **E.** gain 3 electrons

4. As an ion, it has an ionic charge (valence) of
A. 1+ **B.** 2+ **C.** 5+ **D.** 2− **E.** 3−

5. To achieve an octet, a calcium atom
A. loses 1 electron **B.** loses 2 electrons **C.** loses 3 electrons
D. gains 1 electron **E.** gains 2 electrons

6. To achieve an octet, a chlorine atom
A. loses 1 electron **B.** loses 2 electrons **C.** loses 3 electrons
D. gains 1 clcctron **E.** gains 2 clcctrons

7. Another name for a positive ion is
A. anion **B.** cation **C.** proton **D.** positron **E.** sodium

8. The correct ionic charge (valence) for calcium ion is
A. 1+ **B.** 2+ **C.** 1− **D.** 2− **E.** 3−

9. The silver ion has a charge of
A. 1+ **B.** 2+ **C.** 1− **D.** 2− **E.** 3−

10. The correct ionic charge (valence) for phosphate ion is
A. 1+ **B.** 2+ **C.** 1− **D.** 2− **E.** 3−

11. The correct ionic charge (valence) for fluoride is
A. 1+ **B.** 2+ **C.** 1− **D.** 2− **E.** 3−

12. The correct ionic charge (valence) for sulfate ion is
A. 1+ **B.** 2+ **C.** 1− **D.** 2− **E.** 3−

13. When the elements magnesium and sulfur are mixed,
A. an ionic compound forms.
B. a nonpolar covalent compound forms.
C. no reaction occurs.
D. the two repel each other and won't combine.
E. none of the above.

14. An ionic bond typically occurs between
A. two different nonmetals.
B. two of the same type of nonmetals.
C. two noble gases.
D. two different metals.
E. a metal and a nonmetal.

15. A nonpolar covalent bond typically occurs between
A. two different nonmetals.
B. two of the same type of nonmetals.
C. two noble gases.
D. two different metals.
E. a metal and a nonmetal.

16. A polar covalent bond typically occurs between
A. two different nonmetals.
B. two of the same type of nonmetals.
C. two noble gases.
D. two different metals.
E. a metal and a nonmetal.

17. The formula for a compound between carbon and chlorine is
A. Cl **B.** CCl_2 **C.** C_4Cl **D.** CCl_4 **E.** C_4Cl_2

18. The formula for a compound between sodium and sulfur is
A. SoS **B.** NaS **C.** Na_2S **D.** NaS_2 **E.** Na_2SO_4

19. The formula for a compound between aluminum and oxygen is
A. AlO **B.** Al_2O **C.** AlO_3 **D.** Al_2O_3 **E.** Al_3O_2

20. The formula for a compound between barium and sulfur is
A. BaS **B.** Ba_2S **C.** BaS_2 **D.** Ba_2S_2 **E.** $BaSO_4$

21. The correct formula for iron(III) chloride is
A. FeCl **B.** $FeCl_2$ **C.** Fe_2Cl **D.** Fe_3Cl **E.** $FeCl_3$

22. The correct formula for ammonium sulfate is
A. AmS **B.** $AmSO_4$ **C.** $(NH_4)_2S$ **D.** NH_4SO_4 **E.** $(NH_4)_2SO_4$

23. The correct formula for copper(II) chloride is
A. CoCl **B.** CuCl **C.** $CoCl_2$ **D.** $CuCl_2$ **E.** Cu_2Cl

24. The correct formula for lithium phosphate is
A. $LiPO_4$ **B.** Li_2PO_4 **C.** Li_3PO_4 **D.** $Li_2(PO_4)_3$ **E.** $Li_3(PO_4)_2$

25. The correct formula for silver oxide is
A. AgO **B.** Ag_2O **C.** AgO_2 **D.** Ag_3O_2 **E.** Ag_3O

26. The correct formula for magnesium carbonate is
A. $MgCO_3$ **B.** Mg_2CO_3 **C.** $Mg(CO_3)_2$ **D.** MgCO **E.** $Mg_2(CO_3)_3$

27. The correct formula for copper(I) sulfate is
A. $CuSO_3$ **B.** $CuSO_4$ **C.** Cu_2SO_3 **D.** $Cu(SO_4)_2$ **E.** Cu_2SO_4

28. The name of $AlPO_4$ is
A. aluminum phosphide **B.** alum phosphate **C.** aluminum phosphate
D. aluminum phosphorus oxide **E.** aluminum phosphite

29. The name of CuS is
A. copper sulfide **B.** copper(I) sulfate **C.** copper(I) sulfide
D. cuprous sulfide **E.** copper(II) sulfide

30. The name of $FeCl_2$ is
A. ferric chloride **B.** iron(II) chlorine **C.** iron(II) chloride
D. iron chlorine **E.** iron(III) chloride

31. The name of $ZnCO_3$ is
A. zinc(III) carbonate **B.** zinc(II) carbonate **C.** zinc bicarbonate
D. zinc carbon trioxide **E.** zinc carbonate

32. The name of Al_2O_3 is
A. aluminum oxide **B.** aluminum(II) oxide **C.** aluminum trioxide
D. dialuminum trioxide **E.** aluminum oxygenate

33. The name of NCl_3 is
A. nitrogen chloride **B.** nitrogen trichloride **C.** trinitrogen chloride
D. nitrogen chlorine three **E.** nitrogen chloride(III)

34. The name of CO is
A. carbon monoxide **B.** carbonic oxide **C.** carbon oxide
D. carbonious oxide **E.** carboxide

For questions 35 through 40, indicate the type of bonding expected between the following elements:
A. ionic **B.** nonpolar covalent **C.** polar covalent **D.** none

35. ____ silicon and oxygen

36. ____ barium and chlorine

37. ____ aluminum and chlorine

38. ____ chlorine and chlorine

39. ____ sulfur and oxygen

40. ____ neon and oxygen

Determine the shape and angles of each of the following molecules as

A. tetrahedral, 109° **B.** pyramidal, 109° **C.** bent, 109°

41. PCl_3 **42.** CBr_4 **43.** H_2S

Key Terms

anion A negatively charged ion such as Cl^-, O^{2-}, or SO_4^{2-}.

bent The shape of a molecule with two bonded atoms and two lone pairs.

cation A positively charged ion such as Na^+, Mg^{2+}, Al^{3+}, and NH_4^+.

dipole The separation of positive and negative charge in a polar bond indicated by an arrow that is drawn from the more positive atom to the more negative atom.

double bond A sharing of two pairs of electrons by two atoms.

electronegativity The relative ability of an element to attract electrons.

formula The group of symbols and subscripts that represent the atoms or ions in a compound.

ion An atom or group of atoms having an electrical charge because of a loss or gain of electrons.

ionic charge The difference between the number of protons (positive) and the number of electrons (negative) written in the upper right corner of the symbol for the element or polyatomic ion.

molecule The smallest unit of two or more atoms held together by covalent bonds.

nonpolar covalent bond A covalent bond in which the electrons are shared equally between atoms.

nonpolar molecule A molecule that has only nonpolar bonds or in which the bond dipoles cancel.

octet 8 valence electrons.

octet rule Elements in Groups 1–7A (1, 2, 13–17) react with other elements by forming ionic or covalent bonds to produce a noble gas arrangement, usually 8 electrons in the outer shell.

polar covalent bond A covalent bond in which the electrons are shared unequally between atoms.

polar molecule A molecule containing bond dipoles that do not cancel.

polyatomic ion A group of covalently bonded nonmetal atoms that has an overall electrical charge.

pyramidal The shape of a molecule that has three bonded atoms and one lone pair around a central atom.

tetrahedral The shape of a molecule with four bonded atoms.

triple bond A sharing of three pairs of electrons by two atoms.

valence-shell electron-pair repulsion (VSEPR) theory A theory that predicts the shape of a molecule by placing the electron pairs on a central atom as far apart as possible to minimize the mutual repulsion of the electrons.

5 Chemical Reactions and Quantities

LOOKING AHEAD

"In our food science laboratory I develop a variety of food products, from cake donuts to energy beverages," says Anne Cristofano, senior food technologist at Mattson & Company. "When I started the donut project, I researched the ingredients, then weighed them out in the lab. I added water to make a batter and cooked the donuts in a fryer. The batter and the oil temperature make a big difference. If I don't get the right taste or texture, I adjust the ingredients, such as sugar and flour, or adjust the temperature."

A food technologist studies the physical and chemical properties of food and develops scientific ways to process and preserve it for extended shelf life. The food products are tested for texture, color, and flavor. The results of these tests help improve the quality and safety of food.

http://www.pearsoncustom.com/devry/mycbp

Study Goals

- Classify a change in matter as a chemical change or a physical change.
- Show that a balanced equation has an equal number of atoms of each element on the reactant side and the product side.
- Write a balanced equation for a chemical reaction when given the formulas of the reactants and products.
- Classify an equation as a combination, decomposition, replacement and/or combustion reaction.
- Describe the features of oxidation and reduction in an oxidation–reduction reaction.
- Determine the molar mass of a compound from its formula.
- Use the molar mass to convert between the grams of a substance and the number of moles.
- Using a given number of moles and a mole–mole conversion factor, determine the corresponding number of moles for a reactant or a product.
- Using a given mass of a substance in a reaction and the appropriate mole factor and molar masses, calculate the mass of a reactant or a product.

Chapter Review

Concept Map

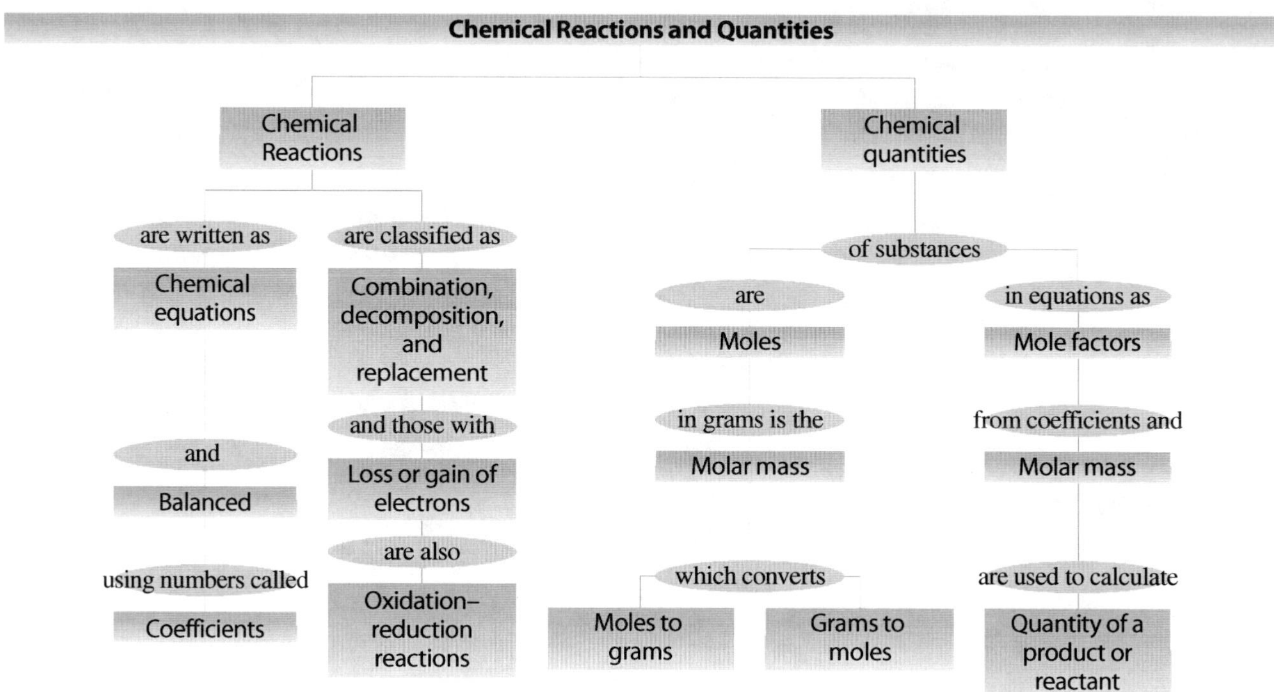

Chapter Concept Review

5.1 Chemical Changes

A chemical change occurs when the atoms of the initial substances rearrange to form new substances. When new substances form, a chemical reaction has taken place.

5.2 Chemical Equations
A chemical equation shows the formulas of the substances that react on the left side of a reaction arrow and the products that form on the right side of the reaction arrow. An equation is balanced by writing the smallest whole numbers (coefficients) in front of formulas to equalize the atoms of each element in the reactants and the products.

5.3 Types of Reactions
Many chemical reactions can be organized by reaction type: combination, decomposition, single replacement, or double replacement.

5.4 Oxidation–Reduction Reactions
When electrons are transferred in a reaction, it is an oxidation–reduction reaction. One reactant loses electrons, and another reactant gains electrons. Overall, the number of electrons lost and gained is equal.

5.5 The Mole
One mole of an element contains 6.02×10^{23} atoms; a mole of a compound contains 6.02×10^{23} molecules or formula units.

5.6 Molar Mass
The molar mass (g/mole) of any substance is the mass in grams equal numerically to its atomic mass, or the sum of the atomic masses, which have been multiplied by their subscripts in a formula. It becomes a conversion factor when it is used to change a quantity in grams to moles, or to change a given number of moles to grams.

5.7 Mole Relationships in Chemical Equations
In a balanced equation, the total mass of the reactants is equal to the total mass of the products. The coefficients in an equation describing the relationship between the moles of any two components are used to write mole–mole factors. When the number of moles for one substance is known, a mole–mole factor is used to find the moles of a different substance in the reaction.

5.8 Energy in Chemical Reactions
In a reaction, the reacting particles must collide with energy equal to or greater than the energy of activation. The heat of reaction is the energy difference between the initial energy of the reactants and the final energy of the products. In exothermic reactions, heat is released. In endothermic reactions, heat is absorbed. The rate of a reaction, which is the speed at which the reactants are converted to products, can be increased by adding more reactants, raising the temperature, or adding a catalyst.

Think About It

1. What causes a slice of apple or an avocado to turn brown?

2. How is a recipe like a chemical equation?

3. Why is the digestion of food a series of chemical reactions?

Key Terms

Match the following terms with the statements below:

a. chemical change **b.** chemical equation **c.** combination reaction **d.** mole
e. molar mass **f.** physical change

1. _____ The amount of a substance that contains 6.02×10^{23} particles of that substance.

2. _____ A change that alters the composition of a substance producing a new substance with new properties.

3. _____ The mass in grams of an element or compound that is equal numerically to its atomic or sum of atomic masses.

4. _____ The type of reaction in which reactants combine to form a single product.

5. _____ A shorthand method of writing a chemical with the formulas of the reactants written on the left side of an arrow and the formulas of the products on the right side.

5.1 Chemical Changes

WEB TUTORIAL
What is Chemistry?

- A chemical change occurs when the atoms of the initial substances rearrange to form new substances.
- Chemical change is indicated by a change in properties of the reactants. For example, a rusting nail, souring milk, and a burning match are all chemical changes.
- When new substances form, a chemical reaction has taken place.

◆ Learning Exercise 5.1

Identify each of the following as a chemical (C) or a physical (P) change:

1. _____ tearing a piece of paper
2. _____ burning paper
3. _____ rusting iron
4. _____ digestion of food
5. _____ dissolving salt in water
6. _____ boiling water
7. _____ chewing gum
8. _____ removing tarnish with silver polish

5.2 Chemical Equations

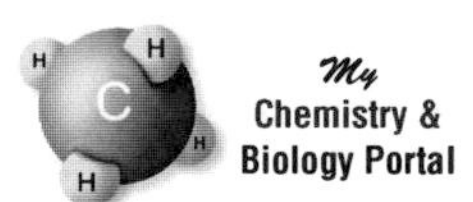

WEB TUTORIAL
Chemical Reactions and Equations

- A chemical equation shows the formulas of the reactants on the left side of the arrow and the formulas of the products on the right side.
- In a balanced equation, *coefficients* in front of the formulas provide the same number of atoms for each kind of element on the reactant and product sides.
- A chemical equation is balanced by placing coefficients in front of the symbols or formulas in the equation.

Example: Balance the following equation:

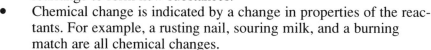

$$N_2\,(g) + H_2\,(g) \rightarrow NH_3\,(g)$$

1. Count the atoms of N and H on the reactant side and on the product side.

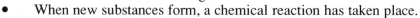

$$N_2\,(g) + H_2\,(g) \rightarrow NH_3\,(g)$$
2N, 2H 1N, 3H

2. Balance the N atoms by placing a coefficient of 2 in front of NH_3. (This increases the H atoms too.) Recheck the number of N atoms and the number of H atoms.

$$N_2\,(g) + H_2\,(g) \rightarrow 2NH_3\,(g)$$

3. Balance the H atoms by placing a coefficient of 3 in front of H_2. Recheck the number of N atoms and the number of H atoms.

$$N_2\,(g) + 3H_2\,(g) \rightarrow 2NH_3\,(g)$$

2N, 6H   2 N, 6H   *The equation is balanced.*

◆ Learning Exercise 5.2A

State the number of atoms of each element on the reactant side and on the product side for each of the following balanced equations:

a. $CaCO_3\,(s) \rightarrow CaO\,(g) + CO_2\,(g)$

Element	**Atoms on reactant side**	**Atoms on product side**
Ca		
C		
O		

b. $2Na\,(s) + H_2O\,(l) \rightarrow Na_2O\,(s) + H_2\,(g)$

Element	**Atoms on reactant side**	**Atoms on product side**
Na		
H		
O		

c. $C_5H_{12}\,(g) + 8O_2\,(g) \rightarrow 5CO_2\,(g) + 6H_2O\,(g)$

Element	**Atoms on reactant side**	**Atoms on product side**
C		
H		
O		

d. $2AgNO_3\,(aq) + K_2S\,(aq) \rightarrow 2KNO_3\,(aq) + Ag_2S\,(s)$

Element	**Atoms on reactant side**	**Atoms on product side**
Ag		
N		
O		
K		
S		

e. $2Al(OH)_3\ (aq)\ +\ 3H_2SO_4\ (aq) \rightarrow Al_2(SO_4)_3\ (s)\ +\ 6H_2O\ (l)$

Element	Atoms on reactant side	Atoms on product side
Al		
O		
H		
S		

◆ Learning Exercise 5.2B

Balance each of the following equations by placing appropriate coefficients in front of the formulas as needed:

a. ____ $MgO(s) \rightarrow$ ____ $Mg(s)\ +$ ____ $O_2(g)$

b. ____ $Zn(s)\ +$ ____ $HCl(aq) \rightarrow$ ____ $ZnCl_2(aq)\ +$ ____ $H_2(g)$

c. ____ $Al(s)\ +$ ____ $CuSO_4(aq) \rightarrow$ ____ $Cu(s)\ +$ ____ $Al_2(SO_4)_3(aq)$

d. ____ $Al_2S_3(s)\ +$ ____ $H_2O(l) \rightarrow$ ____ $Al(OH)_3(aq)\ +$ ____ $H_2S(g)$

e. ____ $BaCl_2(aq)\ +$ ____ $Na_2SO_4(aq) \rightarrow$ ____ $BaSO_4(s)\ +$ ____ $NaCl(g)$

f. ____ $CO(g)\ +$ ____ $Fe_2O_3(s) \rightarrow$ ____ $Fe(s)\ +$ ____ $CO_2(g)$

g. ____ $K(s)\ +$ ____ $H_2O(l) \rightarrow$ ____ $K_2O(s)\ +$ ____ $H_2(g)$

h. ____ $Fe(OH)_3 \rightarrow$ ____ $Fe_2O_3(s)\ +$ ____ $H_2O(l)$

5.3 Types of Reactions

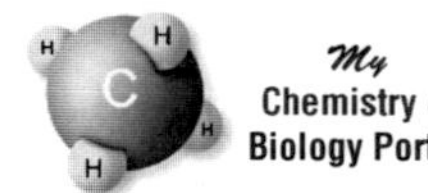

WEB TUTORIAL
Chemical Reactions and Equations

- Reactions are classified as combination, decomposition, single replacement, and double replacement.
- In a *combination* reaction, reactants are combined. In a *decomposition* reaction, a reactant splits into simpler products.
- In *single (or double) replacement* reactions, one (or two) elements in the reacting compounds are replaced with the element(s) from the other reactant(s).

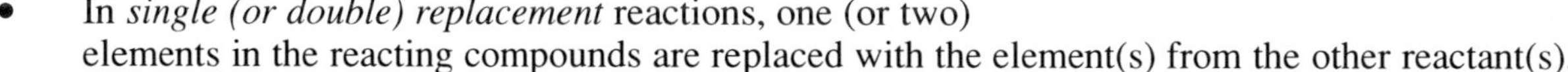
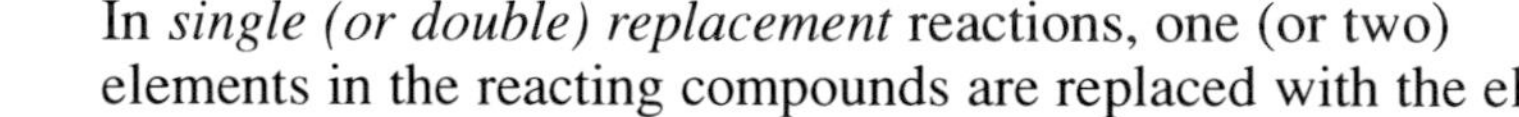

◆ Learning Exercise 5.3A

Match each of the following reactions with the type of reaction:

a. combination **b.** decomposition **c.** single replacement
d. double replacement

1. ____ $N_2(g)\ +\ 3H_2(g) \rightarrow 2\ NH_3(g)$

2. ____ $BaCl_2(aq)\ +\ K_2CO_3(aq) \rightarrow BaCO_3(s)\ +\ 2\ KCl(aq)$

3. ____ $2H_2O_2(aq) \rightarrow 2H_2O(l)\ +\ O_2(g)$

4. ____ $CuO(s)\ +\ H_2(g) \rightarrow Cu(s)\ +\ H_2O(l)$

5. ____ $N_2(g)\ +\ 2O_2(g) \rightarrow 2NO_2(g)$

6. ____ $2NaHCO_3(s) \rightarrow Na_2O(s)\ +\ 2CO_2(g)\ +\ H_2O(l)$

7. ____ $PbCO_3(s) \rightarrow PbO(s)\ +\ CO_2(g)$

8. ____ $Al(s)\ +\ Fe_2O_3(s) \rightarrow Fe(s)\ +\ Al_2O_3(s)$

◆ Learning Exercise 5.3B

One way to remove tarnish from silver is to place the silver object on a piece of aluminum foil and add boiling water and some baking soda. The unbalanced equation is the following:

$$Al(s) + Ag_2S(s) \rightarrow Ag(s) + Al_2S_3(s)$$

a. What is the balanced equation?

b. What type of reaction takes place?

5.4 Oxidation–Reduction Reactions

- An oxidation–reduction reaction consists of a loss and gain of electrons. In an oxidation, electrons are lost. In a reduction, there is a gain of electrons.
- An oxidation must always be accompanied by a reduction. The number of electrons lost in the oxidation reaction and gained in the reduction reaction are equal.
- In biological systems, the term oxidation describes the gain of oxygen or the loss of hydrogen. The term reduction is used to describe a loss of oxygen or a gain of hydrogen.

◆ Learning Exercise 5.4

For each of the following reactions, indicate whether the underlined element is *oxidized* or *reduced*.

a. $4\underline{Al}(s) + 3O_2(g) \rightarrow 2Al_2O_3(s)$ Al is ______________

b. $\underline{Fe}^{3+}(aq) + 1e^- \rightarrow Fe^{2+}(aq)$ Fe^{3+} is ______________

c. $\underline{Cu}O(s) + H_2(g) \rightarrow Cu(s) + H_2O(l)$ Cu^{2+} is ______________

d. $2\underline{Cl}^-(aq) \rightarrow Cl_2(g) + 2e^-$ Cl^- is ______________

e. $2H\underline{Br}(aq) + Cl_2(g) \rightarrow 2HCl(aq) + Br_2(g)$ Br^- is ______________

f. $2\underline{Na}(s) + Cl_2(g) \rightarrow 2NaCl(s)$ Na is ______________

g. $\underline{Cu}Cl_2(aq) + Zn(g) \rightarrow ZnCl_2(aq) + Cu(g)$ Cu^{2+} is ______________

5.5 The Mole

- A mole of any element contains Avogadro's number 6.02×10^{23} of atoms; a mole of any compound contains 6.02×10^{23} molecules or formula units.
- The subscripts in a formula indicate the number of moles of each element in one mole of the compound.

◆ Learning Exercise 5.5A

Calculate each of the following:

a. number of P atoms in 1.50 moles P

b. number of H_2S molecules in 0.0750 mole H_2S

c. moles of Ag in 5.4×10^{24} atoms Ag

d. moles of C_3H_8 in 8.25×10^{24} molecules C_3H_8

◆ Learning Exercise 5.5B

Consider the formula for vitamin C (ascorbic acid), $C_6H_8O_6$.

a. How many moles of carbon are in 2.0 moles of vitamin C?

b. How many moles of hydrogen are in 5.0 moles of vitamin C?

c. How many moles of oxygen are in 1.5 moles of vitamin C?

◆ Learning Exercise 5.5C

For the compound ibuprofen ($C_{13}H_{18}O_2$) used in Advil™ and Motrin™, determine the moles of each of the following:

a. Moles of carbon (C) atoms in 2.20 moles of ibuprofen.

b. Moles of hydrogen (H) in 0.5 mole of ibuprofen.

c. Moles of oxygen (O) in 0.75 mole of ibuprofen.

d. Moles of ibuprofen that contain 36 moles of hydrogen (H).

5.6 Molar Mass

- The molar mass (g/mole) of an element is numerically equal to its atomic mass in grams.
- The molar mass (g/mole) of a compound is the mass in grams equal numerically to the sum of the mass for each element in the formula. $MgCl_2$ has a molar mass that is the sum of the mass of 1 mole of Mg (24.3 g) and 2 moles of Cl (2 × 35.5 g) = 95.3 g/mole.
- The molar mass is useful as a conversion factor to change a given quantity in moles to grams.

$$\cancel{\text{Moles of substance}} \times \frac{\text{number of grams}}{1\ \cancel{\text{mole of substance}}} = \text{grams}$$

Study Note

The molar mass of an element or compound is determined as follows:

1. Determine the moles of each element (from subscripts) in the compound.
2. Calculate the total mass contributed by each element.
3. Total the masses of all the elements.

Example: What is the molar mass of silver nitrate, $AgNO_3$?

$$\begin{aligned} 1\text{ mole Ag} \times 107.9\text{ g/mole} &= 107.9\text{ g} \\ 1\text{ mole N} \times 14.0\text{ g/mole} &= 14.0\text{ g} \\ 3\text{ moles O} \times 16.0\text{ g/mole} &= \underline{48.0\text{ g}} \\ \text{molar mass } AgNO_3 &= 169.9\text{ g} \end{aligned}$$

◆ Learning Exercise 5.6A

Determine the molar mass for each of the following:

a. K_2O

b. $AlCl_3$

c. $C_{13}H_{18}O_2$ ibuprofen

d. C_4H_{10}

e. $Ca(NO_3)_2$

f. Mg_3N_2

g. $FeCO_3$

h. $(NH_4)_3PO_4$

◆ Learning Exercise 5.6B

Study Note

Use the molar mass as a conversion factor to change the number of moles of a substance to its mass in grams. Find the mass in grams of 0.25 mole of Na_2CO_3.

Molar mass
Grams ↔ Moles

$$\textit{Example: } 0.25 \ \cancel{\text{mole } Na_2CO_3} \times \frac{106.0\text{g } Na_2CO_3}{1 \ \cancel{\text{mole } Na_2CO_3}} = 27 \text{ g } Na_2CO_3$$

Find the number of grams in each of the following quantities:

a. 0.100 mole SO_2

b. 0.100 mole H_2SO_4

c. 2.50 moles NH_3

d. 1.25 moles O_2

e. 0.500 mole Mg

f. 5.00 moles H_2

g. 10.0 moles PCl_3

h. 0.400 mole S

◆ Learning Exercise 5.6C

Study Note

When the grams of a substance are given, the molar mass is used to calculate the number of moles of substance present.

$$\cancel{\text{grams of substance}} \times \frac{1 \text{ mole}}{\cancel{\text{grams of substance}}} = \text{moles}$$

Example: How many moles of NaOH are in 4.0 g of NaOH?

$$4.0 \cancel{\text{ g NaOH}} \times \frac{1 \text{ mole NaOH}}{40.0 \cancel{\text{ g NaOH}}} = 0.10 \text{ mole NaOH}$$

Molar Mass (inverted)

Calculate the number of moles in each of the following quantities:

a. 32.0 g of CH_4

b. 391 g of K

c. 8.00 g of C_3H_8

d. 25.0 g of Cl_2

e. 0.220 g of CO_2

f. 5.00 g of Al_2O_3

g. The methane burned in a gas heater has a formula of CH_4. If 725 grams of methane are used in 1 month, how many moles of methane were burned?

h. There is 18 mg of iron in a vitamin tablet. If there are 100 tablets in a bottle, how many moles of iron are contained in the vitamins in the bottle?

5.7 Mole Relationships in Chemical Equations

- The coefficients in a balanced chemical equation describe the moles of reactants and products in the reactions.
- Using the coefficients, mole–mole conversion factors are written for any two substances in the equation.
- For the reaction of oxygen forming ozone, $3O_2(g) \rightarrow 2O_3(g)$, the mole–mole conversion factors are the following:

$$\frac{3 \text{ moles } O_2}{2 \text{ moles } O_3} \text{ and } \frac{2 \text{ moles } O_3}{3 \text{ moles } O_2}$$

◆ Learning Exercise 5.7A

Write the conversion factors that are possible from the following equation: $N_2(g) + O_2(g) \rightarrow 2NO(g)$

Study Note

The appropriate mole factor is used to change the number of moles of the given to moles of a product. *Example:* Using the equation, $N_2(g) + O_2(g) \rightarrow 2NO(g)$, calculate the moles of NO obtained from 3 moles N_2.

$$3\ \cancel{\text{moles } N_2} \times \frac{2 \text{ moles NO}}{1\ \cancel{\text{mole } N_2}} = 6 \text{ moles NO}$$

Mole–mole factor

◆ Learning Exercise 5.7B

Use the equation below to answer the following questions:

$$C_3H_8\,(g) + 5O_2\,(g) \rightarrow 3CO_2\,(g) + 4\,H_2O\,(g)$$

a. How many moles of O_2 are needed to react with 2.00 moles of C_3H_8?

b. How many moles CO_2 are produced when 4.00 moles O_2 react?

c. How many moles of C_3H_8 react with 3.00 moles O_2?

d. How many moles of H_2O are produced from 0.50 mole C_3H_8?

5.8 Energy in Chemical Reactions

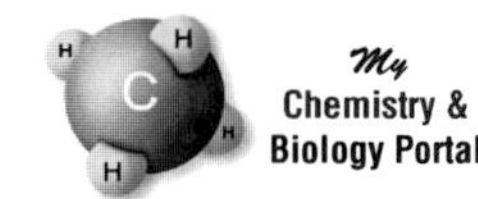

WEB TUTORIAL
Activation Energy and Transition State

- In a reaction, molecules (or atoms) must collide with energy equal to or greater than the energy of activation.
- The heat of reaction is the energy difference between the energy of the reactants and the products.
- In exothermic reactions, the heat of reaction is the energy released. In endothermic reactions, the heat of reaction is the energy absorbed.
- The rate of a reaction (the speed at which products form) can be increased by adding more reacting molecules, raising the temperature of the reaction, or by adding a catalyst.

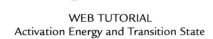

◆ Learning Exercise 5.8

Indicate whether each of the following is an endothermic or exothermic reaction:

1. $2H_2(g) + O_2(g) \rightarrow 2H_2O(g) + 582\ kJ$ ________________
2. $C_2H_4(g) + 176\ kJ \rightarrow H_2(g) + C_2H_2(g)$ ________________
3. $2C(s) + O_2(g) \rightarrow 2CO(g) + 220\ kJ$ ________________
4. $C_6H_{12}O_6(s) + 6\,O_2(g) \rightarrow 6CO_2(g) + 6\,H_2O(l) + 1350\ kcal$ ________________
   glucose
5. $C_2H_4(g) + H_2O(g) \rightarrow C_2H_5OH(l) + 21\ kcal$ ________________

Exercises in Chemical Reactions

Balancing Chemical Equations

In a balanced chemical equation the number of times each element appears as a reactant is equal to the number of times it appears as a product. For example,

$$2\ H_2 + O_2 \dashrightarrow 2\ H_2O$$

Recall that *coefficients* (the integer appearing before the chemical formula) indicate the number of times each chemical formula is to be counted and *subscripts* indicate when a particular element occurs more than once within the formula.

Check whether or not the following chemical equations are balanced.

$3\ NO \dashrightarrow N_2O + NO_2$ ☐ balanced ☐ unbalanced

$SiO_2 + 4\ HF \dashrightarrow SiF_4 + 2\ H_2O$ ☐ balanced ☐ unbalanced

$4\ NH_3 + 5\ O_2 \dashrightarrow 4\ NO + 6\ H_2O$ ☐ balanced ☐ unbalanced

Unbalanced equations are balanced by changing the coefficients. Subscripts, however, should never be changed because this changes the chemical's identity—H_2O is water, but H_2O_2 is hydrogen peroxide! The following steps may help guide you:

1. Focus on balancing only one element at a time. Start with the left-most element and modify the coefficients such that this element appears on both sides of the arrow the same number of times.

2. Move to the next element and modify the coefficients so as to balance this element. Do not worry if you incidentally unbalance the previous element. You will come back to it in subsequent steps.

3. Continue from left to right balancing each element individually.

4. Repeat steps 1–3 until all elements are balanced.

Use the above methodology to balance the following chemical equations.

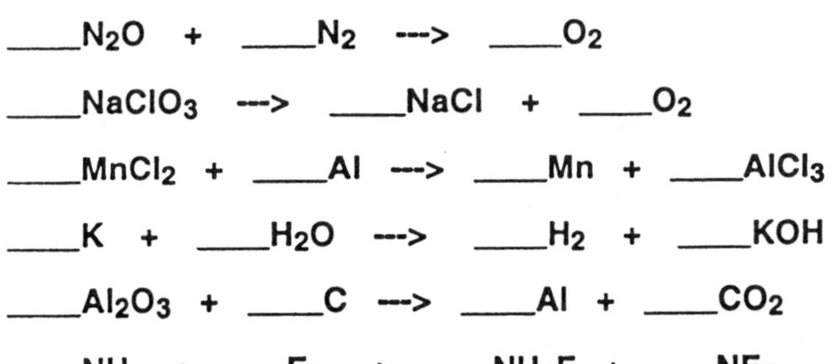
____N_2O + ____N_2 ---> ____O_2
____$NaClO_3$ ---> ____NaCl + ____O_2
____$MnCl_2$ + ____Al ---> ____Mn + ____$AlCl_3$
____K + ____H_2O ---> ____H_2 + ____KOH
____Al_2O_3 + ____C ---> ____Al + ____CO_2
____NH_3 + ____F_2 ---> ____NH_4F + ____NF_3

This is just one of the many methods that chemists have developed to balance chemical equations.

Knowing how to balance a chemical equation is a useful technique, but understanding why a chemical equation needs to be balanced in the first place is far more important.

Exothermic and Endothermic Reactions

During a chemical reaction atoms are neither created nor destroyed. Instead, atoms rearrange—they change partners. This rearrangement of atoms necessarily involves the input and output of energy. First, energy must be supplied to break chemical bonds that hold atoms together. Separated atoms then form new chemical bonds, which involves the release of energy. In an **exothermic** reaction more energy is released than is consumed. Conversely, in an **endothermic** reaction more energy is consumed than is released.

Table 1 Bond Energies

Bond	Bond Energy*	Bond	Bond Energy*
H—H	436	Cl—Cl	243
H—C	414	N—N	159
H—N	389	O=O	498
H—O	464	O=C	803
H—Cl	431	N≡N	946

*In kJ/mol

Table 1 shows bond energies—the amount of energy required to break a chemical bond, and also the amount of energy released when a bond is formed. Use these bond energies to determine whether the following chemical reactions are exothermic or endothermic.

H—H + Cl—Cl ⟶ H—Cl + H—Cl

Hydrogen Chlorine Hydrogen chloride

Total Amount of Energy Required to Break Bonds	Total Amount of Energy Released Upon Bond Formation
______ kJ/mol	______ kJ/mol

Net Energy Change of Reaction: ____________ kJ/mole (absorbed) (released)

circle one

Exothermic and Endothermic Reactions—*continued*

1. Is this reaction exothermic or endothermic?

2. Write the balanced equation for this reaction using chemical formulas and coefficients. If it is exothermic, write "Energy" as a product. If it is endothermic, write "Energy" as a reactant.

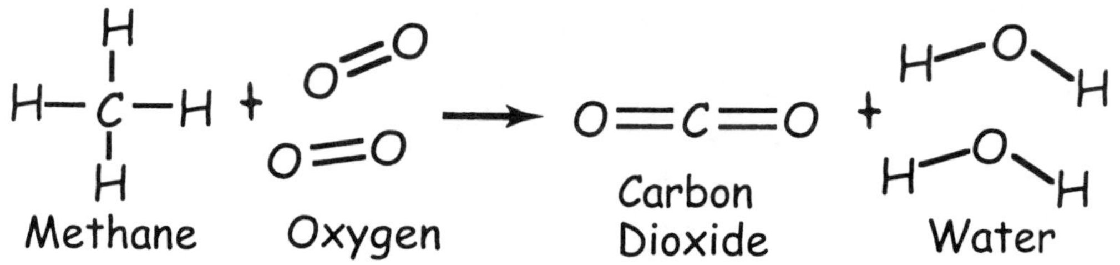

Methane + Oxygen → Carbon Dioxide + Water

Total Amount of Energy Required to Break Bonds	Total Amount of Energy Released Upon Bond Formation
______kJ/mol	______kJ/mol

Net Energy Change of Reaction: ______________kJ/mole (absorbed/released)
circle one

3. Is this reaction exothermic or endothermic?

4. Write the balanced equation for this reaction using chemical formulas and coefficients. If it is exothermic write "Energy" as a product. If it is endothermic write "Energy" as a reactant.

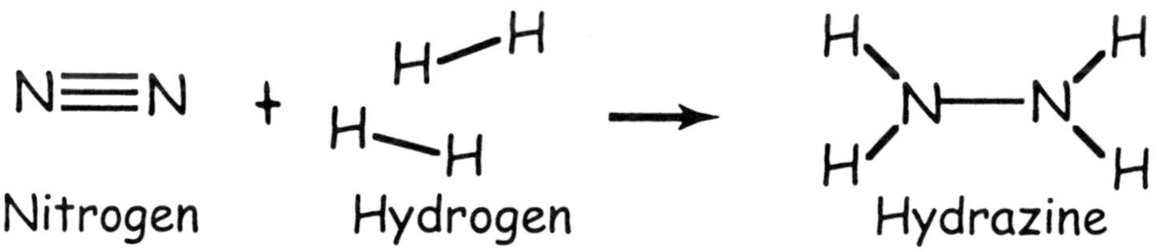

Nitrogen + Hydrogen → Hydrazine

Total Amount of Energy Required to Break Bonds	Total Amount of Energy Released Upon Bond Formation
______ kJ/mol	______ kJ/mol

Net Energy Change of Reaction: ______________kJ/mole (absorbed/released)
circle one

5. Is this reaction exothermic or endothermic?

6. Write the balanced equation for this reaction using chemical formulas and coefficients. If it is exothermic write "Energy" as a product. If it is endothermic write "Energy" as a reactant.

Donating and Accepting Hydrogen Ions

A chemical reaction that involves the transfer of a hydrogen ion from one molecule to another is classified as an acid-base reaction. The molecule that donates the hydrogen ion behaves as an acid. The molecule that accepts the hydrogen ion behaves as a base.

On paper, the acid-base process can be depicted through a series of frames:

Frame 1

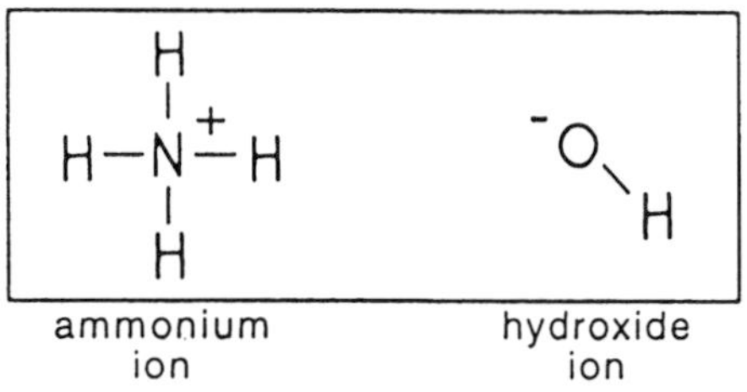

ammonium ion

hydroxide ion

Ammonium and hydroxide ions in close proximity.

Frame 2

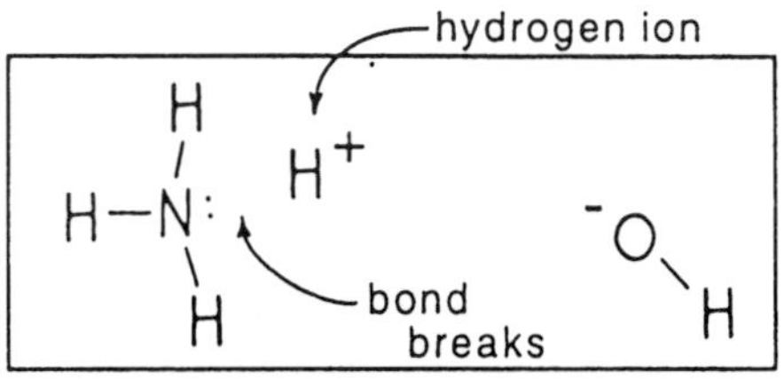

hydrogen ion

bond breaks

Bond is broken between the nitrogen and a hydrogen of the ammonium ion. The two electrons of the broken bond stay with the nitrogen leaving the hydrogen with a positive charge.

Frame 3

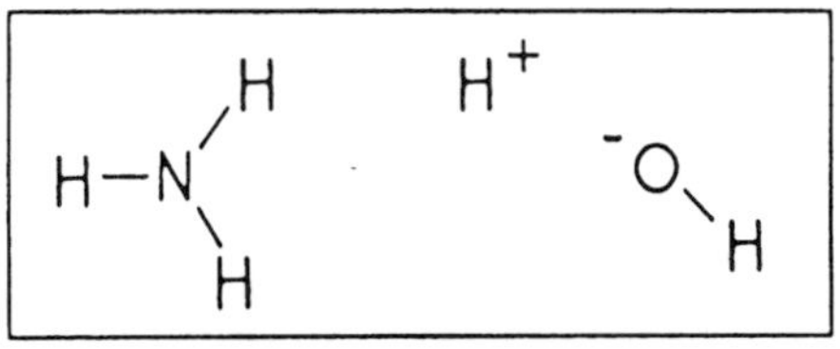

The hydrogen ion migrates to the hydroxide ion.

Frame 4

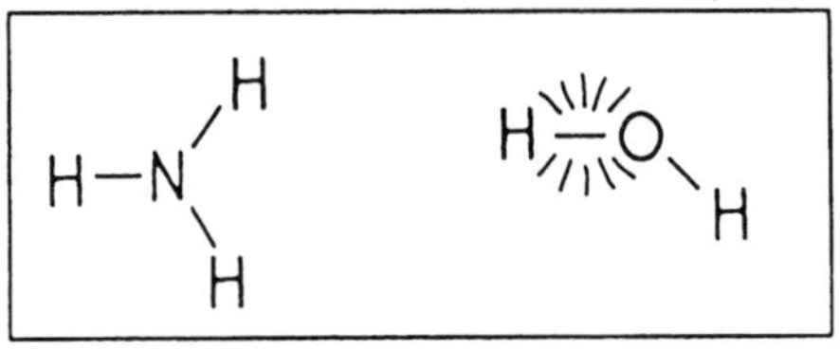

The hydrogen ion bonds with the hydroxide ion to form a water molecule.

In equation form we abbreviate this process by only showing the before and after:

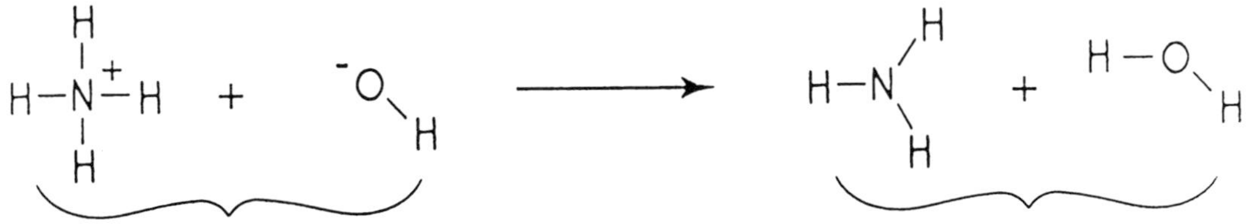

frame 1

frame 4

Donating and Accepting Hydrogen Ions—*continued*

We see from the previous reaction that because the ammonium ion donated a hydrogen ion, it behaved as an acid. Conversely, the hydroxide ion by accepting a hydrogen ion behaved as a base. How do the ammonia and water molecules behave during the reverse process?

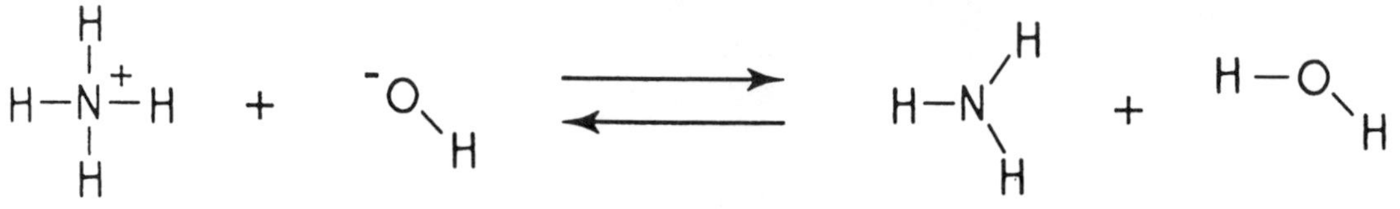

$$NH_4^+ + {}^-OH \rightleftharpoons NH_3 + H_2O$$

acid	base	ammonia	water

Identify the following molecules as behaving as an acid or a base:

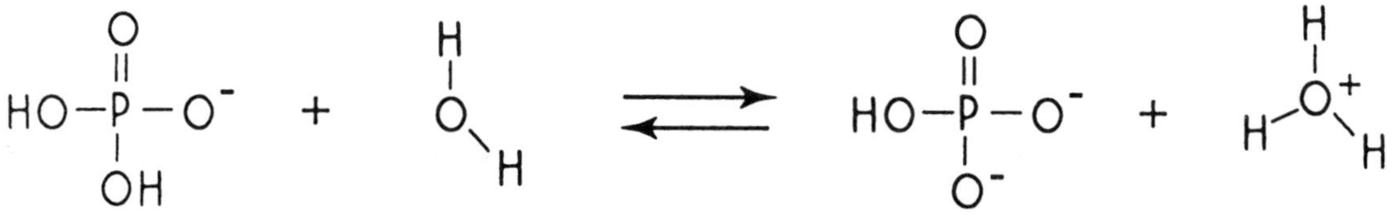

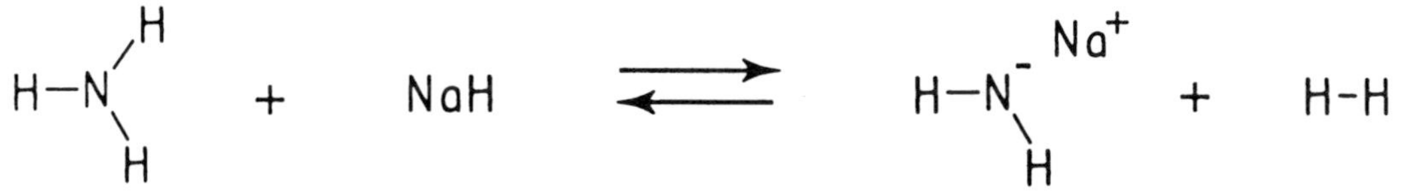

$$HO\text{-}P(=O)(OH)\text{-}O^- + H_2O \rightleftharpoons HO\text{-}P(=O)(O^-)\text{-}O^- + H_3O^+$$

______ ______ ______ ______

$$NH_3 + NaH \rightleftharpoons H_2N^- \; Na^+ + H\text{-}H$$

______ ______ ______ ______

$$H\text{-}H + {}^-H \rightleftharpoons H^- + H\text{-}H$$

______ ______ ______ ______

$$HNO_3 + NH_3 \rightleftharpoons {}^-NO_3 + {}^+NH_4$$

______ ______ ______ ______

Loss and Gain of Electrons

A chemical reaction that involves the transfer of an electron is classified as an oxidation–reduction reaction. Oxidation is the process of losing electrons, while reduction is the process of gaining them. Any chemical that causes another chemical to lose electrons (become oxidized) is called an *oxidizing agent.* Conversely, any chemical that causes another chemical to gain electrons is called a *reducing agent.*

1. What is the relationship between an atom's ability to behave as an oxidizing agent and its electron affinity?

2. Relative to the periodic table, which elements tend to behave as strong oxidizing agents?

3. Why don't the noble gases behave as oxidizing agents?

4. How is it that an oxidizing agent is itself reduced?

5. Specify whether each reactant is about to be oxidized or reduced.

$$2\,K + H_2O \longrightarrow 2\,K^+ + {}^-OH$$

_____ _____

$$2\,Mg + O_2 \longrightarrow 2\,Mg^{2+}O^{2-}$$

_____ _____

$$2\,Na + Cl_2 \longrightarrow 2\,Na^+Cl^-$$

_____ _____

$$CH_4 + 2\,O_2 \longrightarrow O{=}C{=}O + H{-}O{-}H$$

_____ _____

6. Which oxygen atom enjoys a greater negative charge?

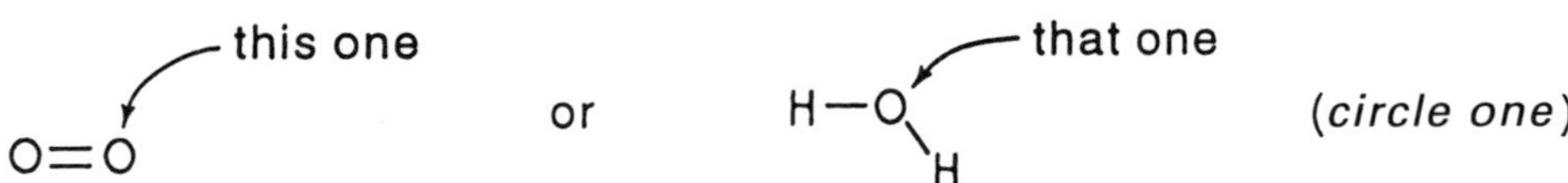

7. Relate your answer to Question 6 to how it is that O_2 is reduced upon reacting with CH_4 to form carbon dioxide and water.

Check List for Chapter 5

You are ready to take the practice test for Chapter 5. Be sure that you have accomplished the following learning goals for this chapter. If you are not sure, review the section listed at the end of the goal. Then apply your new skills and understanding to the practice test.
After studying Chapter 5, I can successfully:

_____ Identify a chemical and physical change (5.1).

_____ State a chemical equation in words and calculate the total atoms of each element in the reactants and products (5.2).

_____ Write a balanced equation for a chemical reaction from the formulas of the reactants and products (5.2).

_____ Identify a reaction as a combination, decomposition, and single or double replacement (5.3).

_____ Identify an oxidation and reduction reaction (5.4).

_____ Calculate the number of particles in a mole of a substance (5.5).

_____ Calculate the molar mass given the formula of a substance (5.6).

_____ Convert the grams of a substance to moles; moles to grams (5.6).

_____ Use mole–mole factors for the mole relationships in an equation to calculate the moles of another substance in an equation for a chemical reaction (5.7).

_____ Identify an exothermic and endothermic reactions from the heat in a chemical reaction. (5.8)

Practice Test for Chapter 5

Indicate whether each change is a (A) physical change or a (B) chemical change:

1. _____ a melting ice cube

2. _____ breaking glass

3. _____ bleaching a stain

4. _____ a burning candle

5. _____ milk turning sour

For each of the *unbalanced equations* in questions 6 through 10, balance and indicate the correct coefficient for the component in the equation written in boldface type.

A. 1 **B.** 2 **C.** 3 **D.** 4 **E.** 5

6. _____ $Sn(s) + \mathbf{Cl_2}(g) \rightarrow SnCl_4(s)$

7. _____ $Al(s) + H_2O(l) \rightarrow Al_2O_3(s) + \mathbf{H_2}(g)$

8. _____ $C_3H_8(g) + \mathbf{O_2}(g) \rightarrow CO_2(g) + H_2O(g)$

9. _____ $\mathbf{NH_3}(g) + O_2(g) \rightarrow N_2(g) + H_2O(g)$

10. _____ $N_2O(g) \rightarrow N_2(g) + \mathbf{O_2}(g)$

For questions 11 through 15, classify each reaction as one of the following:

A. combination **B.** decomposition **C.** single replacement **D.** double replacement

11. _____ $S(s) + O_2(g) \rightarrow SO_2(g)$

12. _____ $Fe_2O_3(s) + 3C(s) \rightarrow 2Fe(s) + 3CO(g)$

13. _____ $CaCO_3(s) \rightarrow CaO(s) + CO_2(g)$

14. _____ $Mg(s) + 2AgNO_3(aq) \rightarrow Mg(NO_3)_2(aq) + 2Ag(s)$

15. _____ $Na_2S(aq) + Pb(NO_3)_2(aq) \rightarrow PbS(s) + 2NaNO_3(aq)$

For questions 16 through 20, identify as an (A) oxidation or a (B) reduction.

16. $Ca \rightarrow Ca^{2+} + 2e^-$ ____

17. $Fe^{3+} + 3e^- \rightarrow Fe$ ____

18. $Al^{3+} + 3e^- \rightarrow Al$ ____

19. $Br_2 + 2e^- \rightarrow 2Br^-$ ____

20. $Sn^{2+} \rightarrow Sn^{4+} + 2e^-$ ____

21. The moles of oxygen (O) in 2.0 moles of $Al(OH)_3$ is
A. 1 **B.** 2 **C.** 3 **D.** 4 **E.** 6

22. What is the molar mass of Li_2SO_4?
A. 55.1 g **B.** 62.1 g **C.** 100.1 g **D.** 109.9 g **E.** 103.1 g

23. What is the molar mass of $NaNO_3$?
A. 34.0 g **B.** 37.0 g **C.** 53.0 g **D.** 75.0 g **E.** 85.0 g

24. The number of grams in 0.600 mole of Cl_2 is
A. 71.0 g **B.** 118 g **C.** 42.6 g **D.** 84.5 g **E.** 4.30 g

25. How many grams are in 4.00 moles of NH_3?
A. 4.00 g **B.** 17.0 g **C.** 34.0 g **D.** 68.0 g **E.** 0.240 g

26. How many moles is 8.0 g NaOH?
A. 0.10 mole **B.** 0.20 mole **C.** 0.40 mole **D.** 2.0 moles **E.** 4.0 moles

27. The number of moles of aluminum in 54 g of Al is
A. 0.50 mole **B.** 1.0 mole **C.** 2.0 moles **D.** 3.0 moles **E.** 4.0 moles

28. The number of moles of water in 36 g of H_2O is
A. 0.50 mole **B.** 1.0 mole **C.** 2.0 moles **D.** 3.0 moles **E.** 4.0 moles

29. What is the number of moles in 2.2 g CO_2?
A. 2.0 moles **B.** 1.0 mole **C.** 0.20 mole **D.** 0.050 mole **E.** 0.010 mole

30. 0.20 g H_2 = ____ mole H_2
A. 0.10 mole **B.** 0.20 mole **C.** 0.40 mole **D.** 0.040 mole **E.** 0.010 mole

For questions 31 to 35, use the reaction: $\underset{\text{Ethanol}}{C_2H_5OH(g)} + 3O_2(g) \rightarrow 2CO_2(g) + 3H_2O(g)$

31. How many grams of oxygen are needed to react with 1.0 mole of ethanol?
A. 8.0 g **B.** 16 g **C.** 32 g **D.** 64 g **E.** 96 g

32. How many moles of water are produced when 12 moles of oxygen react?
A. 3.0 moles **B.** 6.0 moles **C.** 8.0 moles **D.** 12.0 moles **E.** 36.0 moles

33. How many grams of carbon dioxide are produced when 92 g of ethanol react?
A. 22 g **B.** 44 g **C.** 88 g **D.** 92 g **E.** 176 g

34. How many moles of oxygen would be needed to produce 44 g of CO_2?
A. 0.67 mole **B.** 1.0 mole **C.** 1.5 moles **D.** 2.0 moles **E.** 3.0 moles

35. How many grams of water will be produced if 23 g of ethanol react?
A. 54 g **B.** 27 g **C.** 18 g **D.** 9.0 g **E.** 6.0 g

For questions, 36 to 38, indicate if the reactions are (1) exothermic or (2) endothermic:

36. $N_2(g) + 3H_2(g) \rightarrow 2NH_3(g) + 22$ kcal

37. $2HCl(g) + 44$ kcal $\rightarrow H_2(g) + Cl_2(g)$

38. $C_3H_8(g) + 5O_2(g) \rightarrow 3CO_2(g) + 4H_2O(g) + 531$ kcal

Key Terms

activation energy The energy needed upon collision to break apart the bonds of the reacting molecules.

Avogadro's number The number of items in a mole, equal to 6.02×10^{23}.

balanced equation The final form of a chemical equation that shows the same number of atoms of each element in the reactants and products.

catalyst A substance that increases the rate of reaction by lowering the activation energy.

chemical change The formation of a new substance with a different composition and properties than the initial substance.

chemical equation A shorthand way to represent a chemical reaction using chemical formulas to indicate the reactants and products and coefficients to show reacting ratios.

chemical reaction The process by which a chemical change takes place.

coefficients Whole numbers placed in front of the formulas to balance the number of atoms or moles of atoms of each element on both sides of an equation.

combination reaction A reaction in which reactants combine to form a single product.

decomposition reaction A reaction in which a single reactant splits into two or more simpler substances.

double replacement reaction A reaction in which parts of two different reactants exchange places.

endothermic reaction A reaction that requires heat; the energy of the products is higher than the energy of the reactants.

exothermic reaction A reaction that releases heat; the energy of the products is lower than the energy of the reactants.

formula unit The group of ions represented by the formula of an ionic compound.

molar mass The mass in grams of 1 mole of an element equal numerically to its atomic mass. The molar mass of a compound is equal to the sum of the masses of the elements in the formula.

mole A group of atoms, molecules, or formula units that contains 6.02×10^{23} of these items.

mole–mole factor A conversion factor that relates the number of moles of two compounds derived from the coefficients in an equation.

oxidation The loss of electrons by a substance. Biological oxidation may involve the addition of oxygen, or the loss of hydrogen.

oxidation–reduction reaction A reaction in which the oxidation of one reactant is always accompanied by the reduction of another reactant.

physical change A change in which the physical appearance of a substance changes but the chemical composition stays the same.

products The substances formed as a result of a chemical reaction.

reactants The initial substances that undergo change in a chemical reaction.

reduction The gain of electrons by a substance. Biological reduction may involve the loss of oxygen or the gain of hydrogen.

single replacement reaction An element replaces a different element in a compound.

6 Solutions and Gases

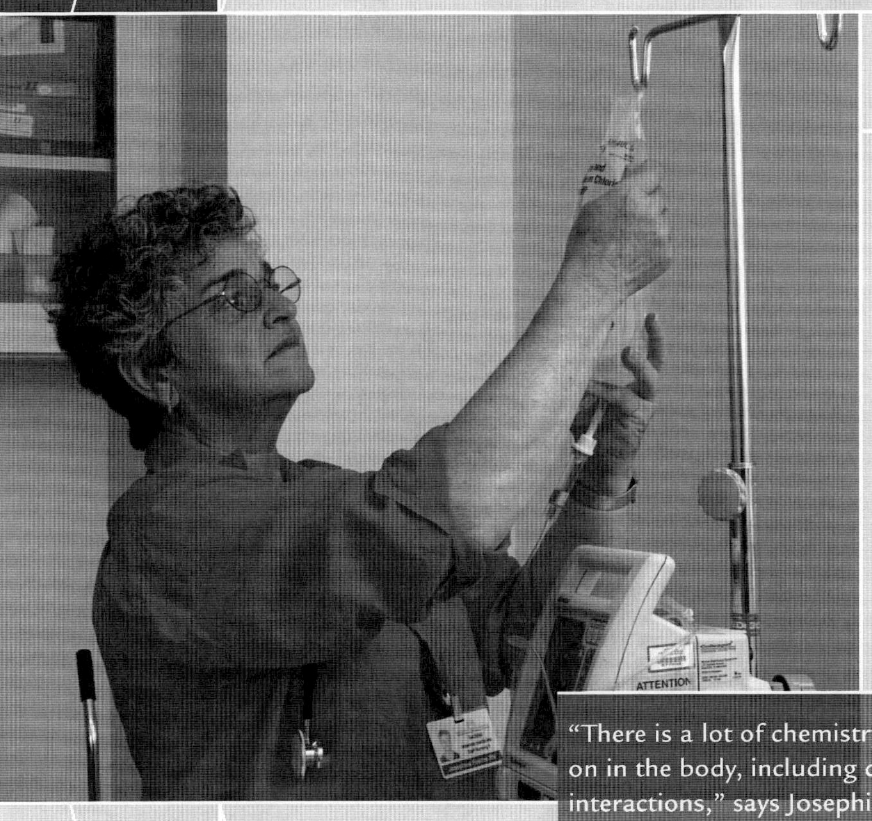

LOOKING AHEAD

"There is a lot of chemistry going on in the body, including drug interactions," says Josephine Firenze, registered nurse, Kaiser Hospital.

Normally, the body maintains a homeostasis of fluids and electrolytes. Conditions that alter the composition of body fluids can lead to convulsions, coma, or death. To halt the disease process and to establish homeostasis, a patient may be given intravenous fluid therapy. Solutions that are compatible with body fluids such as a 5% glucose or a 0.9% saline are used. An infusion pump delivers the desired number of milliliters per hour to the patient. During IV therapy, a patient is checked for fluid overload as indicated by edema, which is swelling, or a greater fluid input than output.

http://www.pearsoncustom.com/devry/mycbp

Study Goals

- Identify the solute and solvent in a solution.
- Describe hydrogen bonding in water.
- Describe electrolytes in a solution.
- Define solubility.
- Calculate the percent concentrations and molarity of a solution.
- Use the molarity of a solution in a chemical reaction to calculate the volume or quantity of a reactant or product.
- Distinguish between a solution, a colloid, and a suspension.
- Describe osmosis and dialysis.
- Describe the behavior of a red blood cell in hypotonic, isotonic, and hypertonic solutions.

Chapter Review

Concept Map

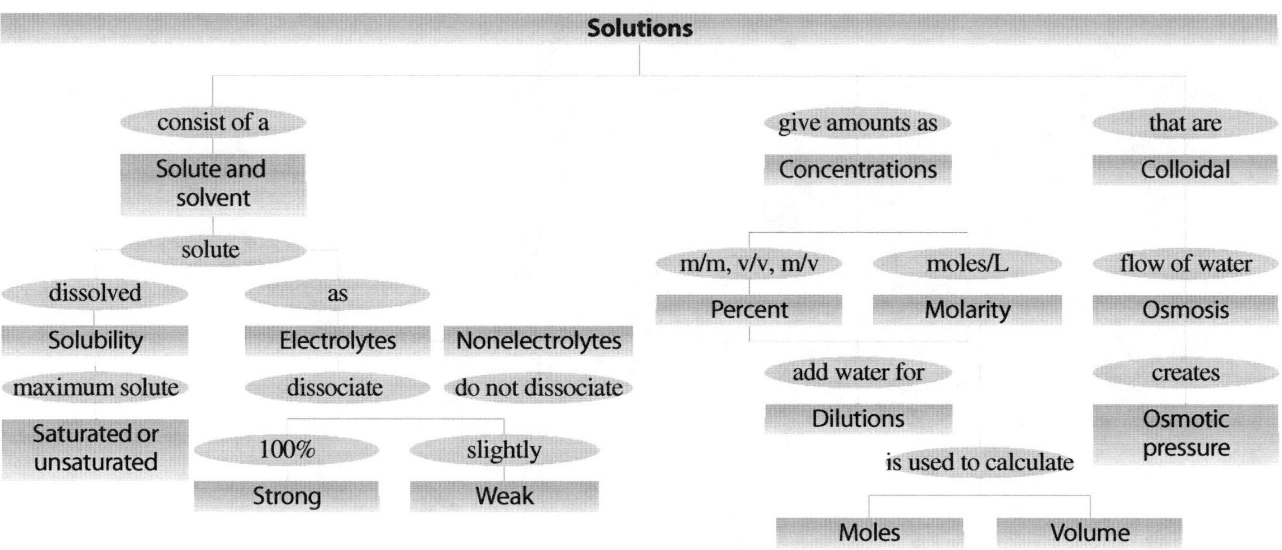

Chapter Concept Review

6.1 Solutions

A solution forms when a solute dissolves in a solvent. In a solution, the particles of solute are evenly distributed in the solvent. The solute and solvent may be solid, liquid, or gas. The polar O—H bond leads to hydrogen bonding in water molecules. An ionic solute dissolves in water, a polar solvent, because the polar water molecules attract and pull the ions into solution, where they become hydrated. The expression "like dissolves like" means that a polar ionic solute dissolves in a polar solvent while a nonpolar solute requires a nonpolar solvent.

6.2 Electrolytes and Nonelectrolytes

Substances that release ions in water are called electrolytes because the solution will conduct an electrical current. Strong electrolytes are completely ionized, whereas weak electrolytes are only partially ionized. Nonelectrolytes are substances that dissolve in water to produce molecules and cannot conduct electrical currents. An equivalent is the amount of a electrolyte that carries one mole of positive or negative charge. One mole of Na^+ is 1 equivalent. One mole of Ca^{2+} has 2 equivalents. In fluid replacement solutions, the concentrations of electrolytes are expressed as mEq/L of solution.

6.3 Solubility
A solution that contains the maximum amount of dissolved solute is a saturated solution. The solubility of a solute is the maximum amount of a solute that can dissolve in 100 g of solvent. A solution containing less than the maximum amount of dissolved solute is unsaturated. An increase in temperature increases the solubility of most solids in water, but decreases the solubility of gases in water.

6.4 Percent Concentration
The concentration of a solution is the amount of solute dissolved in a certain amount of solution. Mass percent expresses the ratio of the mass of solute to the mass of solution multiplied by 100. Percent concentration is also expressed as volume/volume and mass/volume ratios. In calculations of grams or milliliters of solute or solution, the percent concentration is used as a conversion factor.

6.5 Molarity and Dilution
Molarity is the moles of solute per liter of solution. Units of molarity, moles/liter, are used in conversion factors to solve for moles of solute or volume of solution. In dilution, the volume of solvent increases and the solute concentration decreases.

6.6 Properties of Solutions
Colloids contain particles that do not settle out and pass through filters but not through semipermeable membranes. Suspensions have very large particles that settle out of solution.

In osmosis, solvent (water) passes through a semipermeable membrane from a solution of a lower solute concentration to a solution of a higher concentration. Isotonic solutions have osmotic pressures equal to that of body fluids. A red blood cell maintains its volume in an isotonic solution, but swells and may burst (hemolyzes) in a hypotonic solution, and shrinks (crenates) in a hypertonic solution. In dialysis, water and small solute particles pass through a dialyzing membrane, while larger particles are retained.

Think About It

1. Why is salt used to preserve foods?

2. Why do raisins or dried prunes swell when placed in water?

3. Why are pickles made in a brine solution with a high salt concentration?

4. Why can't you drink seawater?

5. How do your kidneys remove toxic substances from the blood but retain the usable substances?

Key Terms

Match the following terms with the correct statement shown below:

a. solution　　**b.** concentration　　**c.** molarity
d. osmosis　　**e.** electrolyte

1. _____ A substance that dissociates into ions when it dissolves in water.

2. _____ The flow of solvent through a semipermeable membrane into a solution with a higher solute concentration.

3. _____ The amount of solute that is dissolved in a specified amount of solution.

4. _____ The number of moles of solute in one liter of solution.

5. _____ A mixture of at least two components called a solute and a solvent.

6.1 Solutions

WEB TUTORIAL
Hydrogen Bonding

- A polar solute is soluble in a polar solvent; a nonpolar solute is soluble in a nonpolar solvent; "like dissolves like."
- A solution forms when a solute dissolves in a solvent.
- The partial positive charge of hydrogen and the partial negative charge of oxygen permits water molecules to hydrogen bond to other water molecules.
- An ionic solute dissolves in water, a polar solvent, because the polar water molecules attract and pull the positive and negative ions into solution. In solution, water molecules surround the ions in a process called hydration.

◆ Learning Exercise 6.1A

Indicate the solute and solvent in each of the following:

	Solute	Solvent
a. 10 g KCl dissolved in 100 g of water	______	______
b. Soda water: $CO_2(g)$ dissolved in water	______	______
c. An alloy composed of 80% Zn and 20% Cu	______	______
d. A mixture of O_2 (200 mm Hg) and He (500 mm Hg)	______	______
e. A solution of 40 mL CCl_4 and 2 mL Br_2	______	______

◆ Learning Exercise 6.1B

Essay: How does the polarity of the water molecule allow it to hydrogen bond?

◆ Learning Exercise 6.1C

Water is polar and hexane is nonpolar. In which solvent is each of the following soluble?

a. Bromine, Br_2, nonpolar ______

b. HCl, polar ______

c. Cholesterol, nonpolar ______

d. Vitamin D, nonpolar ______

e. Vitamin C, polar ______

6.2 Electrolytes and Nonelectrolytes

- Electrolytes conduct an electrical current because they produce ions in aqueous solutions.
- Strong electrolytes are nearly completely ionized, whereas weak electrolytes are slightly ionized. Nonelectrolytes do not form ions in solution but dissolve as molecules.
- An equivalent is the amount of an electrolyte that carries 1 mole of electrical charge.
- There are 1, 2, or 3 equivalents per mole of a positive or negative ion depending on the charge.

◆ Learning Exercise 6.2A

Write an equation for the formation of an aqueous solution of each of the following strong electrolytes:

a. LiCl ______

b. $Mg(NO_3)_2$ ______

c. Na_3PO_4 ______

d. K_2SO_4 ______

e. $MgCl_2$ ______

◆ Learning Exercise 6.2B

Indicate whether an aqueous solution of each of the following contains mostly ions, molecules only, or mostly molecules with some ions. Write an equation for the formation of the solution:

a. glucose, $C_6H_{12}O_6$, a nonelectrolyte ______________________________

b. NaOH, a strong electrolyte ______________________________

c. K_2SO_4, a strong electrolyte ______________________________

d. HF, a weak electrolyte ______________________________

◆ Learning Exercise 6.2C

Calculate the following:

a. Number of equivalents in 1 mole Mg^{2+}

b. Number of equivalents of Cl^- in 2.5 moles Cl^-

c. Number of equivalents of Ca^{2+} in 2.0 moles Ca^{2+}

6.3 Solubility

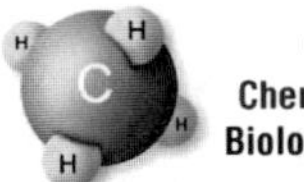

CASE STUDY
1. Solubility
2. Kidney Stones and Saturated Solutions

- The amount of solute that dissolves depends on the nature of the solute and solvent.
- Solubility describes the maximum amount of a solute that dissolves in 100 g of solvent at a given temperature.
- A saturated solution contains the maximum amount of dissolved solute at a certain temperature.
- An increase in temperature increases the solubility of most solids, but decreases the solubility of gases in water.

◆ Learning Exercise 6.3A

Identify each of the following as a saturated solution (S) or an unsaturated solution (U):

1. A sugar cube dissolves when added to a cup of coffee. ______

2. A KCl crystal added to a KCl solution does not change in size. ______

3. A layer of sugar forms in the bottom of a glass of ice tea. ______

4. The rate of crystal formation equals the rate of solution. ______

5. Upon heating, all the sugar dissolves. ______

◆ Learning Exercise 6.3B

Use the KNO_3 solubility chart for the following problems:

Solubility of KNO_3

Temperature (°C)	g KNO_3 /100 g H_2O
0	15
20	30
40	65
60	110
80	170
100	250

a. How many grams of KNO_3 will dissolve in 100 g of water at 40°C?

b. How many grams of KNO_3 will dissolve in 300 g of water at 60°C?

c. A solution is prepared using 200 g of water and 350 g of KNO_3 at 80°C. Will any solute remain undissolved? If so, how much?

d. Will 200 g of KNO_3 dissolve when added to 100 g of water at 100°C?

6.4 Percent Concentration

- The concentration of a solution is the relationship between the amount of solute (g or mL) and the amount (g or mL) of solution.
- A mass percent (mass/mass) expresses the ratio of the mass of solute to the mass of solution multiplied by 100.

$$\text{Percent (m/m)} = \frac{\text{grams of solute}}{\text{grams of solution}} \times 100$$

- Percent concentrations can also be expressed as a mass/volume ratio.

$$\text{Percent (m/v)} = \frac{\text{grams of solute}}{\text{volume (mL) of solution}} \times 100$$

Study Note

Calculate mass percent concentration (% m/m) as

$$\frac{\text{grams of solute}}{\text{grams of solution}} \times 100$$

Example: What is the percent (mass/mass) when 2.4 g of $NaHCO_3$ dissolves in 120 g of solution?

Solution: $$\frac{2.4\text{ g } NaHCO_3}{120\text{ g solution}} \times 100 = 2.0\%\text{ (m/m)}$$

◆ Learning Exercise 6.4A

Determine the percent concentration of the following solutions:

a. The mass/mass % of 18.0 g NaCl in 90.0 g of solution.

b. The mass/volume % of 5.0 g KCl in 2.0 liters of solution.

c. The mass/mass % of 4.0 g KOH in 50.0 g of solution.

d. The mass/volume % of 0.25 kg glucose in 5.0 liters of solution.

Study Note

In solution problems, the percent concentration is useful as a conversion factor. The factor is obtained by rewriting the % as g solute/100 g (or mL) solution.

Example 1: How many g of KI are needed to prepare 250 mL of a 4% (m/v) KI solution?

Solution:
$$250\ \cancel{\text{mL solution}} \times \underbrace{\frac{4\text{ g KI}}{100\ \cancel{\text{mL solution}}}}_{\%\ (m/v)\ factor} = 10\text{ g KI}$$

Example 2: How many grams of a 25% (m/m) NaOH solution can be prepared from 75 g NaOH?

Solution:
$$75\ \cancel{\text{g NaOH}} \times \underbrace{\frac{100\text{ g NaOH solution}}{25\ \cancel{\text{g NaOH}}}}_{\%\ (m/v)\ factor\ (inverted)} = 300\text{ g NaOH solution}$$

◆ Learning Exercise 6.4B

Calculate the number of grams of solute needed to prepare each of the following solutions:

a. How many grams of glucose are needed to prepare 400 mL of a 10.0% (m/v) solution?

b. How many grams of lidocaine hydrochloride are needed to prepare 50.0 g of a 2.0% (m/m) solution?

c. How many grams of KCl are needed to prepare 0.80 liter of a 0.15% (m/v) KCl solution?

d. How many grams of NaCl are needed to prepare 250 mL of a 1.0% (m/v) solution?

◆ Learning Exercise 6.4C

Use percent-concentration factors to calculate the volume (mL) of each solution that contains the amount of solute stated in each problem.

a. 2.00 g NaCl from a 1.00% (m/v) NaCl solution

b. 25 g glucose from a 5% (m/v) glucose solution

c. 1.5 g KCl from a 0.50% (m/v) KCl solution

d. 75.0 g NaOH from a 25.0% (m/v) NaOH solution

6.5 Molarity and Dilution

- Molarity is a concentration term that describes the number of moles of solute dissolved in 1 L (1000 mL) of solution.

$$M = \frac{\text{moles of solute}}{\text{L solution}}$$

- *Dilution* is the process of mixing a solution with solvent to obtain a lower concentration.
- For dilutions, use the expression $C_1V_1 = C_2V_2$ and solve for the unknown value.

◆ Learning Exercise 6.5A

Calculate the molarity of the following solutions:

a. 2.0 moles HCl in 1.0 liter

b. 10.0 moles glucose ($C_6H_{12}O_6$) in 2.0 liters

c. 80.0 g NaOH in 4.0 liters (Hint: Find moles NaOH.)

Study Note

Molarity can be used as a conversion factor to convert between the amount of solute and the volume of solution.

Example 1: How many grams of NaOH are in 0.20 L of a 4.0 M NaOH solution?

Solution: The concentration 4.0 M can be expressed as the conversion factors:

$$\frac{4.0 \text{ moles NaOH}}{1 \text{ L NaOH}} \text{ and } \frac{1 \text{ L NaOH}}{4.0 \text{ moles NaOH}}$$

$$0.20 \cancel{\text{L NaOH}} \times \frac{4.0 \cancel{\text{moles NaOH}}}{1 \cancel{\text{L NaOH}}} \times \frac{40.0 \text{ g NaOH}}{1 \cancel{\text{mole NaOH}}} = 32 \text{ g NaOH}$$

Example 2: How many mL of a 6 M HCl solution will provide 0.36 mole HCl?

Solution:

$$0.36 \cancel{\text{mole HCl solution}} \times \underbrace{\frac{1 \cancel{\text{L}}}{6 \cancel{\text{moles HCl}}}}_{\text{Molarity facto (inverted)}} \times \frac{1000 \text{ mL}}{1 \cancel{\text{L}}} = 60 \text{ mL HCl solution}$$

◆ Learning Exercise 6.5B

Calculate the quantity of solute in the following solutions:

a. How many moles of HCl are in 1.50 liter of a 2.50 M HCl solution?

b. How many moles of KOH are in 125 mL of a 2.40 M KOH solution?

c. How many grams of NaOH are needed to prepare 225 mL of a 3.00 M NaOH solution? (Hint: Find moles of NaOH.)

d. How many grams of NaCl are in 415 mL of a 1.30 M NaCl solution?

◆ Learning Exercise 6.5C

Calculate the milliliters needed of each solution to obtain each of the following:

a. 0.200 mole of $Mg(OH)_2$ from a 2.50 M $Mg(OH)_2$ solution

b. 0.125 mole of glucose from a 5.00 M glucose solution

c. 0.250 mole of KI from a 4.00 M KI solution

d. 16.0 g NaOH from a 3.20 M NaOH solution

◆ Learning Exercise 6.5D

Solve each of the following dilution problems (assume the volumes add):

a. What is the final concentration after 100 mL of a 5.0 M KCl solution is diluted with water to give a final volume of 200 mL?

b. What is the final concentration of the diluted solution if 5.0 mL of a 15% (m/v) KCl solution is diluted to 25 mL?

c. What is the final concentration after 250 mL of an 8% (m/v) NaOH is diluted with 750 mL of water?

d. 160 mL of water is added to 40 mL of an 1.0 M NaCl solution. What is the final concentration?

e. What volume of water must be added to 2.0 L of 12% (m/v) KCl to obtain a 4.0 % (m/v) KCl solution? What is the total volume of the solution?

f. What volume of 6.0 M HCl is needed to prepare 300. mL of 1.0 M HCl? How much water must be added?

6.6 Properties of Solutions

WEB TUTORIAL
Diffusion
Osmosis

- Colloids contain particles that do not settle out and pass through filters but not through semipermeable membranes.
- Suspensions are composed of large particles that settle out of solution.
- In the process of osmosis, water (solvent) moves through a semipermeable membrane from the solution that has a lower solute concentration to a solution where the solute concentration is higher.
- Osmotic pressure is the pressure that prevents the flow of water into a more concentrated solution.
- Isotonic solutions have osmotic pressures equal to that of body fluids. A hypotonic solution has a lower osmotic pressure than body fluids; a hypertonic solution has a higher osmotic pressure.
- A red blood cell maintains its volume in an isotonic solution, but it swells (hemolysis) in a hypotonic solution and shrinks (crenation) in a hypertonic solution.
- In dialysis, water and small solute particles can pass through a dialyzing membrane, while larger particles are retained.

◆ Learning Exercise 6.6A

Identify each of the following as a solution, colloid, or suspension:

1. _____ Contains single atoms, ions, or small molecules.
2. _____ Settles out with gravity.
3. _____ Retained by filters.
4. _____ Cannot diffuse through a cellular membrane.
5. _____ Aggregates of atoms, molecules, or ions larger in size than solution particles.
6. _____ Large particles that are visible.

◆ Learning Exercise 6.6B

Fill in the blanks:

In osmosis, the direction of solvent flow is from the (1) ____________ solvent concentration to the (2) ____________ solvent concentration. A semipermeable membrane separates 5% and 10% sucrose solutions. The (3) ____________% solution has the greater osmotic pressure. Water will move from the (4) ____________% solution into the (5) ____________% solution. The compartment that contains the (6) ____________% solution increases in volume.

◆ Learning Exercise 6.6C

What occurs when 2% (A) and 10% (B) starch solutions are separated by a semipermeable membrane?

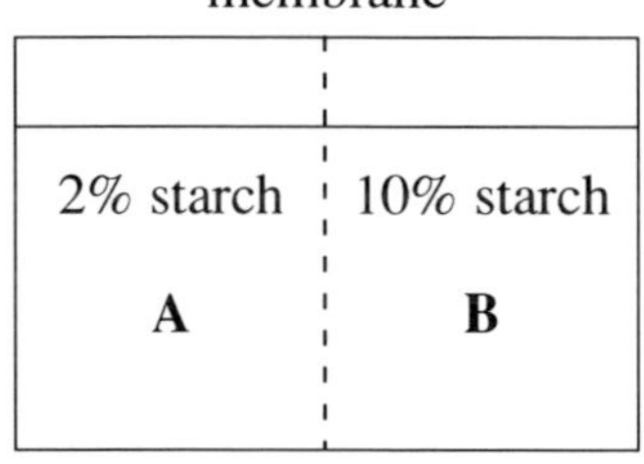

a. Water will flow from side ____________ to side ____________.

b. The volume in compartment __________ will increase and decrease in compartment __________.

c. The final concentration of the solutions in both compartments will be ____________.

◆ Learning Exercise 6.6D

Fill in the blanks:

A (1) __________% NaCl solution and a (2) __________% glucose solution are isotonic to the body fluids. A red blood cell placed in these solutions does not change in volume because these solutions are (3) __________ tonic. When a red blood cell is placed in water, it undergoes (4) __________ because water is (5) __________ tonic. A 20% glucose solution will cause a red blood cell to undergo (6) __________ because the 20% glucose solution is (7) __________ tonic.

◆ Learning Exercise 6.6E

Indicate whether the following solutions are

1. Hypotonic **2.** hypertonic **3.** isotonic

a. _____ 5% (m/v)glucose **d.** _____ water

b. _____ 3% (m/v) NaCl **e.** _____ 0.9% (m/v)NaCl

c. _____ 2% (m/v) glucose **f.** _____ 10% (m/v) glucose

◆ Learning Exercise 6.6F

Indicate whether the following solutions will cause a red blood cell to undergo

1. crenation **2.** hemolysis **3.** no change (stays the same)

a. _____ 10% (m/v) NaCl **d.** _____ 0.5% (m/v) NaCl

b. _____ 1% (m/v) glucose **e.** _____ 10% (m/v) glucose

c. _____ 5% (m/v) glucose **f.** _____ water

◆ Learning Exercise 6.6G

A dialysis bag contains starch, glucose, NaCl, protein, and urea.

a. When the dialysis bag is placed in water, which of the components would you expect to dialyze through the bag? Why?

b. Which components will stay inside the dialysis bag? Why?

Check List for Chapter 6

You are ready to take the practice test for Chapter 6. Be sure that you have accomplished the following learning goals for this chapter. If you are not sure, review the section listed at the end of the goal. Then apply your new skills and understanding to the practice test.
After studying Chapter 6, I can successfully:

_____ Describe hydrogen bonding in water (6.1).

_____ Identify the solute and solvent in a solution (6.1).

_____ Describe the process of dissolving an ionic solute in water (6.1).

_____ Identify the components in solutions of electrolytes and nonelectrolytes (6.2).

_____ Calculate the number of equivalents for an electrolyte (6.2).

_____ Identify a saturated and an unsaturated solution (6.3).

_____ Describe the effects of temperature and nature of the solute on its solubility in a solvent (6.3).

_____ Calculate the percent concentration of a solute in a solution and use percent concentration to calculate the amount of solute or solution (6.4).

_____ Calculate the diluted volume of a solution (6.4).

_____ Calculate the molarity of a solution (6.5)

_____ Identify a mixture as a solution, a colloid, or a suspension (6.6).

_____ Explain the processes of osmosis and dialysis (6.6).

Practice Test for Chapter 6

Indicate if the following are more soluble in (A) water (polar solvent) or (B) benzene (nonpolar solvent).

1. _____ I_2 (g), nonpolar

2. _____ NaBr(s), polar

3. _____ KI(s), polar

4. _____ C_6H_{12}, nonpolar

5. When dissolved in water, $Ca(NO_3)_2$ dissociates into
A. $Ca^{2+} + (NO_3)_2^{2-}$ **B.** $Ca^{+} + NO_3^{-}$ **C.** $Ca^{2+} + 2\,NO_3^{-}$
D. $Ca^{2+} + 2\,N^{5+} + 2\,O_3^{6-}$ **E.** $CaNO_3^{+} + NO_3^{-}$

6. What is the number of equivalents in 2 moles of Mg^{2+}?
A. 0.50 equiv **B.** 1 equiv **C.** 1.5 equiv
D. 2 equiv **E.** 4 equiv

7. CH_3CH_2OH, ethyl alcohol, is a nonelectrolyte. When placed in water it
A. dissociates completely. **B.** dissociates partially. **C.** does not dissociate.
D. makes the solution acidic. **E.** makes the solution basic.

8. The solubility of NH_4Cl is 46 g in 100 g of water at 40°C. How much NH_4Cl can dissolve in 500 g of water at 40°C?
A. 9.2 g **B.** 46 g **C.** 100 g
D. 184 g **E.** 230 g

9. A solution containing 1.20 g sucrose in 50.0 mL of solution has a mass-volume percent concentration of
A. 0.600 % **B.** 1.20% **C.** 2.40%
D. 30.0% **E.** 41.6%

10. The amount of lactose in 250 mL of a 3.0% (m/v) lactose solution of infant formula is
A. 0.15 g **B.** 1.2 g **C.** 6.0 g
D. 7.5 g **E.** 30 g

11. The volume needed to obtain 0.40 g of glucose from a 5.0 % (m/v) glucose solution is
A. 1.0 mL **B.** 2.0 mL **C.** 4.0 mL
D. 5.0 mL **E.** 8.0 mL

12. The amount of NaCl needed to prepare 50.0 mL of a 4.00% (m/v) NaCl solution is
A. 20.0 g **B.** 15.0 g **C.** 10.0 g
D. 4.00 g **E.** 2

13. A solution containing 6.0 g NaCl in 1500 mL of solution has a mass–volume percent concentration of
A. 0.40 (m/v)% **B.** 0.25 (m/v)% **C.** 4.0 (m/v)%
D. 0.90 (m/v)% **E.** 2.5 (m/v)%

For questions 14 through 18, indicate whether each statement describes a
A. solution **B.** colloid **C.** suspension

14. _____ Contains single atoms, ions, or small molecules of solute

15. _____ Settles out upon standing

16. _____ Can be separated by filtering

17. _____ Can be separated by semipermeable membranes

18. _____ Passes through semipermeable membranes

19. The separation of colloids from solution particles by use of a membrane is called
A. osmosis **B.** dispersion **C.** dialysis
D. hemolysis **E.** collodian

20. Any two solutions that have identical osmotic pressures are
A. hypotonic **B.** hypertonic **C.** isotonic
D. isotopic **E.** blue

21. In osmosis, water flows
A. between solutions of equal concentrations.
B. from higher solute concentrations to lower solute concentrations.
C. from lower solute concentrations to higher solute concentrations.
D. from colloids to solutions of equal concentrations.
E. from lower solvent concentrations to higher solvent concentrations.

22. A normal red blood cell will shrink when placed in a solution that is
A. isotonic **B.** hypotonic **C.** hypertonic
D. colloidal **E.** semitonic

23. A red blood cell undergoes hemolysis when placed in a solution that is
A. isotonic **B.** hypotonic **C.** hypertonic
D. colloidal **E.** semitonic

24. A solution that has the same osmotic pressure as body fluids is
A. 0.1% NaCl **B.** 0.9 % NaCl **C.** 5% NaCl
D. 10% glucose **E.** 15% glucose

25. Which of the following is hypertonic to red blood cells?
A. 0.5% NaCl **B.** 0.9% NaCl **C.** 1% glucose
D. 5% glucose **E.** 10% glucose

26. Which of the following is hypotonic to red blood cells?
A. 2.0% NaCl **B.** 0.9% NaCl **C.** 1% glucose
D. 5% glucose **E.** 10% glucose

For questions 27 through 31, select the correct term from the following:
A. isotonic **B.** hypertonic **C.** hypotonic
D. osmosis **E.** dialysis

27. _____ A solution with a higher osmotic pressure than the blood.

28. _____ A solution of 10% NaCl surrounding a red blood cell.

29. _____ A 1% glucose solution.

30. _____ The cleansing process of the artificial kidney.

31. _____ The flow of water up the stem of a plant.

32. _____ In dialysis,

A. dissolved salts and small molecules are separated from colloids.
B. nothing but water passes through the membrane.
C. only ions pass through a membrane.
D. two kinds of colloids are separated.
E. colloids are separated from suspensions.

33. A dialyzing membrane
   A. is a semipermeable membrane.
   B. allows only water and true solution particles to pass through.
   C. does not allow colloidal particles to pass through.
   D. All of the above
   E. None of the above

34. Which substance will remain inside a dialysis bag?
   A. water **B.** NaCl **C.** starch
   D. glucose **E.** Mg^{2+}

35. Waste removal in hemodialysis is based on
   A. concentration gradients between the bloodstream and the dialysate.
   B. a pH difference between the bloodstream and the dialysate.
   C. use of an osmotic membrane.
   D. greater osmotic pressure in the bloodstream.
   E. renal compensation.

36. The moles of KOH needed to prepare 2400 mL of a 2.0 M KOH solution is
   A. 1.2 moles **B.** 2.4 **C.** 4.8
   D. 12 moles **E.** 48 moles

37. The amount in grams of NaOH needed to prepare 7.5 mL of a 5.0 M NaOH is
   A. 1.5 g **B.** 3.8 g **C.** 6.7 g
   D. 15 g **E.** 38 g

For questions 38 through 40, consider a 20.0 mL sample of a solution that contains 2.0 g NaOH.

38. The % concentration of the solution is
   A. 1.0% **B.** 4.0% **C.** 5%
   D. 10% **E.** 20%

39. The number of moles of NaOH in the sample is
   A. 0.050 mole **B.** 0.40 mole **C.** 1.0 mole
   D. 2.5 moles **E.** 4.0 moles

40. The molarity of the sample is
   A. 0.10 M **B.** 0.5 M **C.** 1.0 M
   D. 1.5 M **E.** 2.5 M

Key Terms

colloid A mixture having particles that are moderately large. Colloids pass through filters but cannot pass through semipermeable membranes.

concentration A measure of the amount of solute that is dissolved in a specified amount of solution.

crenation The shriveling of a cell due to water leaving the cell when the cell is placed in a hypertonic solution.

dialysis A process in which water and small solute particles pass through a semipermeable membrane.

dilution A process by which water (solvent) is added to a solution to increase the volume and decrease (dilute) the concentration of the solute.

electrolyte A substance that produces ions when dissolved in water; its solution conducts electricity.

equivalent (Eq) The amount of a positive or negative ion that supplies 1 mole of electrical charge.

hemodialysis A mechanical cleansing of the blood by an artificial kidney using the principle of dialysis.

hemolysis A swelling and bursting of red blood cells in a hypotonic solution due to an increase in fluid volume.

Henry's law The solubility of a gas in a liquid is directly related to the pressure of that gas above the liquid.

hydration The process of surrounding dissolved ions by water molecules.

hydrogen bond The attraction between a partially positive hydrogen atom in one molecule and a highly electronegative atom such as oxygen in another molecule.

hypertonic solution A solution that has a higher osmotic pressure than the red blood cells of the body.

hypotonic solution A solution that has a lower osmotic pressure than the red blood cells of the body.

isotonic solution A solution that has the same osmotic pressure as that of the red blood cells of the body.

mass percent The grams of solute in exactly 100 grams of solution.

mass/volume percent The grams of solute in exactly 100 mL of solution.

molarity (M) The number of moles of solute in exactly 1 L of solution.

nonelectrolyte A substance that dissolves in water as molecules; its solution will not conduct an electrical current.

osmosis The flow of a solvent, usually water, through a semipermeable membrane into a solution of higher solute concentration.

osmotic pressure The pressure that prevents the flow of water into the more concentrated solution.

physiological solution A solution that exerts the same osmotic pressure as normal body fluids.

saturated solution A solution containing the maximum amount of solute that can dissolve at a given temperature. Any additional solute will remain undissolved in the container.

semipermeable membrane A membrane that permits the passage of certain substances while blocking or retaining others.

solubility The maximum amount of solute that can dissolve in exactly 100 g of solvent, usually water, at a given temperature.

solute The component in a solution that changes state upon dissolving; if no change in state occurs, it is the component present in the smaller quantity.

solution A homogeneous mixture in which the solute is made up of small particles (ions or molecules) that can pass through filters and semipermeable membranes.

solvent The substance in which the solute dissolves; usually the component present in greatest amount.

strong electrolyte A polar or ionic compound that ionizes completely when it dissolves in water. Its solution is a good conductor of electricity.

suspension A mixture in which the solute particles are large enough and heavy enough to settle out and be retained by both filters and semipermeable membranes.

unsaturated solution A solution that contains less solute than can be dissolved.

volume percent A percent concentration that relates the volume of the solute to the volume of the solution.

weak electrolyte A substance that produces only a few ions along with many molecules when it dissolves in water. Its solution is a weak conductor of electricity.

7 Acids and Bases

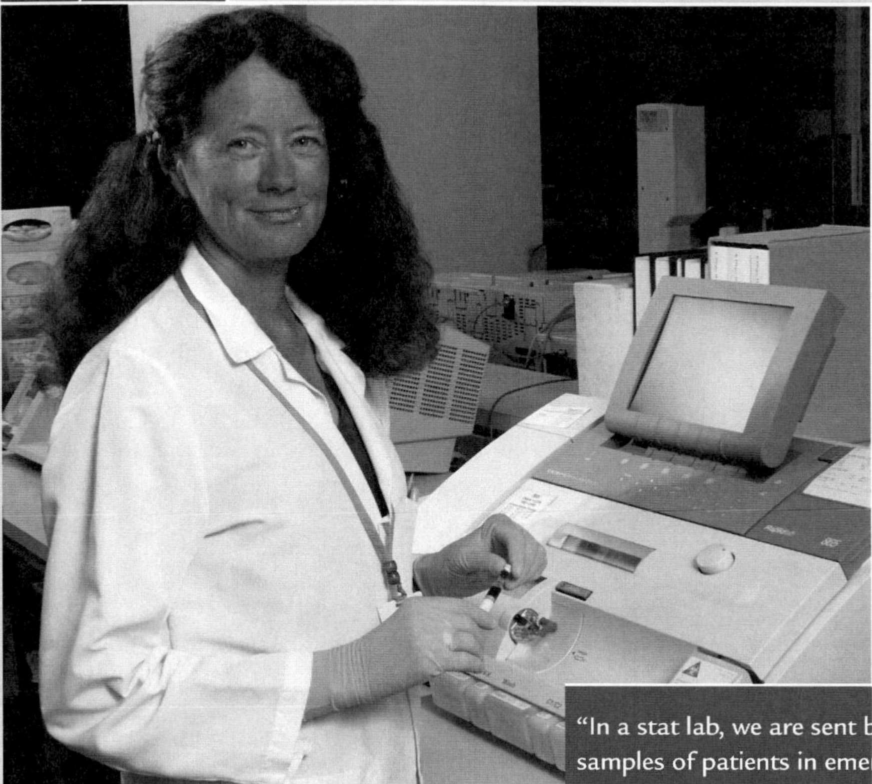

LOOKING AHEAD

"In a stat lab, we are sent blood samples of patients in emergency situations," says Audrey Trautwein, clinical laboratory technician, Stat Lab, Santa Clara Valley Medical Center. "We may need to assess the status of a trauma patient in ER or a patient who is in surgery. For example, an acidic blood pH diminishes cardiac function, and affects the actions of certain drugs. In a stat situation, it is critical that we obtain our results fast. This is done using a blood gas analyzer. As I put a blood sample into the analyzer, a small probe draws out a measured volume, which is tested simultaneously for pH, p_{O_2}, and p_{CO_2} as well as electrolytes, glucose, and hemoglobin. In about one minute we have our test results, which are sent to the doctor's computer."

http://www.pearsoncustom.com/devry/myc

Study Goals

- Describe the characteristics of acids and bases.
- Identify conjugate acid–base pairs in Brønsted–Lowry acids and bases.
- Use the ion product of water to calculate $[H_3O^+]$, $[OH^-]$, and pH.
- Write balanced equations for reactions of an acid with metals, carbonates, and bases.
- Calculate the concentration of an acid solution from titration data.
- Describe the function of a buffer.

Chapter Review

Concept Map

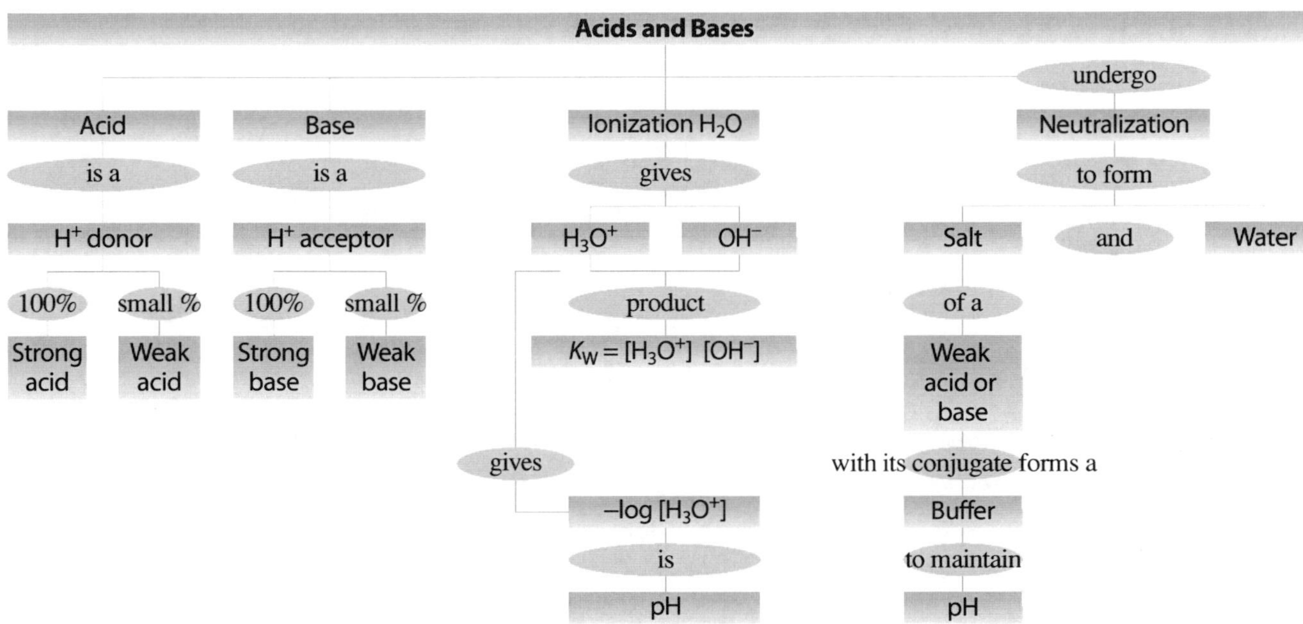

Chapter Concept Review

7.1 Acids and Bases

According to the Arrhenius theory, an acid produces H^+, and a base produces OH^- in aqueous solutions.

7.2 Brønsted–Lowry Acids and Bases

According to the Brønsted–Lowry theory, acids are proton (H^+) donors, and bases are proton acceptors. Two conjugate acid–base pairs are present in an acid–base reaction. Each acid–base pair is related by the loss or gain of one H^+. For example, when the acid HF donates a H^+, the F^- it forms is its conjugate base because F^- is capable of accepting a H^+. The other acid–base pair would be H_2O and H_3O^+.

7.3 Strengths of Acids and Bases

In strong acids, all the H^+ in the acid is donated to H_2O; in a weak acid, only a small percentage of acid molecules produce H_3O^+. Strong bases are hydroxides of Groups 1A (1) and 2A (2) that dissociate completely in water. An important weak base is ammonia, NH_3.

7.4 Ionization of Water

In pure water, a few molecules transfer protons to other water molecules, producing small, but equal, amounts of $[H_3O^+]$ and $[OH^-]$, such that each has a concentration of 1×10^{-7} mole/L. The ion product, K_w, $[H_3O^+][OH^-] = 1 \times 10^{-14}$, applies to all aqueous solutions. In acidic solutions, the $[H_3O^+]$ is greater than the $[OH^-]$. In basic solutions, the $[OH^-]$ is greater than the $[H_3O^+]$.

7.5 The pH Scale

The pH scale is a range of numbers from 0 to 14 related to the $[H_3O^+]$ of the solution. A neutral solution has a pH of 7. In acidic solutions, the pH is below 7, and in basic solutions the pH is above 7. Mathematically, pH is the negative logarithm of the hydronium ion concentration ($-\log[H_3O^+]$).

7.6 Reactions of Acids and Bases

When an acid reacts with a metal, hydrogen gas and a salt are produced. The reaction of an acid with a carbonate or bicarbonate produces carbon dioxide, a salt, and water. In neutralization, an acid reacts with a base to produce a salt and water. In titration, an acid sample is neutralized with a known amount of a base. From the volume and molarity of the base, the concentration of the acid is calculated.

7.7 Buffers

A buffer solution resists changes in pH when small amounts of acid or base are added. A buffer contains either a weak acid and its salt or a weak base and its salt. The weak acid picks up added OH^-, and the anion of the salt picks up added H^+. Buffers are important in maintaining the pH of the blood.

Think About It

1. Why do a lemon, grapefruit, and vinegar taste sour?
2. What do antacids do? What are some bases listed on the labels of antacids?
3. Why are some aspirin products buffered?

Key Terms

a. acid **b.** base **c.** pH **d.** neutralization **e.** buffer

1. _____ A substance that forms hydroxide ions (OH^-) in water and/or accepts protons (H^+)
2. _____ A reaction between an acid and a base to form a salt and water
3. _____ A substance that forms hydrogen ions (H^+) in water
4. _____ A mixture of a weak acid (or base) and its salt that maintains the pH of a solution
5. _____ A measure of the acidity of a solution

7.1 Acids and Bases

- In water, an Arrhenius acid produces H_3O^+, and an Arrhenius base produces OH^-.
- According to the Brønsted–Lowry theory, acids are proton (H^+) donors and bases are proton acceptors.
- Protons form hydronium ions, H_3O^+, in water when they bond to polar water molecules.

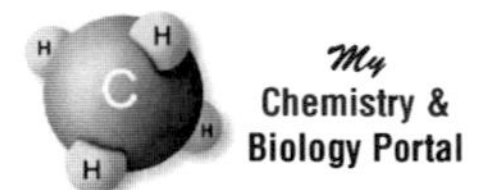

WEB TUTORIAL
Nature of Acids and Bases

◆ Learning Exercise 7.1A

Indicate if the following characteristics describe an (A) acid or (B) base.

1. _____ Turns blue litmus red
2. _____ Tastes sour
3. _____ Contains more OH^- ions than H_3O^+ ions
4. _____ Neutralizes bases
5. _____ Tastes bitter
6. _____ Turns red litmus blue
7. _____ Contains more H_3O^+ ions than OH^- ions
8. _____ Neutralizes acids

◆ Learning Exercise 7.1B

Fill in the blanks with the formula or name of an acid or base:

1. HCl ______________________________
2. _____ sodium hydroxide
3. _____ sulfurous acid
4. _____ nitric acid
5. $Ca(OH)_2$ ______________________________
6. H_2CO_3 ______________________________
7. $Al(OH)_3$ ______________________________
8. _____ potassium hydroxide

7.2 Brønsted–Lowry Acids and Bases

- According to the Brønsted–Lowry theory, acids donate protons (H^+) to bases.
- Conjugate acid–base pairs are molecules or ions linked by the loss and gain of a proton.

Study Note

Identify the conjugate acid–base pairs in the following equation:

$$HCl + H_2O \rightarrow H_3O^+ + Cl^-$$

Solution: HCl (proton donor) and Cl^- (proton acceptor)
H_2O (proton acceptor) and H_3O^+ (proton donor)

◆ Learning Exercise 7.2A

Complete the following conjugate acid–base pairs:

Conjugate Acid	Conjugate Base
1. H_2O	__________
2. HSO_4^-	__________
3. __________	F^-
4. __________	CO_3^{2-}
5. HNO_3	__________
6. NH_4^+	__________
7. __________	HS^-
8. __________	$H_2PO_4^-$

◆ Learning Exercise 7.2B

Identify the conjugate acid–base pairs in each of the following:

1. $HF + H_2O \rightleftarrows H_3O^+ + F^-$

2. $NH_4^+ + SO_4^{2-} \rightleftarrows NH_3 + HSO_4^-$

3. $NH_3 + H_2O \rightleftarrows NH_4^+ + OH^-$

4. $HNO_3 + OH^- \rightleftarrows H_2O + NO_3^-$

7.3 Strengths of Acids and Bases

- In aqueous solution, a strong acid donates nearly all of its protons to water, whereas a weak acid donates only a small percentage of protons to water.
- Most hydroxides of Groups 1A (1) and 2A (2) are strong bases, which dissociate nearly completely in water. In an aqueous ammonia solution, NH_3, which is a weak base, accepts only a small percentage of protons to form NH_4^+.

Study Note

Only six common acids are strong acids: other acids are considered as weak acids.

HCl	HNO_3
HBr	H_2SO_4 (first H)
HI	$HClO_4$

Example: Is H_2S a strong or weak acid?
Solution: H_2S is a weak acid because it is not one of the six strong acids.

◆ Learning Exercise 7.3A

Identify each of the following as a strong or weak acid or base:

1. HNO_3 ________ **4.** NH_3 ________ **7.** $Ca(OH)_2$ ________

2. H_2CO_3 ________ **5.** LiOH ________ **8.** H_2SO_4 ________

3. $H_2PO_4^-$ ________ **6.** H_3BO_3 ________

◆ Learning Exercise 7.3B

Using Table 7.3, identify the stronger acid in each of the following pairs of acids:

1. HCl or H_2CO_3 ____________ **4.** H_2SO_4 or HSO_4^- ____________

2. HNO_2 or HCN ____________ **5.** HF or H_3PO_4 ____________

3. H_2S or HBr ____________

7.4 Ionization of Water

- In pure water, a few water molecules transfer a proton to other water molecules producing small but equal amounts of $[H_3O^+]$ and $[OH^-] = 1 \times 10^{-7}$ moles/L.
- K_w, the ion product, $[H_3O^+][OH^-] = [1 \times 10^{-7}][1 \times 10^{-7}] = 1 \times 10^{-14}$, applies to all aqueous solutions.
- In acidic solutions, the $[H_3O^+]$ is greater than the $[OH^-]$. In basic solutions, the $[OH^-]$ is greater than the $[H_3O^+]$.

Study Note

Example: What is the $[H_3O^+]$ in a solution that has $[OH^-] = 2.0 \times 10^{-9}$ M?

Solution: $$[H_3O^+] = \frac{1.0 \times 10^{-14}}{2.0 \times 10^{-9}} = 5.0 \times 10^{-6}\ M$$

◆ Learning Exercise 7.4

Write the $[H_3O^+]$ when the $[OH^-]$ has the following values:

a. $[OH^-] = 1.0 \times 10^{-10}$ M $[H_3O^+] =$

b. $[OH^-] = 2.0 \times 10^{-5}$ M $[H_3O^+] =$

c. $[OH^-] = 4.5 \times 10^{-7}$ M $[H_3O^+] =$

d. $[OH^-] = 8.0 \times 10^{-4}$ M $[H_3O^+] =$

e. $[OH^-] = 5.5 \times 10^{-8}$ M $[H_3O^+] =$

7.5 The pH Scale

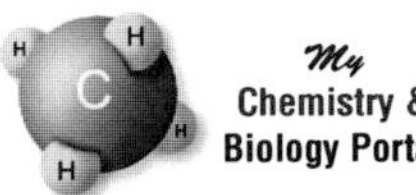

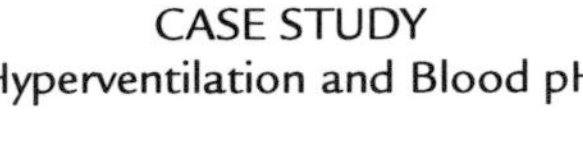

WEB TUTORIAL
The pH Scale

- The pH scale is a range of numbers from 0 to 14 related to the $[H_3O^+]$ of the solution.
- A neutral solution has a pH of 7. In acidic solutions, the pH is below 7, and in basic solutions the pH is above 7.
- Mathematically, pH is the negative logarithm of the hydronium ion concentration:

$$pH = -\log [H_3O^+]$$

◆ Learning Exercise 7.5A

State whether the following pH values are acidic, basic or neutral:

1. _____ plasma, pH = 7.4

2. _____ soft drink, pH = 2.8

3. _____ maple syrup, pH = 6.8

4. _____ beans, pH = 5.0

5. _____ tomatoes, pH = 4.2

6. _____ lemon juice, pH = 2.2

7. _____ saliva, pH = 7.0

8. _____ eggs, pH = 7.8

9. _____ lime, pH = 12.4

10. _____ strawberries, pH = 3.0

◆ Learning Exercise 7.5B

Calculate the pH of each of the following solutions.

a. $[H_3O^+] = 1 \times 10^{-8}$ M ____________

b. $[OH^-] = 1 \times 10^{-12}$ M ____________

c. $[H_3O^+] = 1 \times 10^{-3}$ M ____________

d. $[OH^-] = 1 \times 10^{-10}$ M ____________

◆ Learning Exercise 7.5C

Calculate the pH of each of the following solutions.

a. $[H_3O^+] = 1 \times 10^{-3}$ M   **b.** $[OH^-] = 1 \times 10^{-6}$ M

c. $[H_3O^+] = 1 \times 10^{-8}$ M   **d.** $[OH^-] = 1 \times 10^{-10}$ M

◆ Learning Exercise 7.5D

Complete the following table:

$[H_3O^+]$	$[OH^-]$	pH
a.	1×10^{-12} M	
b.		8.0
c. 1×10^{-10} M		
d.		7.0
e.		1.0

7.6 Reactions of Acids and Bases

- Acids react with many metals to yield hydrogen gas (H_2) and the salt of the metal.
- Acids react with carbonates and bicarbonates to yield CO_2, H_2O, and the salt of the metal.
- Acids neutralize bases in a reaction that produces water and a salt.
- The net ionic equation for any neutralization is $H^+ + OH^- \rightarrow H_2O$.
- In a balanced neutralization equation, an equal number of moles of H^+ and OH^- must react.
- The concentration of an acid can be determined by titration.

◆ Learning Exercise 7.6A

Complete and balance each of the following reactions of acids:

1. ____ $Zn(s)$ + ______ $HCl(aq)$ → ______ $ZnCl_2(aq)$ + ____________

2. ____ $HCl(aq)$ + ______ $Li_2CO_3(s)$ → ______ + ____________

3. ____ $HCl(aq)$ + ______ $NaHCO_3(s)$ → ______ $CO_2(g)$ ______ + $H_2O(l)$ + ______ $NaCl(aq)$

4. ____ $Al(s)$ + ______ $H_2SO_4(aq)$ → ______ $Al_2(SO_4)_3(aq)$ + ____________

◆ Learning Exercise 7.6B

Balance each of the following neutralization reactions:

1. ____ $NaOH(aq)$ + ______ $H_2SO_4(aq)$ → ______ $Na_2SO_4(aq)$ + ______ $H_2O(l)$

2. ____ $Mg(OH)_2(aq)$ + ______ $HCl(aq)$ → ______ $MgCl_2(aq)$ + ______ $H_2O(l)$

3. ____ $Al(OH)_3(aq)$ + ____ $HNO_3(aq)$ → ____ $Al(NO_3)_3(aq)$ + ____ $H_2O(l)$

4. ____ $Ca(OH)_2(aq)$ + ____ $H_3PO_4(aq)$ → ____ $Ca_3(PO_4)_2(s)$ + ____ $H_2O(l)$

◆ Learning Exercise 7.6C

Complete each of the following neutralization reactions and then balance:

a. $KOH(aq)$ + ________ $H_3PO_4(aq)$ → ________ + ________ $H_2O(l)$

b. $NaOH(aq)$ + ________ → ________ $Na_2SO_4(aq)$ + ________

c. ________ + ________ → ________ $AlCl_3(aq)$ + ________

d. ________ + ________ → ________ $Fe_2(SO_4)_3(s)$ + ________

◆ Learning Exercise 7.6D

1. A 24.6 ml sample of HCl reacts with 33.0 ml of 0.222 M NaOH solution. What is the molarity of the HCl solution?

2. A 15.7 ml sample of H_2SO_4 reacts with 27.7 ml of 0.187 M KOH solution. What is the molarity of the H_2SO_4 solution?

7.7 Buffers

- A buffer solution resists a change in pH when small amounts of acid or base are added.
- A buffer contains either (1) a weak acid and its salt, or (2) a weak base and its salt. The weak acid picks up excess OH^-, and the anion of the salt picks up excess H_3O^+.
- The pH of a buffer can be calculated by rearranging the K_a for $[H_3O^+]$.

◆ Learning Exercise 7.7

State whether each of the following represents a buffer system or not.

a. HCl + NaCl b. K_2SO_4 c. H_2CO_3 d. H_2CO_3 + $NaHCO_3$

Check List for Chapter 7

You are ready to take the practice test for Chapter 7. Be sure that you have accomplished the following learning goals for this chapter. If you are not sure, review the section listed at the end of the goal. Then apply your new skills and understanding to the practice test.
After studying Chapter 7, I can successfully:

____ Describe the properties of Arrhenius acids and bases and write their names (7.1).

____ Describe the Brønsted–Lowry concept of acids and bases; write conjugate acid–base pairs for an acid–base reaction (7.2).

____ Write equations for the ionization of strong and weak acids and bases (7.3).

____ Use the ion product of water to calculate $[H_3O^+]$ and $[OH^-]$ (7.4).

____ Calculate pH from the $[H_3O^+]$ of a solution (7.5).

____ Write a balanced equation for the reactions of acids with metals, carbonates, and/or bases (7.6).

____ Describe the role of buffers in maintaining the pH of a solution and calculate the pH of a buffer solution. (7.7).

Practice Test for Chapter 7

1. An acid is a compound which when placed in water yields this characteristic ion:
   A. H_3O^+ **B.** OH^- **C.** Na^+
   D. Cl^- **E.** CO_3^{2-}

2. $MgCl_2$ would be classified as a(n)
   A. acid **B.** base **C.** salt
   D. buffer **E.** nonelectrolyte

3. $Mg(OH)_2$ would be classified as a
   A. weak acid **B.** strong base **C.** salt
   D. buffer **E.** nonelectrolyte

4. In the K_w expression for pure H_2O, the $[H_3O^+]$ has the value
   A. 1×10^{-7} M **B.** 1×10^{-1} M **C.** 1×10^{-14} M
   D. 1×10^{-6} M **E.** 1×10^{-12} M

5. Of the following pH values, which is the most acidic?
   A. 8.0 **B.** 5.5 **C.** 1.5
   D. 3.2 **E.** 9.0

6. Of the following pH values, which is the most basic pH?
   A. 10.0 **B.** 4.0 **C.** 2.2
   D. 11.5 **E.** 9.0

For questions 7 through 9, consider a solution with $[H_3O^+] = 1 \times 10^{-11}$ M.

7. The pH of the solution is
   A. 1.0 **B.** 2.0 **C.** 3.0
   D. 11.0 **E.** 14.0

8. The hydroxide ion concentration is
   A. 1×10^{-1} M **B.** 1×10^{-3} M **C.** 1×10^{-4} M
   D. 1×10^{-7} M **E.** 1×10^{-11} M

9. The solution is
   A. acidic **B.** basic **C.** neutral
   D. a buffer **E.** neutralized

For questions 10 through 12, consider a solution with a $[OH^-] = 1 \times 10^{-5}$ M.

10. The hydrogen ion concentration of the solution is
    A. 1×10^{-5} M **B.** 1×10^{-7} M **C.** 1×10^{-9} M
    D. 1×10^{-10} M **E.** 1×10^{-14} M

11. The pH of the solution is
    A. 2.0 **B.** 5.0 **C.** 9.0
    D. 11 **E.** 14

12. The solution is
    A. acidic **B.** basic **C.** neutral
    D. a buffer **E.** neutralized

13. Acetic acid is a weak acid because
A. it forms a dilute acid solution. **B.** it is isotonic.
C. it is less than 50% ionized in water. **D.** it is a nonpolar molecule.
E. it can form a buffer.

14. A weak base when added to water
A. makes the solution slightly basic. **B.** does not affect the pH.
C. dissociates completely. **D.** does not dissociate.
E. makes the solution slightly acidic.

15. Which is an equation for neutralization?
A. $CaCO_3(s) \rightarrow CaO(s) + CO_2(g)$
B. $Na_2SO_4(s) \rightarrow 2Na^+(aq) + SO_4^{2-}(aq)$
C. $H_2SO_4(aq) + 2\,NaOH(aq) \rightarrow Na_2SO_4(aq) + 2H_2O(l)$
D. $Na_2O(s) + SO_3(g) \rightarrow Na_2SO_4(s)$
E. $H_2CO_3(s) \rightarrow CO_2(g) + H_2O(l)$

16. What is the name given to components in the body that keep blood pH within its normal 7.35 to 7.45 range?
A. nutrients **B.** buffers **C.** metabolites
D. fluids **E.** neutralizers

17. What is true of a typical buffer system?
A. It maintains a pH of 7.0.
B. It contains a weak base.
C. It contains a salt.
D. It contains a strong acid and its salt.
E. It maintains the pH of a solution.

18. Which of the following would act as a buffer system?
A. HCl **B.** Na_2CO_3 **C.** $NaOH + NaNO_3$
D. NH_4OH **E.** $NaHCO_3 + H_2CO_3$

19. Which of the following pairs is a conjugate acid–base pair?
A. HCl/HNO_3 **B.** HNO_3/NO_3^- **C.** NaOH/KOH
D. HSO_4^-/HCO_3^- **E.** Cl^-/F^-

20. The conjugate base of $HSO_4{}^-$ is
A. SO_4^{2-} **B.** H_2SO_4 **C.** HS^-
D. H_2S **E.** SO_3^{-2}

21. In which reaction does H_2O act as an acid?
A. $H_3PO_4(aq) + H_2O(l) \rightarrow H_3O^+(aq) + H_2PO_4^-(aq)$
B. $H_2SO_4(aq) + H_2O(l) \rightarrow H_3O^+(aq) + HSO_4^-(aq)$
C. $H_2O(l) + HS^-(aq) \rightarrow H_3O^+(aq) + S^{2-}(aq)$
D. $NaOH(aq) + HCl(aq) \rightarrow NaCl(aq) + H_2O(l)$
E. $NH_3(aq) + H_2O(l) \rightarrow NH_4^+(aq) + OH^-(aq)$

22. 23.7 ml of HCl reacts with 19.6 ml of 0.179 M NaOH. The molarity of the HCl solution is
A. 6.76 M **B.** 0.216 M **C.** 0.148 M
D. 0.163 M **E.** 0.333 M

Key Terms for Crossword Puzzle

acid
aqueous solution
atom
atomic number
base
buffer
chemical bond
chemical reaction
cohesion
compound
covalent bond
electron
element
evaporative cooling
heat
hydrogen bond
ion
ionic bond
isotope
mass
mass number
matter
molecule
neutron
nucleus
pH scale
polar molecule
product
proton
radioactive isotope
reactant
solute
solution
solvent
temperature
trace element

Crossword Puzzle

Use the Key Terms list from this chapter to fill in the crossword puzzle.

ACROSS

3. a fluid mixture of two or more substances
6. a starting material in a chemical reaction
8. a type of isotope whose nucleus decays spontaneously
9. a subatomic particle that is electrically neutral
10. a substance containing two or more elements in a fixed ratio
12. an attraction between atoms that share one or more pairs of electrons
13. a variant form of an atom
14. an atom or molecule that has gained or lost one or more electrons
17. a substance that increases the hydrogen ion concentration in a solution
18. the amount of energy associated with the movement of the atoms and molecules in a body of matter
20. anything that occupies space and has mass
22. a molecule that has opposite charges on opposite ends
24. the attraction between molecules of the same kind
26. a substance that cannot be broken down into other substances
28. a measure of the amount of material in an object
29. an attraction between two atoms
30. the smallest unit of matter that retains the properties of an element
31. a chemical substance that resists changes in pH
32. the sum of the number of protons and neutrons in an atom's nucleus
34. a weak chemical bond between a partially positive hydrogen and a partially negative atom
35. surface cooling that results when a substance evaporates

DOWN

1. an element that is essential for the survival of an organism but only in minute quantities
2. the dissolving agent in a solution
4. an atom's central core
5. a subatomic particle with a single positive electrical charge
7. an attraction between two ions with opposite electrical charges
10. a process leading to chemical changes in matter
11. a measure of the relative acidity of a solution, ranging in value from 0 to 14
15. a measure of the intensity of heat
16. a substance that is dissolved in a solution
19. an ending material in a chemical reaction
21. a mixture of two or more substances, one of which is water
23. a group of two or more atoms held together by covalent bonds
25. the number of protons in each atom of a particular element
27. a subatomic particle with a negative charge
33. a substance that decreases the hydrogen concentration in a solution

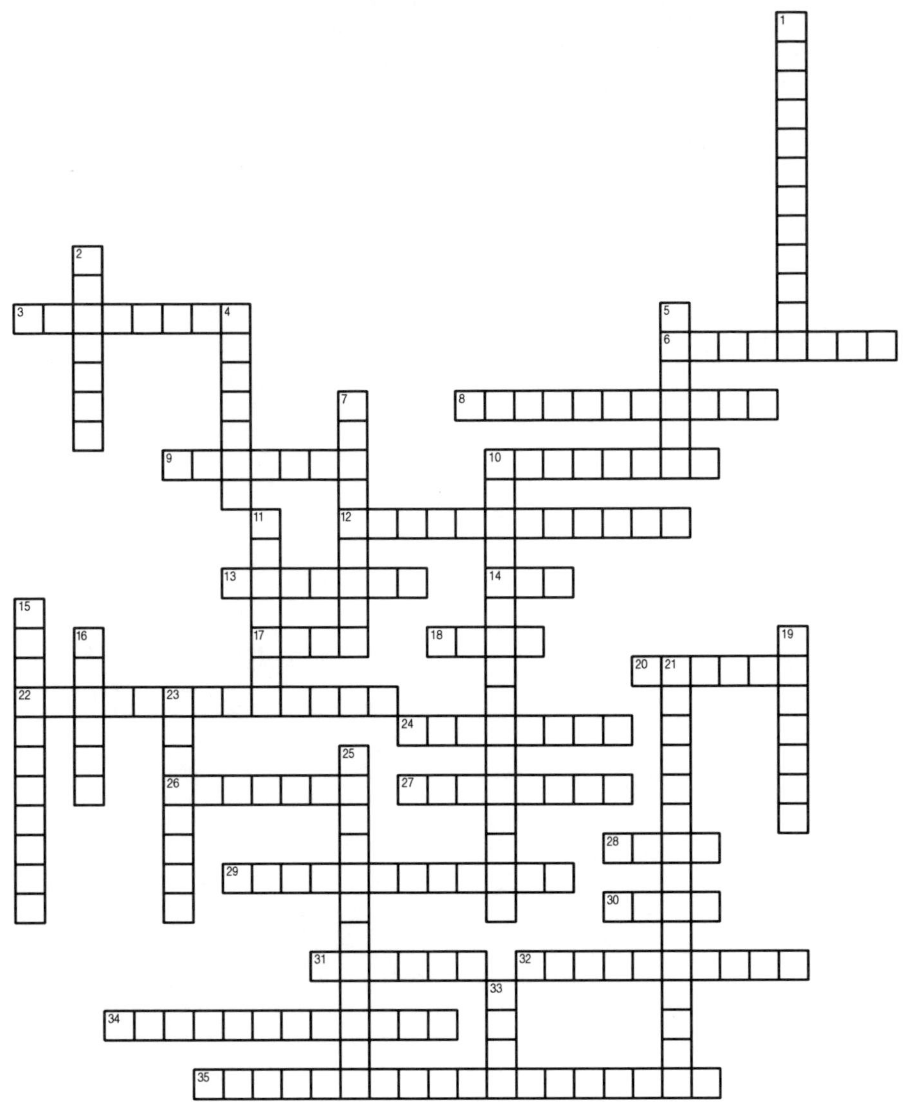

Key Terms

acid A substance that dissolves in water and produces hydrogen ions (H^+), according to the Arrhenius theory. All acids are proton donors, according to the Brønsted–Lowry theory.

acidosis A physiological condition in which the blood pH is lower than 7.35.

alkalosis A physiological condition in which the blood pH is higher than 7.45.

base A substance that dissolves in water and produces hydroxide ions (OH^-) according to the Arrhenius theory. All bases are proton acceptors, according to the Brønsted–Lowry theory.

Brønsted–Lowry acids and bases An acid is a proton donor, and a base is a proton acceptor.

buffer solution A mixture of a weak acid or a weak base and its salt that resists changes in pH when small amounts of an acid or base are added.

conjugate acid–base pair An acid and base that differ by one H^+. When an acid donates a proton, the product is its conjugate base, which is capable of accepting a proton in the reverse reaction.

hydronium ion, H_3O^+ The ion formed by the attraction of a proton (H^+) to an H_2O molecule.

ion-product constant of water, *K*w The product of $[H_3O^+]$ and $[OH^-]$ in solution; $Kw = [H_3O^+][OH^-]$.

neutral The term that describes a solution with equal concentrations of $[H_3O^+]$ and $[OH^-]$.

neutralization A reaction between an acid and a base to form a salt and water.

pH A measure of the $[H_3O^+]$ in a solution; $pH = -\log[H_3O^+]$.

strong acid An acid that completely ionizes in water.

strong base A base that completely ionizes in water.

titration The addition of base to an acid sample to determine the concentration of the acid.

weak acid An acid that ionizes only slightly in solution.

weak base A base that ionizes only slightly in solution.

8 Introduction to Organic Chemistry and Macromolecules

LOOKING AHEAD

You perceive the flavor of vanilla when the sensory organs of your mouth and nose detect the organic compound vanillin. The flavor of chocolate, on the other hand, derives from a wide assortment of carbon-based molecules. One of the major flavor ingredients in chocolate is the organic compound tetramethylpyrazine, a ringlike structure built of nitrogen, carbon, and hydrogen atoms.

Chapter Review: Summary of Essential Chemistry

Atoms

Matter is defined as anything that takes up space and has mass. The smallest chemical units of matter are **atoms**.

Atomic Structure

Atoms contain negatively charged particles called **electrons** spinning around a nucleus composed of uncharged particles called **neutrons** and positively charged particles called **protons**. (A hydrogen atom contains only one proton and no neutrons.) The number of electrons in an atom typically equals the number of protons, so atoms are electrically neutral overall.

An **element** is matter that is composed of a single type of atom. Of the 93 naturally occurring elements, organisms utilize only about 20, including, for example, carbon, oxygen, and nitrogen. Elements differ from one another in their **atomic number**, which is the number of protons in their nuclei. The **atomic mass** (or *atomic weight*) of an atom is the sum of the masses of its protons, neutrons, and electrons. Since electrons have little mass, the atomic mass is estimated by adding the number of protons and neutrons. Thus hydrogen has an atomic mass of 1.

Isotopes

Isotopes are atoms of an element that differ only in the numbers of neutrons they contain. For example, there are three naturally occurring isotopes of carbon, all of which have 6 protons: carbon-12 has 6 neutrons, carbon-13 has 7 neutrons, and carbon-14 has 8 neutrons.

Electron Configurations

Since only the electrons of atoms come close enough to interact, they determine an atom's chemical behavior. Electrons orbit their nucleus in three-dimensional electron shells, each of which can hold only a certain maximum number of electrons. For example, the first shell of any atom has a capacity of just two electrons, whereas the second shell has a capacity of eight. The number of electrons in the **valence shell**—the outermost shell—determines the atom's reactivity: atoms with valence shells not containing the maximum number of electrons are more likely to give up or accept electrons from another atom until their outermost shell is full.

Chemical Bonds

The sharing or transferring of electrons to fill a valence shell results in the formation of **chemical bonds**. Two or more atoms held together by chemical bonds form a **molecule**. Any molecule containing atoms of more than one element is called a **compound**. For example, two hydrogen atoms bonded to an oxygen atom form a molecule of water (H_2O), which is a compound.

Nonpolar Covalent Bonds

A **covalent bond** is the sharing of a pair of electrons by two atoms. Two hydrogen atoms bind covalently to form a stable molecule of hydrogen in which both atoms have full valence shells. Atoms such as oxygen that share two pairs of electrons have a *double covalent bond* with each other. The attraction of an atom for electrons is called its **electronegativity**. When atoms with similar electronegativities bind, the shared electrons tend to spend an equal amount of time around each nucleus of the pair. Since neither nucleus acts as a "pole" to exert an unequal pull, these are called **nonpolar covalent bonds**.

Since carbon atoms have four electrons in their valence shells, they have an equal tendency to lose or gain four electrons, and form nonpolar covalent bonds with one another and with many other atoms. One result of this feature is that carbon atoms easily form very long chains that constitute the "backbone" of many biologically important molecules. Compounds that contain carbon and hydrogen atoms are called **organic compounds**.

Polar Covalent Bonds

When atoms with significantly different electronegativities combine, the electron pair will spend more time orbiting the "pole"; that is, the nucleus of the atom with greater electronegativity. Bonds with an unequal sharing of electrons are therefore called **polar covalent bonds**. A water molecule, for example, has two polar covalent bonds. Although they can form between many different elements, the most biologically important polar covalent bonds are those involving hydrogen because they allow hydrogen bonding.

Ionic Bonds

When two atoms with vastly different electronegativities approach each other, the atom with the higher electronegativity will strip one or more electrons from the valence shell of the other. This happens, for example, when chlorine, with seven electrons in its valence shell, encounters sodium, which has just one valence electron. When sodium loses an electron, it becomes positively charged; when chlorine gains an electron, it becomes negatively charged. Charged atoms are called **ions**; specifically, an ion like sodium with a positive charge is called a **cation**, whereas an atom like chlorine with a negative charge is called an **anion**. The opposite charges of cations and anions attract each other strongly to form an **ionic bond**. Molecules with ionic bonds form crystalline compounds known as **salts**, such as sodium chloride (NaCl). Notice that, in ionic bonds, electrons are *transferred* from one molecule to another; in contrast to covalent bonds, there is no sharing of electrons.

The polar bonds of water molecules interfere with the ionic bonds of salts, causing *dissociation* (also called *ionization*). When cations and anions dissociate in water, they are called **electrolytes** because they can conduct electricity through the solution.

Hydrogen Bonds

Like ionic bonds, **hydrogen bonds** do not involve the sharing of electrons. Instead, a partially charged hydrogen atom is attracted to a full or partial negative charge on either a different region of the same molecule or another molecule. The cumulative effect of numerous hydrogen bonds is to stabilize the three-dimensional shapes of large molecules, such as DNA. Thus, although weak, they are essential to life.

Chemical Reactions

Chemical reactions result from the making or breaking of chemical bonds in a process in which **reactants**—the atoms, ions, or molecules that exist at the beginning of a reaction—are changed into **products**—the atoms, ions, or molecules that remain after the reaction is complete.

Synthesis Reactions

Synthesis reactions involve the formation of larger, more complex molecules. An important type is **dehydration synthesis**, in which two smaller molecules are joined together by a covalent bond, and a water molecule is removed from the reactants. Synthesis reactions require energy to break bonds in the reactants and to form new bonds to make products. They are said to be **endothermic reactions** because they trap energy within new molecular bonds. **Anabolism** is the sum of all synthesis reactions in an organism.

Decomposition Reactions

Decomposition reactions are the opposite of synthesis reactions in that they break bonds within larger reactants to form smaller atoms, ions, and molecules. Because these reactions release energy, they are called **exothermic**. A common type of decomposition reaction is **hydrolysis**, the reverse of dehydration synthesis, in which a covalent bond in a large molecule is broken, and the ionic components of water (H^+ and OH^-) are added to the products. Collectively, all the decomposition reactions in an organism are called **catabolism**.

Exchange Reactions

Exchange reactions involve exchanging atoms between reactants. An important example is the phosphorylation of glucose. The sum of all chemical reactions in an organism is called **metabolism**.

Water, Acids, Bases, and Salts

Inorganic chemicals lack carbon. Many, including water, acids, bases, and salts, are essential to life.

Water

Water constitutes 50–99% of the mass of living organisms. It is vital to life because of its solvent properties, its liquidity, its capacity to absorb heat, and its participation in chemical reactions. In addition, water molecules are cohesive; they stick to one another via hydrogen bonding. This property generates surface tension, which enables water to form a thin layer on the surface of cells through which dissolved molecules can be transported into and out of the cell.

Acids and Bases

An **acid** is a substance that dissociates into one or more hydrogen ions (H^+) and one or more anions. A **base** is a molecule that binds with H^+ when dissolved in water. Many bases dissociate into hydroxyl ions and cations. The concentration of hydrogen ions in a solution is expressed using a logarithmic **pH** scale in which acidity increases as pH values decrease. Organisms can tolerate only a narrow pH range. Thus, most organisms contain natural **buffers**, substances that prevent drastic changes in internal pH.

Salts

A *salt* is a compound that dissociates in water into cations and anions other than H^+ and OH^-. A cell uses the cations and anions of salts—electrolytes—to create electrical differences between its internal and external environments, to transfer electrons from one location to another, and as important components of many enzymes. Some organisms use salts to provide structural support for their cells.

Organic Macromolecules

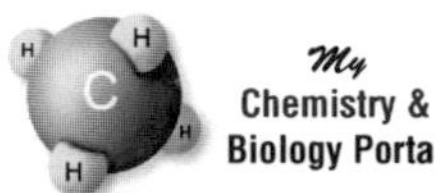

Organic Molecules & Isomers

Organic *macromolecules* are large, complex molecules containing carbon and hydrogen atoms linked together in branched and unbranched chains, and rings bound to one or more other elements, such as oxygen, nitrogen, phosphorus, or sulfur.

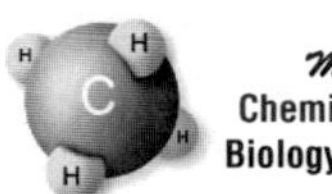

Introduction to Organic Molecules

Functional Groups and Monomers

In organic macromolecules, atoms often appear in certain common arrangements called **functional groups**. For example, the hydroxyl functional group is common to all alcohols. In addition, the organic macromolecules of proteins, carbohydrates, and nucleic acids are composed of simple subunits called **monomers** that can be covalently linked to form chainlike **polymers**, which may be hundreds of thousands of monomers long.

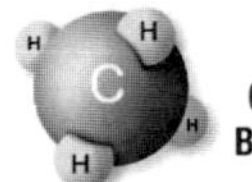

Polymers

Lipids

Lipids are organic macromolecules composed almost entirely of carbon and hydrogen atoms linked by nonpolar covalent bonds. They are thus **hydrophobic**; that is, they are insoluble in water. The four major groups of lipids are:

- **Fats** composed of glycerol and three chainlike fatty acids. **Saturated fatty acids** contain more hydrogen in their structural formulas than **unsaturated fatty acids**, which contain double bonds between some of their carbon atoms. If several double bonds exist, the fatty acid is called a **polyunsaturated fat**.
- **Phospholipids** contain two fatty acid chains and a phosphate functional group. Whereas the fatty acid "tail" of the molecule is nonpolar and thus hydrophobic, the phospholipid "head" is polar and thus hydrophilic. This means that phospholipids placed in a watery environment will always self-assemble into one of two forms that keep the fatty acid tails away from water: a single-layered *micelle* or a *bilayer* such as is found in the outer membranes of all cells.
- **Waxes** contain one long-chain fatty acid linked covalently to a long-chain alcohol by an ester bond. They are completely water insoluble and are sometimes used as energy storage molecules.
- **Steroids** consist of four carbon rings that are fused to one another and attached to various side chains and functional groups. Many organisms have sterol molecules in their cell membranes that keep them fluid at low temperatures.

Carbohydrates

Carbohydrates are organic molecules composed solely of atoms of carbon, hydrogen, and oxygen. They are used for immediate and long-term storage of energy, as structural components of DNA and RNA and some cell walls, and for conversion into amino acids. They also serve as recognition sites during intercellular interactions. Three basic groups are:

- **Monosaccharides** are simple sugars such as glucose and fructose. They usually take cyclic forms.
- **Disaccharides** are formed when two monosaccharides are linked together via dehydration synthesis. Sucrose, lactose, and maltose are examples.
- **Polysaccharides** are polymers composed of tens or thousands of monosaccharides that have been covalently linked in dehydration synthesis reactions. Cellulose and glycogen are examples.

Proteins

The most complex organic macromolecules are **proteins**, which are composed mostly of carbon, hydrogen, oxygen, nitrogen, and sulfur. They function as structural components of cells, enzymatic catalysts, regulators of various activities, transporters of substances, and defense molecules. The monomers of proteins are **amino acids**, in which a central carbon is attached to an amino group, a hydrogen atom, a carboxyl group, and a side group that varies according to the amino acid. These are linked by **peptide bonds** into specific structural patterns determined genetically. Every protein has at least three levels of structure, and some have four. **Denaturation** of a protein disrupts its structure and subsequently its function.

Nucleic Acids

The two nucleic acids **deoxyribonucleic acid (DNA)** and **ribonucleic acid (RNA)** comprise the genetic material of cells and viruses. These differ primarily in the structure of their monomers, which are called **nucleotides.** Each nucleotide consists of phosphoric acid, a pentose sugar (deoxyribose or ribose) and one of five cyclic nitrogenous bases: **adenine (A), guanine (G), cytosine (C), thymine (T), uracil (U**). DNA contains A, G, C, and T nucleotides, whereas RNA contains A, G, C, and U nucleotides.

The structure of nucleic acids allows for genetic diversity, correct copying of genes for their passage on to the next generation, and the accurate synthesis of proteins. **Adenosine triphosphate (ATP)**, which is made up of the nitrogenous base adenine, ribose sugar, and three phosphate groups, is the most important short-term energy storage molecule in cells. It is also incorporated into the structure of many coenzymes.

Practice Test for Chapter 8

Exercises in Organic Chemistry

Structures of Organic Compounds

1. What are the chemical formulas for the following structures?

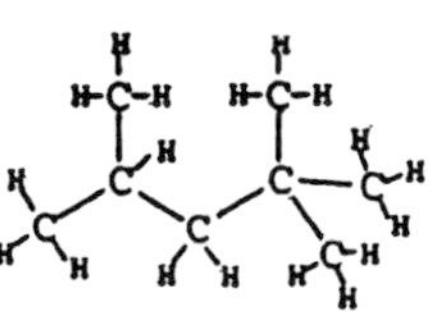

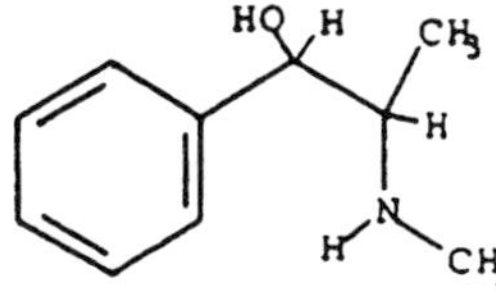

Formula: ______ ______ ______ ______

2. How many covalent bonds is carbon able to form? ______

3. What is wrong with the structure shown in the box at right?

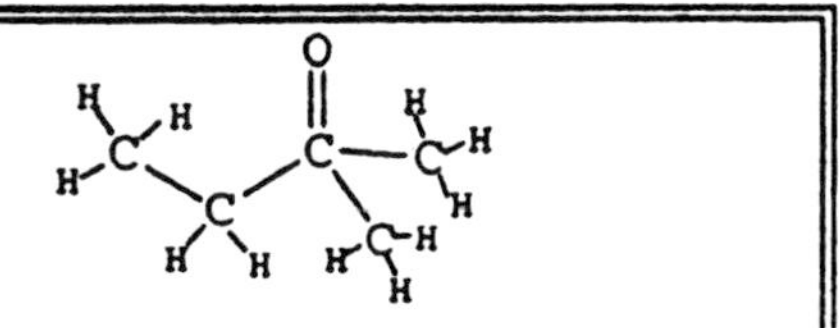

____

4. **a.** Draw a hydrocarbon that contains 4 carbon atoms.

b. Redraw your structure and transform it into an amine.

c. Transform your amine into an amide. You may need to relocate the nitrogen.

d. Redraw your amide, transforming it into a carboxylic acid.

e. Redraw your carboxylic acid, transforming it into an alcohol.

f. Rearrange the carbons of your alcohol to make an ether.

Polymers

1. Circle the monomers that may be useful for forming an addition polymer and draw a box around the ones that may be useful for forming a condensation polymer.

$H_2C{=}CH_2$

$HO{-}C(=O){-}CH_2CH_2CH_2CH_3$

$H_2N{-}C_6H_{10}{-}NH_2$ (1,3-diaminocyclohexane)

$H_2N{-}CH(CH_3){-}C(=O){-}OH$

$HO{-}C(=O){-}CH_2{-}C(H){=}CH_3$

$HO{-}C(=O){-}CH_2CH_2CH_2CH_2{-}C(=O){-}OH$

2. Which type of polymer always weighs less than the sum of its parts? Why?

3. Would a material with the following arrangement of polymer molecules have a relatively high or low melting point? Why?

Multiple Choice

1. Which element has the greatest number of protons in its nucleus?
   - **a.** Carbon-12
   - **b.** Carbon-13
   - **c.** Carbon-14
   - **d.** All have the same number of protons

2. A nonpolar covalent bond:
   - **a.** Shares electrons equally between atoms
   - **b.** Shares electrons unequally between atoms
   - **c.** Forms when one atom strips the valence electrons from another atom
   - **d.** Does not form between the electrons of different atoms

3. Which of the following acids is an organic acid?
   - **a.** HNO_3 (nitric acid)
   - **b.** HCl (hydrochloric acid)
   - **c.** CH_3COOH (acetic acid)
   - **d.** H_3PO_4 (phosphoric acid)

4. Salts are held together by what types of bonds?
   - **a.** Nonpolar covalent bonds
   - **b.** Polar covalent bonds
   - **c.** Ionic bonds
   - **d.** Hydrogen bonds

5. Exchange, or transfer reactions, are:
   - **a.** Endothermic
   - **b.** Exothermic
   - **c.** Both endothermic and exothermic
   - **d.** Neither endothermic nor exothermic

6. Lemon juice, with a pH of 2, contains how many more hydrogen atoms than milk with a pH of 6?
   - **a.** 10 times
   - **b.** 100 times
   - **c.** 1,000 times
   - **d.** 10,000 times

7. Which of the following is not considered a macromolecule?
   - **a.** DNA
   - **b.** Sucrose
   - **c.** Phospholipids
   - **d.** Antibodies

8. Lipids are composed almost entirely of carbon and hydrogen atoms linked together by:
   - **a.** Nonpolar covalent bonds
   - **b.** Polar covalent bonds
   - **c.** Ionic bonds
   - **d.** Hydrogen bonds

9. What type of fatty acids would you expect to see predominating in the membranes of microbes living in extremely hot environments?
   - **a.** Saturated fatty acids
   - **b.** Unsaturated fatty acids
   - **c.** Polyunsaturated fatty acids
   - **d.** All types of fatty acids would be present in equal amounts

10. The cell walls of bacteria are made out of what materials?
  a. Monosaccharides and amino acids
  b. Polysaccharides and amino acids
  c. Monosaccharides and lipids
  d. Polysaccharides and lipids

11. The most abundant polysaccharide on Earth is:
  a. Amylose **c.** Glucose
  b. Cellulose **d.** Glycogen

12. Which of the following is not a function of nucleic acids?
  a. Nucleic acids carry the genetic instructions of the cell
  b. Nucleic acids are involved in protein synthesis
  c. Nucleic acids provide energy for cellular functions
  d. All of these are functions of nucleic acids

Fill in the Blanks

1. The atomic number of an element corresponds to the number of ______________________ in its nucleus.

2. Chemical bonds form between two or more ______________________ to create a ______________________.

3. The two ways to write the structural formula for O_2 are ______________________ and ______________________.

4. For each of the following reactions, indicate the type of reaction that is occurring:
  a. $C_6H_{12}O_6 + 6O_2 \rightarrow 6H_2O + 6CO_2$ ______________________
  b. $C_6H_{12}O_6 + ATP \rightarrow C_6H_{12}O_6\text{–}P + ADP$ ______________________
  c. Glucose + Fructose $\rightarrow$ sucrose + H_2O ______________________

5. Acids characteristically dissociate to release ______________________ ions. Bases dissociate to release ______________________ ions. (Give the name and the molecular formula for each.)

6. Organisms cannot tolerate large changes in internal pH and so they contain natural ______________________ to protect themselves. An example is ______________________.

7. Phospholipids form membranes by orienting their ______________________ head groups toward the water environment and their ______________________ tails away from the water.

8. Covalent bonds formed between amino acids in a protein are called __________________ bonds. Other bonds, mostly __________________ bonds, help to hold the protein in its tertiary form.

9. In DNA, the pentose sugar that forms each nucleotide is ______________________ whereas in RNA the sugar is ______________________.

10. Write the complementary DNA strand sequence and the complementary RNA strand sequence for the following sequence: 5' - ATTGCTACCGAT - 3'.
  a. DNA sequence: ______________________.
  b. RNA sequence: ______________________.

Short-Answer

1. Describe the difference between an element, a molecule, and a compound. Give one example of each.

2. Using a periodic table, draw the electron shells of calcium and chlorine. Indicate the valence for each element. Draw the molecule $CaCl_2$, indicating the type of bonds formed.

3. Fats are believed to contribute to certain types of heart disease, such as atherosclerosis, by building up in the arteries of the heart and blocking them. Which types of fatty acids—saturated, unsaturated, or polyunsaturated—would you expect to contribute *least* to heart disease and why?

4. List the five primary functions of proteins. For each function, explain in one sentence what would happen to an organism if proteins could no longer perform that function.

Critical Thinking

1. In metabolism, catabolism provides the energy necessary for anabolism to occur. Consider a bacterium living in the human intestinal tract versus one living in the water of an abandoned flowerpot. Which one would you predict to have the higher metabolic activity and why? Define the terms metabolism, catabolism, and anabolism in your answer.

2. While microbes require a relatively neutral internal pH, many species can survive and even thrive in highly acidic or basic external environments. Some microbes even physically alter the pH of their environment to better suit themselves. How does this ability to change the acidic or basic nature of the environment confer a growth advantage on the microbes that do it?

3. Mutations, in the form of amino acid substitutions, happen at a relatively high frequency in microbes. Some are lethal and destroy protein function, while others are not. These neutral, nonharmful substitutions are generally believed to predominate in nature. Explain why this might be so.

Concept Building Questions

1. One of the key questions posed during the Golden Age of Microbiology was that of what caused fermentation to occur. What type(s) of chemical reactions is/are occurring in the microbial production of alcohol from sugar? In general, why are these types of reactions useful for the cell?

2. The role microbes play in the environment is an important question to microbiologists. Reread the section in Chapter 1 that describes this question and then explain how a firm understanding of chemical bonds and chemical reactions is crucial to answering this question.

Word Roots

di = two (disaccharide: two monosaccharides joined together)
glyco = sweet (glycogen: a polysaccharide sugar used to store energy in animals)
hydro = water (hydrolysis: breaking chemical bonds by adding water)
iso = equal (isomers: molecules with similar molecular formulas but different structures)
lyse = break (hydrolysis: breaking chemical bonds by adding water)
macro = big (macromolecule: a giant molecule in living organisms)
meros = part (polymer: a chain made from smaller organic molecules)

mono = single (monosaccharide: simplest type of sugar)
philic = loving (hydrophilic: water-loving property of a molecule)
phobos = fearing (hydrophobic: water-hating property of a molecule)
poly = many (polysaccharide: many monosaccharides joined together)
sacchar = sugar (monosaccharide: simplest type of sugar)
sclero = hard (atherosclerosis: hardening of the arteries)
tri = three (triglyceride: a glycerol molecule joined with three fatty acid molecules)

Key Terms for Crossword Puzzle

amino acids
anabolic steroids
atherosclerosis
carbohydrates
cellulose
dehydration reaction
denaturation
disaccharides
DNA
double helix
fats
functional groups
glycogen
hydrocarbons
hydrogenation
hydrolysis
hydrophilic
hydrophobic
isomers
lipids
low-carb diets
macromolecules
monomers
monosaccharides
nitrogenous base
nucleic acids
nucleotides
organic chemistry
organic compounds
peptide bond
polymers
polypeptide
polysaccharides
primary structure
protein
protein shape
RNA
saturated
starch
steroids
sugar-phosphate backbone
trans fats
triglyceride
unsaturated

Crossword Puzzle

Use the Key Terms list from this chapter to fill in the crossword puzzle.

ACROSS

1. a type of diet that avoids starches and sugars
3. type of bond between adjacent amino acids
4. water-hating property of a molecule
5. first level of protein structure
6. unhealthy unsaturated fats produced by hydrogenation
8. molecules with similar formulas but different structures
9. the addition of hydrogens to unsaturated fats
11. the type of backbone forming polynucleotides
12. a polysaccharide used to store energy in plants
13. the simplest organic molecule
16. monomer of a nucleic acid
18. a chain of amino acids used to make a protein
20. type of group of atoms usually involved in chemical reactions
23. the part of the molecule that varies between different types of nucleotides
25. gigantic molecule
26. a change in the shape of a protein
27. simplest type of sugar
29. cardiovascular disease in which lipid deposits accumulate in walls of arteries
30. the type of chemistry that studies organic molecules
31. a type of nucleic acid that uses the base uracil
32. monomer of a protein
34. the most abundant organic compound on Earth
35. macromolecule made of one or more polypeptides
36. type of organic molecule that includes sugars and starch
37. a large lipid molecule made from glycerol and three fatty acids
38. the genetic material that organisms inherit from their parents
39. shape of DNA

DOWN
1. a type of organic molecule that includes fats, steroids, and phospholipids
2. a type of lipid with a carbon skeleton in the form of four fused rings
4. water-loving property of a molecule
7. type of fatty acid with the maximum number of hydrogens
10. process that links monomers together
14. many monosaccharides joined together
15. a polysaccharide used to store energy in animals
17. breaking chemical bonds by adding water
19. a chain made from smaller organic molecules
21. building block of a polymer
22. type of organic molecule including DNA and RNA
24. synthetic variant of testosterone
28. two monosaccharides joined together
33. type of fatty acid with less than the maximum hydrogens

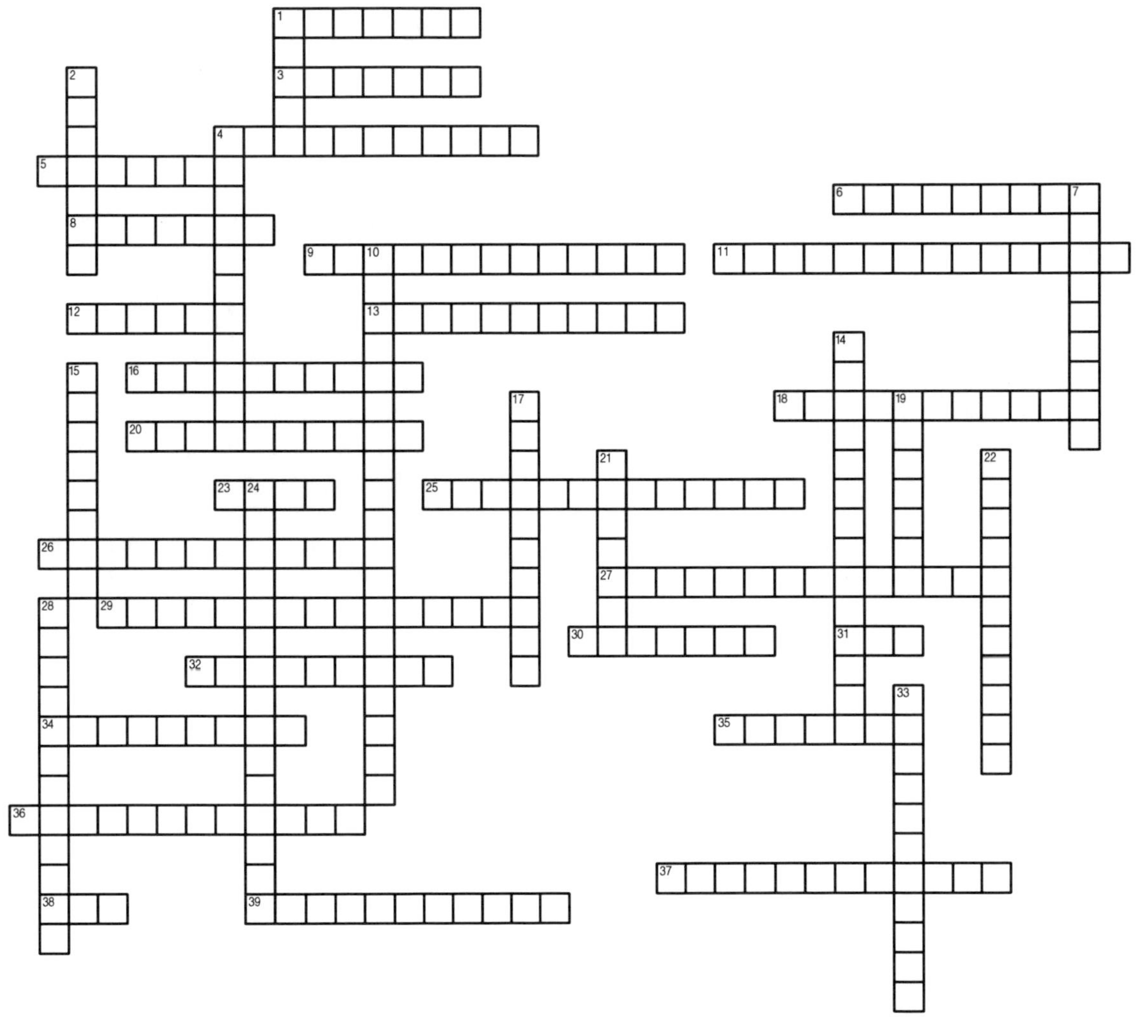

Key Terms

Adenosine triphosphate (ATP), which is related to adenine nucleotide, is the most important short-term energy storage molecule in cells. It is also incorporated into the structure of many coenzymes.

Alcohol An organic molecule that contains a hydroxyl group bonded to a saturated carbon.

Aldehyde An organic molecule containing a carbonyl group in which the carbon is bonded either to one carbon atom and one hydrogen atom or to two hydrogen atoms.

Amide An organic molecule containing a carbonyl group in which the carbon is bonded to a nitrogen atom.

Amine An organic molecule containing a nitrogen atom bonded to one or more saturated carbon atoms.

Aromatic compound Any organic molecule containing a benzene ring.

Carbohydrates such as **monosaccharides, disaccharides**, and **polysaccharides** serve as energy sources, structural molecules, and recognition sites during intercellular interactions.

Carboxylic acid An organic molecule containing a carbonyl group in which the carbon is bonded to a hydroxyl group.

Certain groups of atoms in common arrangements, called **functional groups**, are found in organic macromolecules. **Monomers** are simple subunits that can be covalently linked to form chainlike polymers.

Deoxyribonucleic acid (DNA) and **ribonucleic acid (RNA)** are unbranched macromolecular polymers of **nucleotides**, each composed either of deoxyribose or ribose sugar, phosphoric acid, and a nitrogenous base. Five different bases exist: **adenine, guanine, cytosine, thymine**, and **uracil**. DNA contains A, G, C, and T nucleotides. RNA uses U nucleotides instead of T nucleotides.

Ester An organic molecule containing a carbonyl group in which the carbon is bonded to one carbon atom and one oxygen atom is bonded to another carbon atom.

Ether An organic molecule containing an oxygen atom bonded to two carbon atoms.

Fat molecules are formed from a glycerol and three chainlike fatty acids. **Saturated fatty acids** contain more hydrogen in their structural formulas than **unsaturated fatty acids**, which contain double bonds between some carbon atoms. If several double bonds exist in the fatty acids of a molecule of fat, it is a **polyunsaturated** fat.

Functional group A specific combination of atoms that behave as a unit in an organic molecule.

Heteroatom Any atom other than carbon or hydrogen in an organic molecule.

Hydrocarbon A chemical compound containing only carbon and hydrogen atoms.

Ketone An organic molecule containing a carbonyl group in which the carbon is bonded to two carbon atoms.

Lock-and-key model A conceptual model that explains how drugs interact with receptor sites.

Lipids, which include fats, phospholipids, waxes, and steroids, are bold **hydrophobic** (insoluble in water) macromolecules.

Monomer The small molecular unit from which a polymer is formed.

Organic chemistry The study of carbon-containing compounds.

Phenol An organic molecule in which a hydroxyl group is bonded to a benzene ring.

Polymer A long organic molecule made of many repeating units.

Phospholipids contain two fatty acid chains and a phosphate functional group. The phospholipid head is **hydrophilic**, whereas the fatty acid portion of the molecule is hydrophobic.

Proteins are structural components of cells, enzymatic catalysts, regulators of various activities, molecules involved in the transportation of substances, and molecules involved in an organism's defense. They are composed of **amino acids** linked by **peptide bonds**, and they possess primary, secondary, tertiary, and (sometimes) quaternary structures that affect their function. **Denaturation** of a protein disrupts its structure and subsequently its function.

Saturated hydrocarbon A hydrocarbon containing no multiple covalent bonds, with each carbon atom bonded to four other atoms.

Structural isomers Molecules that have the same molecular formula but different chemical structures.

Steroid lipids such as cholesterol help maintain the structural integrity of membranes as temperature fluctuates.

The structure of nucleic acids allows for genetic diversity, correct copying of genes for their passage on to the next generation, and the accurate synthesis of proteins.

Unsaturated hydrocarbon A hydrocarbon containing at least one multiple covalent bond.

Waxes contain a long-chain fatty acid covalently linked to a long-chain alcohol. Waxes, which are water insoluble, are components of cell walls and are sometimes used as energy storage molecules.

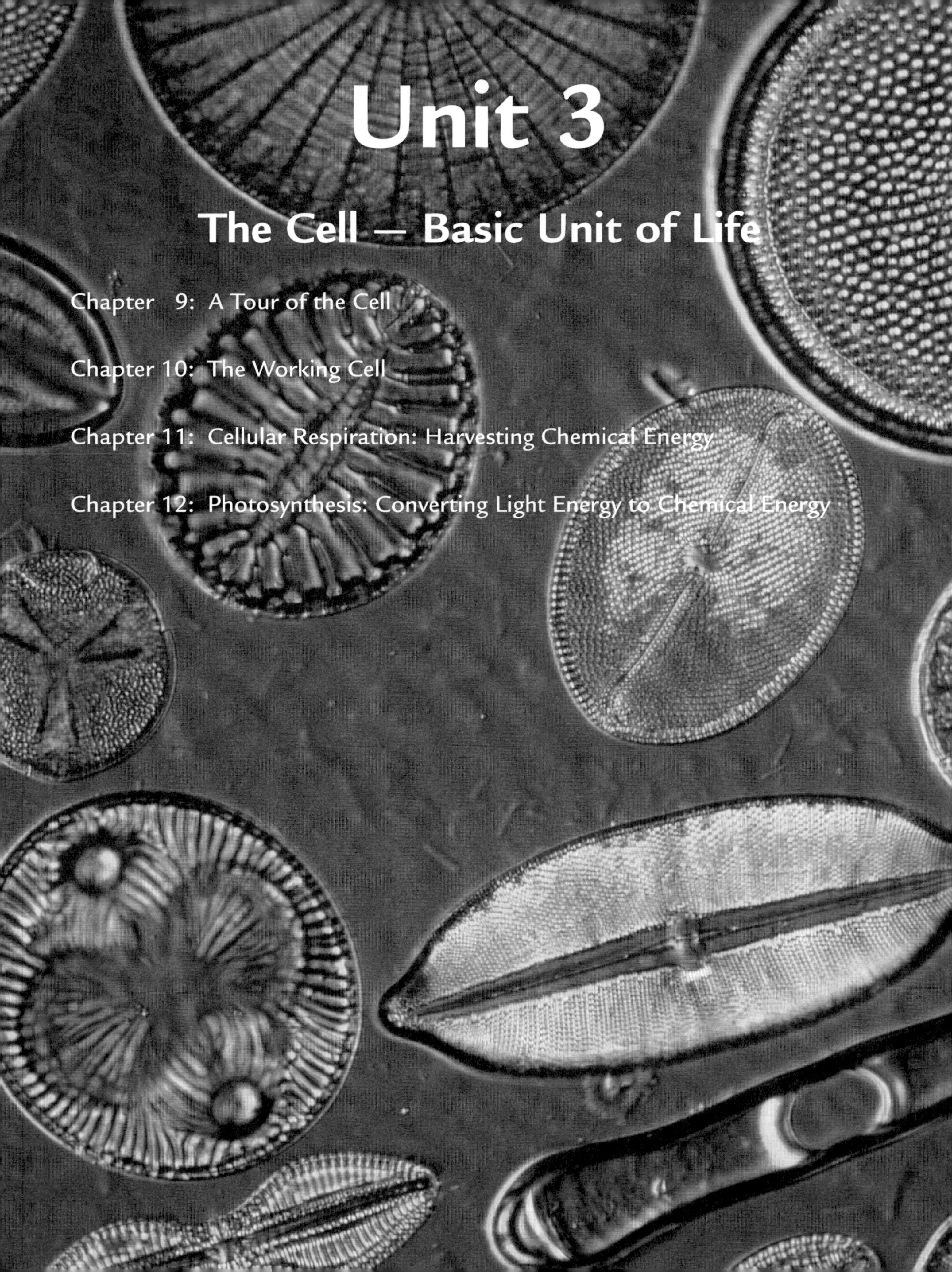

Unit 3

The Cell — Basic Unit of Life

9 A Tour of the Cell

An electron microscope can visualize objects a million times smaller than the head of a pin.
If you stacked up 8,000 cell membranes, they would only be as thick as a page in this book.
The cells of a whale are about the same size as the cells of a mouse.
Every second, your body produces about 2 million red blood cells.

LOOKING AHEAD

My
Chemistry &
Biology Portal

http://www.pearsoncustom.com/devry/myc

Study Goals

A Tour of the Cell

a. Before you begin reading this chapter, examine Figure 9.6 of your text. How many of these cell parts do you recognize from prior courses? Also refer to Figure 9.3 of your text to become familiar with the relative sizes of cells and their parts.

b. The organizing tables below will be especially useful in this chapter. Many basic parts of cells are introduced. These tables will help you keep the information organized for review.

Chapter Review

Concept Map

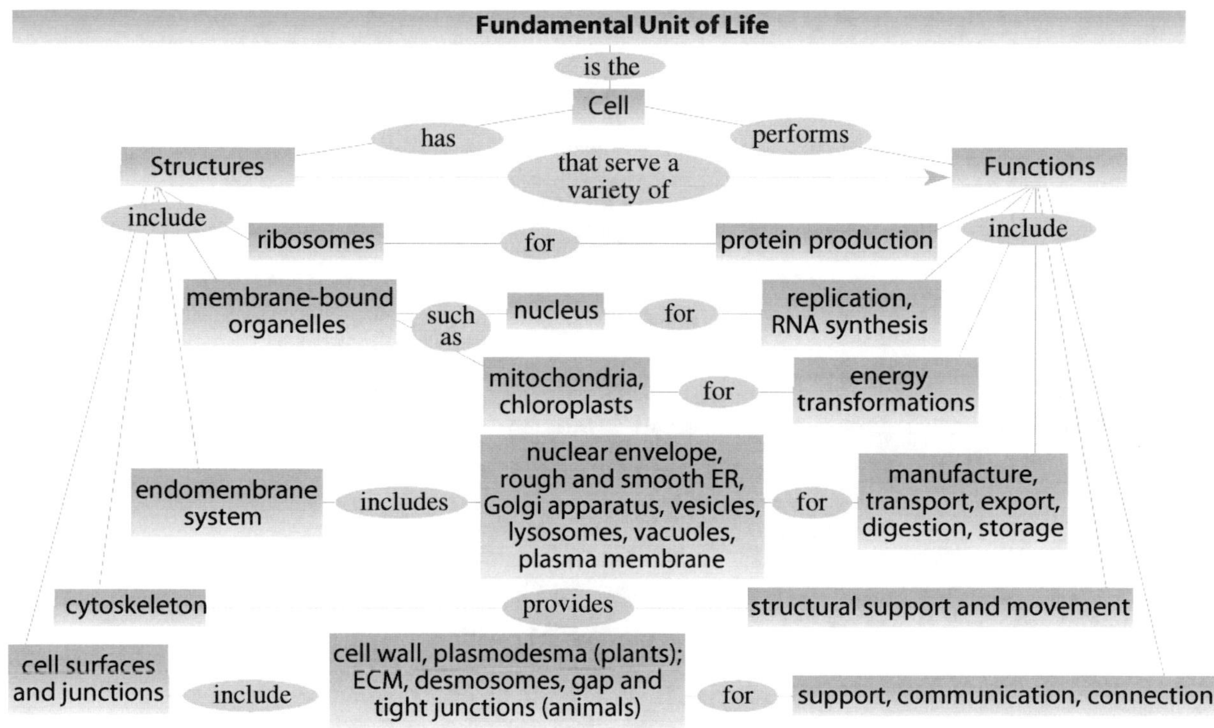

Chapter Concept Review

For study help and activities, go to campbellbology.com or the student CD-ROM.

The Microscopic World of Cells

- **Microscopes as a Windows on the World of Cells** Using early microscopes, biologists discovered that all organisms are made of cells. Resolving power limits the useful magnification of microscopes. A light microscope (LM) has useful magnifications of up to about 1,000×. Electron microscopes, both scanning (SEM) and transmission (TEM), are much more powerful.

Activity *Metric System Review*

Case Study in the Process of Science *What is the Size and Scale of Our World?*

- The Two Major Categories of Cells

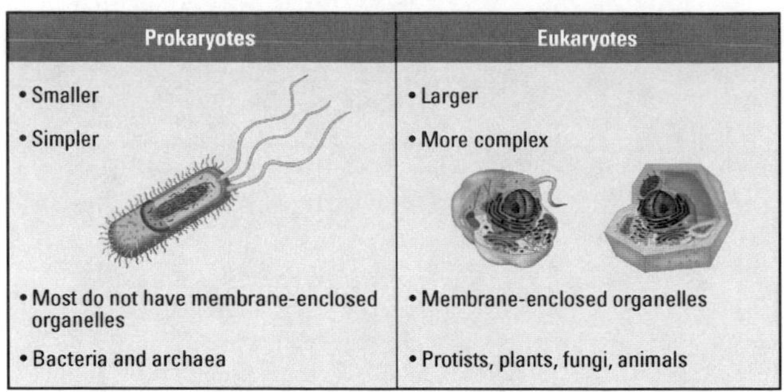

Prokaryotes
Eukaryotes
• Smaller
• Simpler
• Most do not have membrane-enclosed organelles
• Bacteria and archaea
• Larger
• More complex
• Membrane-enclosed organelles
• Protists, plants, fungi, animals

Activity *Prokaryotic cell structure and function*

- **A Panoramic View of Eukaryotic Cells** Many cellular functions are partitioned by membranes in the complex organization of eukaryotic cells. The largest organelle is usually the nucleus. Other organelles are located in the cytoplasm, the region between the nucleus and the plasma membrane.

eTutor *A Tour of the Animal Cell*

Activity *Comparing Cells*

Activity *Build an Animal Cell and a Plant Cell*

Membrane Structure

- **The Plasma Membrane: A Fluid Mosaic of Lipids and Proteins**

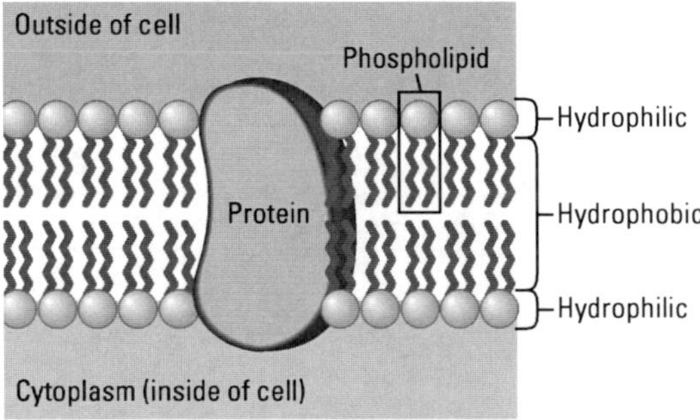

Activity *Membrane Structure*

- **Cell Surfaces** Most cells secrete an extracellular coat that helps protect and support the cell. The walls that encase plant cells support plants against the pull of gravity and also prevent cells from absorbing too much water. Animal cells are coated by a sticky extracellular matrix.

The Nucleus and Ribosomes: Genetic Control of the Cell

- **Structure and Function of the Nucleus** An envelope consisting of two membranes encloses the nucleus. Within the nucleus, DNA and proteins make up chromatin fibers; each very long fiber is a single chromosome. The nucleus also contains the nucleolus, which produces components of ribosomes.
- **Ribosomes** Ribosomes produce proteins in the cytoplasm.
- **How DNA Controls the Cell** Genetic messages are transmitted to the ribosomes via messenger RNA, which travels from the nucleus to the cytoplasm.

Activity *Overview of Protein Synthesis*

The Endomembrane System: Manufacturing and Distributing Cellular Products

- **The Endoplasmic Reticulum** The ER consists of membrane-enclosed tubes and sacs within the cytoplasm. Rough ER, named for the ribosomes attached to its surface, makes membrane and secretory proteins. The functions of smooth ER include lipid synthesis and detoxification.
- **The Golgi Apparatus** The Golgi refines certain ER products and packages them in transport vesicles targeted for other organelles or export from the cell.
- **Lysosomes** Lysosomes, sacs containing digestive enzymes, function in digestion within the cell and chemical recycling.
- **Vacuoles** These membrane-enclosed organelles include the contractile vacuoles that expel water from certain freshwater protists and the large, multifunctional central vacuoles of plant cells.

Activity *The Endomembrane System*

Chloroplasts and Mitochondria: Energy Conversion

- **Chloroplasts** The sites of photosynthesis in plant cells, chloroplasts convert light energy to the chemical energy of food. Grana, stacks of membranous sacs within the chloroplasts, trap the light energy.
- **Mitochondria** These are the sites of cellular respiration, which converts food energy to ATP energy. ATP drives most cellular work. Both chloroplasts and mitochondria contain small amounts of DNA.

Activity *Build a Chloroplast and a Mitochondrion*

The Cytoskeleton: Cell Shape and Movement

- **Maintaining Cell Shape** Straight, hollow microtubules are an important component of the cytoskeleton, an organelle that gives support to and maintains the shape of cells.
- **Cilia and Flagella** Cilia and eukaryotic flagella are both motile appendages made primarily of microtubules. Cilia are short, numerous, and move by coordinated beating. Flagella are long, often occur singly, and propel a cell through whiplike movements.

Activity *Cilia and Flagella*

Activity *Review: Animal Cell Structure and Function*

Activity *Review: Plant Cell Structure and Function*

Organizing Tables

Compare the features of prokaryotic and eukaryotic cells. (See your text and Figure 9.4 of your text.)

TABLE 9.1

	Prokaryotic Cells	Eukaryotic Cells
Which group has a nucleus bordered by a membrane?		
Which group has organelles?		
How do the sizes compare?		
What are examples of each group?		

Compare the structure, location, and function of the following components of the endomembrane system.

TABLE 9.2

	Structure	**Location in the Cytoplasm**	**Function(s)**
Smooth endoplasmic reticulum			
Rough endoplasmic reticulum			
Golgi apparatus			
Lysosome			
Central vacuole			

Compare the features of cilia and flagella.

TABLE 9.3

	Cilia	**Flagella**
Which are usually longer?		
Which are usually more numerous?		
How does their basic architecture compare?		
Where are they found?		

Compare the structures and functions of mitochondria and chloroplasts.

TABLE 9.4

	Mitochondria	**Chloroplasts**
These organelles are found in the cells of organisms in what kingdoms?		
Which organelle is involved in cellular respiration and which is involved in photosynthesis?		
Compare the number of membranes and compartments found in each organelle.		
Consider drawing a general sketch to show these parts.		
What part of each organelle is the most active region?		

Practice Test for Chapter 9

Directions: Identify the *one* best answer for the multiple-choice questions. For true/false questions, determine if the statement is true or false. If false, change the underlined word(s) to make the statement true. Finally, add the correct word(s) to the fill-in-the-blank questions to make the statements true.

Biology and Society: Cells That Cure

1. Cell therapy to repair damage caused by a heart attack:
  A. genetically modifies muscle cells surrounding the damage to promote the replacement of the damaged cells.
  B. uses a series of drugs to encourage the damaged cells to grow and reproduce to repair the damaged region.
  C. transplants into the damaged heart region mouse stem cells that have been changed into heart muscle.
  D. injects immature muscle cells from another area of the body into the damaged areas of the heart.
  E. none of the above.

2. True or False? Even though many patients respond positively to cell therapy to treat damage caused by a heart attack, scientists <u>do not</u> yet understand how cell therapy works.

3. True or False? Heart muscle cells <u>regenerate</u> over time.

4. During a heart attack, heart muscle cells die because they are starved for ___________.

The Microscopic World of Cells

5. Which one of the following is most closely associated with the term "resolution"?
  A. clarity
  B. larger size
  C. greater color
  D. lighter image

6. Examine Figure 9.6 of your text. Which one of the following organelles is physically connected to the nucleus?
  A. mitochondrion
  B. Golgi apparatus
  C. rough and smooth endoplasmic reticulum
  D. lysosome
  E. plasma membrane

7. Which one of the following statements about prokaryotic and eukaryotic cells is *false*?
  A. Eukaryotic cells have membrane-enclosed organelles.
  B. Prokaryotic cells evolved before eukaryotic cells evolved.
  C. Eukaryotic cells are generally smaller than prokaryotic cells.
  D. Eukaryotic cells divide the labor of life among many internal compartments.
  E. Most bacteria are surrounded by a rigid cell wall.

8. Which one of the following has prokaryotic cells?
  A. a mushroom
  B. a bacterium
  C. an oak tree
  D. a crawfish
  E. a virus

9. True or False? Bacteria and archaea both consist of <u>prokaryotic</u> cells.

10. True or False? The genetic material of eukaryotic cells is housed in the <u>endoplasmic reticulum</u>.

11. Small parts of eukaryotic cells with specific functions are called ___________.

12. The magnification of a transmission electron microscope is about ___________ times greater than that of a typical light microscope.

13. Cell surfaces are best revealed by a(n) ___________ electron microscope.

14. Internal details of cells are best revealed by a(n) ___________ electron microscope.

15. A nucleus bordered by a membranous envelope is found in ___________ cells, but not in ___________ cells.

16. The generalization that all living things are composed of cells is called ___________ theory.

17. Some prokaryotic cells have ___________, which help attach them to surfaces.

18. In a eukaryotic cell, the region between the nucleus and the plasma membrane is the ___________.

19. In a eukaryotic cell, organelles are suspended in a fluid called the ___________.

Membrane Structure

20. The membranes of cells are primarily composed of:
- **A.** lipids and nucleic acids.
- **B.** proteins and nucleic acids.
- **C.** lipids and carbohydrates.
- **D.** proteins and carbohydrates.
- **E.** lipids and proteins.

21. Which one of the following statements about cellular membranes is *false*?
- **A.** Membrane molecules can move freely past one another.
- **B.** Most membranes have carbohydrates embedded in the phospholipid bilayer.
- **C.** Diverse proteins float like icebergs in the phospholipid sea.
- **D.** The structure of the plasma membrane is similar to the structure of the other internal membranes of eukaryotic cells.
- **E.** Phospholipids in the membrane form a bilayer.

22. Which one of the following statements about plant cell walls is *false*? Plant cell walls:
- **A.** help the cells maintain their shape.
- **B.** protect the cells from physical damage.
- **C.** restrain plant cells from absorbing too much water.
- **D.** are the primary site of photosynthesis.

23. True or False? Animal cells are often bound to the extracellular matrix by surface <u>lipids</u> in the plasma membrane.

24. The phospholipids and most of the proteins in a membrane are free to drift about in what is called the fluid ___________.

25. The surfaces of most animal cells contain cell ___________, structures that connect them to another cell.

The Nucleus and Ribosomes: Genetic Control of the Cell

26. Which one of the following statements about the nucleus and ribosomes of eukaryotic cells is *false*?
- **A.** Chromosomes are composed of long strands of DNA attached to certain proteins.
- **B.** Pores in the nuclear envelope allow messenger RNA to move from the nucleus to the cytoplasm.
- **C.** Ribosomes are constructed in the cytoplasm from parts produced in the nucleolus.
- **D.** DNA moves from the nucleus to the cytoplasm to direct the production of proteins.
- **E.** Ribosomes may work either suspended in the cytosol or attached to the endoplasmic reticulum.

27. If we think of the cell as a factory, then the nucleus is its executive boardroom and the top managers are the:
- **A.** genes.
- **B.** ribosomes.
- **C.** chromosomes.
- **D.** mitochondria.
- **E.** endoplasmic reticulum.

28. True or False? The directions to make a protein move from <u>DNA</u> to <u>messenger RNA</u> and then to <u>ribosomes</u>.

29. Proteins are made on ribosomes in the cytoplasm using the directions from a(n) ___________ molecule.

30. Differences in the structures of ___________ allow humans to use antibiotics that do not harm human cells.

The Endomembrane System: Manufacturing and Distributing Cellular Products

31. Which one of the following statements about the components of the endomembrane system is *false*?
- **A.** Products from the endoplasmic reticulum are modified in the Golgi apparatus.
- **B.** Lysosomes have several types of digestive functions.
- **C.** Lipids are typically produced by the rough endoplasmic reticulum.
- **D.** Central vacuoles contribute to plant growth and may contain pigments and poisons.
- **E.** The smooth endoplasmic reticulum helps detoxify poisons.

32. Examine Figures 9.11–9.15 of your text. Which one of the following sequences best represents the steps an enzyme would take from initial production to joining with a food vacuole?
- **A.** rough endoplasmic reticulum, Golgi apparatus, lysosome
- **B.** Golgi apparatus, rough endoplasmic reticulum, lysosome
- **C.** lysosome, smooth endoplasmic reticulum, Golgi apparatus
- **D.** smooth endoplasmic reticulum, Golgi apparatus, lysosome

33. The smooth endoplasmic reticulum:
- **A.** synthesizes lipids and helps to detoxify drugs.
- **B.** synthesizes carbohydrates and proteins.
- **C.** is the primary site of ribosome production.
- **D.** regulates the import of drugs and hormones.
- **E.** helps to destroy lysosomes.

34. True or False? The final destination of some proteins in the cell is determined by chemical tags applied by the <u>rough endoplasmic reticulum</u>.

35. Found in animal cells but absent from most plant cells, ___________ are membrane-bounded sacs of digestive enzymes.

36. Membrane proteins and secretory proteins are the typical products of the ___________ endoplasmic reticulum.

Chloroplasts and Mitochondria: Energy Conversion

37. In a plant cell, where is light energy trapped and converted to chemical energy?
- **A.** the inner mitochondrial membrane
- **B.** the outer mitochondrial membrane
- **C.** the outer chloroplast membrane
- **D.** the stroma of a chloroplast
- **E.** the grana in the chloroplast

38. Compare Figures 9.16 and 9.17 of your text. Which of the following pairs of structures are the largest membranes in chloroplasts and mitochondria?
- **A.** outer chloroplast membrane and outer mitochondrial membrane
- **B.** inner chloroplast membrane and outer mitochondrial membrane
- **C.** outer chloroplast membrane and inner mitochondrial membrane
- **D.** the grana of chloroplasts and the outer mitochondrial membrane
- **E.** the grana of chloroplasts and the inner mitochondrial membrane

39. True or False? Plant cells have <u>chloroplasts and mitochondria</u>.

40. Cells use molecules of ___________ as the direct energy source for most of their work.

41. The extensive folds of the inner mitochondrial membrane are called ___________.

The Cytoskeleton: Cell Shape and Movement

42. Which one, if any, of the following is *not* a function of the cytoskeleton?
- **A.** gives mechanical support to the cell
- **B.** anchors organelles
- **C.** helps a cell maintain its shape
- **D.** helps a cell move
- **E.** All of the above are functions of the cytoskeleton.

43. Which one of the following statements about the cilia and flagella is *false*?
- **A.** Cilia are generally shorter than flagella.
- **B.** Cilia are more numerous than flagella.
- **C.** Cilia and flagella have the same basic architecture.
- **D.** Flagella line the inside of your windpipe.
- **E.** Human sperm rely on flagella for movement.

44. True or False? A specialized arrangement of <u>microfilaments</u> helps move cilia and flagella.

45. The movement of dividing chromosomes is guided by ___________.

Evolution Connection: The Origin of Membranes

46. One of the first steps in the evolution of the first cells was likely the origin of:
- **A.** mitochondria.
- **B.** membranes.
- **C.** chloroplasts.
- **D.** photosynthesis.
- **E.** DNA.

47. The first cell membranes allowed cells to:
- **A.** regulate their chemical exchanges with the environment.
- **B.** form an impermeable barrier between the inside and outside of the cell.
- **C.** use photosynthesis.
- **D.** reproduce.
- **E.** make ATP.

48. True or False? Phosphoplipids require <u>no</u> genetic information to assemble into membranes.

49. The main lipids in the earliest cell membranes were probably ___________.

Exercises in the Basic Unit of Life—The Cell

Features of Prokaryotic and Eukaryotic Cells

1. Are the following associated with prokaryotic cells, eukaryotic cells, or both?
a. nucleic acids
b. cell membrane
c. nucleus
d. organelles
e. mitochondria
f. chloroplasts
g. bacteria
h. circular chromosome
i. cytoplasm
j. human cells

2. Match the following organelles with their functions:
ribosome
rough endoplasmic reticulum
smooth endoplasmic reticulum
golgi apparatus
lysosome
mitochondrion
chloroplast
cytoskeleton

a. assembles proteins destined to go either to the cell membrane or to leave the cell
b. obtains energy for the cell to use
c. in plant cells, captures energy from sunlight to build organic molecules
d. receives products from the endoplasmic reticulum and packages them for transport
e. helps cell hold its shape
f. assembles membranes and performs other specialized functions in certain cells
g. assembles proteins for the cell
h. breaks down organic materials

3. What are the three components of a cell membrane? Draw a portion of a cell membrane showing each of these components.

4. What are some functions carried out by membrane proteins?

5. What are the functions of short carbohydrates?

Transport In and Out of Cells

1. Assume that the square-shaped molecules shown below can pass freely across the cell membrane. What is the name of the process by which they move across the cell membrane?

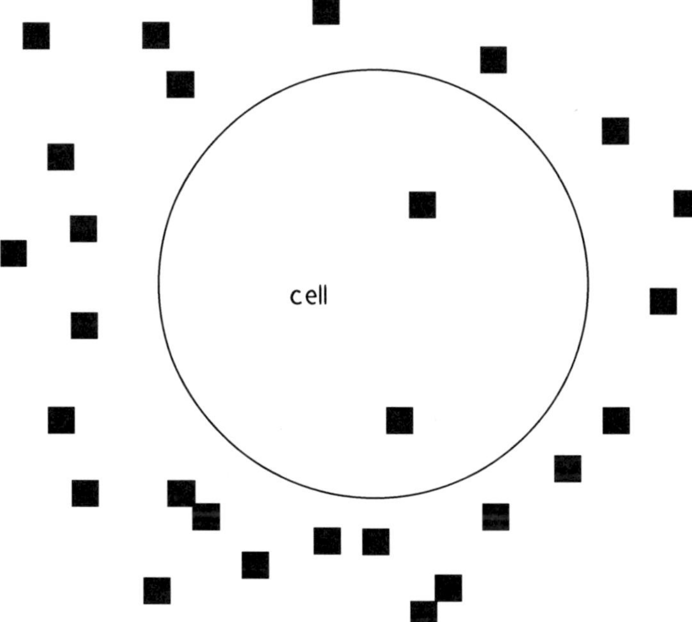

Will the square-shaped molecules tend to move out of the cell or into the cell? Why?

2. The diffusion of water has a special name. It is called ______________________________.
In the figure below, a membrane allows water to move freely between two compartments. The dark circles represent solute molecules, which are not free to move between the two compartments. Which way will water tend to flow? Why?

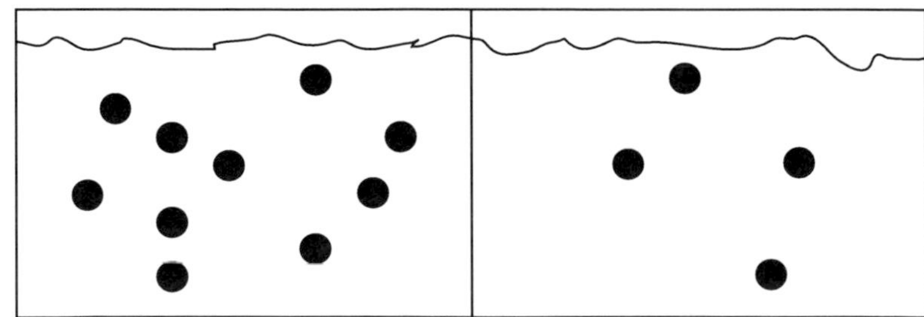

3. a. If a molecule needs a carrier protein, but no energy input in order to cross a cell membrane, it provides an example of ____.

b. If a molecule requires energy input in order to cross a cell membrane, it provides an example of ____.

c. Which process is illustrated in (a)? Which is illustrated in (b)?

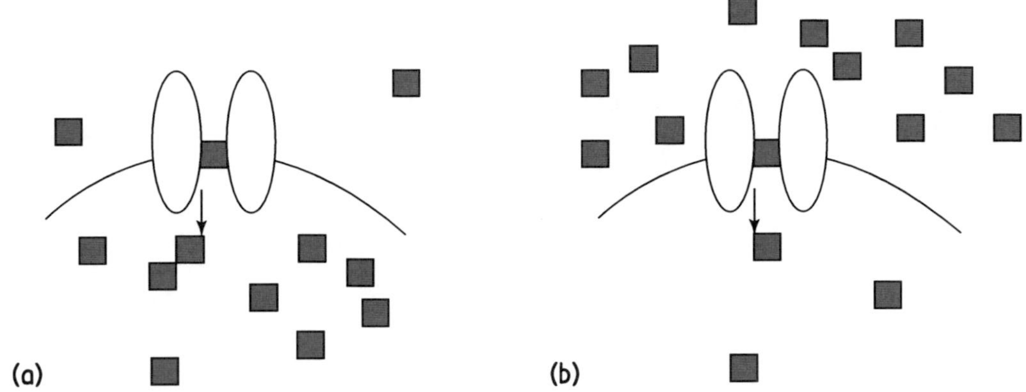

4. The cell below is going to take in the triangular molecule below via endocytosis. Draw what happens.

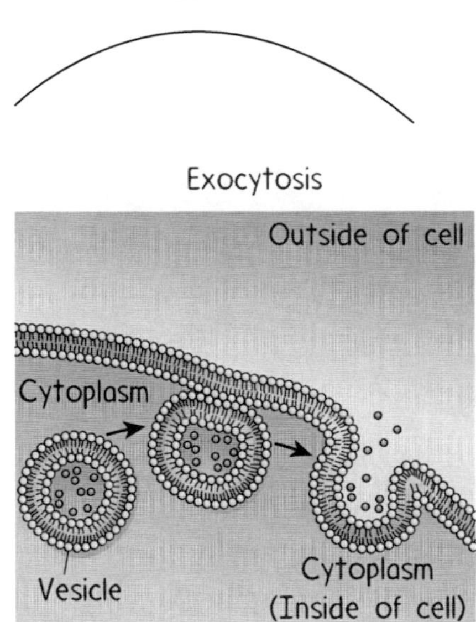

Photosynthesis and Cellular Respiration

1. The chemical reaction for photosynthesis is (use words or chemical formulae):

   ______ + _______ + _______ → ______ + _______

2. a. Where in plant cells does photosynthesis take place?
   b. Where do plants get carbon dioxide from?
   c. Where do plants get water from?
   d. What parts of plants capture sunlight?

3. For each of the following events that occur during photosynthesis, indicate whether it occurs during the light-dependent or light-independent reactions:
   a. sunlight strikes a chlorophyll molecule
   b. Calvin cycle
   c. energy is generated in the form of molecules of ATP and NADPH
   d. free oxygen is produced
   e. carbon is fixed
   f. glucose is produced

4. The chemical reaction for cellular respiration is

   _____ + ______ + ______ → _____ + ______ + _______

5. Cellular respiration allows cells to produce ATP. How do cells later obtain energy from ATP?

6. Which of the following processes requires oxygen?
   glycolysis
   Krebs cycle and electron transport
   alcoholic fermentation
   lactic acid fermentation

Word Roots

chloro = green (chloroplast: the green organelle of photosynthesis)
chromo = color (chromosome: a thread-like, darkly staining structure packaging DNA in the nucleus)
cili = small hair (cilium: a short, hair-like cellular appendage with a microtubule core)
cyto = cell (cytoplasm: cell region between the nucleus and the plasma membrane)
endo = inner (endomembrane system: an internal system of membranous organelles)
eu = true (eukaryotic: cell type with a membrane-enclosed nucleus and other organelles)
extra = outside (extracellular: the substance around animal cells)
flagell = whip (flagellum: a long, whip-like cellular appendage that moves cells)

micro = small (microtubules: microscopic tubular filaments contributing to the cytoskeleton)
plasm = molded (plasma membrane: the thin layer that sets a cell apart from its surroundings)
pro = before (prokaryotic: the first cells, lacking a membrane-enclosed nucleus and other organelles)
reticul = network (endoplasmic reticulum: membranous network where proteins are produced)
trans = across (transport vesicles: membranous spheres that move materials across a cell)
vacu = empty (vacuole: sac that buds from the ER, Golgi apparatus, or plasma membrane)

Key Terms

cell junctions
cell theory
central vacuole
chloroplast
chromatin
chromosome
cilia
cristae
cytoplasm
cytoskeleton
cytosol
electron microscope (EM)
endomembrane system
endoplasmic reticulum (ER)
eukaryotic cell
extracellular matrix
flagella
fluid mosaic
food vacuoles
gene
Golgi apparatus
grana
light microscope (LM)
lysosomal storage disease
lysosome
magnification
matrix
microtubule
mitochondria
nuclear envelope
nucleolus
nucleus
organelles
phospholipid
phospholipid bilayer
plasma membrane
prokaryotic cell
resolving power
ribosome
rough ER
scanning electron microscope (SEM)
smooth ER
stroma
transmission electron microscope (TEM)
transport vesicles
vacuole

Crossword Puzzle

Use the Key Terms list from this chapter to fill in the crossword puzzle.

ACROSS

1. a type of cell found only in the bacteria and archaea
4. a double membrane, perforated with pores, that encloses the nucleus
6. the thickest of the three main kinds of fibers making up a eukaryotic cytoskeleton
7. a membranous network of tubules not associated with ribosomes in a eukaryotic cell
9. a digestive organelle in eukaryotic cells
10. the organelles in eukaryotic cells where cellular respiration occurs
12. an increase in the apparent size of an object
13. a network of interconnected membranous sacs studded with ribosomes
16. initials for a type of microscope that uses an electron beam to study a specimen's surface
18. the thick fluid within the chloroplast
19. a type of cell that has a membrane-enclosed nucleus and organelles
21. interconnected stacks where sunlight is captured during photosynthesis
23. a discrete unit of hereditary information
24. a type of system of membranous organelles subdividing eukaryotic cells
28. a description of the flowing nature of membrane structure
29. initials for an instrument that focuses an electron beam to see fine details
30. a membrane-enclosed sac in a eukaryotic cell with diverse functions
32. a sticky coat secreted by most animal cells
33. a measure of the clarity of an image
34. a type of theory that all living things are composed of cells and all cells come from other cells
36. the combination of DNA and proteins that constitutes eukaryotic chromosomes
37. a membrane-enclosed sac occupying most of the interior of a mature plant cell
39. a photosynthetic organelle found in plants and some protists
40. the place in a eukaryotic cell nucleus where ribosomes are made
41. a thread-like, gene-carrying structure found in the nucleus of a eukaryotic cell
42. structures with specialized functions within a cell
43. the semifluid medium of a cell's cytoplasm
44. a membrane fat with a hydrophilic "head" and two hydrophobic "tails"
45. infoldings of the inner mitochondrial membrane

DOWN

2. membranous spheres that bud from the endoplasmic reticulum
3. initials for a type of microscope that uses a penetrating electron beam to study internal cellular details
5. a type of hereditary disease associated with abnormal lysosomes
8. a sticky coat outside of cells
11. an organelle that functions as the site of protein synthesis in the cytoplasm
14. the simplest type of digestive cavity, found in protists
15. similar to cilia in structure, these cellular appendages propel protists and sperm
17. the thin layer of lipids and proteins that sets a cell off from its surroundings
20. a network of fine fibers that provides structural support for a eukaryotic cell
22. a double layer that makes up the basic fabric of biological membranes
25. initials for a membranous organelle connected to the outer nuclear membrane
26. everything inside a cell between the plasma membrane and the nucleus
27. an organelle that modifies, stores, and ships products of the endoplasmic reticulum
31. a type of connection between cells
35. initials for an optical instrument with lenses that bend visible light to magnify images
38. an atom's central core, containing protons and neutrons
41. cellular appendages similar to flagella that move some protists through water

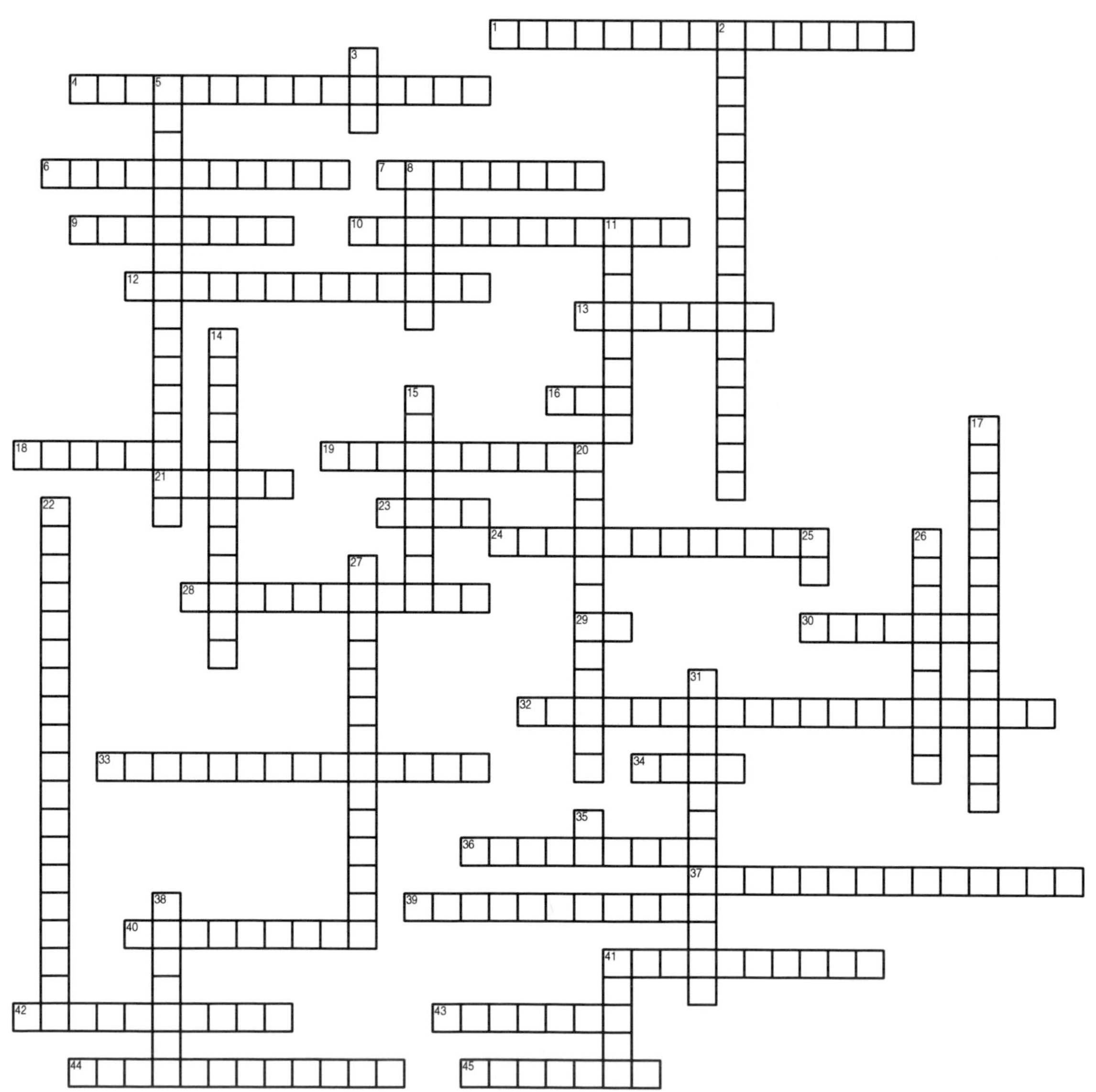

10 The Working Cell

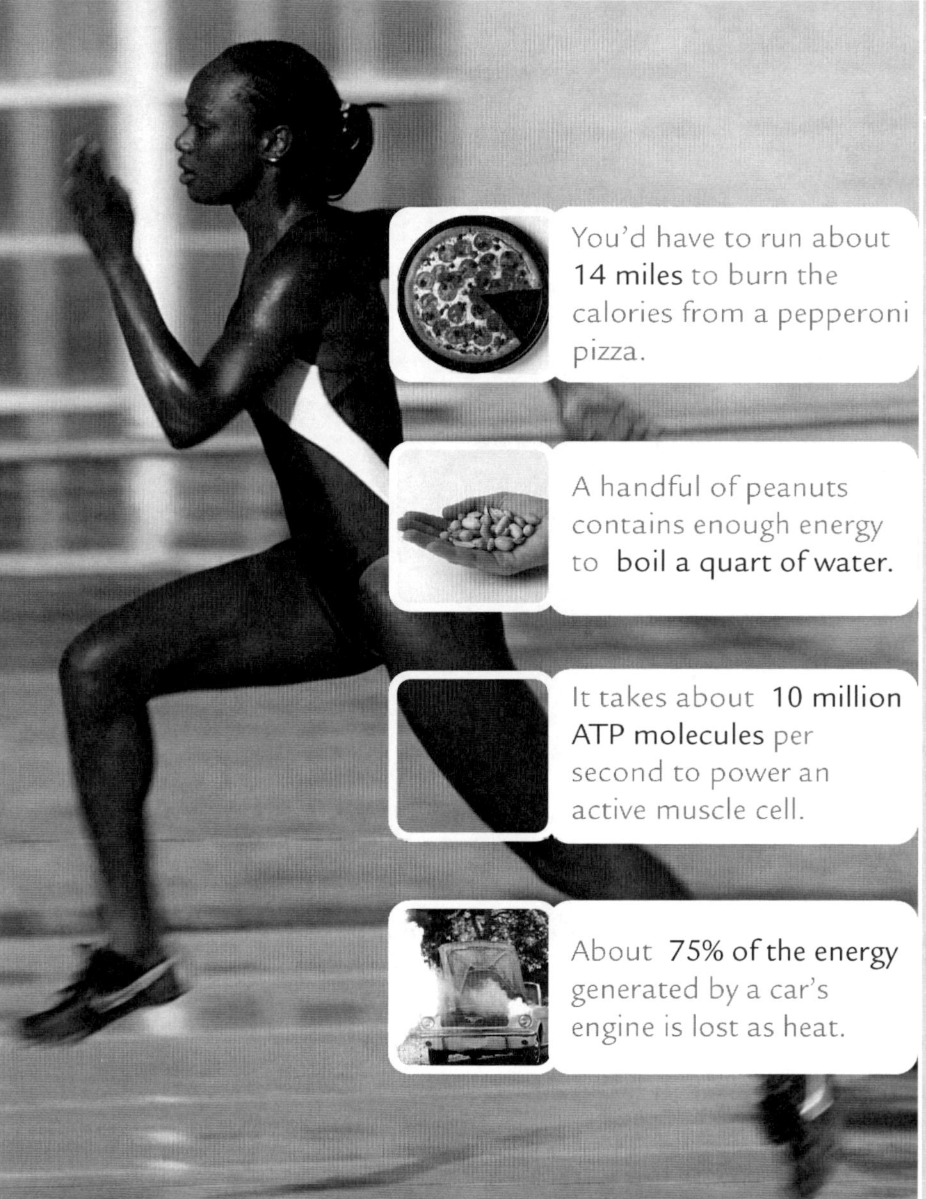

You'd have to run about 14 miles to burn the calories from a pepperoni pizza.
A handful of peanuts contains enough energy to boil a quart of water.
It takes about 10 million ATP molecules per second to power an active muscle cell.
About 75% of the energy generated by a car's engine is lost as heat.

LOOKING AHEAD

My Chemistry & Biology Portal

http://www.pearsoncustom.com/devry/mycbp

Study Goals

- This chapter addresses many abstract ideas that may initially be difficult to grasp. Do not try to understand all of this chapter in a single night. Read the material slowly and carefully and study the figures as you go along. Take frequent study breaks and review what you have already read before continuing further into the chapter.
- Many of the concepts in this chapter relate to events in your life. It is always easier to remember a new idea by relating it to something you already know or have experienced. Look for these connections as you study.

Chapter Review

Concept Map

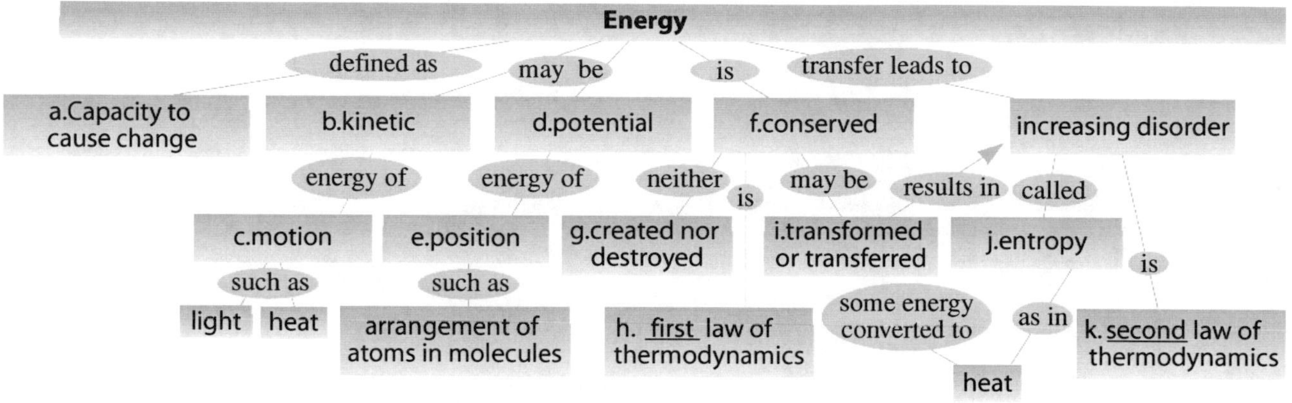

Chapter Concept Review

For study help and activities, go to campbellbiology.com or the student CD-ROM.

Some Basic Energy Concepts

MP3 Tutor ***Basic Energy Concepts***

- **Conservation of Energy** Machines and organisms can transform kinetic energy (energy of motion) to potential energy (stored energy) and vice versa. In all such energy transformations, total energy is conserved. Energy cannot be created or destroyed.
- **Entropy** Every energy conversion releases some randomized energy in the form of heat. This is an example of the tendency for the entropy, or disorder, of the universe to increase.
- **Chemical Energy** Molecules store varying amounts of potential energy in the arrangement of their atoms. Organic molecules are relatively rich in such chemical energy.

Activity ***Energy Concepts***

- **Food Calories** Actually kilocalories, food Calories are units used for the amount of energy in our foods and also for the amount of energy we expend in various activities.

ATP and Cellular Work

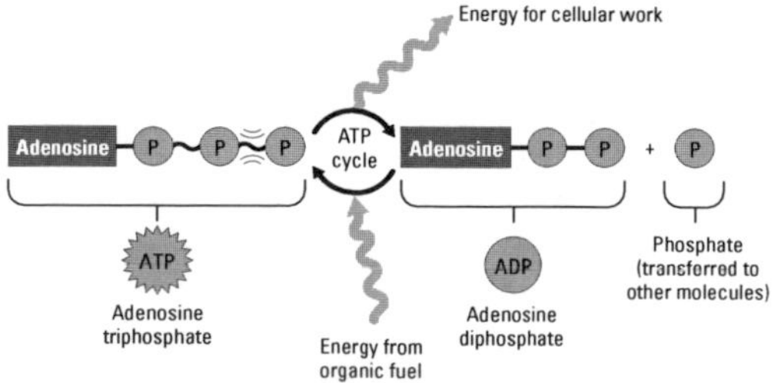

Activity ***The Structure of ATP***

Enzymes

- **Activation Energy** Enzymes are biological catalysts that speed up metabolic reactions by lowering the activation energy required to break the bonds of reactant molecules.
- **Induced Fit** The entry of a substrate into the active site of an enzyme causes the enzyme to change shape slightly, allowing for a better fit and thereby promoting the interaction of enzyme with substrate.

Activity ***How Enzymes Work***

Case Study in the Process of Science *How Is the Rate of Enzyme Catalysis Measured?*

- **Enzyme Inhibitors** Enzyme inhibitors are molecules that can disrupt metabolic reactions by binding to enzymes, either at the active site or elsewhere.

Membrane Function

Proteins embedded in the plasma membrane perform a wide variety of functions, including regulating transport.

- **Passive Transport, Osmosis, and Active Transport**

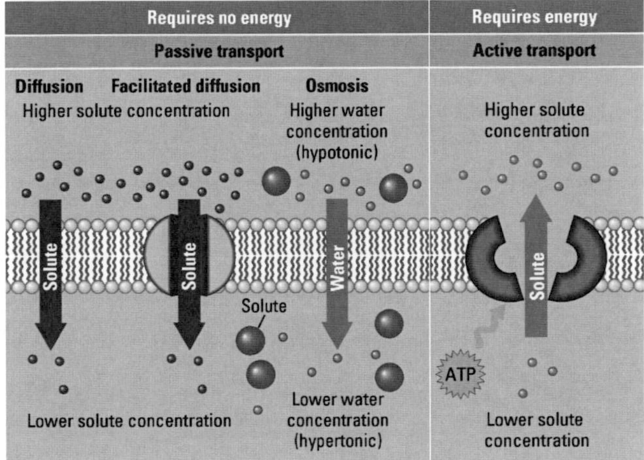

Most animal cells require an isotonic environment. Plant cells need a hypotonic environment, which keeps the walled cells turgid. Osmoregulation is the control of water balance within a cell or organism.

Activity ***Membrane Structure***

Activity ***Diffusion***

Activity ***Facilitated Diffusion***

Activity ***Osmosis and Water Balance in Cells***

Case Study in the Process of Science *How Does Osmosis Affect Cells?*

Activity ***Active Transport***

- **Exocytosis and Endocytosis: Traffic of Large Molecules**

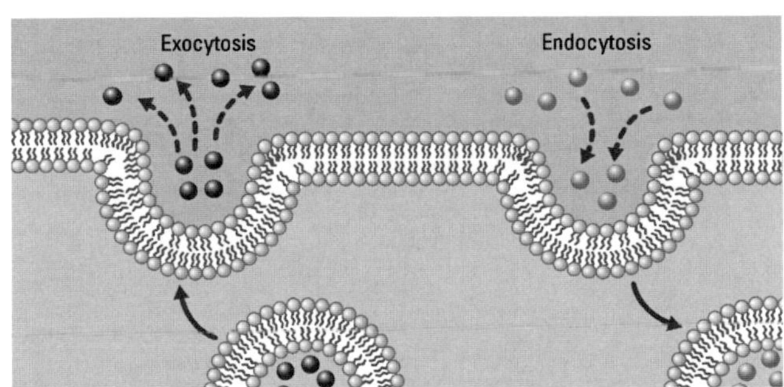

The three kinds of endocytosis are phagocytosis ("cellular eating"), pinocytosis ("cellular drinking"), and receptor-mediated endocytosis, which enables the cell to take in specific large molecules.

Activity ***Exocytosis and Endocytosis***

- **The Role of Membranes in Cell Signaling** Receptors on the cell surface trigger signal transduction pathways that control processes within the cell.

Activity ***Cell Signaling***

Case Study in the Process of Science *How Do Cells Communicate with Each Other?*

Organizing Tables

Compare the reactants, products, and efficiencies of cellular respiration and the use of gasoline in an engine by completing the table below.

TABLE 10.1

	Reactants	Products	Efficiency (Percent of energy used to do work)
Cellular respiration			
Burning of gasoline in an automobile engine			

Compare the processes of passive transport, facilitated diffusion, and active transport.

TABLE 10.2

	Passive Transport	Facilitated Diffusion	Active Transport
Does the process require the use of ATP?			
What special membrane proteins, if any, are needed?			
Describe an example in a cell.			

Compare the reactions of animal and plant cells when placed into isotonic, hypotonic, and hypertonic solutions. Compare your results to Figure 10.14 of your text.

TABLE 10.3

	Isotonic Solution	Hypotonic Solution	Hypertonic Solution
Animal cell			
Plant cell			

Practice Test for Chapter 10

Basic Energy Concept

Directions: Identify the *one* best answer for the multiple-choice questions. For true/false questions, determine if the statement is true or false. If false, change the underlined word(s) to make the statement true. Finally, add the correct word(s) to the fill-in-the-blank questions to make the statements true.

Biology and Society: Stonewashing Without the Stones

1. Which one of the following statements about cellulase is *false*? Cellulase:
- **A.** is a protein.
- **B.** breaks down cellular membranes.
- **C.** is a catalyst.
- **D.** is used by bacteria and fungi to break down plant material.
- **E.** is used in the process of biostoning.

2. True or False? Using pumice stones is <u>more</u> friendly to the environment than using enzymes to produce stonewashed jeans.

3. The enzyme cellulase breaks down the polysaccharide ___________.

Some Basic Energy Concepts

Conservation of Energy

4. You are riding a bike up and down hills. At which point do you have the greatest potential energy?
- **A.** at the bottom of the hill
- **B.** at the top of the hill
- **C.** riding down the hill at the fastest speed
- **D.** climbing the hill

5. True or False? Energy is defined as the <u>capacity to do work</u>.

6. The principle known as ___________ states that it is not possible to destroy or create energy.

Entropy

7. All energy conversions:
- **A.** destroy some energy.
- **B.** decrease the entropy of the universe.
- **C.** generate some heat.
- **D.** produce ATP.

8. True or False? The heat produced by an automobile engine is a type of <u>kinetic energy</u>.

9. The term ___________ is used as a measure of disorder or randomness.

Chemical Energy

10. We feel warmer when we exercise because of extra heat produced by:
- **A.** cellular respiration.
- **B.** breathing faster.
- **C.** friction of blood flowing through the body.
- **D.** our movement through the air around us.
- **E.** sweating.

11. Examine Figure 10.3 of your text. Which one of the following is *not* produced by the engine and cellular respiration?
  A. heat
  B. water
  C. oxygen
  D. carbon dioxide

12. True or False? The chemical energy in molecules of glucose and other fuels is a special type of <u>kinetic</u> energy.

13. Molecules of carbohydrates, fats, and gasoline all have structures that make them especially rich in ___________ energy.

Food Calories

14. The energy in a 300-food-calorie cheeseburger could raise the temperature of:
  A. 1 kilogram (kg) of water by 30°C.
  B. 3 kg of water by 100°C.
  C. 3 kg of water by 1°C.
  D. 30 kg of water by 30°C.
  E. 30 kg of water by 100°C.

15. True or False? The calories in food are a form of <u>potential</u> energy.

16. The amount of energy needed to raise 1 gram of water 1° Celsius is a(n) ___________ while 1,000 times this amount of energy is a(n) ___________.

ATP and Cellular Work

The Structure of ATP, Phosphate Transfer

17. Moving ions across cell membranes is an example of what type of ATP work?
  A. chemical work
  B. transport work
  C. neutral work
  D. mechanical work

18. True or False? ATP has <u>less</u> potential energy than ADP.

19. The energy for most cellular work is found in the ___________ of the ATP molecule.

The ATP Cycle

20. What happens to the ADP molecule produced when ATP loses a phosphate during an energy transfer?
  A. ADP is used to build carbohydrates, fats, and proteins for use throughout the cell.
  B. ADP is released from the cells.
  C. ADP is broken down further into carbon atoms that are then reassembled into proteins.
  D. Energy from cellular respiration is used to convert ADP back to ATP.
  E. None of the above statements are correct.

21. Which one of the following processes is most like energy coupling?
  A. burning coal to produce electricity to run a factory
  B. running a furnace to heat a home
  C. using a car to drive to work
  D. using the energy from the sun to make sugar

22. During the process of energy coupling in a cell, ___________ molecules are recycled.

Enzymes

Activation Energy

23. Which of the following can be used to initiate a chemical reaction?
- **A.** addition of ATP
- **B.** heat and the addition of ATP
- **C.** enzymes
- **D.** heat
- **E.** heat or enzymes

24. True or False? Enzymes <u>raise</u> the activation energy to break the bonds of reactant molecules.

25. The many chemical reactions that occur in organisms are collectively called ___________.

Induced Fit

26. When a substrate molecule slips into an active site, the active site changes shape slightly to embrace the substrate and catalyze the reaction. This interaction is called:
- **A.** substrate locking.
- **B.** active engagement.
- **C.** active site shifting.
- **D.** induced fit.
- **E.** substrate embracing.

27. True or False? Most enzymes are named for their <u>inhibitors</u>.

28. The reactant molecule called the ___________ binds at an enzyme's ___________.

Enzyme Inhibitors

29. Examine the role of an inhibitor in Figure 10.10 of your text. The inhibitor functions most like a:
- **A.** teacher giving you instructions for a laboratory exercise.
- **B.** friend who helps you do your laundry.
- **C.** person who has parked in your parking spot.
- **D.** screwdriver used to tighten screws.
- **E.** traffic light indicating to a driver when it is safe to cross an intersection.

30. True or False? The inhibition of an enzyme by its product is an example of <u>feedback regulation</u>.

31. Many antibiotics that kill disease-causing bacteria are also enzyme ___________.

Membrane Function

Passive Transport: Diffusion Across Membranes

32. Releasing fish into a pond and seeing them swim in all directions is most like the process of:
- **A.** diffusion.
- **B.** osmosis.
- **C.** osmoregulation.
- **D.** active transport.
- **E.** pinocytosis.

33. Which one of the following most relies upon the process of diffusion?
- **A.** recognizing a friend eating at another table in a cafeteria
- **B.** discussing a subject in preparation for an exam
- **C.** selecting a new perfume or cologne
- **D.** listening to a song on the radio
- **E.** checking your pulse after exercise

34. True or False? Cells <u>do not</u> need to spend energy for diffusion to occur.

35. A cell does not have to use ___________ for passive transport to occur.

36. Some substances have properties that prevent them from directly diffusing across a membrane. Such substances, however, can diffuse across a membrane with the help of specific transport proteins in the process of ___________.

Osmosis and Water Balance in Cells

37. If you soak your hands in dishwater, you may notice that your skin soaks up water and swells into distinct wrinkles. This is because your skin cells are ___________ to the ___________ dishwater.
- **A.** hypotonic . . . hypertonic
- **B.** hypertonic . . . hypotonic
- **C.** hypotonic . . . hypotonic
- **D.** isotonic . . . hypotonic
- **E.** hypertonic . . . isotonic

38. You decide to buy a new angelfish for your freshwater aquarium. When you introduce the fish into its new tank, the fish swells up and dies. You later learn it was an angelfish from the ocean. The unfortunate fish went from a ___________ solution into a(n) ___________ solution.
- **A.** mesotonic . . . hypotonic
- **B.** hypertonic . . . isotonic
- **C.** hypertonic . . . hypotonic
- **D.** hypotonic . . . isotonic

39. Examine Figure 10.14 of your text. Why does the animal cell but not the plant cell burst when it is in a hypotonic solution?
- **A.** The plant cell does not absorb as much salt.
- **B.** The plant cell is less hypertonic.
- **C.** The cell wall keeps the cell from bursting.
- **D.** The water cannot easily move through the plant cell wall.

40. True or False? A crab in the ocean has the same salt concentration in its body as the surrounding seawater. Thus, the ocean is <u>hypotonic</u> to the crab.

41. When a *Paramecium* uses its contractile vacuole to remove excess water, it is engaged in the process called ___________.

Active Transport: The Pumping of Molecules Across Membranes

42. Moving a molecule across a membrane and against its concentration gradient requires:
- **A.** phospholipids using passive transport.
- **B.** phospholipids using active transport.
- **C.** membrane transport proteins using active transport.
- **D.** membrane transport proteins using passive transport.
- **E.** membrane transport proteins using receptor-mediated endocytosis.

43. True or False? Membrane proteins using <u>passive</u> transport require ATP as a source of energy.

44. A nerve cell maintains a higher concentration of potassium ions inside itself than in its surroundings. This nerve cell is most likely using ___________ transport to keep the potassium levels high.

Exocytosis and Endocytosis: Traffic of Large Molecules

45. Which one of the following is a type of endocytosis in which very specific molecules are brought into a cell using specific membrane protein receptors?
- **A.** osmoregulation
- **B.** phagocytosis
- **C.** pinocytosis
- **D.** receptor-mediated endocytosis
- **E.** none of the above

46. True or False? Tears and saliva are products released by cells using endocytosis.

47. In ___________, the cell gulps droplets of fluid by forming tiny vesicles.

The Role of Membranes in Cell Signaling

48. In a cell, the ___________ relays a signal and converts it to chemical forms that work within the cell.
- **A.** process of exocytosis
- **B.** process of endocytosis
- **C.** process of pinocytosis
- **D.** receptor protein
- **E.** signal transduction pathway

49. True or False? The three stages of cell signaling are reception, transduction, and response.

50. In a signal transduction pathway, external signals are received by specific receptor ___________.

Evolution Connection: Evolving Enzymes

51. Which one of the following statements is *false*? Directed evolution:
- **A.** has a specific purpose chosen by the researchers.
- **B.** may require just a few weeks to produce a new enzyme.
- **C.** relies upon the natural environment.
- **D.** can be used to produce enzymes that perform a new function.

52. True or False? Natural selection does not have purpose or direction.

53. Research data suggest that many of our human genes arose through ___________ evolution.

Word Roots

endo = within, inner (endocytosis: taking material into a cell)
exo = outside (exocytosis: eliminating some materials outside of a cell)
hyper = excessive (hypertonic: in comparing two solutions, it refers to the one with the greater concentration of solutes)
hypo = lower (hypotonic: in comparing two solutions, it refers to the one with the lower concentration of solutes)
iso = same (isotonic: solutions with equal concentrations of solutes)
kinet = move (kinetic: type of energy, it is the energy of motion)
phago = eat (phagocytosis: cellular eating)
pino = drink (pinocytosis: cellular drinking)
tonus = tension (isotonic: solutions with equal concentrations of solutes)

Key Terms

activation energy
active site
active transport
ADP
ATP
calorie
cellular respiration
chemical energy
conservation of energy
diffusion
energy
energy coupling
entropy
enzyme
enzyme inhibitor
endocytosis
exocytosis
facilitated diffusion
feedback regulation
heat
hypertonic
hypotonic
induced fit
isotonic
kinetic energy
metabolism
osmoregulation
osmosis
passive transport
phagocytosis
pinocytosis
plasmolysis
potential energy
receptor-mediated endocytosis
signal transduction pathway
substrate
transport proteins

Crossword Puzzle

Use the Key Terms list from this chapter to fill in the crossword puzzle.

ACROSS

2. the type of endocytosis in which specific molecules move into a cell by inward budding
3. the interaction between a substrate molecule and the active site of an enzyme
5. a specific substance (reactant) on which an enzyme acts
6. cellular eating
8. the control of water and solute balance in an organism
9. having the same solute concentration as another solution
10. of two solutions, the one with the greater concentration of solutes
11. the energy of motion
12. the amount of energy associated with the movement of the atoms and molecules in a body of matter
13. protein that serves as a biological catalyst
14. the passage of a substance across a biological membrane down its concentration gradient
16. the type of energy that is stored
18. the transfer of energy from processes that yield energy to those that consume it
19. the many chemical reactions that occur in organisms
21. the movement of materials into the cytoplasm of a cell via membranous vesicles
23. the type of energy stored in the chemical bonds of molecules
24. type of pathway that converts a signal on a cell's surface to an inner response
26. the movement of materials out of the cytoplasm of a cell via membranous vesicles
28. diffusion across a membrane without the input of energy
29. the capacity to perform work
30. the type of energy that reactants must absorb before a chemical reaction will start
32. plant cell shriveling when there is a shortage of water
34. the part of an enzyme molecule where a substrate molecule attaches
35. the principle that energy can neither be created nor destroyed

DOWN

1. cellular drinking
4. a metabolic control in which the product inhibits the process that produced it
7. of two solutions, the one with the lesser concentration of solutes
13. a measure of disorder, or randomness
15. chemical that interferes with an enzyme's activities
17. the aerobic harvesting of energy from food molecules
20. the type of protein that helps move substances across a cell membrane
22. the tendency of molecules to move from high to low concentrations
25. the amount of energy that raises the temperature of 1 gram of water by 1° C
27. the passive transport of water across a selectively permeable membrane
30. a molecule composed of adenosine and two phosphate groups
31. the type of transport moving a substance across a membrane against its concentration gradient
33. a molecule composed of adenosine and three phosphate groups

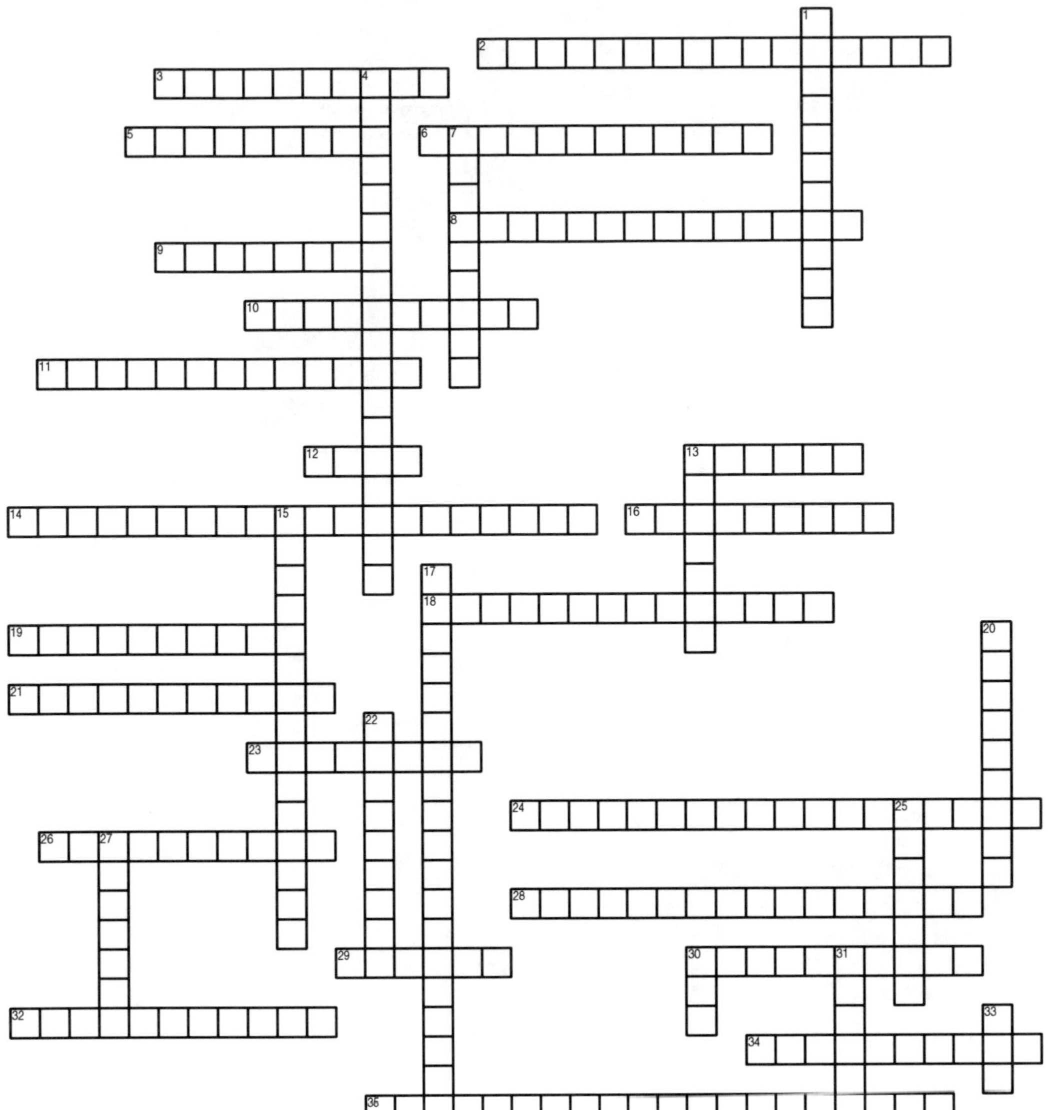
1
2
3
4
5
6
7
8
9
10
11
12
13
14
15
16
17
18
19
20
21
22
23
24
25
26
27
28
29
30
31
32
33
34
35

11 Cellular Respiration: Harvesting Chemical Energy

Yeast is used to produce bread, beer, and champagne.
All the energy in all the food you eat can be traced back to sunlight.
Both carbon monoxide and cyanide kill by disrupting cellular respiration.
If you exercise too hard, your muscles shut down from a lack of oxygen.

LOOKING AHEAD

My Chemistry & Biology Portal

http://www.pearsoncustom.com/devry/myc

Chapter Review

Concept Map

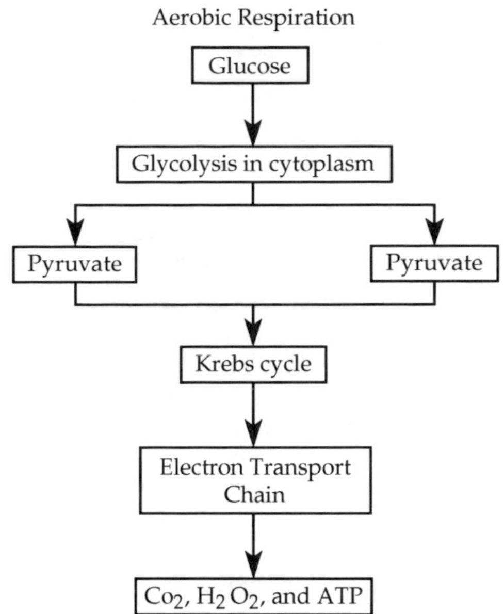

Chapter Concept Review

For study help and activities, go to campbellbiology.com or the student CD-ROM.

Biology and Society: Feeling the Burn

- Aerobic metabolism occurs when cells receive enough oxygen to support their energy needs. If a body exceeds its aerobic capacity, the demand for oxygen is greater than the body's ability to deliver it, and metabolism becomes anaerobic.

Energy Flow and Chemical Cycling in the Biosphere

- **Producers and Consumers** Autotrophs (producers) make organic molecules from inorganic nutrients via photosynthesis. Heterotrophs (consumers) must consume organic material and obtain energy via cellular respiration.
- **Chemical Cycling between Photosynthesis and Cellular Respiration**

Activity *Build a Chemical Cycling System*

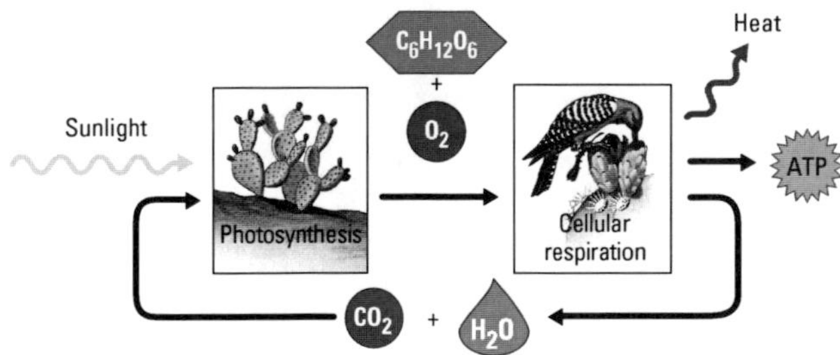

Cellular Respiration: Aerobic Harvest of Food Energy
eTutor *Cellular Respiration*
MP3 Tutor *Cellular Respiration Part 1: Glycolysis*
MP3 Tutor *Cellular Respiration Part 2: Citric Acid Cycle and Electron Transport Chain*

- **The Relationship between Cellular Respiration and Breathing** The bloodstream distributes O_2 from the lungs to all the cells of the body and transports CO_2 waste from the cells to the lungs for disposal.
- **The Overall Equation for Cellular Respiration**

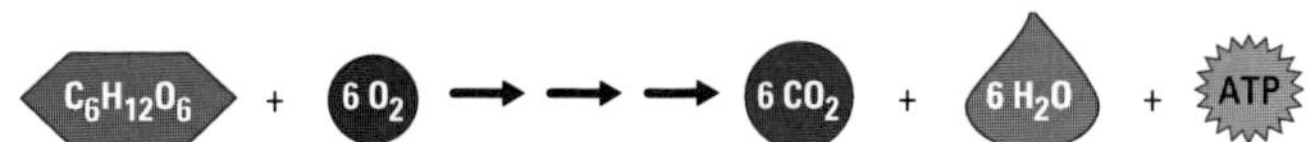

- **The Role of Oxygen in Cellular Respiration**

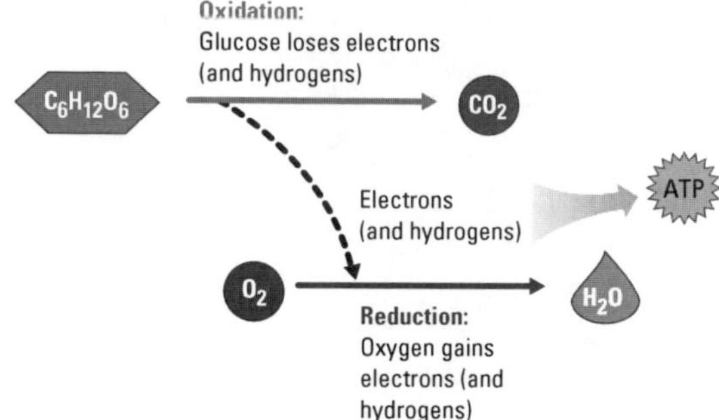

Redox reactions transfer electrons from food molecules to an electron acceptor called NAD^+, forming NADH. The NADH then passes the high-energy electrons to an electron transport chain that eventually "drops" them to O_2. The energy released during this electron transport is used to regenerate ATP from ADP. The affinity of oxygen for electrons keeps the redox reactions of cellular respiration working.

- **The Metabolic Pathway of Cellular Respiration** You can follow the flow of molecules through the process of cellular respiration in the following diagram:

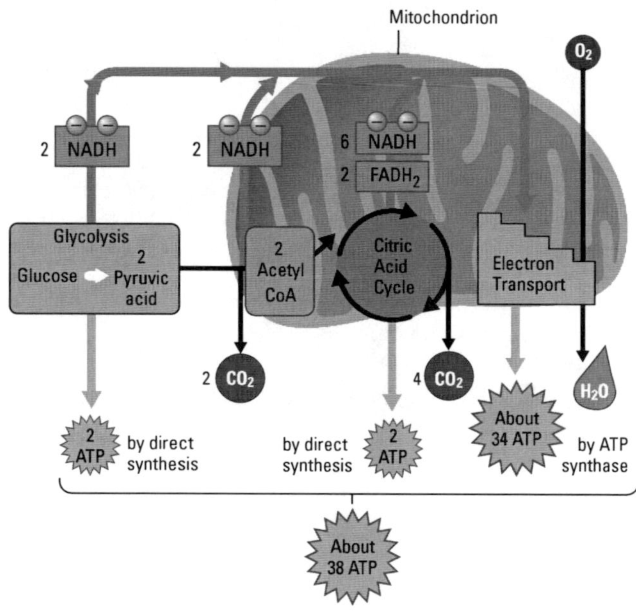

The electron transport chains pump H^+ across the membrane as electrons flow stepwise from NADH to oxygen. Backflow of H^+ across the membrane powers the ATP synthases, which attach phosphate to ADP to make ATP.

Activity *Overview of Cellular Respiration*

Activity *Glycolysis*

Activity *The Citric Acid Cycle*

Activity *Electron Transport*

Case Study in the Process of Science *How Is the Rate of Cellular Respiration Measured?*

Fermentation: Anaerobic Harvest of Food Energy

- **Fermentation in Human Muscle Cells** When muscle cells consume ATP faster than O_2 can be supplied for cellular respiration, they regenerate ATP by fermentation. The waste product under these anaerobic conditions is lactic acid. The ATP yield per glucose is much lower during fermentation than during cellular respiration.

- **Fermentation in Microorganisms** Yeast and other facultative anaerobes can survive with or without O_2. Wastes from fermentation can be ethyl alcohol, lactic acid, or other compounds, depending on the species. Some microorganisms are obligate anaerobes, which are poisoned by O_2.

Activity *Fermentation*

Organizing Tables

Compare the definitions of the following pairs of terms.

TABLE 11.1

Photosynthesis	vs.	Respiration
Autotrophs	vs.	Heterotrophs
Producers	vs.	Consumers
Aerobic	vs.	Anaerobic
Facultative anaerobe	vs.	Obligate anaerobe
Obligate aerobe	vs.	Obligate anaerobe

Compare the processes of glycolysis, citric acid cycle, and electron transport chain in the table below. Some cells are already filled in to make the job a little easier!

TABLE 11.2

	Location	Reactants	Products	Energy Yield
Glycolysis			Two molecules of pyruvic acid	
Citric acid cycle		Acetyl CoA	CO_2	
Electron transport chain		NADH		

Compare the products of each of the following reactions.

TABLE 11.3

Process	Products
Fermentation in human muscle cells	
Fermentation in yeast	

Practice Test for Chapter 11

Directions: Identify the *one* best answer for the multiple-choice questions. For true/false questions, determine if the statement is true or false. If false, change the underlined word(s) to make the statement true. Finally, add the correct word(s) to the fill-in-the-blank questions to make the statements true.

Biology and Society: Feeling the Burn

1. Which one of the following does *not* occur as you approach your aerobic capacity?
A. You use aerobic metabolism.
B. Oxygen is used to generate ATP.
C. Your muscle cells use increasing amounts of oxygen.
D. Your muscle cells produce lactic acid.

2. True or False? Lactic acid is produced during aerobic metabolism.

3. The burning sensation of an overexercised muscle results from the buildup of ___________.

Energy Flow and Chemical Cycling in the Biosphere

Producers and Consumers

4. Which one of the following statements about photosynthesis is *false*? Photosynthesis:
A. occurs mainly within the roots of plants.
B. provides the food for most ecosystems.
C. provides the energy to power chemical processes that make organic molecules.
D. occurs within chloroplasts.

5. True or False? Chlorophyll in chloroplasts makes plant leaves appear green.

6. True or False? Plants and other photosynthetic organisms are the consumers in an ecosystem.

7. Organisms that *cannot* make organic molecules from inorganic ones are called ___________.

Chemical Cycling Between Photosynthesis and Cellular Respiration

8. Plants use photosynthesis to join together:
A. carbon dioxide and water to make oxygen and glucose.
B. carbon dioxide and glucose to make water and oxygen.
C. carbon dioxide and oxygen to make water and glucose.
D. glucose and oxygen to make water and carbon dioxide.
E. water and oxygen to make glucose and carbon dioxide.

9. Cellular respiration:
A. occurs in chloroplasts.
B. is used by plants, but not animals.
C. is part of photosynthesis.
D. harvests energy stored in sugars and other organic molecules.
E. produces glucose and oxygen.

10. Examine Figure 11.3 of your text. In this ecosystem, the carbon dioxide that the trees use in photosynthesis came from:
A. plants.
B. wolves.
C. rabbits.
D. all of the above.
E. none of the above.

11. True or False? Cellular respiration occurs in plant and animal cells in organelles called chloroplasts.

12. Cellular respiration typically uses energy extracted from organic fuel to produce another form of chemical energy called ___________.

13. Photosynthesis combines together ___________ and ___________, which are products of cellular respiration.

Cellular Respiration: Aerobic Harvest of Food Energy

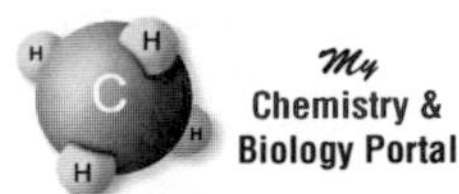

eTutor
Cellular Respiration
Overview of Cellular Respiration

The Relationship Between Cellular Respiration and Breathing

14. What do cellular respiration and breathing have in common? Both processes:

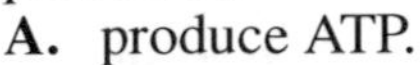

- **A.** produce ATP.
- **B.** produce glucose.
- **C.** take in carbon dioxide and release oxygen.
- **D.** take in oxygen and release carbon dioxide.

15. True or False? An aerobic cellular process requires <u>carbon dioxide</u>.

16. The aerobic harvesting of chemical energy from organic food molecules defines ___________.

The Overall Equation for Cellular Respiration

17. Which one of the following is *not* produced as a result of the breakdown of a single glucose molecule by cellular respiration?

- **A.** 6 molecules of carbon dioxide
- **B.** 6 molecules of water
- **C.** 6 molecules of oxygen
- **D.** up to 38 ATP molecules

18. True or False? Cellular respiration consists of <u>many</u> steps.

19. Oxygen is a vital part of aerobic respiration because it accepts ___________ atoms from glucose.

The Role of Oxygen in Cellular Respiration

20. Which one of the following occurs during the transfer of hydrogen in cellular respiration?

- **A.** Glucose is reduced, oxygen is oxidized, and energy is released.
- **B.** Glucose is oxidized, oxygen is reduced, and energy is released.
- **C.** Glucose is reduced, oxygen is oxidized, and energy is consumed.
- **D.** Glucose is oxidized, oxygen is reduced, and energy is consumed.

21. Which one of the following does *not* occur during the cellular respiration of glucose?

- **A.** NAD^+ donates electrons to NADH.
- **B.** NADH transfers electrons from glucose to the top of the electron transport chain.
- **C.** Electrons cascade down the electron transport chain giving up a small amount of energy with each transfer.
- **D.** Oxygen is the final electron acceptor at the bottom of the electron transport chain.

22. Examine Figure 11.6 of your text. The transfer of electrons during cellular respiration is most like:

- **A.** a giant waterfall.
- **B.** walking down a set of stairs.
- **C.** climbing a mountain.
- **D.** running up a set of stairs.
- **E.** playing catch with a baseball.

23. True or False? In the electron transport chain, NAD^+ functions like gravity, pulling electrons down the chain.

24. NADH undergoes the process of ___________ when it donates its electrons to the electron transport chain.

The Metabolic Pathway of Cellular Respiration

25. Which one of the following statements about cellular respiration is *false*?
- **A.** ATP synthase, located within the inner mitochondrial membrane, helps form ATP.
- **B.** Cellular respiration is a metabolic pathway consisting of more than two dozen chemical reactions, each catalyzed by a specific enzyme.
- **C.** Inside mitochondria, glycolysis joins a pair of three-carbon pyruvic acid molecules to form a molecule of glucose.
- **D.** The citric acid cycle breaks down molecules of acetyl-CoA to release CO_2 and energy trapped by NADH.

26. The extensive infolding of the inner mitochondrial membrane is likely an adaptation to:
- **A.** make it more difficult for oxygen to pass through.
- **B.** increase the flexibility of mitochondria.
- **C.** make it more difficult for glucose to pass through.
- **D.** increase the surface area of the electron transport system.
- **E.** increase the surface area for glycolysis.

27. Examine Figure 11.11 of your text. What happens to the two carbons in Acetyl CoA during the citric acid cycle? The two carbons are:
- **A.** attached to NADH.
- **B.** used to make glucose.
- **C.** released as CO_2.
- **D.** added to ADP to make ATP.
- **E.** destroyed in the process.

28. Most ATP is generated during the process of:
- **A.** glycolysis.
- **B.** fermentation.
- **C.** electron transport.
- **D.** citric acid cycle.

29. Energy from the electron transport chain pumps ___________ across the inner mitochondrial membrane.

30. Cellular respiration is an example of ___________, the sum of all of the chemical processes that occur in cells.

Fermentation: Anaerobic Harvest of Food Energy

Fermentation in Human Muscle Cells

31. Which one of the following statements about fermentation is *false*?
- **A.** Your cells can produce ATP when no oxygen is present.
- **B.** When your muscles use fermentation, glucose is produced.
- **C.** Fermentation in your cells uses the process of glycolysis.
- **D.** Fermentation produces about two ATP per glucose molecule.
- **E.** Fermentation occurs when oxygen levels are not sufficient to support cellular respiration.

32. True or False? Fermentation is an <u>anaerobic</u> process.

33. During the process of fermentation, pyruvic acid is converted to ___________.

Fermentation in Microorganisms

34. Yeast used to make beer and bread use fermentation to produce:
  A. ATP, carbon dioxide, and oxygen.
  B. ATP, water, and oxygen.
  C. ATP, ethyl alcohol, and carbon dioxide.
  D. ethyl alcohol and oxygen.
  E. carbon dioxide and water.

35. True or False? Although our cells behave as facultative anaerobes, our entire body is an obligate aerobe.

36. Some organisms, called ___________ anaerobes, are unable to live in the presence of oxygen.

Matching: For each of the following, indicate whether it is a facultative anaerobe, obligate anaerobe, or obligate aerobe.

_____ **37.** yeast	**A.** facultative anaerobe
_____ **38.** human muscle cells	**B.** obligate anaerobe
_____ **39.** an entire human organism	**C.** obligate aerobe
_____ **40.** bacteria living in stagnant ponds or deep soil	

Evolution Connection: Life on an Anaerobic Earth

41. Glycolysis is considered to be an ancient metabolic process because:
  A. oxygen was abundant in the early Earth atmosphere.
  B. glycolysis is found only in animals.
  C. glycolysis occurs in the cytosol.
  D. it produces more ATP per glucose molecule than cellular respiration.

42. True or False? The process of glycolysis may be more than 3 billion years old.

43. The early Earth atmosphere had very little ___________, favoring anaerobic organisms that could use glycolysis.

Word Roots

aero = air (aerobic: chemical reaction using oxygen)
auto = self; **troph** = food (autotroph: organism that makes its own organic matter)
glyco = sweet; **lysis** = split (glycolysis: process that splits glucose into two molecules)
hetero = other (heterotroph: Greek word that means "other feeder")
oblig = bound (obligate aerobe: organism that must have oxygen)
photo = light (photosynthesis: process using light energy to make organic molecules)

Key Terms

aerobic
aerobic capacity
anaerobic
ATP synthase
autotroph
cellular respiration
citric acid cycle
consumer
electron transport chain
facultative anaerobe
fermentation
glycolysis
heterotroph
NADH
obligate aerobe
obligate anaerobe
oxidation
photosynthesis
producer
redox reaction
reduction

Crossword Puzzle

Use the Key Terms list from this chapter to fill in the crossword puzzle.

ACROSS

1. type of organism that uses photosynthesis
3. abbreviation for type of reaction that transfers electrons
4. process using light energy to make organic molecules
6. type of chemical reaction that does not use oxygen
7. organism that cannot make its own organic food molecules
9. chemical reaction using oxygen
11. organism that makes all of its own organic matter
12. a type of anaerobe that can make ATP using aerobic or anaerobic respiration
14. cluster of proteins built into the inner mitochondrial membrane
16. a molecule that carries electrons from glucose to the electron transport chain
17. process that harvests energy stored in sugars
18. anaerobic harvest of food energy
20. type of cycle that continues breakdown of glucose after glycolysis

DOWN

2. loss of electrons during a redox reaction
5. the maximum rate that oxygen can be taken in and used by muscle cells
8. a type of chain composed of electron carrier molecules used to make ATP
10. a type of anaerobe that cannot survive around oxygen
13. heterotroph that eats other heterotrophs or autotrophs
15. process that splits glucose into two molecules
19. acceptance of electrons during a redox reaction

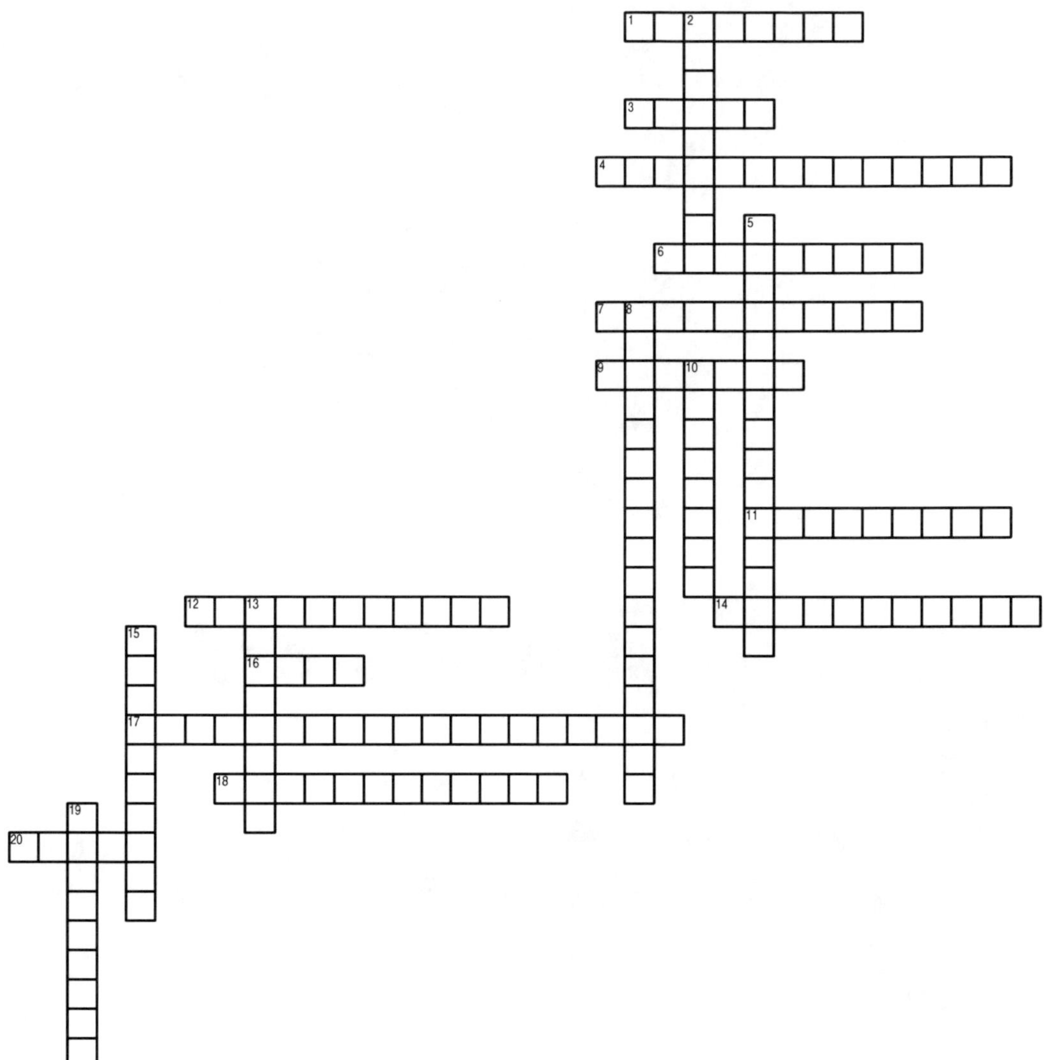

12 Photosynthesis: Converting Light Energy to Chemical Energy

Life on Earth is solar powered.
Without the greenhouse effect of the atmosphere, Earth would be about 10°C (18°F) colder.
Photosynthesis produces 160 billion metric tons of carbohydrates each year.
Each square millimeter of a leaf contains about 500,000 photosynthesis factories called chloroplasts.

LOOKING AHEAD

My Chemistry & Biology Portal

http://www.pearsoncustom.com/devry/my

Study Goals

- This chapter addresses many abstract ideas that may initially be difficult to grasp. Do not try to understand this entire chapter in a single night. Read the material slowly and carefully and study the figures as you go along. Figures 12.10–12.13 are especially helpful in understanding the molecular details of photosynthesis. Take frequent study breaks and review what you have already read before continuing further into the chapter.
- The organizing table below should help you understand the two basic steps of photosynthesis and compare these to cellular respiration.

Chapter Review

Concept Map

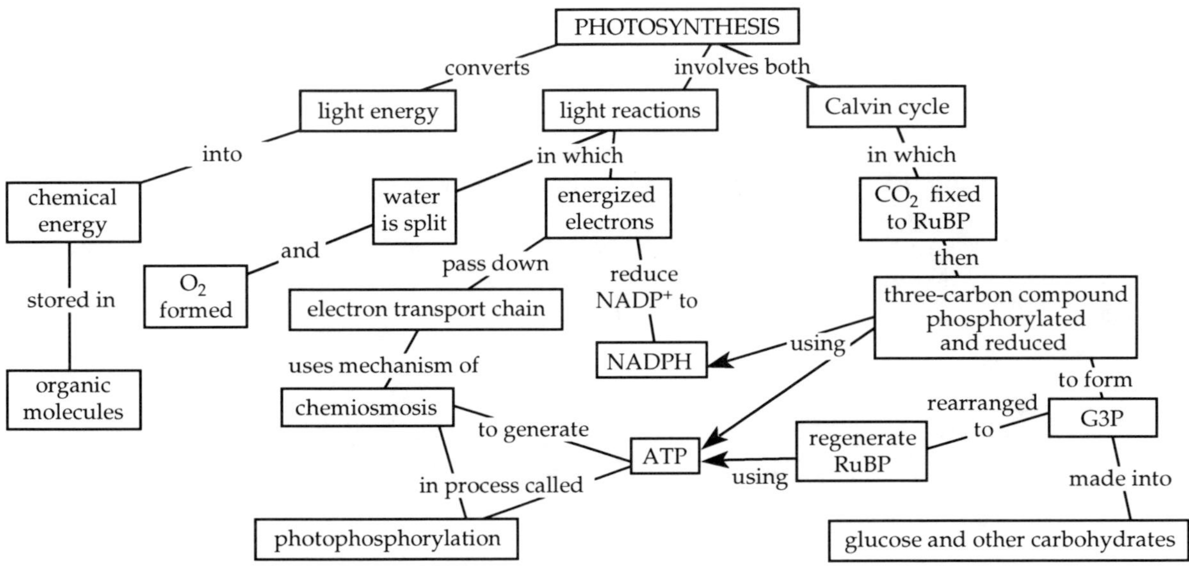

FIGURE

Photosynthesis converts light energy to the chemical energy of food.

Chapter Concept Review

The Basics of Photosynthesis

eTutor *Photosynthesis*

MP3Tutor *Photosynthesis*

- **Chloroplasts: Sites of Photosynthesis** Chloroplasts contain a thick fluid called stroma surrounding a network of membranes called thylakoids.

Activity *Plants in Our Lives*

Activity *The Sites of Photosynthesis*

- **The Overall Equation for Photosynthesis**

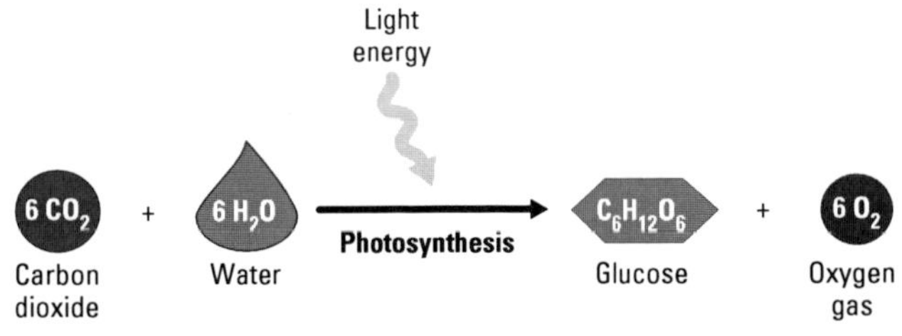

- A Photosynthesis Road Map

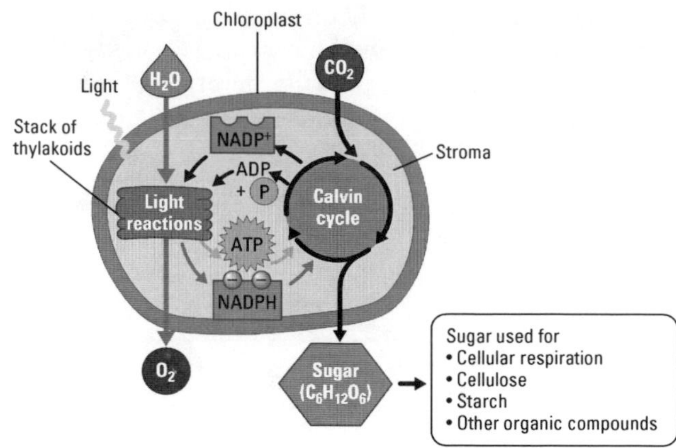

Activity *Overview of Photosynthesis*

The Light Reactions: Converting Solar Energy to Chemical Energy

- **The Nature of Sunlight** Visible light is part of the spectrum of electromagnetic energy (radiation). It travels through space as waves.
- **Chloroplast Pigments** Pigment molecules absorb light energy of certain wavelengths and reflect other wavelengths. We see the reflected wavelengths as the color of the pigment. Several chloroplast pigments absorb light of various wavelengths, but it is the green pigment chlorophyll *a* that participates directly in the light reactions.

Activity *Light Energy and Pigments*

Case Study in the Process of Science *How Does Paper Chromatography Separate Plant Pigments?*

- **How Photosystems Harvest Light Energy; How the Light Reactions Generate ATP and NADPH**

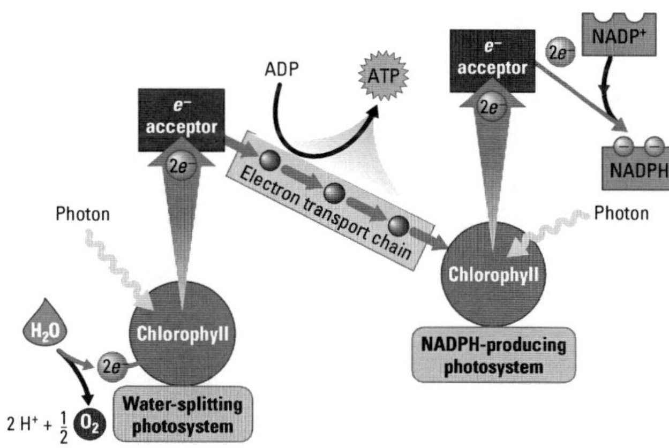

Case Study in the Process of Science *How is the process of photosynthesis measured*?

Activity *The Light Reactions*

The Calvin Cycle: Making Sugar from Carbon Dioxide

Activity *The Calvin Cycle*

- Water-Saving Adaptations of C4 and CAM Plants Photosynthetic adaptations of C4 and CAM plants enable sugar production to continue even when stomata are closed, thereby reducing water loss in arid environments.

Activity *Photosynthesis in Dry Climates*

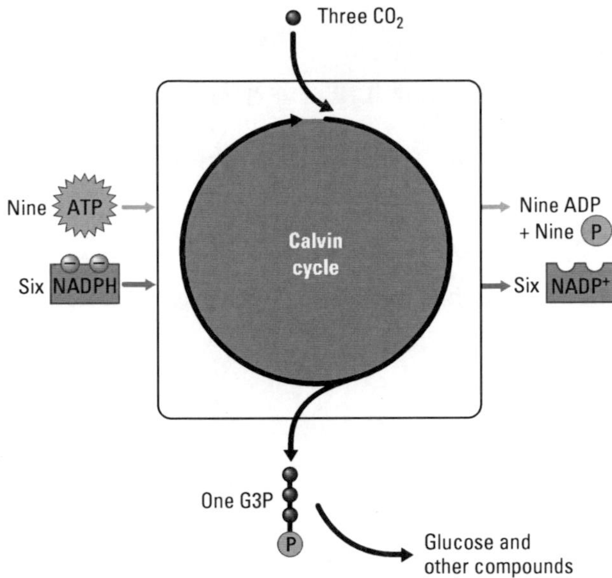

The Environmental Impact of Photosynthesis

- The process of photosynthesis provides organic material and chemical energy for life on Earth. Photosynthesis also swaps O_2 for CO_2 in the atmosphere.
- **How Photosynthesis Moderates Global Warming** Atmospheric CO_2 traps heat and raises our planet's temperature. Photosynthesis makes use of some of this CO_2. Levels of CO_2 in the atmosphere are increasing, raising concerns about global warming. Deforestation and the burning of fossil fuels appear to be contributing to these global changes in atmosphere and climate.

Activity *The Greenhouse Effect*

Organizing Tables

Compare the reactants, products, and location in the cell for the three reactions listed at the left.

TABLE 12.1

	Reactants	Products	Location in the Cell
Cellular respiration			
Light reaction			
Calvin cycle			

Practice Test for Chapter 12

eTutor
Photosynthesis
Overview of Photosynthesis

Directions: Identify the *one* best answer for the multiple-choice questions. For true/false questions, determine if the statement is true or false. If false, change the underlined word(s) to make the statement true. Finally, add the correct word(s) to the fill-in-the-blank questions to make the statements true.

Biology and Society: Plant Power for Power Plants

1. During most of human history, what has been the main source of energy for heat, light, and fuel for cooking?
A. wood
B. oil
C. coal
D. natural gas
E. nuclear

2. Burning wood for fuel has many advantages over using fossil fuels. Which one of the following is *not* an advantage of burning wood instead of fossil fuels? Energy plantations:
A. provide wildlife habitat.
B. reduce soil erosion.
C. renew the soil.
D. increase carbon dioxide in the air.

3. True or False? All of the food consumed by humans can be traced back to <u>animals</u>.

4. Over the last century, wood has been largely displaced as an energy source by ___________.

The Basics of Photosynthesis

Chloroplasts: Sites of Photosynthesis

5. Photosynthesis commonly occurs when sunlight hits chlorophyll pigments in the:
A. thylakoid membrane of a mitochondrion in a leaf.
B. stroma of a chloroplast in a cell of a leaf.
C. thylakoid membrane of a chloroplast in a cell surrounding a stoma of a leaf.
D. thylakoid membrane of a chloroplast in a cell of a leaf.

6. Examine Figure 12.3 to compare the drawing and photograph of a chloroplast. How is the drawing different from the photograph of an actual chloroplast from a plant leaf?
A. The grana are not stacked in the drawing.
B. The grana are not interconnected in the drawing.
C. There is no stroma in the drawing.
D. The intermembrane space is much larger in the drawing.

7. True or False? Sugars are made in the <u>grana</u> of a chloroplast.

8. Carbon dioxide enters the leaf, and oxygen exits, through tiny pores called ___________.

The Overall Equation for Photosynthesis

9. Which one of the following statements about photosynthesis is *false*? Photosynthesis:
- **A.** uses the products of respiration.
- **B.** produces carbon dioxide and oxygen.
- **C.** uses energy from sunlight to split water and release oxygen into the atmosphere.
- **D.** boosts the energy in electrons "uphill" to join carbon dioxide and hydrogens.

10. True or False? Inside chloroplasts, <u>carbon dioxide</u> is split to form hydrogen and oxygen.

11. The largest molecule produced by photosynthesis is __________.

A Photosynthesis Road Map

12. ATP and NADPH, produced by the:
- **A.** light reaction, are used to reduce carbon dioxide to form glucose.
- **B.** light reaction, are used to reduce glucose to form carbon dioxide.
- **C.** Calvin cycle, are used to reduce carbon dioxide to form glucose.
- **D.** Calvin cycle, are used to reduce glucose to form carbon dioxide.

13. Examine the overall equation for photosynthesis. Which one of the following is a product of the Calvin cycle?
- **A.** ATP
- **B.** NADPH
- **C.** G3P
- **D.** carbon dioxide
- **E.** water

14. True or False? The light reaction <u>does not</u> produce sugar.

15. The Calvin cycle depends on a supply of __________ and __________ from the light reactions.

The Light Reactions: Converting Solar Energy to Chemical Energy

The Nature of Sunlight

16. Which one of the following statements about radiation is *false*?
- **A.** Waves in the electromagnetic spectrum carry energy.
- **B.** The electromagnetic spectrum is the full range of radiation.
- **C.** Energy in wavelengths of visible light is absorbed by components of the Calvin cycle.
- **D.** The wavelengths of visible light that we see were not absorbed by what we are looking at.
- **E.** A wavelength is the distance between the crests of two adjacent waves.

17. True or False? We can see <u>only a small portion of</u> the entire electromagnetic spectrum.

18. A dark blue shirt will absorb __________ light energy than a very light blue shirt.

The Process of Science: What Colors of Light Drive Photosynthesis?

19. What did Engelmann use to determine where the highest concentrations of oxygen were produced?
- **A.** oxygen-sensitive bacteria
- **B.** an electronic oxygen probe
- **C.** signs of bubbles of oxygen gas accumulating
- **D.** the speed of particles moving away from the oxygen-producing algae
- **E.** a change in the color of the water around the oxygen-producing algae

20. True or False? Chloroplasts use <u>all</u> of the wavelengths of light to drive photosynthesis.

21. Most plants least use the wavelengths of light that form the color __________.

Chloroplast Pigments

22. Chlorophyll *b*:

A. absorbs mainly blue-violet and red light.
B. participates directly in the light reactions.
C. absorbs and dissipates excessive light that could damage chlorophyll.
D. participates indirectly in the light reactions by transferring light energy to chlorophyll *a*.

23. True or False? Chloroplast pigments are all located within the outer membrane of the chloroplast.

24. Only the pigment ___________ participates directly in the light reactions.

How Photosystems Harvest Light Energy

25. The photosynthetic pigments work together to function most like:

A. a telephone.
B. a brain.
C. a mirror.
D. an umbrella.
E. an antenna.

26. Which one of the following is the general sequence of energy transfer during photosynthesis? Light energy in a photon is transferred first to:

A. a primary electron acceptor, then to chlorophyll *a*, and finally to pigment molecules.
B. pigment molecules, then to a primary electron acceptor, and finally to chlorophyll *a*.
C. pigment molecules, then to chlorophyll *b*, and finally to a primary electron acceptor.
D. pigment molecules, then to chlorophyll *a*, and finally to a primary electron acceptor.
E. none of the above.

27. True or False? The reaction center of a photosystem consists of a chlorophyll *a* molecule next to a primary electron acceptor.

28. A fixed quantity of light energy is a(n) ___________.

How the Light Reactions Generate ATP and NADPH

29. Which one of the following parts of a mitochondrion functions most like the thylakoid membrane?

A. mitochondrial matrix
B. outer mitochondrial membrane
C. inner mitochondrial membrane
D. the intermembrane space

30. The extensive infolding of the inner thylakoid membrane is likely an adaptation to:

A. make it more difficult for oxygen to pass through.
B. increase the flexibility of chloroplasts.
C. make it more difficult for hydrogen ions to pass through.
D. increase the surface area of the light reactions.
E. increase the surface area for glycolysis.

31. Oxygen is produced during the:

A. water-splitting photosystem.
B. electron transport chain.
C. NADPH-producing photosystem.
D. Calvin cycle.

32. True or False? Both cellular respiration and photosynthesis have ATP synthases that use the energy stored by the H^+ gradient.

33. The electron transport chain in the chloroplast releases energy used to produce ___________.

The Calvin Cycle: Making Sugar from Carbon Dioxide

Water-Saving Adaptations of C_4 And Cam Plants

34. Which of the following are produced by the Calvin cycle?
- **A.** $NADP^+$, ADP + P, and G3P
- **B.** NADPH, ATP, and glucose
- **C.** $NADP^+$, ADP + P, and glucose
- **D.** NADPH, ATP, and G3P
- **E.** glucose and oxygen

35. Which of the following *only* includes CAM plants?
- **A.** pineapples, cacti, and aloe
- **B.** soybeans, wheat, and jade
- **C.** soybeans, wheat, and cacti
- **D.** oats, wheat, and pineapples

36. True or False? Plant cells use <u>G3P</u> to make glucose and other organic molecules they need.

37. CAM plants are most likely to have their ___________ open mainly at night.

38. During a hot and dry summer, C_3 plants can lose dangerous amounts of ___________ if their stomata remain open during the day.

The Environmental Impact of Photosynthesis

How Photosynthesis Moderates Global Warming

39. Deforestation contributes to global warming by:
- **A.** decreasing the number of producers and adding CO2 to the atmosphere.
- **B.** decreasing the number of consumers and adding CO2 to the atmosphere.
- **C.** increasing the number of producers and removing CO2 from the atmosphere.
- **D.** increasing the number of consumers and removing CO2 from the atmosphere.

40. True or False? Increasing the total amount of photosynthesis on Earth would <u>increase</u> global warming by removing CO_2 from the atmosphere.

41. The ___________ is a gradual warming of Earth caused by increased atmospheric carbon dioxide.

Evolution Connection: The Oxygen Revolution

42. Large amounts of oxygen were first added to Earth's atmosphere by:
- **A.** land plants.
- **B.** algae in the oceans.
- **C.** cyanobacteria.
- **D.** fungi.
- **E.** the greenhouse effect.

43. True or False? The widespread production of oxygen by cyanobacteria 2.7–3.5 billion years ago permitted the evolution of <u>photosynthetic</u> organisms.

44. Many anaerobic prokaryotes die if they are exposed to ___________.

Word Roots

chloro = green; **plast** = formed or molded (chloroplast: the organelle of photosynthesis)
electro = electricity; **magne** = magnetic (electromagnetic spectrum: the full range of radiation)
photo = light (photosystem: cluster of pigment molecules)
phyll = leaf (chlorophyll: photosynthetic pigment in chloroplasts)
stoma = mouth (stomata: tiny pores in leaves through which gases are exchanged)
thylac = a sac or pouch (thylakoids: membranous sacs suspended in the stroma)

Key Terms

C_3 plants
C_4 plants
Calvin cycle
CAM plants
chlorophyll *a*
chloroplast
electromagnetic spectrum
global warming
grana
greenhouse effect
greenhouse gases
light reaction
NADPH
photon
photosystem
primary electron acceptor
reaction center
stomata
stroma
thylakoids
wavelength

Crossword Puzzle

Use the Key Terms list from this chapter to fill in the crossword puzzle.

ACROSS

1. a type of electron acceptor that harvests light
2. in a chloroplast, the chlorophyll *a* molecule and primary electron acceptor
4. tiny pores in leaves through which gases are exchanged
5. thick fluid deep inside a chloroplast
6. the gases in the atmosphere that absorb heat radiation
8. pigment that absorbs blue-violet and red light
9. the type of spectrum of all types of radiation
12. stacks of hollow disks inside chloroplasts
16. membranous sacs suspended in the stroma
17. changes in the surface air temperature induced by emission of greenhouse gases
18. the process of atmospheric carbon dioxide trapping heat
19. a fixed quantity of light energy

DOWN

1. cluster of pigment molecules
3. process that makes sugar from carbon dioxide
7. the organelle of photosynthesis
8. the type of plant that uses crassulacean acid metabolism
10. type of plant that prefaces the Calvin cycle with reactions that incorporate carbon dioxide into four-carbon compounds
11. type of plant that uses the Calvin cycle to form three-carbon compounds as the first stable intermediate
13. distance between crests of adjacent light waves
14. the type of reaction converting solar energy to chemical energy
15. electron carrier involved in photosynthesis

1
2
3
4
5
6
7
8
9
10
11
12
13
14
15
16
17
18
19

Unit 4

Genetics: The Plan of Life

13 The Cellular Basis of Reproduction: Cells from Cells

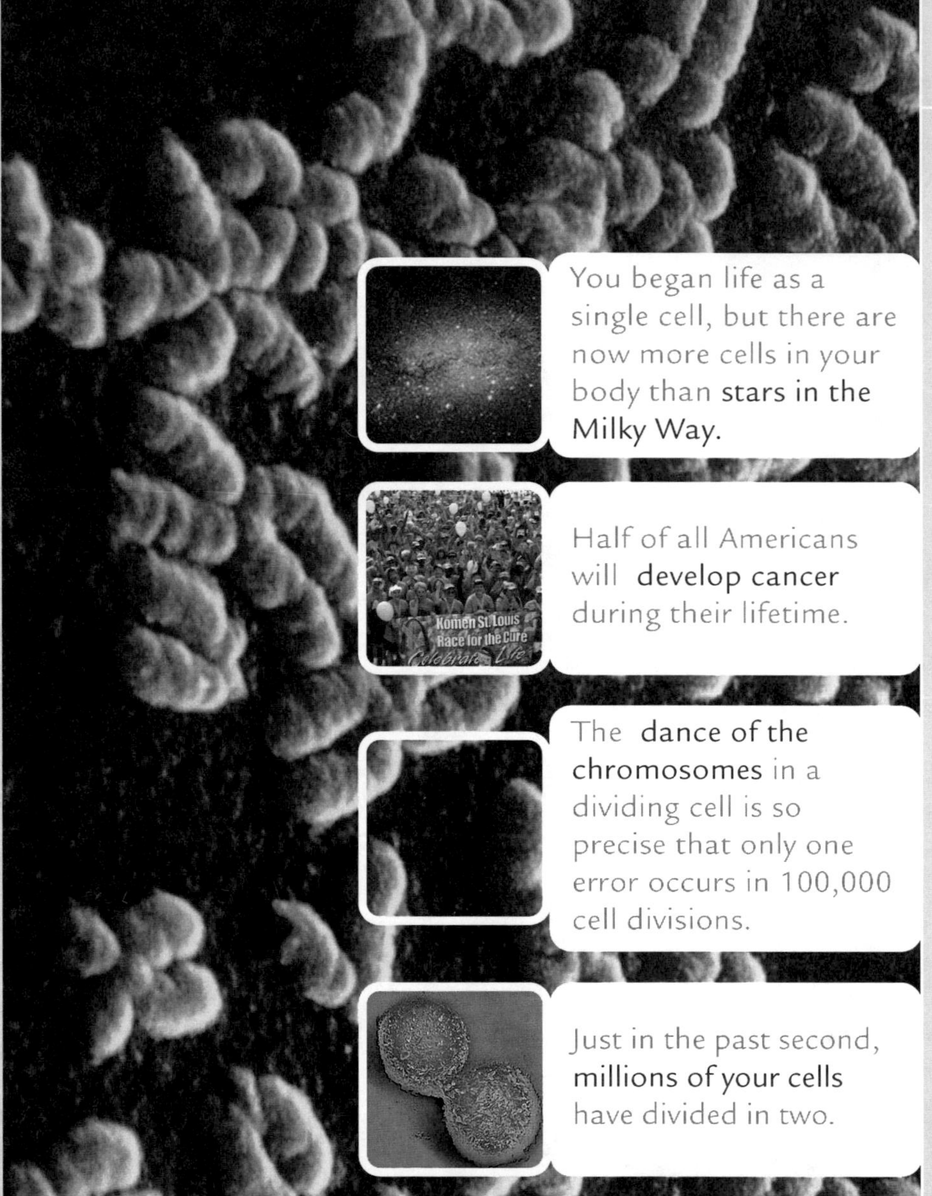
You began life as a single cell, but there are now more cells in your body than stars in the Milky Way.
Komen St. Louis
Race for the Cure
Celebrate Life
Half of all Americans will develop cancer during their lifetime.
The dance of the chromosomes in a dividing cell is so precise that only one error occurs in 100,000 cell divisions.
Just in the past second, millions of your cells have divided in two.

LOOKING AHEAD

My
Chemistry &
Biology Portal

http://www.pearsoncustom.com/devry/mycbp

Study Goals

- Read carefully and study Figures 13.8 and 13.16 of your text describing the key events of mitosis and meiosis. Figure 13.17 is a very useful comparison of both processes.
- The key to understanding mitosis and meiosis is learning how the chromosomes are arranged and how they separate during metaphase. Again, Figures 13.8 and 13.16 of your text are crucial.
- The organizing tables below should help you sort out the important details of the cell cycle, mitosis, and meiosis.

Chapter Review

Concept Map

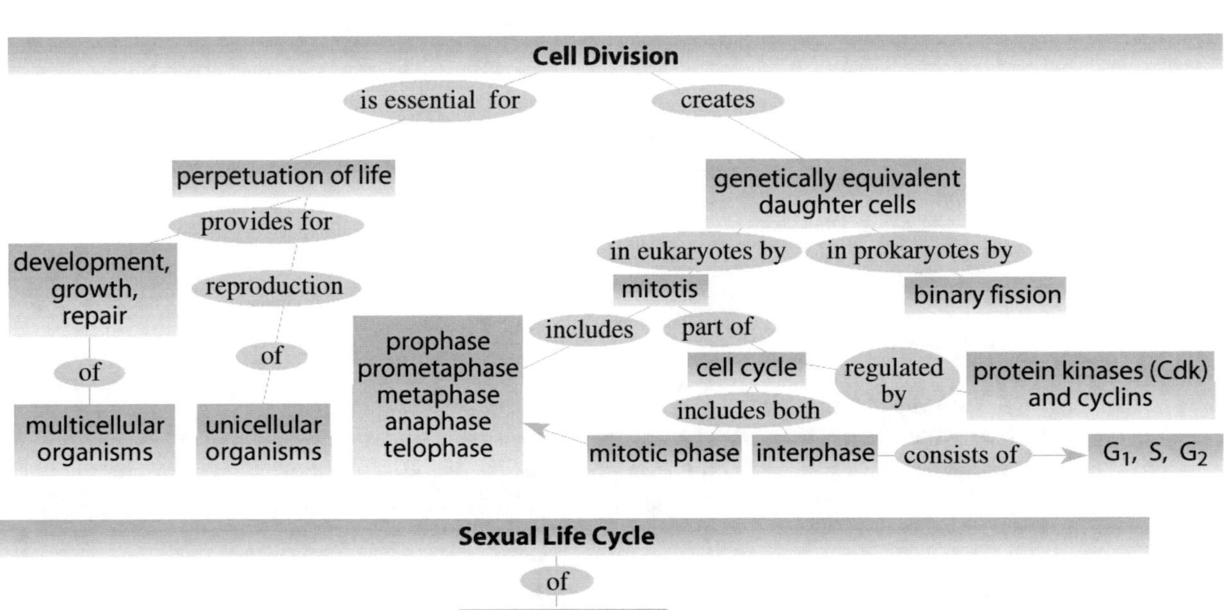

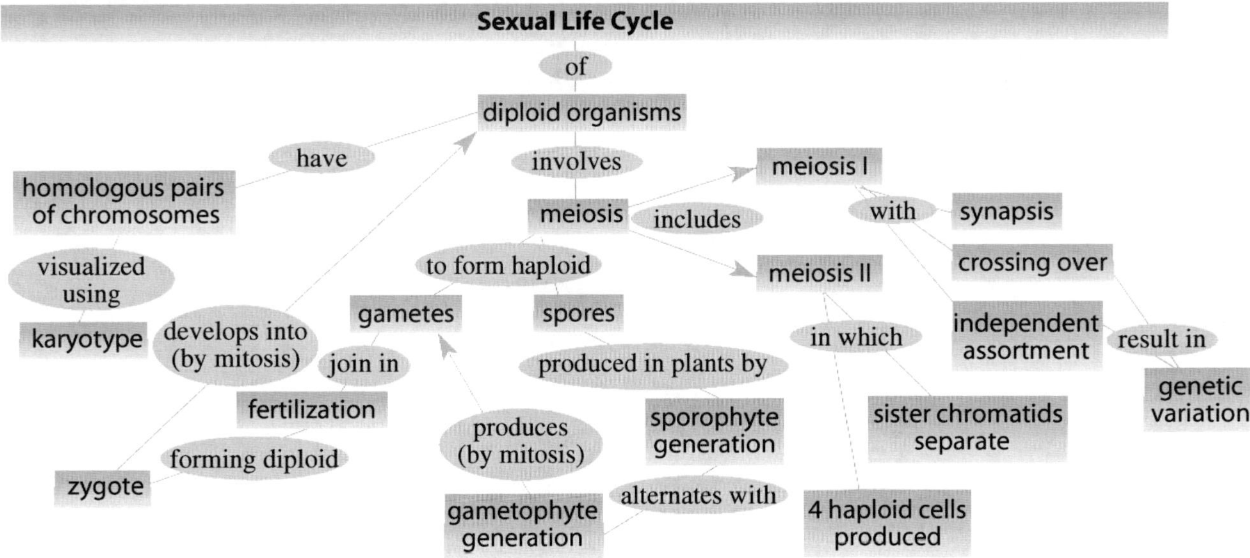

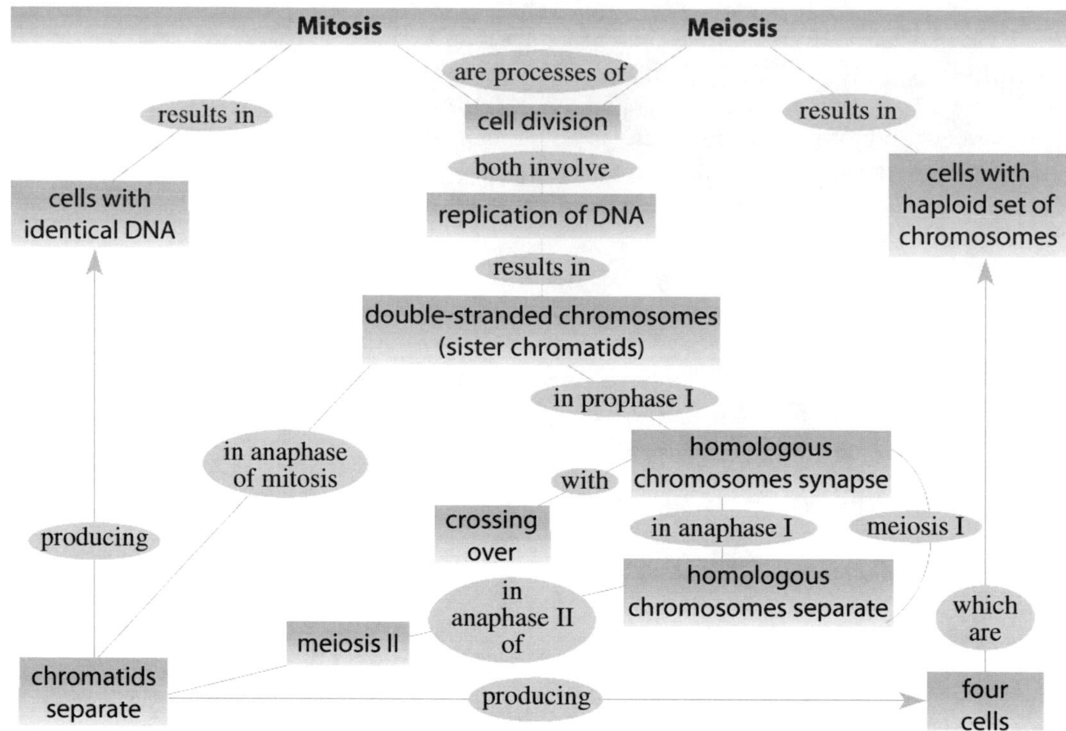

Chapter Concept Review

What Cell Reproduction Accomplishes

- **Passing On Genes from Cell to Cell** Cell reproduction, also called cell division, involves the duplication of all the chromosomes, followed by the distribution of the two identical sets of chromosomes to two "daughter" cells. The daughter cells are genetically identical.
- **The Reproduction of Organisms** Some organisms use mitosis (ordinary cell division) to reproduce. This is called asexual reproduction, and it results in offspring that are genetically identical to the lone parent and to each other. Mitosis also enables multicellular organisms to grow and develop and to replace damaged or lost cells. Organisms that reproduce sexually, by the union of a sperm with an egg cell, carry out meiosis, a type of cell division that yields gametes with only half as many chromosomes as body (somatic) cells.

Activity *Asexual and Sexual Reproduction*

The Cell Cycle and Mitosis

eTutor *Mitosis*
MP3 Tutor *Mitosis*

- **Eukaryotic Chromosomes** The many genes of a eukaryotic genome are grouped into multiple chromosomes in the nucleus. Each chromosome contains one very long DNA molecule, with many genes, that is tightly packed around histone proteins. Individual chromosomes are visible with a light microscope only when the cell is in the process of dividing; otherwise, they are in the form of thin, loosely packed chromatin fibers. Before a cell starts dividing, the chromosomes duplicate, producing sister chromatids (containing identical DNA) joined together at the centromere.

- **The Cell Cycle**

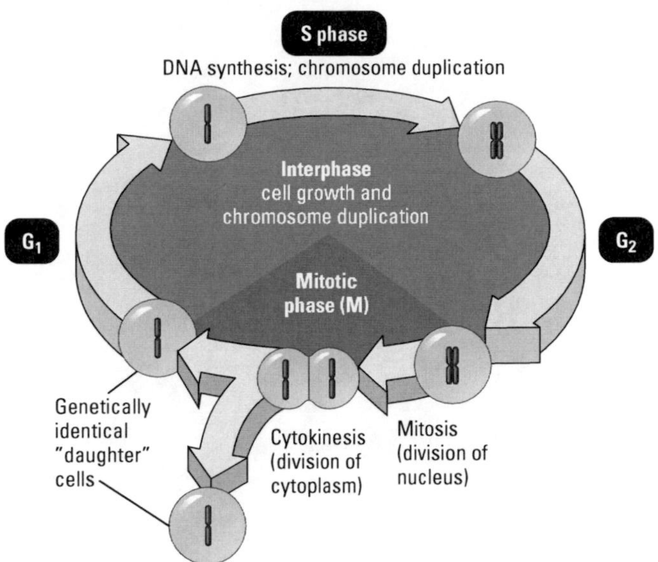

Activity *The Cell Cycle*

- **Mitosis and Cytokinesis** Mitosis is divided into four phases: prophase, metaphase, anaphase, and telophase. At the start of mitosis, the chromosomes coil up and the nuclear envelope breaks down (prophase). Then a mitotic spindle made of microtubules moves the chromosomes to the middle of the cell (metaphase). The sister chromatids then separate and are moved to opposite poles of the cell (anaphase), where two new nuclei form (telophase). Cytokinesis overlaps the end of mitosis. Mitosis and cytokinesis produce genetically identical cells. In animals, cytokinesis occurs by cleavage, which pinches the cell in two. In plants, a membranous cell plate splits the cell in two.

Activity *Mitosis and Cytokinesis Animation*

Activity *Mitosis and Cytokinesis Video*

Case Study in the Process of Science *How Much Time Do Cells Spend in Each Phase of Mitosis?*

- **Cancer Cells: Growing Out of Control** When the cell cycle control system malfunctions, a cell may divide excessively and form a tumor. Cancer cells may grow to form malignant tumors, invade other tissues (metastasize), and even kill the organism. Surgery can remove tumors, and radiation and chemotherapy are effective as treatments because they interfere with cell division. You can protect yourself against some forms of cancer through lifestyle changes and regular screenings.

Activity *Causes of Cancer*

Meiosis, the Basis of Sexual Reproduction

eTutor *Meiosis*

MP3 Tutor *Meiosis*

- **Homologous Chromosomes** The somatic cells (body cells) of each species contain a specific number of chromosomes; human cells have 46, made up of 23 pairs of homologous chromosomes. The chromosomes of a homologous pair carry genes for the same characteristics at the same places. Mammalian males have X and Y sex chromosomes (only partly homologous), while females have two X chromosomes.

- **Gametes and the Life Cycle of a Sexual Organism**

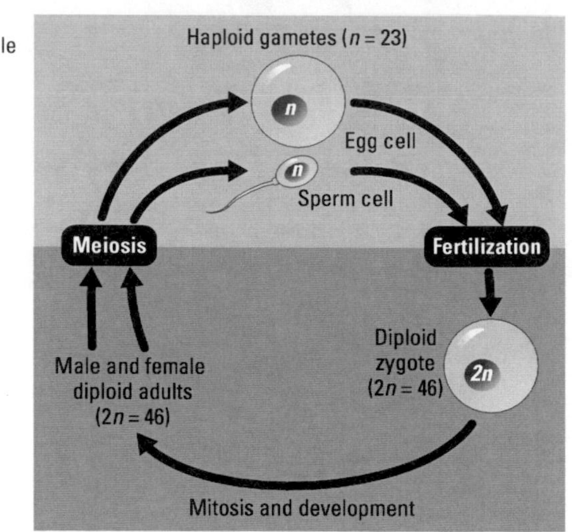

Activity *Human Life Cycle*

- **The Process of Meiosis** Meiosis, like mitosis, is preceded by chromosome duplication. But in meiosis, the cell divides twice to form four daughter cells. The first division, meiosis I, starts with the pairing of homologous chromosomes. In crossing over, homologous chromosomes exchange corresponding segments. Meiosis I separates the members of the homologous pairs and produces two daughter cells, each with one set of (duplicated) chromosomes. Meiosis II is essentially the same as mitosis; in each of the cells, the sister chromatids of each chromosome separate.

Activity *Meiosis Animation*

Case Study in the Process of Science *How Can the Frequency of Crossing Over Be Estimated?*

- **Review: Comparing Mitosis and Meiosis**

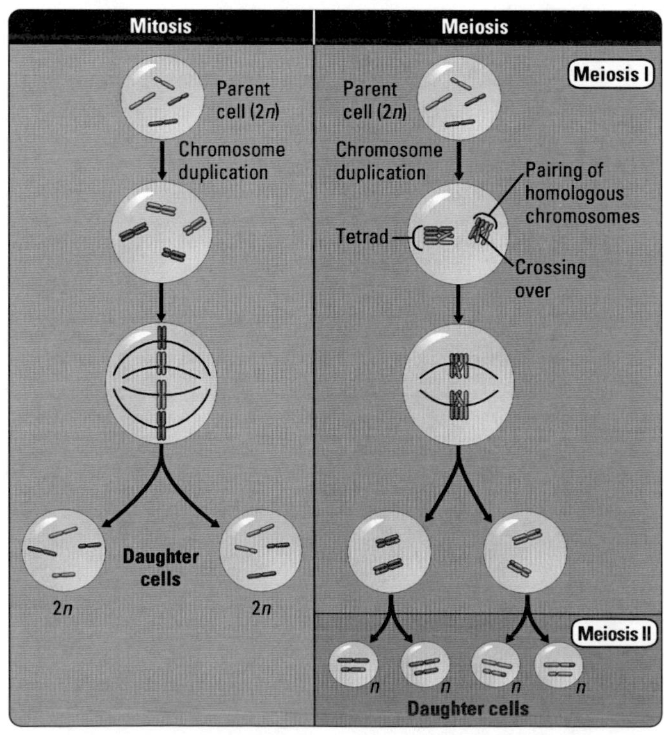

MP3 Tutor *Mitosis-Meiosis Comparison*

- **The Origins of Genetic Variation** Because the chromosomes of a homologous pair come from different parents, they carry different versions of many of their genes. The large number of possible arrangements of chromosome pairs at metaphase of meiosis I leads to many different combinations of chromosomes in eggs and sperm. Random fertilization of eggs by sperm greatly increases the variation. Crossing over during prophase of meiosis I increases variation still further.

Activity *The Origins of Genetic Variation*

- **When Meiosis Goes Awry** Sometimes a person has an abnormal number of chromosomes, which causes problems. Down syndrome is caused by an extra copy of chromosome 21. The abnormal chromosome count is a product of nondisjunction, the failure of a homologous pair of chromosomes to separate during meiosis I or of sister chromatids to separate during meiosis II. Nondisjunction can also produce gametes with extra or missing sex chromosomes, which lead to varying degrees of malfunction in humans but do not usually affect survival.

Activity *Polyploid Plants*

Organizing Tables

Compare the key events of each stage of the cell cycle.

TABLE 13.1

	Key Events
M phase	
G_1 phase	
G_2 phase	
S phase	

Compare the following aspects of the G_2 phase of interphase and the stages of mitosis.

TABLE 13.2

Stages	**The Arrangement and Behavior of the Chromosomes**	**The Structure and Functions of the Mitotic Spindle**	**Other Cellular Details**
G_2 Interphase: Preparing for mitosis			
Prophase			
Metaphase			
Anaphase			
Telophase			

Compare the following aspects of meiosis I and meiosis II.

TABLE 13.3

Stage of Meiosis	How Are the Chromosomes Arranged During Metaphase? (Draw the Arrangement of Two Tetrads)	What Separates During Anaphase: Homologous Chromosomes or Sister Chromatids?	Where Does Crosing Over Begin?
Meiosis I			
Meiosis II			

Practice Test for Chapter 13

Directions: Identify the *one* best answer for the multiple-choice questions. For true/false questions, determine if the statement is true or false. If false, change the underlined word(s) to make the statement true. Finally, add the correct word(s) to the fill-in-the-blank questions to make the statements true.

Biology and Society: A $50,000 Egg!

1. Which one of the following does not occur in the process of *in vitro* fertilization (IVF)?
- **A.** cloning sperm cells in a petri dish
- **B.** joining sperm and egg in a petri dish
- **C.** allowing an embryo to grow to the 8-cell stage
- **D.** implanting the embryo into the uterus of the mother

2. True or False? Infertility affects one in <u>a thousand</u> American couples.

3. The inability to produce children after one year of trying defines ___________.

What Cell Reproduction Accomplishes

Passing On Genes from Cell to Cell

4. Daughter cells formed during typical cell division have:
- **A.** identical sets of chromosomes with identical genes.
- **B.** different sets of chromosomes with identical genes.
- **C.** identical sets of chromosomes with different genes.
- **D.** different sets of chromosomes with different genes.

5. True or False? Growth of an organism and the replacement of lost or damaged cells are the main roles of <u>cell division</u>.

6. Before a cell divides, it duplicates its ___________.

The Reproduction of Organisms

7. Sexual reproduction:
- **A.** uses only meiosis.
- **B.** involves the production of daughter cells with double the genetic material of the parent cell.
- **C.** uses only ordinary cell division.
- **D.** requires the fertilization of an egg by a sperm.
- **E.** is the normal process by which the cells of most organisms divide.

8. True or False? A sperm or egg has twice as many chromosomes as its parent cell.

9. In ___________ reproduction, the offspring and parent have identical genes.

The Cell Cycle and Mitosis

Eukaryotic Chromosomes

My Chemistry & Biology Portal

eTutor
Mitosis

10. Which one of the following statements about chromosomes is *false*?
    A. Sister chromatids remain attached until anaphase.
    B. The number of chromosomes in a eukaryotic cell depends upon the species.
    C. Chromosomes are made of a combination of DNA, carbohydrate, and lipid molecules.
    D. Human body cells each typically have 46 chromosomes.
    E. Once separated, sister chromatids go to different cells.

11. True or False? The lipids in chromosomes help control the activity of the genes.

12. Sister chromatids remain attached at a region called the ___________.

The Cell Cycle

13. What stage of the cell cycle is marked by the presence of sister chromatids and the preparation of the cell for division?
    A. S
    B. M
    C. G_1
    D. G_2
    E. G_3

14. True or False? Some highly specialized cells do not undergo a cell cycle.

15. True or False? Prokaryotes do not undergo mitosis.

16. The M phase of the cell cycle includes ___________ and ___________.

17. During the ___________ stage of the cell cycle, the chromosomes are duplicated.

Mitosis and Cytokinesis

18. Which one of the following statements about mitosis is *false*?
    A. During prophase, the sister chromatids are clearly seen, the nuclear envelope breaks up, and the mitotic spindle begins to form.
    B. Toward the end of prophase, the sister chromatids replicate again, but remain attached to each other.
    C. During metaphase, the chromosomes line up in the middle of the mitotic spindle.
    D. At the start of anaphase, the sister chromatids are pulled apart and start to move toward opposite spindle poles.
    E. Telophase is like the opposite of prophase: The nuclear envelope reforms, the chromosomes uncoil, and the spindle disappears.

19. Dividing an animal cell into two cells is most like:
    A. building a new wall that divides one room into two.
    B. overtightening the drawstring of sweatpants.
    C. peeling an apple.
    D. cutting a pie into two pieces with a knife.

20. Examine the prophase stages of mitosis in Figure 13.8 of your text. Which of the following structures invade(s) the nuclear space after the nuclear membrane disintegrates?
   A. chromosomes
   B. centrioles
   C. nucleolus
   D. spindle microtubules

21. Compare the cell stages in Figure 13.8 of the text to the photograph in Figure 13.4. What stage is indicated by the cell in Figure 13.4?
   A. interphase
   B. early prophase
   C. late prophase
   D. metaphase
   E. anaphase

22. Spindle microtubules grow from ___________, clouds of cytoplasmic material that in animal cells contains centrioles.

Cancer Cells: Growing Out of Control

23. The most dangerous property of cancer cells is that they:
   A. divide slowly.
   B. spread throughout the body.
   C. form tumors.
   D. do not divide by mitosis.
   E. do not live very long.

24. Which one of the following can *reduce* your risk of developing cancer?
   A. smoking
   B. overexposure to the sun
   C. exercising
   D. Eating a low-fiber high-fat diet.

25. True or False? Radiation and chemotherapy both fight cancer by <u>disrupting cell division.</u>

26. An abnormal mass of cells that remains at its original site is a ___________ tumor.

27. The use of drugs to disrupt division of cancerous cells is called ___________.

Meiosis, the Basis of Sexual Reproduction

My Chemistry & Biology Portal

eTutor Meiosis

Homologous Chromosomes

28. A male human somatic cell has:
   A. 46 pairs of chromosomes.
   B. 23 pairs of sex chromosomes.
   C. 23 pairs of autosomes.
   D. 22 pairs of autosomes and 1 pair of sex chromosomes.
   E. 22 pairs of sex chromosomes and 1 pair of autosomes.

29. True or False? Most of the chromosomes in humans are <u>sex chromosomes.</u>

30. The same sequence of genes is found on ___________ chromosomes.

Gametes and the Life Cycle of a Sexual Organism

31. In the human life cycle somatic cells are:
- **A.** diploid, and gametes are diploid.
- **B.** diploid, and gametes are haploid.
- **C.** haploid, and gametes are diploid.
- **D.** haploid, and gametes are haploid.

32. True or False? If the human reproductive cycle only included diploid cells, the offspring of each generation would have <u>twice as much</u> genetic material in each cell as the parent cells.

33. If the somatic cells of a species have 25 pairs of homologous chromosomes, the number of chromosomes in haploid gametes would be __________.

The Process of Meiosis

34. Which one of the following statements about meiosis is *false*?
- **A.** Cells dividing by meiosis undergo two consecutive divisions.
- **B.** Homologous chromosomes exchange segments before separating from each other.
- **C.** Homologous chromosomes separate during meiosis I.
- **D.** Sister chromatids separate during meiosis II.
- **E.** The chromosomes replicate before meiosis and between meiosis I and meiosis II.

35. In sexually reproducing organisms, cells entering mitosis have:
- **A.** half the amount of DNA as cells entering meiosis.
- **B.** the same amount of DNA as cells entering meiosis.
- **C.** twice the amount of DNA as cells entering meiosis.
- **D.** four times the amount of DNA as cells entering meiosis.

36. True or False? Before crossing over occurs, sister chromatids are <u>identical</u>.

37. The result of meiosis is four __________ cells.

Review: Comparing Mitosis and Meiosis

38. Which one of the following is an actual difference between mitosis and meiosis?
- **A.** A single cell is divided into two cells in mitosis and four cells in meiosis.
- **B.** Mitosis produces haploid cells, and meiosis produces diploid cells.
- **C.** Mitosis involves two cellular divisions, and meiosis involves just one cellular division.
- **D.** The chromosomes replicate before mitosis and meiosis, but in meiosis they replicate again between the first and second division.

39. True or False? The two daughter cells produced by meiosis I <u>do not</u> undergo cytokinesis before meiosis II.

40. Sister chromatids are separated during mitosis and __________.

The Origins of Genetic Variation

41. The random segregation of one member of each homologous pair of chromosomes into gametes defines:
- **A.** random fertilization.
- **B.** crossing over.
- **C.** independent assortment.
- **D.** random assortment.
- **E.** independent fertilization.

42. True or False? Crossing over only occurs in <u>mitosis</u>.

43. The site of crossing over is a called a(n) __________.

When Meiosis Goes Awry

44. In general:

- **A.** the absence of a Y chromosome results in maleness.
- **B.** the presence of only a single X chromosome results in maleness.
- **C.** a human embryo with an abnormal number of chromosomes is usually normal.
- **D.** nondisjunction occurs only in males of sexually reproducing, diploid organisms.
- **E.** the incidence of Down syndrome increases markedly with the age of the mother.

45. Examine the chart in Figure 13.23 of your text. At which of the following intervals do we find the greatest *increase* in risk of having a child with Down syndrome?

- **A.** 25–30 years
- **B.** 30–35 years
- **C.** 35–40 years
- **D.** 40–45 years
- **E.** 45–50 years

46. True or False? Klinefelter syndrome and Turner syndrome result from nondisjunction of <u>autosomes</u>.

47. A person with trisomy 21 is said to have __________.

Evolution Connection: New Species from Errors in Cell Division

48. Polyploid species:

- **A.** are common in mammals.
- **B.** are more common in animals than in plants.
- **C.** can result if gametes are produced by mitosis.
- **D.** have two sets of chromosomes in each somatic cell.

49. True or False? At least half of all species of flowering plants are <u>polyploid.</u>

50. The union of a diploid egg and a diploid sperm will produce a __________ zygote.

Exercises in Genetics

Meiosis

Consider the following diploid cell. The long, dot-filled chromosomes are homologous, but are shaded differently to distinguish them from each other. This is true for the shorter checkerboard chromosomes as well.

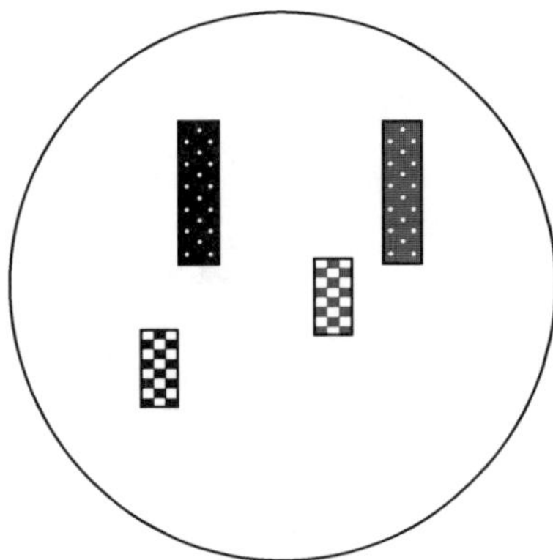

1. a. How many chromosomes are there in this diploid cell?

b. If this cell were to undergo meiosis, how many chromosomes would there be in the resulting haploid cells?

2. Draw the cell during the following phases of meiosis:

a. What does the cell look like when it has duplicated its genetic material in preparation for meiosis?

b. What does the cell look like during metaphase I, before crossing over and recombination have occurred?

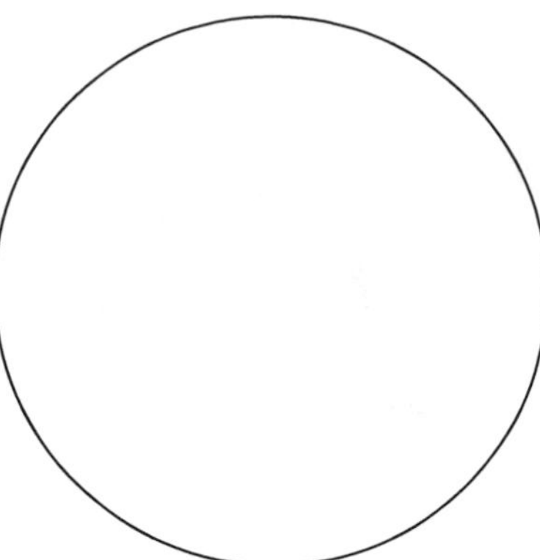

c. Suppose each chromosome experiences a single crossing over event with its homologue. Draw the cell during metaphase I, after crossing over has occurred.

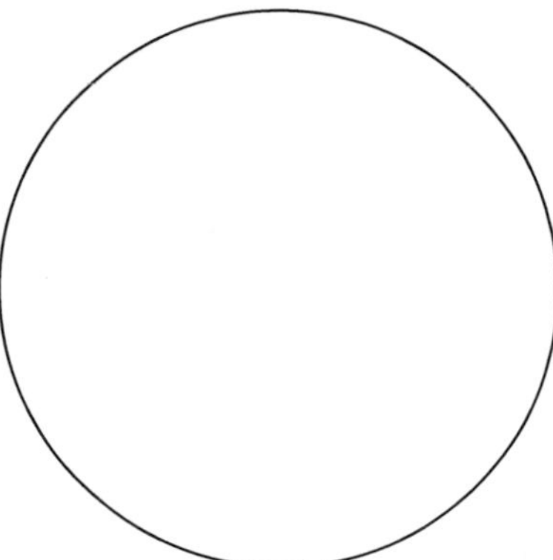

d. Draw the two daughter cells at the end of meiosis I.

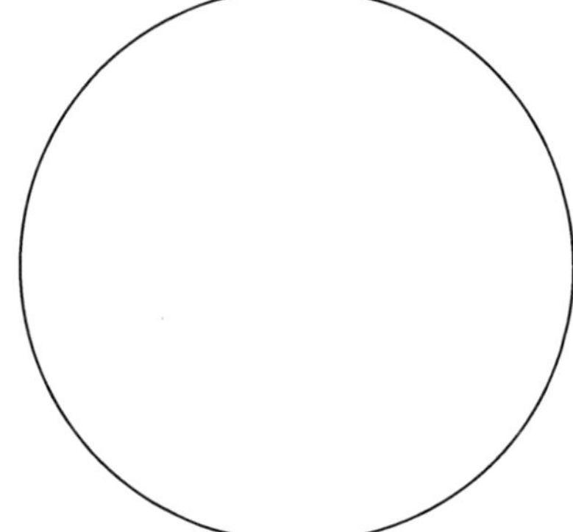

e. Draw the four daughter cells at the end of meiosis II.

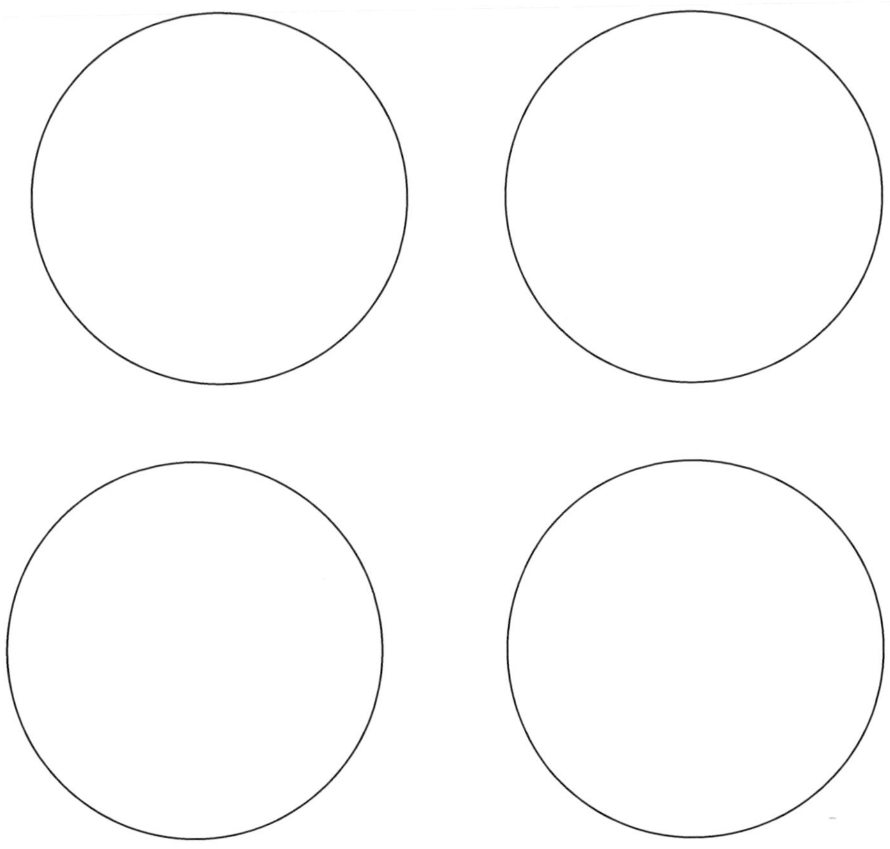

Word Roots

a = not or without (asexual: type of reproduction not involving fertilization)
ana = again (anaphase: mitotic stage when sister chromatids separate)
auto = self (autosomes: the chromosomes that do not determine gender)
carcin = an ulcer (carcinoma: cancer originating in the external or internal coverings of the body)
centro = the center; **mere** = a part (centromere: the centralized region joining two sister chromatids)
chemo = chemical (chemotherapy: type of cancer therapy using drugs that disrupt cell division)
chiasm = cross-mark (chiasma: the sites where crossing over have occurred)
chroma = colored (chromosome: DNA-containing structure)
cyto = cell; **kinet** = move (cytokinesis: division of the cytoplasm)
di = two (diploid: cells that contain two homologous sets of chromosomes)
fertil = fruitful (fertilization: process of fusion of sperm and egg cell)
gamet = a wife or husband (gamete: egg or sperm)
haplo = single (haploid: cells that contain only one chromosome of each homologous pair)
homo = like (homologous: like chromosomes that form a pair)
inter = between (interphase: time when a cell metabolizes and performs its various functions)
karyo = nucleus (karyotype: a display of the chromosomes of a cell)
leuko = white (leukemia: cancer of white blood cells)

mal = bad or evil (malignant: type of tumor that migrates away from its site of origin)
mei = less (meiosis: the division of a diploid nucleus into four haploid daughter nuclei)
meta = between (metaphase: mitotic stage when the chromosomes are lined up in the cell's middle)
mito = a thread (mitosis: the division of a diploid cell into two diploid cells)
non = not; **dis** = separate (nondisjunction: the result when paired chromosomes fail to separate)
poly = many (polyploid: having more than two sets of homologous chromosomes in each somatic cell)
pro = before (prophase: mitotic stage when the nuclear membrane first breaks up)
sarco = flesh (sarcoma: cancer that arises in tissues that support the body)
soma = body (somatic: body cells with 46 chromosomes in humans)
telo = end (telophase: final mitotic stage when the nuclear envelope reforms)
tetra = four (tetrad: the orientation of homologous pairs of chromosomes with four apparent "arms")
tri = three (trisomy 21: a condition in which a person has three number 21 chromosomes)

Key Terms

anaphase
asexual reproduction
autosome
benign tumor
cancer
carcinomas
cell cycle
cell cycle control system
cell division
cell plate
centromere
centrosome
chemotherapy
chiasma
chromatin
chromosome
cleavage furrow
crossing over
cytokinesis
diploid
Down syndrome
fertilization
gamete
genetic recombination
haploid
histone
homologous chromosome
interphase
karyotype
leukemia
life cycle
lymphoma
malignant tumor
meiosis
metaphase
metastasis
mitosis
mitotic phase
mitotic spindle
nucleosome
nondisjunction
polyploid
prophase
radiation therapy
sarcoma
sex chromosome
sexual reproduction
sister chromatid
somatic cell
telophase
tetrad
trisomy 21
tumor
zygote

Crossword Puzzle

Use the Key Terms list from this chapter to fill in the crossword puzzle.

ACROSS

1. final mitotic stage when the nuclear envelope reforms
3. type of cancer therapy exposing parts of the body to high energy
5. cancer that arises in tissues that support the body
6. a bead-like structure consisting of DNA wrapped around histone molecules
9. cancer of the tissue that forms white blood cells
11. a condition in which a person has three number 21 chromosomes
12. part of cell cycle when cell is dividing
16. time when a cell metabolizes and performs its various functions
17. mitotic stage when the chromosomes are lined up in the cell's middle
20. the division of a diploid cell into two diploid cells
22. type of chromosome that forms a pair
24. stages leading from the adults of one generation to the adults of the next
26. a display of the chromosomes of a cell
27. football-shaped structure of microtubules important in mitosis
28. long strands of DNA attached to certain proteins
30. trisomy 21
31. type of reproduction requiring fertilization
32. a thread-like, gene-carrying structure formed from chromatin
33. small protein associated with DNA
35. cells that contain two homologous sets of chromosomes

38. cell reproduction
39. egg or sperm
40. sequence of events from cell formation to cell division
43. type of tumor that stays at its original site of origin
44. the orientation of homologous pairs of chromosomes
45. a chromosome that does not determine sex
46. cloud of cytoplasmic material with centrioles in animal cells
47. type of reproduction not involving fertilization
48. indentation at the equator of a cell where it will divide
49. production of gene combinations unlike the parent chromosomes

DOWN

2. mitotic stage when the nuclear membrane first breaks up
4. the fertilized egg
7. type of chromosome that determines the sex of a child
8. the spread of cancer cells beyond their original site
9. cancer of blood-forming tissues
10. one of two identical parts of a replicated chromosome
11. an abnormally growing mass of body cells
13. process of fusion of haploid sperm and haploid egg cell
14. having more than two sets of homologous chromosomes in each somatic cell
15. the division of a diploid nucleus into four haploid daughter nuclei
18. type of cell with 46 chromosomes in humans
19. exchange of genetic material between homologous chromosomes
21. the result when paired chromosomes fail to separate
23. type of tumor that migrates away from its site of origin
25. the use of drugs to disrupt the division of cancer cells
29. division of the cytoplasm
33. cells that contain only one chromosome of each homologous pair
34. disease of cells that divide excessively and exhibit bizarre behavior
36. membranous disk containing cell wall material in plants
37. the region where two chromatids are joined
40. site where crossing over has occurred
41. cancer originating in the external or internal coverings of the body
42. mitotic stage when sister chromatids separate

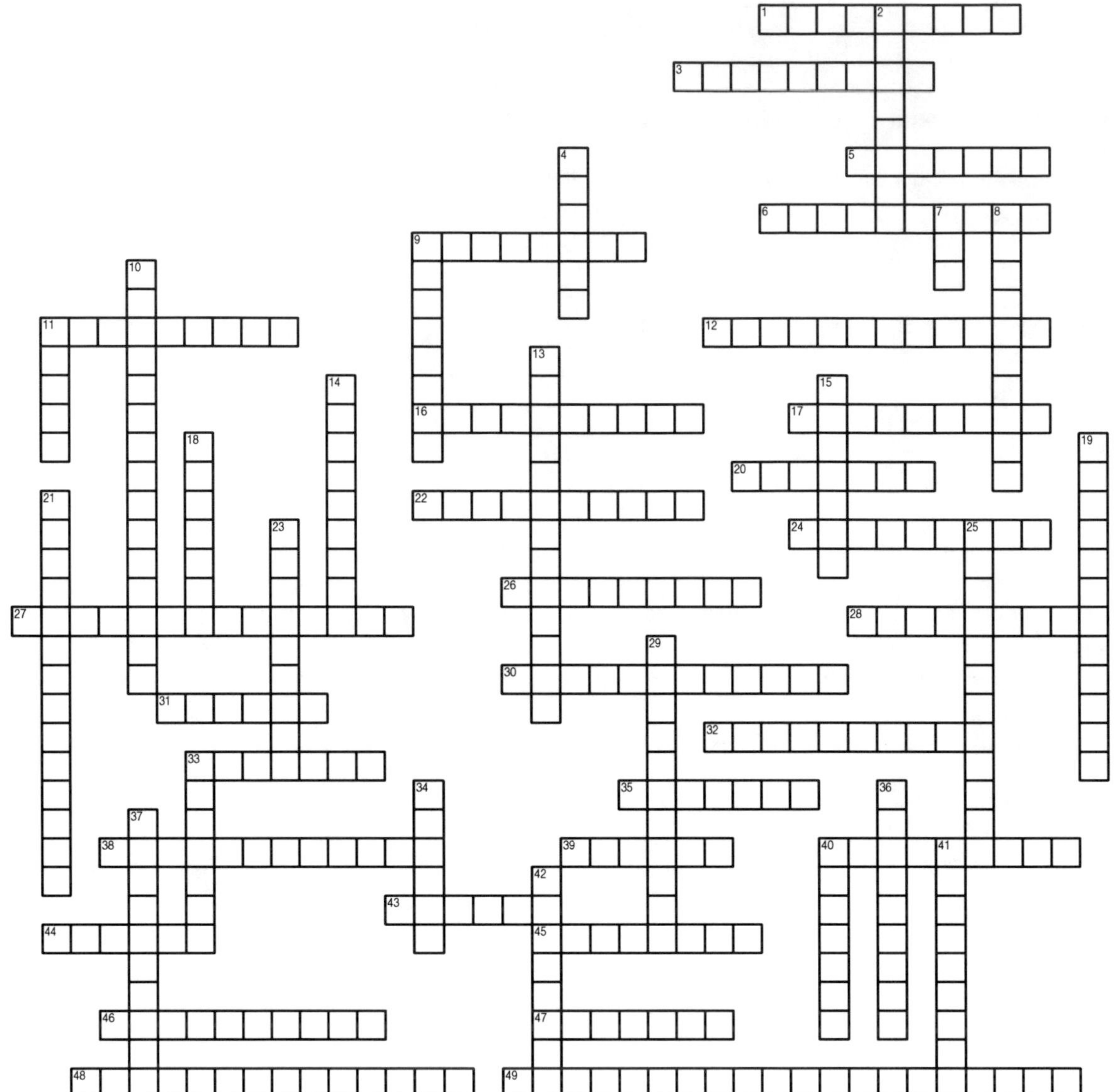

14 Patterns of Inheritance

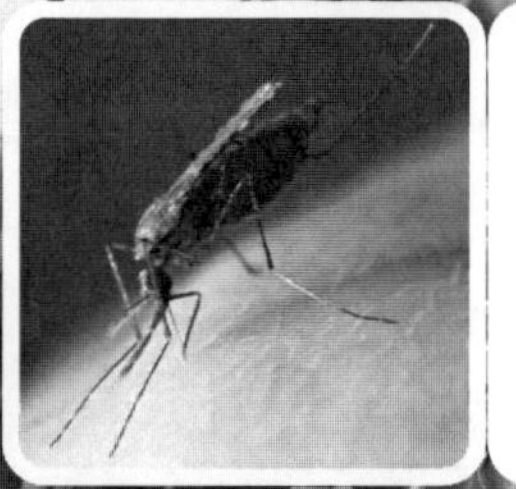

The same genetic defect that causes sickle-cell disease can also protect against malaria.

The first genetics research "lab" was a monk's abbey garden.

Intermarriage caused the disease hemophilia to be inherited by many members of Europe's royal families.

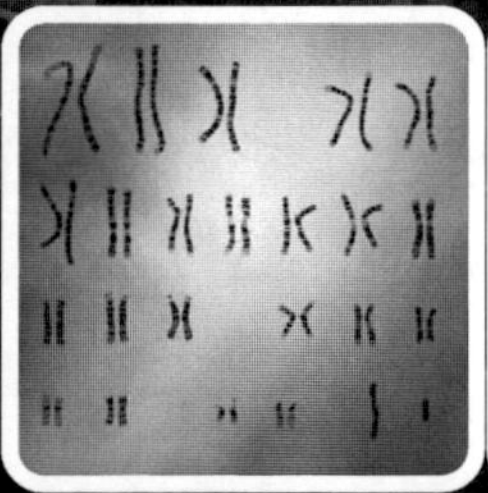

In some isolated communities, 1% of boys are born with a genetic defect that causes Duchenne muscular dystrophy.

LOOKING AHEAD

http://www.pearsoncustom.com/devry/mycbp

Study Goals

- Have you ever wondered how your sex was determined, why people have different skin colors, and how diseases such as hemophilia and sickle-cell disease are inherited? This chapter addresses some of the most interesting questions and relevant information in all of your biological studies!
- This chapter includes many examples of different types of inheritance. To help you organize these definitions, Table 14.2 provides space for you to define and describe key terms and phrases related to inheritance.
- If you have not recently studied Chapter 13, you will need to review the process of meiosis to best understand the Chapter 14 section titled "The Chromosomal Basis of Inheritance."

Chapter Review

Concept Map

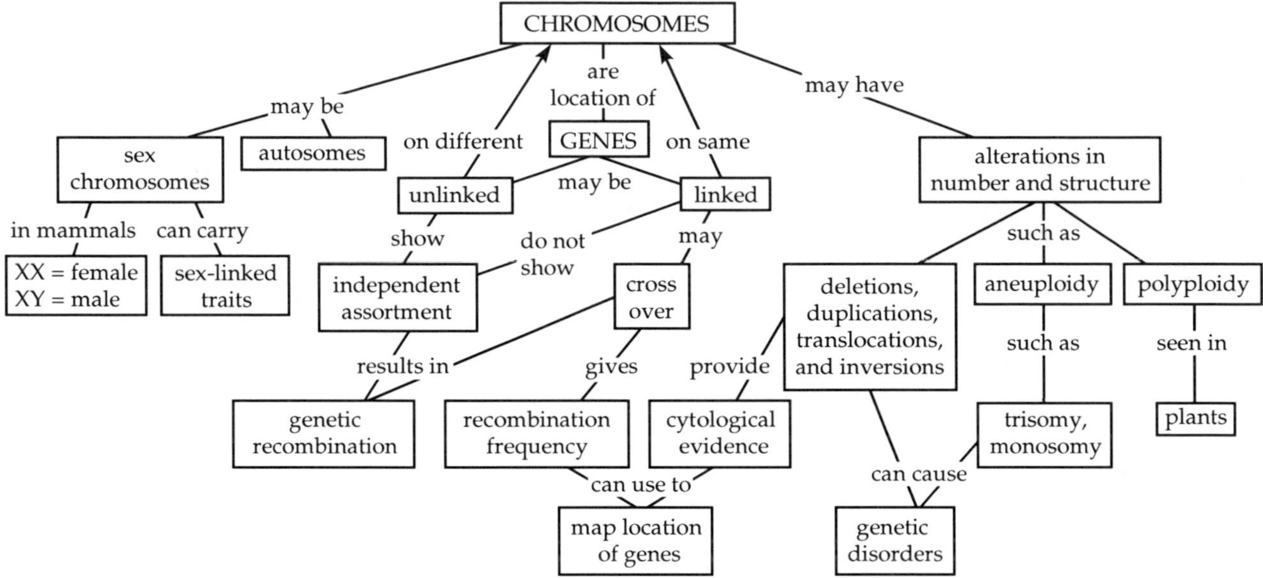

Chapter Concept Review

Heritable Variation and Patterns of Inheritance

- Gregor Mendel was the first to study genetics, the science of heredity, by analyzing patterns of inheritance. In his 1866 paper, he emphasized that heritable factors (genes) retain permanent identities.
- **In an Abbey Garden** Mendel started with true-breeding varieties of pea plants representing two alternative variants of a hereditary characteristic, such as flower color. He then crossed the different varieties and traced the inheritance of traits from generation to generation.
- **Mendel's Law of Segregation** Pairs of alleles separate during gamete formation; fertilization restores the pairs.

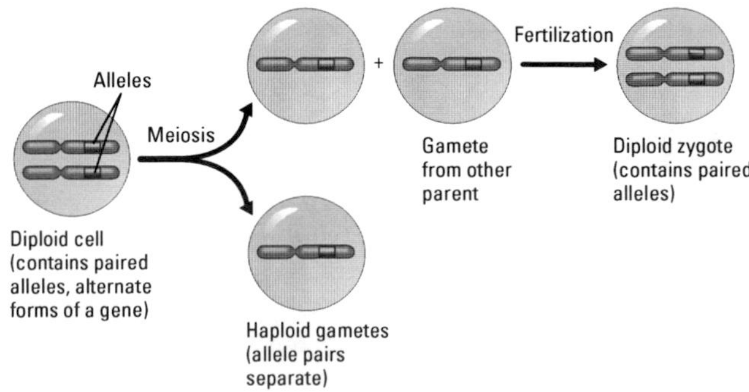

If an individual's genotype (genetic makeup) has two different alleles for a gene and only one influences the organism's phenotype (appearance), that allele is said to be dominant and the other allele recessive. Alleles of a gene reside at the same locus, or position, on homologous chromosomes. Where the allele pair match, the organism is homozygous; where they're different, the organism is heterozygous.

Activity *Monohybrid Cross*

- **Mendel's Law of Independent Assortment** By following two characteristics at once, Mendel found that the alleles of a pair segregate independently of other allele pairs during gamete formation.

Activity *Dihybrid Cross*

Activity *Gregor's Garden*

- **Using a Testcross to Determine an Unknown Genotype**

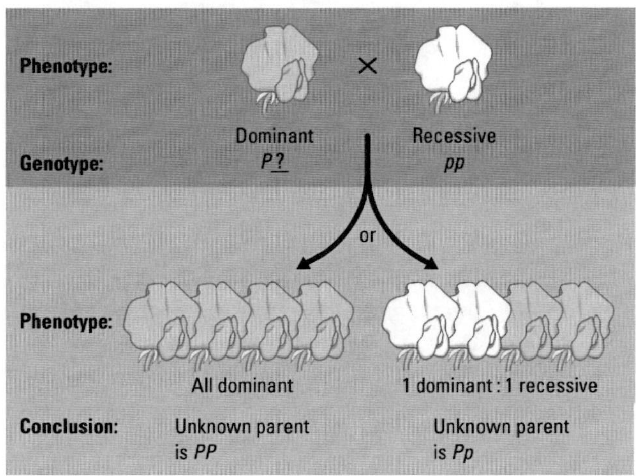

- **The Rules of Probability** Inheritance follows the rules of probability. The chance of inheriting a recessive allele from a heterozygous parent is $\frac{1}{2}$ The chance of inheriting it from both of two heterozygous parents is $\frac{1}{2} \times \frac{1}{2} = \frac{1}{4}$, illustrating the rule of multiplication for calculating the probability of two independent events.
- **Family Pedigrees** The inheritance of many human traits, from freckles to genetic diseases, follows Mendel's laws and the rules of probability. Geneticists use family pedigrees to determine patterns of inheritance and individual genotypes among humans.
- **Human Disorders Controlled by a Single Gene** For traits that vary within a population, the one most commonly found in nature is called the wild type. Many inherited disorders in humans are controlled by a single gene (represented by two alleles). Most such disorders, such as cystic fibrosis, are caused by autosomal recessive alleles. A few, such as Huntington's disease, are caused by dominant alleles.

Variations on Mendel's Laws

- **Incomplete Dominance in Plants and People**

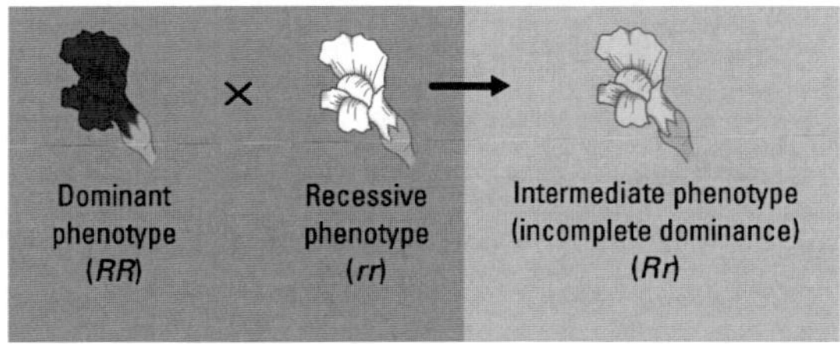

Activity *Incomplete Dominance*

- **ABO Blood Type: An Example of Multiple Alleles and Codominance** Within a population, there are often multiple kinds of alleles for a characteristic, such as the three alleles for the ABO blood groups. The alleles determining the A and B blood factors are codominant; that is, both are expressed in a heterozygote.

- **Pleiotropy and Sickle-Cell Disease**

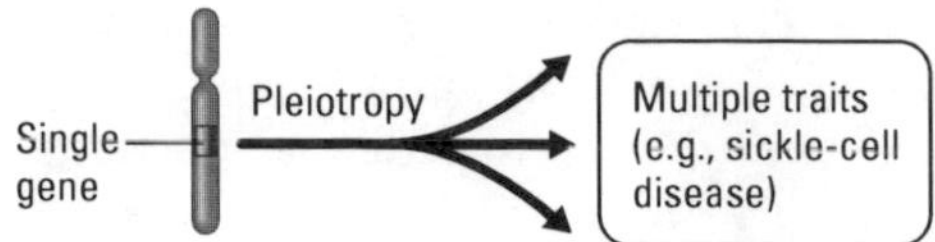

The presence of two copies of the sickle-cell allele at a single gene locus brings about the many symptoms of sickle-cell disease. But having just one copy of the sickle-cell allele may be beneficial because it provides some protection against the disease malaria.

- **Polygenic Inheritance**

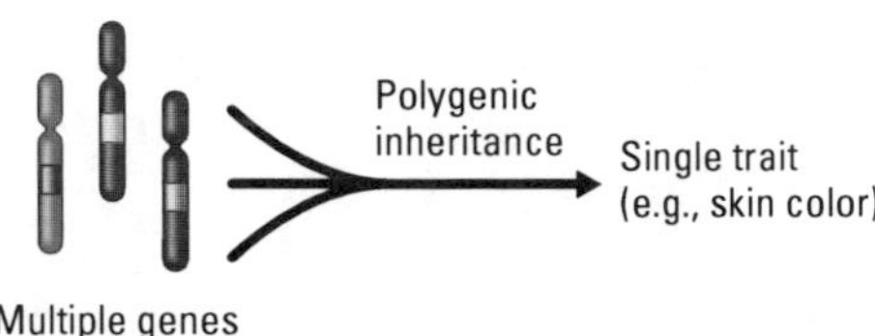

- **The Role of Environment** Many human characteristics result from a combination of genetic and environmental effects, but only genetic influences are biologically heritable.

The Chromosomal Basis of Inheritance
MP3 Tutor *Chromosomal Basis of Inheritance*

- Genes are located on chromosomes, whose behavior during meiosis and fertilization accounts for inheritance patterns (see Figure 14.23).
- **Linked Genes** Certain genes are linked: They tend to be inherited together because they lie close together on the same chromosome.
- **Genetic Recombination: Crossing Over** Crossing over can separate linked alleles, producing gametes with recombinant chromosomes and offspring with recombinant phenotypes.
- **Linkage Maps** The fact that crossing over between linked genes is more likely to occur between genes that are farther apart enables geneticists to map the relative positions of genes on chromosomes.

Activity *Linked Genes and Crossing Over*
Sex Chromosomes and Sex-Linked Genes

- **Sex Determination in Humans and Fruit Flies** In humans, the Y chromosome has a gene that triggers the development of testes; an absence of this gene triggers the development of ovaries.

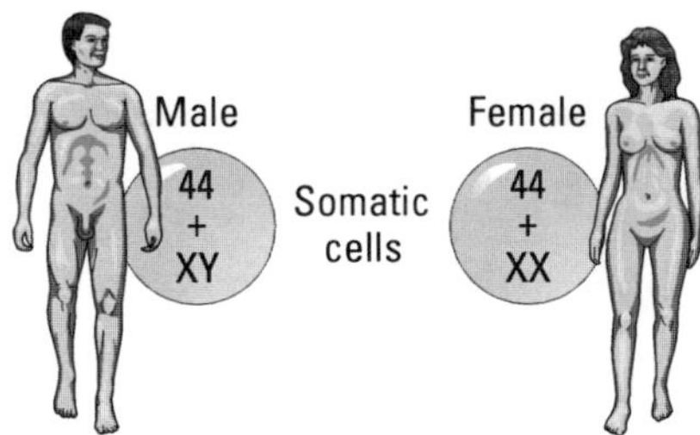

- **Sex-Linked Genes** Genes on the sex chromosomes are said to be sex-linked. In both fruit flies and humans, the X chromosome carries many genes unrelated to sex. Their inheritance pattern reflects the fact that females have two homologous X chromosomes, but males have only one.

Activity *Sex-Linked Genes*
Case Study in the Process of Science *What Can Fruit Flies Reveal about Inheritance?*

- **Sex-Linked Disorders in Humans** Most sex-linked human disorders, such as red-green color blindness and hemophilia, are due to recessive alleles and are seen mostly in males. A male receiving a single sex-linked recessive allele from his mother will have the disorder; a female has to receive the allele from both parents to be affected.

Organizing Tables

The table below shows the results of a cross between plants heterozygous for purple flower color. Write the genotypes of the plants in each square as either (a) homozygous dominant, (b) heterozygous, or (c) homozygous recessive. Next, write the phenotypes of the flowers for each square as either (a) purple (the dominant trait) or (b) white (the recessive trait).

TABLE 14.1

Genotype: *PP*	Genotype: *Pp*
Genotype in words ______________________ Phenotype ____________________________	Genotype in words ______________________ Phenotype ____________________________
Genotype: *pP*	Genotype: *pp*
Genotype in words ______________________ Phenotype ____________________________	Genotype in words ______________________ Phenotype ____________________________

Organizing the key terms related to inheritance: This table should help you organize the definitions of key aspects of inheritance.

TABLE 14.2

Term	**Definition**
Recessive disorders	
Dominant disorders	
Incomplete dominance	
Multiple-allele inheritance	
Codominance	
Pleiotropy	
Polygenic inheritance	
Linked genes	
Sex-linked genes	

Practice Test for Chapter 14

Directions: Identify the *one* best answer for the multiple-choice questions. For true/false questions, determine if the statement is true or false. If false, change the underlined word(s) to make the statement true. Finally, add the correct word(s) to the fill-in-the-blank questions to make the statements true.

Biology and Society: Testing Before Birth

1. When amniocentesis is performed:
A. a piece of placenta is removed.
B. sound waves are used to view the fetus.
C. the fetus is viewed directly through a thin tube inserted into the uterus.
D. amniotic fluid is sampled.

2. True or False? Amniocentesis or chorionic villus sampling could be used to test for Down syndrome.

3. Amniocentesis and chorionic villus sampling require the collection of ___________.

Heritable Variation and Patterns of Inheritance

In an Abbey Garden

4. Crossing members of two different true-breeding varieties of organisms produces:
A. F_1 hybrids.
B. F_2 hybrids.
C. P_1 hybrids.
D. P_2 hybrids.
E. F_1 true breeders.

5. True or False? When Mendel wanted to cross-fertilize his pea plants, he covered the flower with a small bag.

6. Fertilization between members of the F_1 generation produces members of the ___________ generation.

Mendel's Law of Segregation

7. What are the phenotypes of two pea plants with the flower-color genotypes *Pp* and *PP*?
A. Both are purple.
B. Both are white.
C. One is white and the other is purple.
D. A Punnett square is needed to figure this out.

8. If we crossed two pea plants with genotypes *Pp* and *PP* as noted above, we would expect that the phenotypes of the offspring would be:
A. all purple.
B. half purple and half white.
C. three-quarters purple and one-quarter white.
D. three-quarters white and one-quarter purple.
E. all white.

9. Mendel's principle of segregation states that:
A. pairs of alleles stay together during gamete formation and the alleles separate at fertilization.
B. pairs of alleles segregate during gamete formation and the alleles separate at fertilization.
C. pairs of alleles stay together during gamete formation and the alleles pair again at fertilization.
D. pairs of alleles segregate during gamete formation and the alleles pair again at fertilization.

10. True or False? An individual that has two different alleles for a gene is said to be homozygous.

11. The physical location of a gene on a chromosome is that gene's ___________.

Mendel's Law of Independent Assortment

12. If Mendel's principle of independent assortment *did not apply* to the pea shape and color experiment, and the two traits in a dihybrid cross of heterozygous individuals *were* inherited together, what would be the expected phenotypic ratio of the F_2 generation?
A. 9:3:3:1
B. 1:6:1
C. 1:2:1
D. 3:1
E. 1:1

13. True or False? Mendel performed dihybrid crosses involving all seven of his pea characteristics and found 9:3:3:1 ratios in <u>half</u> of them.

14. Mendel's pea shape and color experiment showed that this dihybrid cross was the equivalent of two ___________ crosses occurring simultaneously.

Using a Testcross to Determine an Unknown Genotype

15. A testcross is a mating between:
- **A.** an organism of unknown genotype and a homozygous dominant individual.
- **B.** an organism of unknown genotype and a heterozygous individual.
- **C.** an organism of unknown genotype and a homozygous recessive individual.
- **D.** two heterozygous individuals.
- **E.** a homozygous dominant and a homozygous recessive individual.

16. True or False? Mendel used <u>testcrosses</u> to determine whether he had true-breeding varieties of plants.

17. Testcrosses are used to determine the ___________ of an organism.

The Rules of Probability

18. Using a standard deck of 52 playing cards, the chance of drawing a red card is 1/2 and the chance of drawing a queen is 1/13. To determine the probability of drawing a red queen, we should use the rule of:
- **A.** addition.
- **B.** subtraction.
- **C.** multiplication.
- **D.** division.

19. True or False? If we know the <u>phenotypes</u> of the parents, we can predict the probability for any genotype among the offspring.

Family Pedigrees

20. Consider a trait in which *T* represents the dominant allele and *t* represents the recessive allele. Which of the following genotypes will exhibit the recessive phenotype?
- **A.** *TT*
- **B.** *Tt*
- **C.** *tT*
- **D.** *tt*
- **E.** more than one of the above
- **F.** none of the above

21. Examine the patterns of inheritance of deafness in Figure 14.13 of your text. How many of the seven children of Jonathan and Elizabeth are carriers for the deafness trait?
- **A.** 0
- **B.** 2
- **C.** 5
- **D.** 7

22. True or False? Dominant phenotypes <u>are</u> more common than recessive phenotypes.

23. True or False? A family <u>pedigree</u> is used to assemble information about the occurrence of heritable characteristics in parents and their offspring across several generations.

24. People who are heterozygous with just one copy of an allele for a recessive disorder do not show symptoms of the disorder. They are considered to be ___________ of the disorder.

Human Disorders Controlled by a Single Gene

25. Dominant lethal alleles:
   A. are more common than lethal recessive alleles.
   B. are commonly carried by heterozygotes without affecting them.
   C. are never inherited from a heterozygote.
   D. cause most human genetic disorders.
   E. cause Huntington's disease.

26. True or False? Inbreeding is less likely to produce offspring that are homozygous for a harmful recessive trait.

27. Most people born with recessive disorders are born to parents who are both ___________ or carriers for the recessive allele.

28. The illness called ___________ is a degeneration of the nervous system that usually does not begin until middle age.

29. The most common lethal genetic disease in the United States is ___________.

Variations on Mendel's Laws

Incomplete Dominance in Plants and People

30. If a mating occurs between two parent plants that are both heterozygous for a trait with incomplete dominance, the expected ratio of phenotypes will be:
   A. 1:3.
   B. 1:2:1.
   C. 1:1.
   D. 9:3:3:1.
   E. 2:1.

31. True or False? Mendel's work involved plants that showed incomplete dominance.

32. Humans with the disease ___________ are homozygous or heterozygous for an allele that causes dangerously high cholesterol levels in the blood.

ABO Blood Type: An Example of Multiple Alleles and Codominance

33. What is the expected *phenotypic* ratio of children from parents with the following blood genotypes? $I^A I^A$ and $I^B I^i$?
   A. 1/2 AB and 1/2 A
   B. 1/2 AB and 1/2 B
   C. 1/4 A, 1/2 AB, and 1/4 B
   D. 1/2 AB and 1/2 O
   E. 1/4 B, 1/2 A, and 1/4 O

34. Examine the blood test results in Figure 14.19 of your text. Why aren't any of the blood cells clumped in the test of AB blood?
   A. There must have been a mistake.
   B. AB blood has antibodies to type A and type B carbohydrates.
   C. AB blood does not have antibodies to type A or type B carbohydrates.
   D. AB blood has antibodies to type A carbohydrates.
   E. AB blood has antibodies to type B carbohydrates.

35. True or False? When a trait exhibits codominance, both recessive phenotypes are expressed in heterozygotes with two dominant alleles.

36. People with type ___________ blood show codominance because both alleles are expressed.

Pleiotropy and Sickle-Cell Disease

37. In tropical Africa, resistance to malaria occurs in people who are:
- **A.** homozygous for the sickle-cell allele.
- **B.** heterozygous for the sickle-cell allele.
- **C.** homozygous for the non-sickle-cell allele.
- **D.** born with an extra chromosome containing the non-sickle-cell allele.

38. True or False? About one in every ten African Americans are <u>heterozygotes</u> for the sickle-cell trait.

39. Sickle-cell disease is an example of ___________, when a single gene impacts more than one characteristic.

Polygenic Inheritance

40. In the example of polygenic inheritance described in the text, regarding human skin color, which of the following genotypes would produce the darkest skin?
- **A.** AAbbcc
- **B.** AaBbCc
- **C.** aabbcc
- **D.** AAbBcc
- **E.** AaBbCC

41. True or False? In polygenic inheritance of skin-color, only the <u>dominant</u> alleles contribute to darker skin color.

42. The opposite of pleiotropy, ___________ involves two or more genes affecting a single characteristic.

The Role of Environment

43. If we examine a real human population for the skin-color phenotype, we would see more shades than just seven because:
- **A.** of the effects of environmental factors.
- **B.** some genes fade over time, producing light effects.
- **C.** there appear to be more genes involved in skin tone than have been described.
- **D.** skin color has no genetic component.

44. True or False? Height clearly <u>has</u> a large environmental component.

45. Although organisms result from a combination of genetic and environmental factors, only ___________ factors are passed on to the next generation.

The Chromosomal Basis of Inheritance

Chromosomal Basis of Inheritance

46. Linked genes tend to be inherited together because:
- **A.** they affect the same characteristic.
- **B.** they determine different aspects of the same trait.
- **C.** they have similar structures.
- **D.** they are on the same chromosome.
- **E.** they have the same alleles.

47. Which one of the following processes can result in the separate inheritance of linked genes?
- **A.** polygenic inheritance
- **B.** crossing over
- **C.** incomplete dominance
- **D.** pleiotropy
- **E.** independent assortment

48. The probability of crossover between two linked genes is greatest when the genes are:
- **A.** located on separate chromosomes.
- **B.** close together on the same chromosome.
- **C.** farthest apart on the same chromosome.
- **D.** pleiotropic.
- **E.** dominant.

49. True or False? Linked genes do not follow the typical patterns of inheritance.

50. True or False? Researchers used recombination data to assign genes to relative positions on chromosomes to create linkage maps.

51. The ___________ states that genes are located at specific positions on chromosomes and that chromosomal behavior during meiosis and fertilization accounts for inheritance patterns.

52. Early studies of the relationship between chromosome behavior and inheritance relied upon ___________, often seen flying around overripe fruit.

Sex Chromosomes and Sex-Linked Genes

Sex Determination in Humans and Fruit Flies, Sex-Linked Genes

53. Which one of the following statements about sex chromosomes is *false*?
- **A.** Humans have 44 autosomes and 2 sex chromosomes.
- **B.** In both humans and fruit flies, a male inherits an X and a Y sex chromosome.
- **C.** A gene called SRY, found on the Y chromosome, triggers testis development.
- **D.** Each human gamete contains both sex chromosomes.
- **E.** Most sex-linked genes unrelated to sex determination are found on the X chromosome.

54. True or False? Any gene located on a sex chromosome is a sex-linked gene.

55. The ___________ chromosomes of a human female are XX.

Sex-Linked Disorders in Humans

56. For a sex-linked recessive allele to be expressed a man would have to inherit:
- **A.** only one recessive allele, but a woman would have to inherit two.
- **B.** two recessive alleles, but a woman would have to inherit only one allele.
- **C.** two recessive alleles, just like a woman.
- **D.** only one recessive allele, just like a woman.

57. True or False? Sex-linked human diseases do not occur in females.

58. True or False? Red-green color blindness is a common sex-linked disorder involving one X-linked gene(s).

59. Factors involved in blood clotting are missing in people suffering from ___________.

60. A sex-linked recessive disorder called ___________ is a condition characterized by a progressive weakening and loss of muscle tissue.

Evolution Connection: The Telltale Y Chromosome

61. Which one of the following statements about the human Y chromosome is *false*? The human Y chromosome:
- **A.** is only about 1/3 the size of the X chromosome.
- **B.** carries only 1/100 as many genes as the X chromosome.
- **C.** carries most of the genes that code for female fertility.
- **D.** engages in limited crossing over with the X chromosome during meiosis.
- **E.** may have evolved from an X chromosome about 300 million years ago.

62. True or False? Most of the DNA of the Y chromosome passes intact from father to son.

63. Studies of the ___________ chromosome have been used to trace the evolution of humans.

Exercises in Genetics

Inheritance

1. Suppose there exists a species of small woodland creature in which fur is either spotted or striped. It turns out that fur pattern is determined by a single gene, and that the striped phenotype is dominant to the spotted phenotype. Which of the following must be a homozygote?

2. Suppose, in fact, both the woodland creatures above are homozygotes. Their genotypes are aa and AA. Fill in the blanks below:

Genotype	__________	__________
Phenotype	__________	__________

3. What phenotype would an Aa heterozygote have? Draw it below:

Inheritance—continued

4. Now, you breed together an aa individual with an AA individual. Draw the cross below:

Genotype __________ __________

Phenotype __________ __________

What are the progeny like?

Genotype __________

Phenotype __________

5. Cross together two of the progeny from Problem 4 above. Fill in the boxes below.

Allele received from father

Allele received from mother	A	a
A	Genotype: Phenotype:	Genotype: Phenotype:
a	Genotype: Phenotype:	Genotype: Phenotype:

Word Roots

co = together (codominance: phenotype in which both dominant alleles in a heterozygous individual are expressed)
di = two (dihybrid: a type of cross that mates varieties differing in two characteristics)
geno = offspring (genotype: an organism's genetic makeup)
hemo = blood; **philia** = love (hemophilia: a human genetic disease caused by excessive bleeding following an injury)
hetero = different (heterozygous: when an organism has different alleles for a gene)
homo = alike (homozygous: when an organism has the same alleles for a gene)
hyper = excessive (hypercholesterolemia: a condition of incomplete dominance resulting in elevated blood cholesterol levels)
mono = one (monohybrid: a type of cross between organisms that differ in only one trait)
pheno = appear (phenotype: an organism's physical traits)
pleio = more; **trop** = change (pleiotropy: when a single gene impacts more than one characteristic)
poly = many; **gen** = produce (polygenic: type of inheritance in which two or more genes affect a single trait)

Key Terms

ABO blood groups
achondroplasia
alleles
carrier
chromosome theory of inheritance
codominance
cross
cross-fertilization
dihybrid cross
dominant allele
Duchenne muscular dystrophy
F_1 generation
F_2 generation
genetics
genotype
hemophilia
heterozygous
homozygous
Huntington's disease
hybrid
hypercholesterolemia
inbreeding
incomplete dominance
law of segregation
linkage map
linked genes
loci
Mendel's law of independent assortment
monohybrid cross
pedigree
P generation
phenotype
pleiotropy
polygenic inheritance
Punnett square
recessive allele
recombination frequency
red-green color blindness
rule of multiplication
self-fertilize
sex-linked gene
sickle-cell disease
testcross
true-breeding
wild-type traits

Crossword Puzzle

Use the Key Terms list from this chapter to fill in the crossword puzzle.

ACROSS

5. the way to determine the probability that two independent events will both occur
6. a sex-linked recessive trait that causes excessive bleeding
7. when an organism has the same alleles for a gene
8. mating of an organism of unknown genotype with a homozygous recessive organism
9. type of inheritance in which two or more genes affect a single trait
11. any gene located on a sex chromosome
12. hybridization of F_1 organisms
13. the type of traits most often seen in nature
14. when an organism has different alleles for a gene
17. a form of muscular dystrophy characterized by a progressive weakening and loss of muscle tissue
18. the parental organisms
20. a type of color blindness commonly sex-linked in humans
21. a type of cross mating varieties differing in two characteristics
22. in a heterozygote, the type of allele that has no noticeable effect on the phenotype
23. the science of heredity
24. when a single gene impacts more than one characteristic
25. a device for predicting the results of a genetic cross
26. hybrid offspring

28. phenotype in which both dominant alleles in a heterozygous individual are expressed
29. a type of map based on the frequencies of recombinations during crossover
31. a type of cross between organisms that differ in only one trait
32. the three letters representing the three types of human blood alleles
34. the specific locations of genes on chromosomes
35. a type of degenerative disease of the nervous system caused by a dominant allele
36. a hybridization
39. a condition of incomplete dominance resulting in elevated blood cholesterol levels
40. results of a cross of close relatives
41. alternate forms of genes
42. family tree describing the occurrence of heritable characters in parents and offspring
43. type of genes that are located close together on the same chromosome

DOWN

1. production of offspring with inherited trait(s) identical to the parents
2. the percentage of recombinant offspring in a testcross
3. a type of disease characterized by malformed blood cells and other symptoms
4. the genetic makeup of an organism
10. fusion of sperm and egg from different organisms
15. the principle that sperm or eggs carry only one allele for each inherited characteristic
16. an organism's physical traits
19. the law that states that each pair of alleles sorts independently of the other pairs of alleles during gamete production
27. a form of dwarfism caused by a dominant allele
30. type of dominance in which the heterozygote phenotype is intermediate to the homozygous phenotypes
33. in a heterozygote, the type of allele that determines the phenotype
35. the offspring of two different true-breeding varieties
36. the type of theory of inheritance that states that genes are located on specific positions on chromosomes
37. fusion of sperm and egg from the same organism
38. an organism that has one allele for a recessive disorder but shows no symptoms

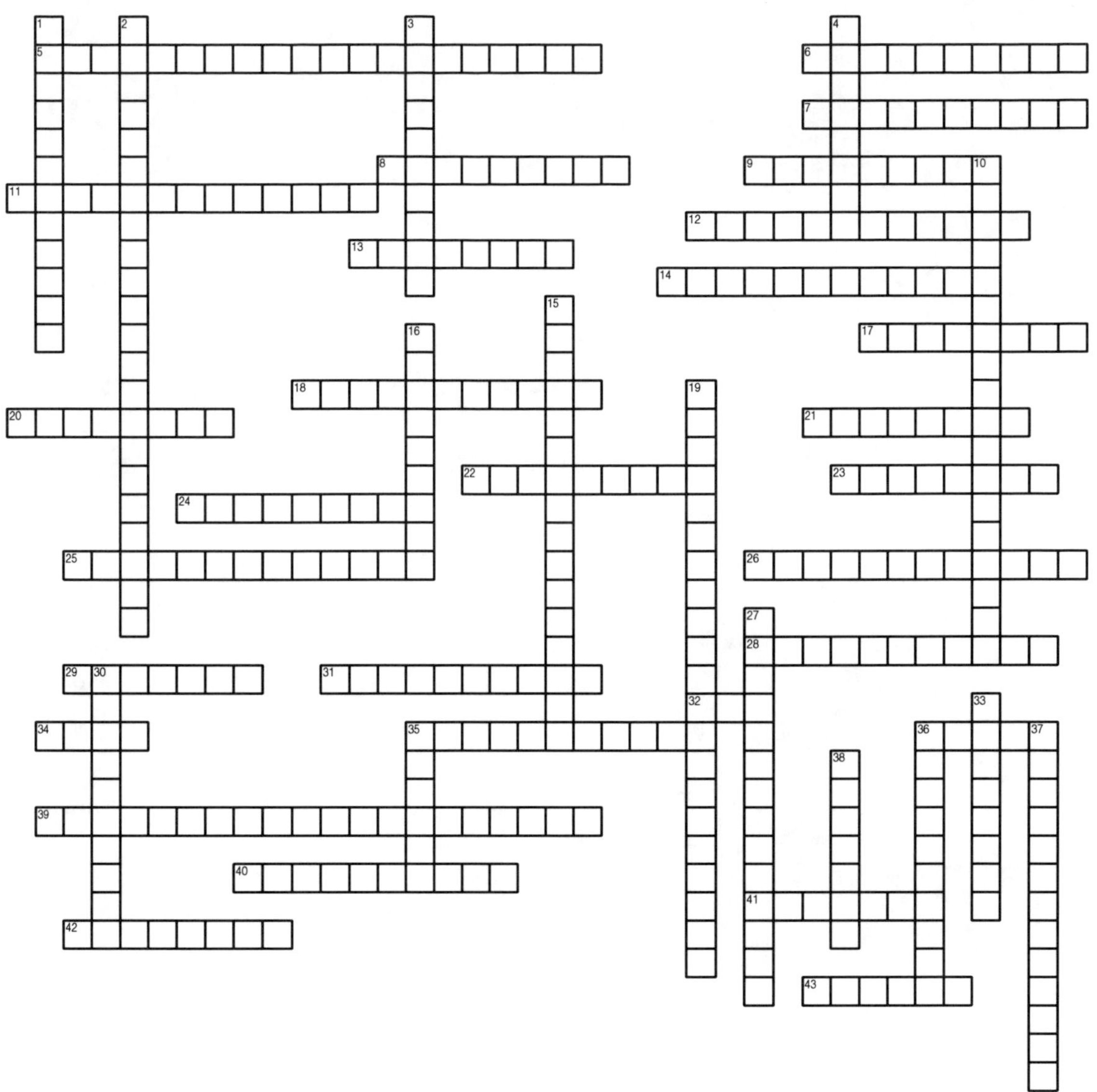

15 The Structure and Function of DNA

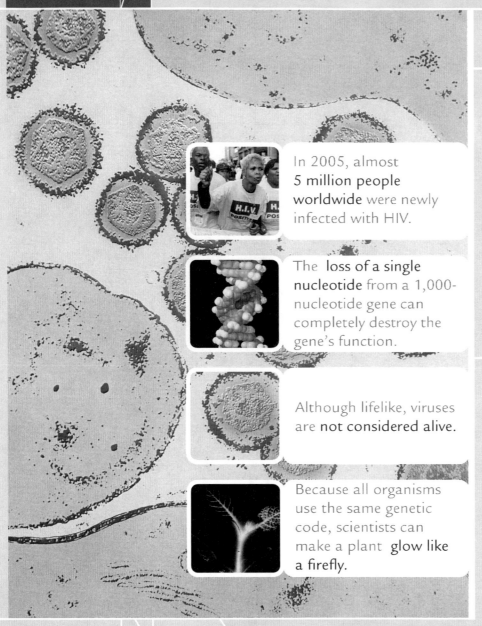

In 2005, almost **5 million people worldwide** were newly infected with HIV.

The **loss of a single nucleotide** from a 1,000-nucleotide gene can completely destroy the gene's function.

Although lifelike, viruses are **not considered alive.**

Because all organisms use the same genetic code, scientists can make a plant **glow like a firefly.**

LOOKING AHEAD

http://www.pearsoncustom.com/devry/mycbp

Chapter Review

Concept Map

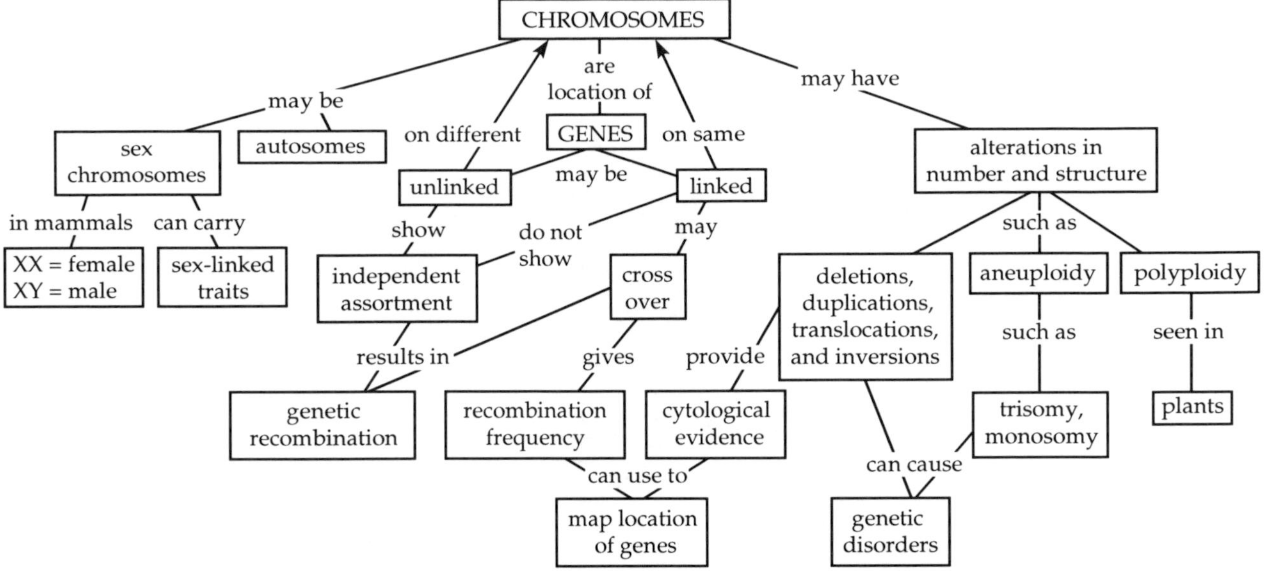

Chapter Concept Review

Biology and Society: Sabotaging HIV

- Molecular biology, the study of heredity at the molecular level, can provide insight into many areas of biology, including the action of anti-HIV drugs.

DNA: Structure and Replication

Activity *The Hershey-Chase Experiment*

- **DNA and RNA Structure**

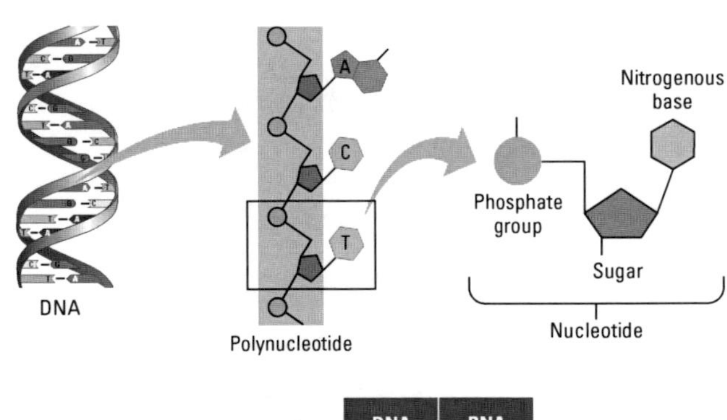

	DNA	RNA
Nitrogenous base	C G A T	C G A U
Sugar	Deoxy-ribose	Ribose
Number of strands	2	1

Activity *DNA and RNA Structure*

- **Watson and Crick's Discovery of the Double Helix** Watson and Crick worked out the three-dimensional structure of DNA: two polynucleotide strands wrapped around each other in a double helix. Hydrogen bonds between bases hold the strands together. Each base pairs with a complementary partner: A with T, and G with C.

Activity *DNA Double Helix*

- **DNA Replication**

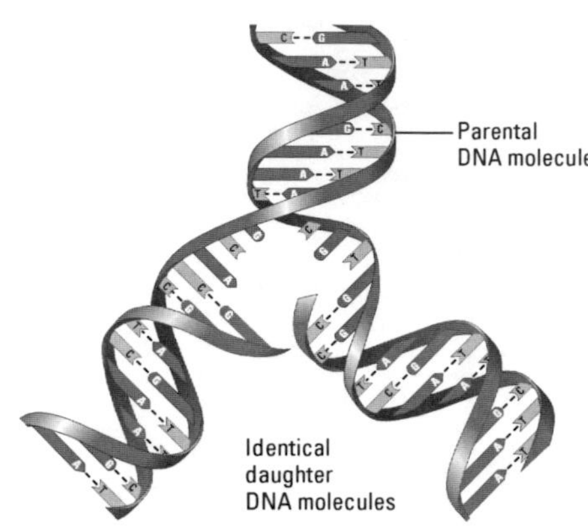

Case Study in the Process of Science *What Is the Correct Model for DNA Replication?*
Activity *DNA Replication*

The Flow of Genetic Information from DNA to RNA to Protein

eTutor *Protein Synthesis*

MP3 Tutor *DNA to RNA to Protein*

- **How an Organism's Genotype Produces Its Phenotype** The information constituting an organism's genotype is carried in the sequence of its DNA bases. Studies of inherited metabolic defects first suggested that phenotype is expressed through proteins. A particular gene—a linear sequence of many nucleotides—specifies a polypeptide. The DNA of the gene is transcribed into RNA, which is translated into the polypeptide.

Activity *Overview of Protein Synthesis*

Case Study in the Process of Science *How Is a Metabolic Pathway Analyzed?*

- **From Nucleotides to Amino Acids: An Overview** The DNA of a gene is transcribed into RNA using the usual base-pairing rules, except that an A in DNA pairs with U in RNA. In the translation of a genetic message, each triplet of nucleotide bases in the RNA, called a codon, specifies one amino acid in the polypeptide.
- **The Genetic Code** In addition to codons that specify amino acids, the genetic code has one codon that is a start signal and three that are stop signals for translation. The genetic code is redundant: There is more than one codon for most amino acids.
- **Transcription: From DNA to RNA** In transcription, RNA polymerase binds to the promoter of a gene, opens the DNA double helix there, and catalyzes the synthesis of an RNA molecule using one DNA strand as a template. As the single-stranded RNA transcript peels away from the gene, the DNA strands rejoin.
- **The Processing of Eukaryotic RNA** The RNA transcribed from a eukaryotic gene is processed before leaving the nucleus to serve as messenger RNA (mRNA). Introns are spliced out, and a cap and tail are added.

Activity *Transcription and RNA Processing*

- **Translation: The Players**

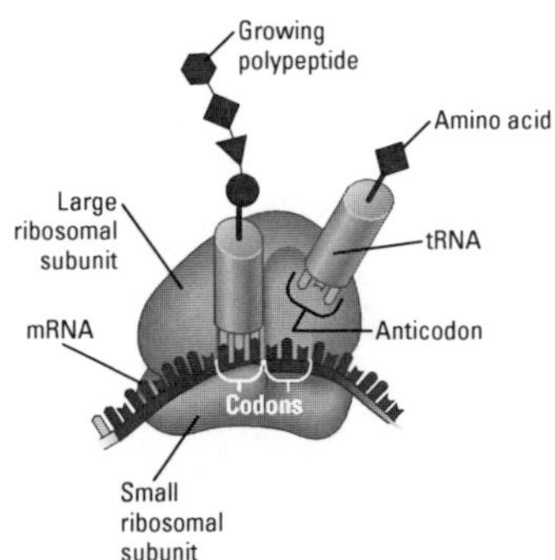

- **Translation: The Process** In initiation, a ribosome assembles with the mRNA and the initiator tRNA bearing the first amino acid. One by one, the codons of the mRNA are recognized by tRNAs bearing succeeding amino acids. The ribosome bonds the amino acids together. With each addition, the mRNA translocates by one codon through the ribosome. When a stop codon is reached, the completed polypeptide is released.

Activity *Translation*

- **Review: DNA → RNA → Protein** Figure 15.20 summarizes transcription, RNA processing, and translation. The sequence of codons in DNA, via the sequence of codons in mRNA, spells out the primary structure of a polypeptide.
- **Mutations** Mutations are changes in the DNA base sequence, caused by errors in DNA replication or by mutagens. Substituting, inserting, or deleting nucleotides in a gene has varying effects on the polypeptide and organism.

Case Study in the Process of Science *How Do You Diagnose a Genetic Disorder?*

Viruses: Genes in Packages

Activity *Simplified Reproductive Cycle of a Virus*

- Viruses can be regarded as genes packaged in protein.
- **Bacteriophages** When phage DNA enters a lytic cycle inside a bacterium, it is replicated, transcribed, and translated. The new viral DNA and protein molecules then assemble into new phages, which burst from the cell. In the lysogenic cycle, phage DNA inserts into the cell's chromosome and is passed on to generations of daughter cells. Much later, it may initiate phage production.

Activity *Phage Lytic Cycle*

Activity *Phage Lysogenic and Lytic Cycles*

- **Plant Viruses** Viruses that infect plants can be a serious agricultural problem. Most have RNA genomes. They enter plants via breaks in the plant's outer layers.
- **Animal Viruses** Many animal viruses, such as flu viruses, have RNA genomes; others, such as hepatitis viruses, have DNA. Some animal viruses "steal" a bit of cell membrane as a protective envelope. Some, such as the herpesviruses, can remain latent inside cells for long periods.
- **HIV, the AIDS Virus** HIV is a retrovirus. Inside a cell it uses its RNA as a template for making DNA, which is then inserted into a chromosome.

Activity *HIV Reproductive Cycle*

Case Study in the Process of Science *What Causes Infections in AIDS Patients?*

Case Study in the Process of Science *Why Do AIDS Rates Differ across the United States?*

Evolution Connection: Emerging Viruses

- Emerging viruses, ones that have appeared recently, result from mutations, contact between species, and spreading from previously isolated populations.

Organizing Tables

Compare the structure of DNA and mRNA in the table that follows.

TABLE 15.1

	Type of Sugar	Types of Bases	Overall Shape of the Molecule
DNA			
mRNA			

Compare the structures and functions of the different types of RNA molecules in the table below.

TABLE 15.2

	Structure	Function	Location in the Cell
mRNA			
tRNA			
rRNA			

Practice Test for Chapter 15

Directions: Identify the *one* best answer for the multiple-choice questions. For true/false questions, determine if the statement is true or false. If false, change the underlined word(s) to make the statement true. Finally, add the correct word(s) to the fill-in-the-blank questions to make the statements true.

Biology and Society: Sabotaging HIV

1. Which one of the following statements is *false*?
  A. AIDS is one of the most significant health challenges facing the world today.
  B. The letters in AIDS stand for acquired immune deficiency syndrome.
  C. AIDS is spread through the exchange of body fluids.
  D. There is no cure for AIDS.
  E. HIV uses special enzymes to convert its DNA into RNA.

2. A molecule of AZT has a shape very similar to:
  A. ATP, an important molecule in energy transport inside cells.
  B. thymine, one of the four nucleotides that comprise DNA.
  C. water.
  D. ribosomal RNA.
  E. glucose, a common type of sugar found in cells.

3. True or False? AZT prevents the synthesis of HIV <u>RNA</u>.

DNA: Structure and Replication

4. In the 1950s, scientists understood the functions of DNA to be all of the following *except*:
  A. the capacity to *store* genetic information.
  B. the capacity to *create* new genetic information.
  C. the capacity to *copy* genetic information.
  D. the capacity to *pass along* genetic information from generation to generation.

5. True or False? Mendel worked on inheritance patterns <u>without knowing</u> about DNA's role in heredity.

6. By the 1950s, a race was on to understand the __________ of DNA.

DNA and RNA Structure

7. The backbone of DNA and RNA polynucleotides consists of a repeating pattern of:
- **A.** sugar, base, sugar, base.
- **B.** phosphate, base, phosphate, base.
- **C.** sugar, phosphate, sugar, phosphate.
- **D.** sugar, base, phosphate, sugar, base, phosphate.

8. True or False? The "D" in DNA comes from deoxyribose because compared to the sugar in RNA, the sugar in DNA <u>has an extra</u> oxygen atom.

9. The sugars of DNA and RNA are different. DNA has the sugar __________, and RNA has the sugar __________.

10. RNA uses the nitrogenous base __________, which DNA does not use.

11. The two types of bases in DNA are the single-ring bases, __________ and __________, and the double-ring structures, __________ and __________.

12. In DNA and RNA, the polymers are __________ and the monomers are __________.

Watson and Crick's Discovery of the Double Helix

13. The genetic information in a chromosome is encoded:
- **A.** in the nucleotide sequence of the molecule.
- **B.** by the base pairing of the DNA molecule.
- **C.** by the interaction between DNA and the associated histone proteins.
- **D.** in the types of sugars used in the molecule.
- **E.** in the types of chemical bonds formed between the bases forming DNA.

14. The shape of a DNA molecule is most like the shape of:
- **A.** railroad tracks.
- **B.** a spiral staircase.
- **C.** the strings on a tennis racquet.
- **D.** the letter X.

15. If adenine paired with guanine and cytosine paired with thymine in DNA, then:
- **A.** DNA would have irregular widths along its length.
- **B.** the DNA molecule would be much longer.
- **C.** the DNA molecule would be much shorter.
- **D.** the sequential information would be lost.
- **E.** the DNA molecule would be circular.

16. True or False? Watson and Crick discovered that the backbone of DNA was located on the <u>inside</u> of the molecule.

17. If one side of a DNA molecule has the bases CGAT, the opposite side would have the bases __________.

DNA Replication

18. When a DNA molecule is copied, how much of the original DNA is included in the new copy?
- **A.** none
- **B.** 25%
- **C.** 50%
- **D.** 75%
- **E.** 100%

19. DNA replication is most like:
- **A.** picking students to make two baseball teams.
- **B.** two people getting divorced followed by each person remarrying.
- **C.** splitting a large plant into two and planting each half.
- **D.** mixing vinegar and oil to make salad dressing.

20. True or False? The DNA molecule of a eukaryotic chromosome has a single replication origin.

21. Covalent bonds between the nucleotides of a new DNA strand are made by the enzyme ___________.

22. DNA repair is accomplished by the enzyme ___________ and some of the proteins associated with DNA replication.

The Flow of Genetic Information from DNA to RNA to Protein

My Chemistry & Biology Portal

eTutor
Protein Synthesis

How an Organism's Genotype Produces its Phenotype

23. The Beadle and Tatum hypothesis about the function of genes is best stated as one gene– ___________:
- **A.** one protein.
- **B.** one enzyme.
- **C.** one DNA.
- **D.** one polypeptide.
- **E.** one monomer.

24. Which one of the following best represents the flow of genetic information in a cell?
- **A.** RNA → transcription → DNA Æ translation → PROTEIN
- **B.** DNA → transcription → RNA Æ translation → PROTEIN
- **C.** DNA → transcription → PROTEIN → translation → RNA
- **D.** DNA → translation → RNA → transcription → PROTEIN

25. True or False? The molecular basis of the phenotype lies in an organism's DNA.

26. An organism's ___________ is its genetic makeup. An organism's specific traits are its ___________.

27. Cells produce RNA by the process of ___________ and proteins by the process of ___________.

From Nucleotides to Amino Acids: An Overview

28. If a gene consisted of 60 bases, the protein made from the gene would be about:
- **A.** 180 amino acids long.
- **B.** 60 amino acids long.
- **C.** 20 amino acids long.
- **D.** 10 amino acids long.

29. True or False? A DNA molecule may contain thousands of genes.

30. True or False? A gene may consist of thousands of nucleotides.

31. A codon consists of ___________ base(s) in a DNA or RNA molecule.

32. The sequence of nucleotides of the RNA molecule dictates the sequence of ___________ of the polypeptide.

The Genetic Code

33. Of the 64 possible codons:
- **A.** 61 code for an amino acid and 3 are stop codons.
- **B.** all of them code for at least one amino acid.
- **C.** 20 code for 2 amino acids and the rest code for a single amino acid.
- **D.** 2 are start codons, 3 are stop codons, and 59 code for a single amino acid.
- **E.** 1 is a start codon, 1 is a stop codon, and the remaining 62 code for a single amino acid.

34. Examine the sets of codons in Figure 15.11 that code for the same amino acid. How do the codons that all code for the same amino acid compare?
- **A.** The first letter in the codon is most likely to be different.
- **B.** The second letter in the codon is most likely to be different.
- **C.** The third letter in the codon is most likely to be different.
- **D.** The second and third letters in the codon are always the same.
- **E.** The first and third letters in the codon are always the same.

35. True or False? There are <u>gaps</u> between the codons of RNA.

36. True or False? Different codons may code <u>for the same amino acid</u>.

37. The set of rules relating nucleotide sequence to amino acid sequence is the ___________.

Transcription: From DNA to RNA

38. Which one of the following statements about transcription is *false*?
- **A.** In RNA, U, rather than T, pairs with A.
- **B.** The RNA molecule is built one nucleotide at a time.
- **C.** Both DNA strands serve as the template for one RNA.
- **D.** Transcription begins when RNA polymerase attaches to the promoter.
- **E.** As the RNA molecule is produced, it peels away from its DNA template.

39. True or False? The terminator sequence indicates the <u>end</u> of a gene.

40. The ___________ dictates which of the two DNA strands is to be transcribed.

41. The RNA nucleotides are linked by the enzyme ___________.

The Processing of Eukaryotic RNA

42. In eukaryotic cells, RNA transcribed from DNA undergoes processing before leaving the nucleus. In this processing:
- **A.** a cap and tail are added, introns are edited out, and exons are joined together to make mRNA.
- **B.** a cap and tail are removed, introns are edited out, and exons are joined together to make mRNA.
- **C.** a cap and tail are added, exons are edited out, and introns are joined together to make mRNA.
- **D.** a cap is removed, a tail is added, exons are edited out, and introns are joined together to make mRNA.

43. True or False? The cap and tail on an mRNA molecule protects mRNA from cellular enzymes and helps ribosomes recognize RNA as mRNA.

44. RNA splicing involves the removal of ___________ and the joining of ___________ to produce mRNA.

Translation: The Players

45. The actual translation of codons into amino acids is the job of:
- **A.** mRNA.
- **B.** tRNA.
- **C.** rRNA.
- **D.** ribosomes.
- **E.** RNA polymerase.

46. Which one of the following statements about tRNA is *false*?
- **A.** An anticodon recognizes a particular mRNA codon by using base-pairing rules.
- **B.** There is a slightly different version of tRNA for each amino acid.
- **C.** Some parts of the tRNA molecule twists, folds around, and base-pairs with itself.
- **D.** Each tRNA molecule must pick up the appropriate amino acid.
- **E.** A tRNA molecule is made of a double strand of RNA about 800 nucleotides long.

47. A ribosome consists of:
- **A.** one subunit made up of proteins and DNA.
- **B.** two subunits, each made up of tRNA and rRNA.
- **C.** two subunits, each made up of proteins and mRNA.
- **D.** two subunits, each made up of proteins and rRNA.
- **E.** three subunits, each made up of proteins, mRNA, and tRNA.

48. True or False? The part of a tRNA molecule that binds to a codon is a parallel codon.

49. A fully assembled ribosome has a binding site for ___________ on its small subunit and a binding site for ___________ on its large subunit.

Translation: The Process, Review: DNA → RNA → Protein

50. During the initiation stage of translation:
- **A.** a ribosome assembles with the mRNA and the initiator tRNA bearing the first amino acid.
- **B.** additional amino acids are brought in, one at a time, as a polynucleotide forms.
- **C.** the ribosomal subunits form by the combination of rRNA and proteins.
- **D.** the mRNA molecule is edited further, beginning with the removal of the cap and tail.

51. Which one of the following is the correct molecular sequence in the combined processes of transcription and translation.
- **A.** DNA → mRNA → polypeptide → protein
- **B.** mRNA → DNA → polypeptide → protein
- **C.** DNA → polypeptide → mRNA → protein
- **D.** DNA → mRNA → protein → polypeptide
- **E.** mRNA → polypeptide → DNA → protein

52. True or False? An incoming tRNA molecule first binds with the mRNA codon at the A site.

53. After a new amino acid is brought in, the polypeptide leaves the tRNA in the P site and attaches to the ___________ on the tRNA in the A site.

54. Once a new amino acid is added to a polypeptide, the tRNA and mRNA move together from the ___________ site to the ___________ site. This process is known as ___________.

55. Elongation continues until a(n) ___________ reaches the ribosome's A site.

Mutations

56. Compare the two sentences below.

The cat hit the red toy pig.
The caz thi tth ere dto ypi.

The second sentence has been changed in a way that is most like a mutation caused by:

A. a base substitution.
B. a single base deletion.
C. a single base addition.
D. a multiple base deletion.
E. a multiple base addition.

57. In the mutation above, the second sentence no longer reads properly because:

A. of a shift in the reading frame.
B. most of the letters are different.
C. several key letters were lost.
D. of word substitutions.
E. of word deletions.

58. True or False? Alleles frequently differ by only a <u>single</u> base pair.

59. True or False? A base substitution <u>shifts</u> the reading frame.

60. True or False? Mutations are usually <u>beneficial</u>.

61. Any change in the nucleotide sequence of DNA is a(n) ___________.

62. Chemicals and X-rays that cause mutations are called ___________.

Viruses: Genes in Packages

Bacteriophages

63. In the lytic cycle of a bacteriophage:

A. the DNA inserts by genetic recombination into the bacterial chromosome.
B. the phage genes remain inactive.
C. the viral DNA can be passed along through many generations of infected bacteria.
D. the DNA immediately turns the cell into a virus-producing factory.
E. the phage DNA is referred to as a prophage.

64. Which one of the following is most like the way that phage DNA is replicated during a lysogenic cycle?

A. having a friend photocopy your two-page essay while he is photocopying a 50-page article
B. having your friend wash a shirt for you while she washes her clothes
C. asking a friend to help you while you change the tires on your truck
D. inviting friends over to your house to share a good home-cooked meal
E. working with a group of friends to design an experiment for a science class

65. True or False? The <u>lysogenic</u> cycle leads to the lysis of the host bacterial cell.

66. True or False? Once a prophage forms, it <u>cannot</u> leave its chromosome.

67. True or False? Prophage DNA is replicated along with the host cell's DNA.

68. Phage DNA that is incorporated into the bacterial chromosome is referred to as a(n) ___________.

Plant Viruses, Animal Viruses

69. Which one of the following statements about plant viruses is *false*?
- **A.** Most plant viruses discovered to date have RNA instead of DNA as their genetic material.
- **B.** Most plant viruses consist of RNA surrounded by proteins.
- **C.** Plant viruses cannot easily penetrate a healthy plant epidermis.
- **D.** Plants infected with viruses can pass the virus on to their offspring.
- **E.** Unlike for animals, there are many simple cures for viral diseases of plants.

70. Which one of the following does *not* typically occur during the reproductive cycle of an enveloped RNA virus?
- **A.** A protein-coated RNA enters the host cell. Once inside the host cell, the protein coat around the virus is removed.
- **B.** A viral enzyme starts making complementary strands of the viral RNA.
- **C.** Some of the new RNA serves as mRNA for the synthesis of new viral proteins.
- **D.** The new viral proteins assemble around new viral RNA.
- **E.** The new viruses escape by killing the cells.

71. True or False? Antibiotics are effective for the treatment of viral infections.

72. True or False? We usually recover from colds by replacing cells damaged by the virus.

73. The herpes virus DNA may remain as ___________ in the nuclei of certain nerve cells.

74. Most RNA viruses get their outer membranes from the ___________ of the host cell. But DNA viruses, such as the herpes virus, get their outer membranes from the ___________ of the host cell.

HIV, the AIDS Virus

75. Which one of the following statements about HIV is *false*?
- **A.** The virus that is transmitted into cells contains RNA.
- **B.** Once in a host cell, the viral RNA synthesizes more RNA from the host's DNA.
- **C.** Double-stranded DNA produced by reverse transcription is inserted into the host cell's chromosomal DNA as a provirus.
- **D.** The provirus is transcribed and translated into viral proteins.
- **E.** New HIV leaves without killing the host cell.

76. The outer envelope of HIV is derived from the ___________ of a previous host cell.

77. HIV is an example of a(n) ___________, a virus that reproduces by means of a DNA molecule.

78. HIV uses the enzyme ___________ to catalyze reverse transcription.

Evolution Connection: Emerging Viruses

79. RNA viruses mutate more quickly than our DNA because RNA viruses:
- **A.** come into contact with many mutagens.
- **B.** are made of more fragile amino acids.
- **C.** are smaller.
- **D.** lack proofreading steps after replication.
- **E.** have weaker covalent bonds between their bases.

80. True or False? Annual flu vaccines are necessary because last year's flu virus may be mutated enough that you have little immunity against it.

81. True or False? New viral diseases may result when an old virus is introduced to a new host.

82. Viruses that have appeared suddenly or may have only recently come to the attention of science are called ___________ viruses.

Exercises in Genetics

DNA Replication, Transcription, and Translation

1. Let's start with the following strand of DNA:

AT
GC
CG
TA
TA
AT
CG
CG
GC
TA
AT
CG
GC

The strand is unwound, so that the DNA can be replicated. Fill in the nucleotides on the new strands.

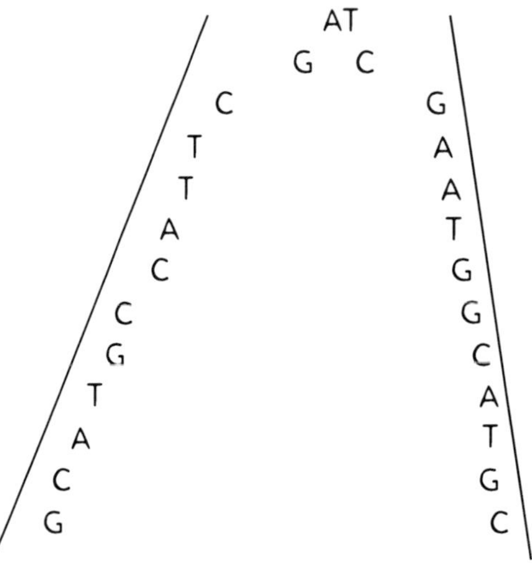

DNA Replication, Transcription, and Translation—*continued*

2. Transcription takes place in the ____________________________.
During transcription, DNA is used to make a molecule of ______________________________________.
If the following length of DNA is being transcribed, what are the bases found on the transcript?

____
ATGGTCATACGTACAATG

3. Translation takes place in the ______ of cells in organelles called _______.
During translation, _____ is used to build a _____.
Divide the transcript from Problem 2 into codons and indicate the sequence of amino acids that is assembled in the ribosome. How many amino acids are coded for by this sequence?
For reference, the genetic code table is shown below:

Second base

First base	U	C	A	G	Third base
U	UUU Phenylalanine	UCU	UAU Tyrosine	UGU Cysteine	U
	UUC (Phe)	UCC Serine	UAC (Tyr)	UGC (Cys)	C
	UUA Leucine	UCA (Ser)	UAA Stop	UGA Stop	A
	UUG (Leu)	UCG	UAG Stop	UGG Tryptophan (Trp)	G
C	CUU	CCU	CAU Histidine	CGU	U
	CUC Leucine	CCC Proline	CAC (His)	CGC Arginine	C
	CUA (Leu)	CCA (Pro)	CAA Glutamine	CGA (Arg)	A
	CUG	CCG	CAG (Gln)	CGG	G
A	AUU	ACU	AAU Asparagine	AGU Serine	U
	AUC Isoleucine	ACC Threonine	AAC (Asn)	AGC (Ser)	C
	AUA (Ile)	ACA (Thr)	AAA Lysine	AGA Arginine	A
	AUG Met or start	ACG	AAG (Lys)	AGG (Arg)	G
G	GUU	GCU	GAU Aspartic	GGU	U
	GUC Valine	GCC Alanine	GAC acid(Asp)	GGC Glycine	C
	GUA (Val)	GCA (Ala)	GAA Glutamic	GGA (Gly)	A
	GUG	GCG	GAG acid (Glu)	GGG	G

Word Roots

muta = change; **gen** = producing (mutagen: a physical or chemical agent that causes mutations)
phage = cat (bacteriophages: viruses that attack bacteria)
poly = many (polynucleotide: a polymer of many nucleotides)
pro = before (prophage: phage DNA inserted into the bacterial chromosome before viral replication)
retro = backward (retrovirus: an RNA virus that reproduces by first transcribing its RNA into DNA then inserting the DNA molecule into a host DNA)
trans = across; **script** = write (transcription: the transfer of genetic information from DNA into an RNA molecule)

Key Terms

adenine (A)
AIDS
bacteriophages
cap
codon
cytosine (C)
DNA
DNA polymerase
double helix
emerging viruses
exons
genetic code
guanine (G)
HIV
introns
lysogenic cycle
lytic cycle
messenger RNA
molecular biology
mutagen
mutation
nucleotide
phages
polynucleotide
prophage
provirus
reading frame
retrovirus
reverse transcriptase
ribosomal RNA (rRNA)
RNA polymerase
RNA splicing
stop codon
sugar-phosphate backbone
tail
terminator
thymine (T)
transcription
transfer RNA (tRNA)
translation
uracil (U)
virus

Crossword Puzzle

Use the Key Terms list from this chapter to fill in the crossword puzzle.

ACROSS

1. the nitrogenous base that pairs with adenine
2. the transfer of genetic information from RNA into a protein
3. a bit of nucleic acid wrapped in a protein coat, these can cause serious disease
4. an RNA virus that reproduces by means of a DNA molecule
7. the selective editing out of introns
9. the transcription enzyme used to link RNA nucleotides
10. the transfer of genetic information from DNA into an RNA molecule
13. the study of heredity at the molecular level
17. the abbreviation for the type of polynucleotide transcribed from a gene
19. the nitrogenous base found only in RNA
20. a triplet that signals for translation to stop
21. a type of viral replication cycle in which viral DNA replication occurs without phage production
23. a physical or chemical agent that causes mutations
24. viral DNA that inserts into a host genome
25. the set of rules relating nucleotide sequence to amino acid sequence
28. the enzyme that makes the covalent bonds during DNA replication
30. a monomer of a nucleic acid
32. the abbreviation for acquired immune deficiency syndrome
33. viruses that attack bacteria
36. phage DNA inserted into the bacterial chromosome
37. the nitrogenous base that pairs with cytosine
38. an enzyme that catalyzes reverse transcription

DOWN

1. a nucleotide sequence that signals the end of a gene
4. the triplet grouping of an mRNA molecule
5. the abbreviation for the type of polynucleotide that helps to form ribosomes
6. a polymer of nucleotides
8. the abbreviation for the type of polynucleotide that serves as a molecular interpreter
11. extra nucleotides added to the end of an RNA transcript
12. a type of viral replication cycle that releases new phages by the death of the host cell
14. the short name for viruses that attack bacteria
15. noncoding stretch of nucleotides in RNA transcripts
16. a change in the nucleotide sequence of DNA
18. the general shape of a DNA molecule
20. the type of structural backbone of polynucleotides
22. the type of virus that has appeared suddenly or recently come to scientific attention
26. coding stretches of nucleotides in RNA transcripts
27. the nitrogenous base that pairs with guanine
29. the three-base word used during translation
31. the abbreviation for the double-stranded nucleic acid stored in the nucleus
32. the nitrogenous base that pairs with thymine
34. extra nucleotides added to the beginning of an RNA transcript
35. the abbreviation for the human immunodeficiency virus

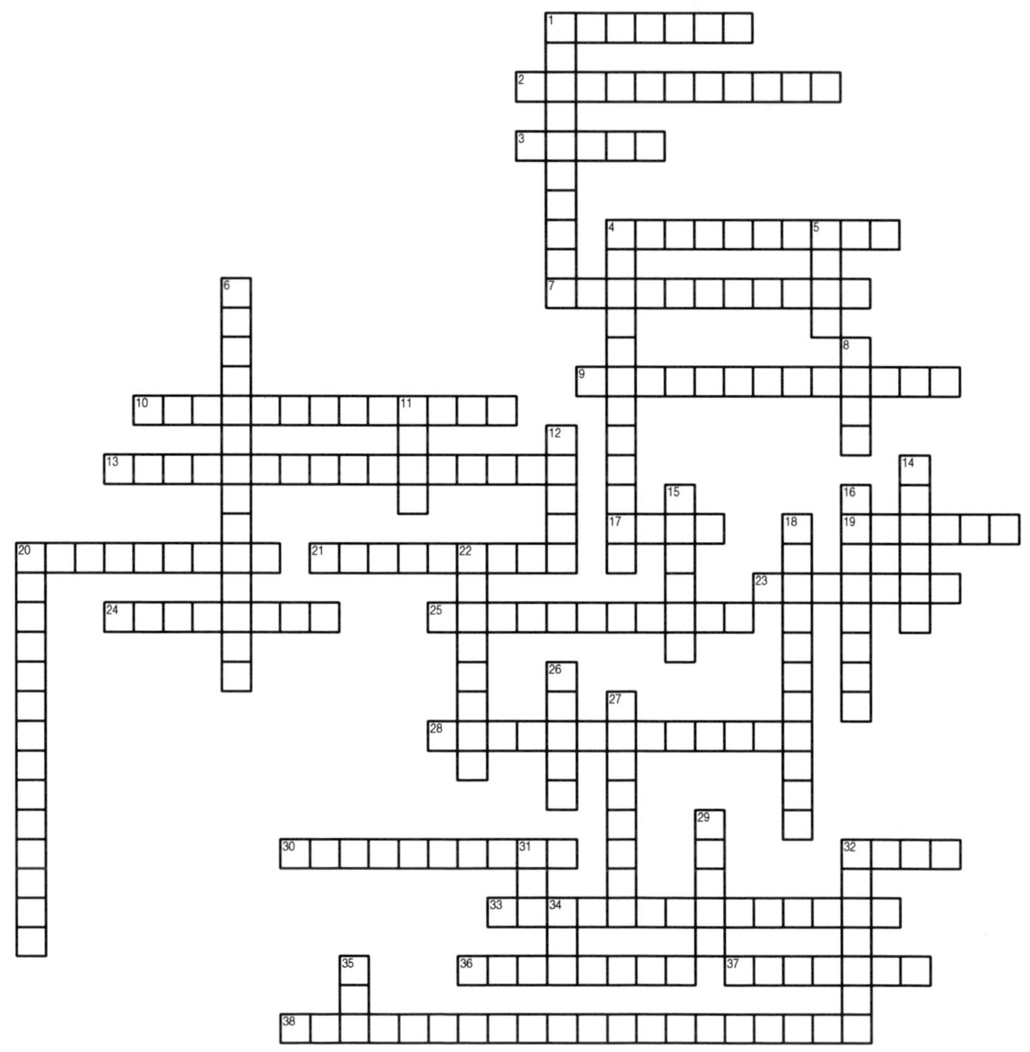

16 How Genes Are Regulated

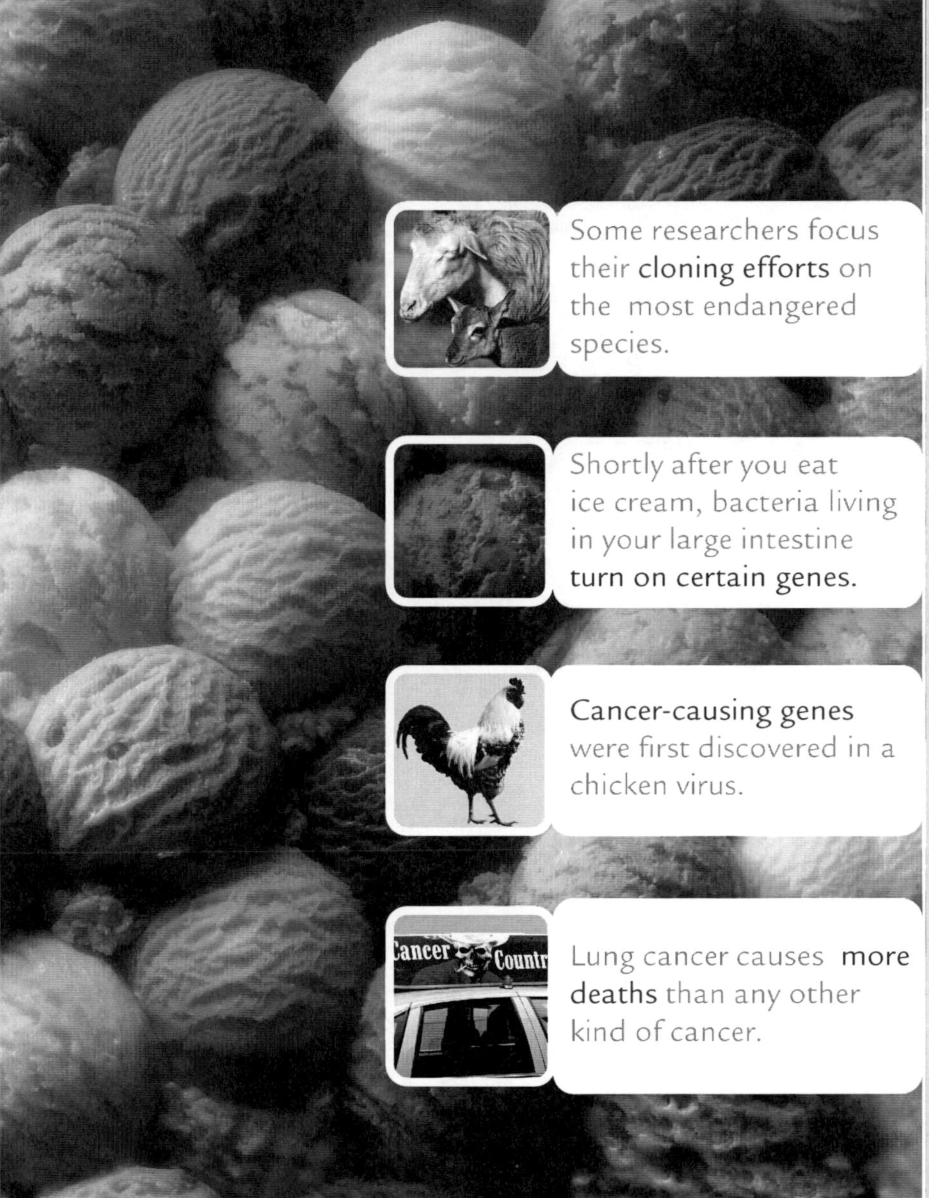
Some researchers focus their cloning efforts on the most endangered species.
Shortly after you eat ice cream, bacteria living in your large intestine turn on certain genes.
Cancer-causing genes were first discovered in a chicken virus.
Cancer
Countr
Lung cancer causes more deaths than any other kind of cancer.

LOOKING AHEAD

C
H
H
H
H
My
Chemistry &
Biology Portal

http://www.pearsoncustom.com/devry/mycbp

Chapter Review

Concept Map

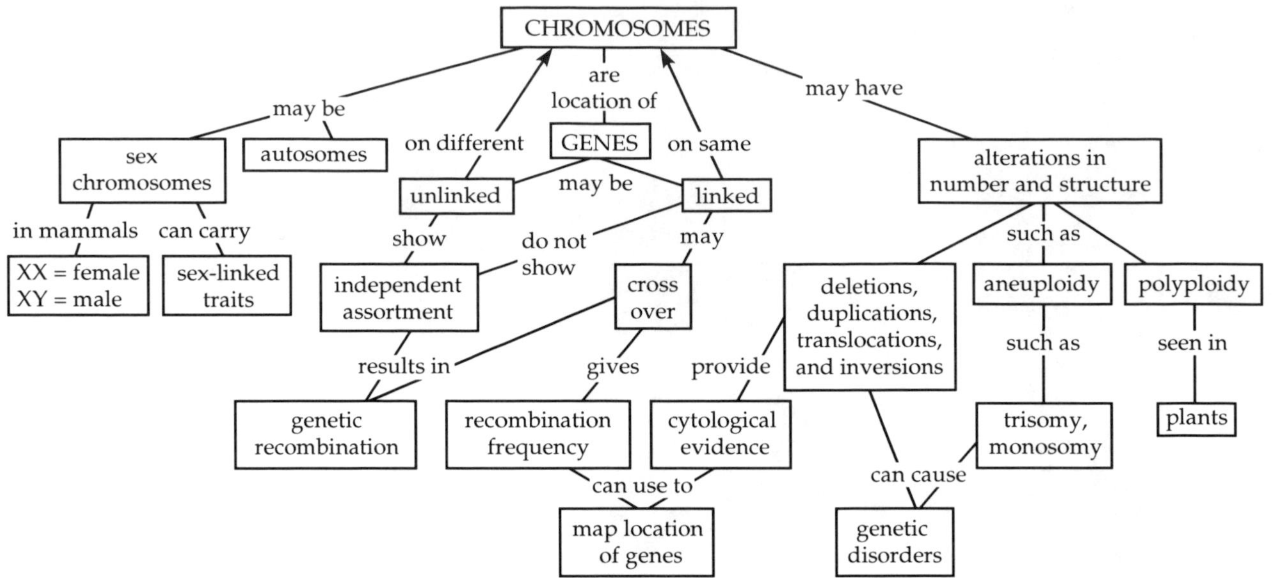

Chapter Concept Review

Biology and Society: Cloning at the Edge of Extinction

- Some scientists focus their efforts on making clones (genetically identical organisms created by asexual reproduction) of endangered species.

How and Why Genes Are Regulated
MP3 Tutor *Control of Gene Expression*

- **Patterns of Gene Expression in Differentiated Cells** The various cell types of a multicellular organism are different because different combinations of genes are turned on and off via gene regulation.
- **Gene Regulation in Bacteria** An operon is a cluster of genes with related functions together with their promoter and other sequences for controlling their transcription. The *lac* operon produces enzymes that break down lactose only when it is present.

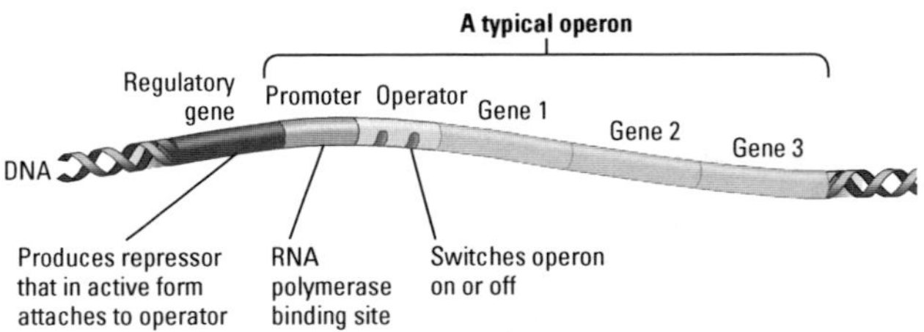

Activity *The* lac *Operon in* E. coli

- **Gene Regulation in Eukaryotic Cells** In the nucleus of eukaryotic cells, there are multiple possible control points in the pathway of gene expression. DNA packing tends to block gene expression, presumably by preventing access of transcription proteins to the DNA. An extreme example is X chromosome inactivation in the cells of female mammals. The most important control point in both eukaryotes and prokaryotes is at gene transcription. A variety of regulatory proteins interact with DNA and with each other to turn the transcription of eukaryotic genes on or off. There are also opportunities for the control of eukaryotic gene expression after transcription, when introns are cut out of the RNA and a cap and tail are added.

- The lifetime of an mRNA molecule helps determine how much protein is made, as do factors involved in translation. Finally, the cell may activate the finished protein in various ways (for instance, by cutting out portions) and later break it down.

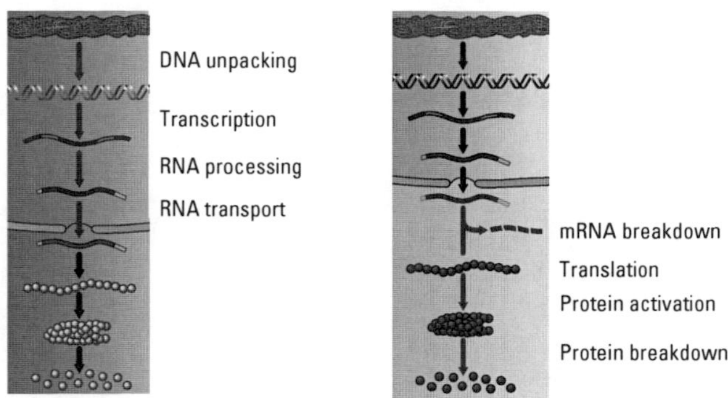

Case Study in the Process of Science *How Do You Design a Gene Expression System?*

Activity *Gene Regulation in Eukaryotes*

Activity *Review: Gene Regulation in Eukaryotes*

- **Cell Signaling** Cell-to-cell signaling is key to the development and functioning of multicellular organisms. Signal transduction pathways convert molecular messages to cell responses, often the transcription of particular genes.

Activity *Signal Transduction Pathway*

- **DNA Microarrays: Visualizing Gene Expression** DNA microarrays can be used to determine which of many genes are turned on in a particular cell type.

Cloning Plants and Animals

- **The Genetic Potential of Cells** Most differentiated cells retain a complete set of genes, so a carrot plant, for example, can be made to grow from a single carrot cell. Under special conditions, animals can also be cloned.
- **Reproductive Cloning of Animals** Nuclear transplantation is a procedure whereby a donor cell nucleus is inserted into a nucleus-free egg. First demonstrated in frogs in the 1950s, reproductive cloning was used in 1997 to clone a sheep from an adult mammary cell and has since been used to create many other cloned animals.

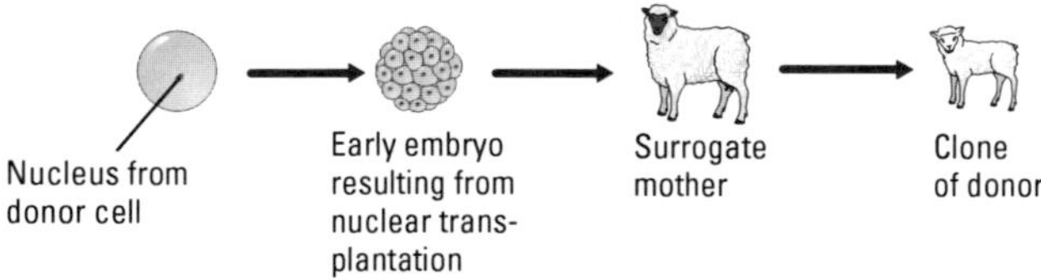

- **Therapeutic Cloning and Stem Cells** The purpose of therapeutic cloning is to produce embryonic stem cells for medical uses. Both embryonic and adult stem cells show promise for future therapeutic uses.

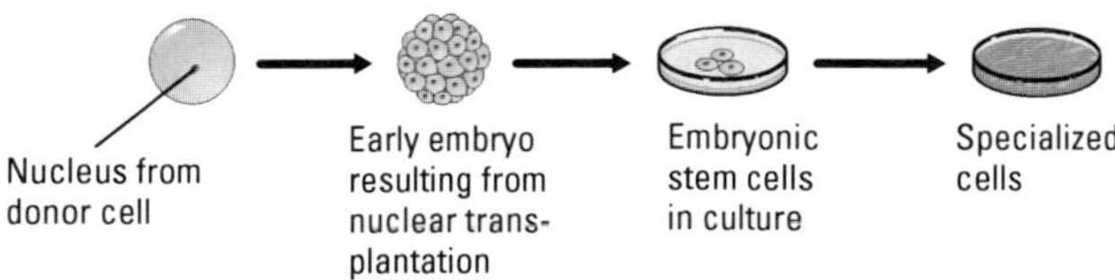

The Genetic Basis of Cancer

- **Genes That Cause Cancer** Cancer cells, which divide uncontrollably, can result from mutations in genes whose protein products regulate the cell cycle.

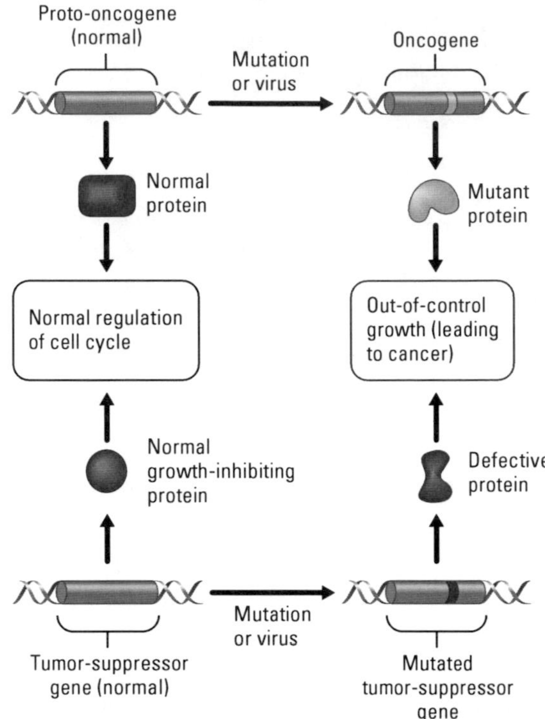

Many proto-oncogenes and tumor-suppressor genes code for proteins active in signal transduction pathways regulating cell division. Mutations of these genes cause malfunction of the pathways. Cancers result from a series of genetic changes in a cell lineage. Researchers have gained insight into the genetic basis of breast cancer by studying families in which a disease-predisposing mutation is inherited.

- **Cancer Risk and Prevention** Reducing exposure to carcinogens (which induce cancer-causing mutations) and other lifestyle choices can help reduce cancer risk.

Activity *Causes of Cancer*

Evolution Connection: Homeotic Genes

- Evidence for the evolutionary importance of gene regulation is apparent in homeotic genes, master genes that regulate groups of other genes that in turn control embryonic development.

Organizing Tables

Using the following table, describe the main functions of each component of the lactose (*lac*) operon and the regulatory genes and repressor proteins that affect the operon. Some of the cells of the table are already filled in to make this task a bit easier.

TABLE 16.1

	Location	Function	What Controls Them
Promoter			
Operator			
Three enzyme genes	All three enzyme genes are located together next to the operator.		
Regulatory gene		Produces the repressor protein.	Nothing regulates it. It is always on!
Repressor protein	The repressor proteins are free-floating in the cytoplasm.		Lactose, when present, binds and prevents the repressor from attaching to the promoter.

Use the following table to compare the genes and process of gene regulation in prokaryotes and eukaryotes. Some of the cells of the table are already filled in to make this task a bit easier.

TABLE 16.2

	Prokaryotes	Eukaryotes
Which group(s) use regulatory proteins that attach to DNA?		
Which group uses genes with their own promoter and control sequences?		
Which are used more often, activators or repressors?		
Are the operators (prokaryotes) or enhancers (eukaryotes) far away or close to the genes they help regulate?		
Which group(s) modify mRNA before it is translated?	Prokaryotes do not usually modify mRNA.	
How long do the mRNA molecules last in the cell?	Prokaryotic mRNA is degraded by enzymes after only a few minutes.	

Practice Test for Chapter 16

Directions: Identify the *one* best answer for the multiple-choice questions. For true/false questions, determine if the statement is true or false. If false, change the underlined word(s) to make the statement true. Finally, add the correct word(s) to the fill-in-the-blank questions to make the statements true.

Biology and Society: Cloning at the Edge of Extinction

1. If adult body cells typically contain the same genetic material, how do different types of cells develop?
- **A.** by turning off and on certain genes
- **B.** through the selective addition of some genes
- **C.** through the selective loss of some genes
- **D.** by joining cells together in unique combinations
- **E.** by mutations

2. True or False? Cloned animals typically <u>have</u> been just as healthy as noncloned animals.

3. The nucleus of an adult body cell contains a complete ___________ capable of directing the production of an entire organism.

How and Why Genes Are Regulated

Patterns of Gene Expression in Differentiated Cells

4. Genes determine the nucleotide sequences of:
- **A.** DNA.
- **B.** proteins.
- **C.** lipids.
- **D.** amino acids.
- **E.** mRNA.

5. The overall process by which genetic information flows from genes to proteins is called:
- **A.** replication.
- **B.** gene expression.
- **C.** gene suppression.
- **D.** transcription.
- **E.** translation.

6. True or False? The genes for specialized proteins are expressed in <u>all</u> cells.

7. Individual cells must undergo ___________; that is, they must become specialized in structure and function.

Gene Regulation in Bacteria

8. In bacteria, gene expression is mainly controlled by:
- **A.** deleting certain genes from chromosomes.
- **B.** moving DNA into special capsules.
- **C.** limiting DNA replication.
- **D.** turning transcription on and off.
- **E.** making extra copies of chromosomes.

9. Examine Figure 16.5 in the text. A gene mutation would produce the greatest effects:
- **A.** when changes are made to the polypeptide in the cytoplasm.
- **B.** during translation.
- **C.** during processing of RNA in the nucleus.
- **D.** during transcription.

10. Which one of the following statements about the *lac* operon is *false*?
A. Enzymes that help absorb and process lactose are produced by *E. coli* when lactose is absent.
B. When RNA polymerase attaches to the promoter, it initiates transcription.
C. The operator helps to determine whether RNA polymerase can attach to the promoter.
D. The repressor protein binds to the operator and blocks the attachment of RNA polymerase to the promoter.
E. When lactose is present, it interferes with the attachment of the *lac* repressor to the promoter by binding to the repressor and changing its shape.

11. The way that lactose works in the *lac* operon is most like:
A. adding milk and sugar to coffee to improve its flavor.
B. a boy distracting his mom while his brother takes some cookies.
C. cooking a meal and serving it to guests.
D. putting an ATM card into an ATM to get some money.
E. advertising a restaurant to attract customers.

12. True or False? RNA polymerase attaches to the <u>operator</u>.

13. A cluster of genes with related functions, along with the control sequences, is called a(n) ___________.

Gene Regulation in Eukaryotic Cells

14. The extra X chromosome in human females:
A. is expressed at about the same level as the other X chromosome.
B. is eliminated from the cell early in embryonic development.
C. is highly compacted and inactivated.
D. is less folded and more frequently expressed.

15. Eukaryotes usually:
A. have operons.
B. have a promoter and other control sequences for each gene.
C. have regulatory proteins that bind to DNA.
D. have more repressor genes than activators.

16. The process in Figure 16.8 is most like:
A. baking a pie and a cake and cutting them up to serve to guests.
B. clipping news and sports articles out of newspapers to make two scrap books.
C. sorting out beads to make two different necklaces.
D. editing 8 hours of film different ways to produce different movies.

17. In eukaryotes, the most important stage for regulating gene expression is the:
A. unpacking of chromosomal DNA.
B. breakdown of mRNA.
C. removal of introns from RNA.
D. initiation of transcription.
E. transport of mRNA from the nucleus to the cytoplasm.

18. Which one of the following is *not* a mechanism used to regulate gene expression after eukaryotic mRNA is transported to the cytoplasm?
A. The mRNA molecule is typically broken down within hours to weeks.
B. Different mRNA molecules combine in the cytoplasm to form new mRNA molecules.
C. Proteins in the cytoplasm regulate translation.
D. Proteins are edited after translation.
E. Some final protein products last only a few minutes or hours.

19. True or False? DNA packing tends to <u>promote</u> gene expression.

20. True or False? Eukaryotic cells have <u>more</u> elaborate mechanisms than bacteria for regulating the expression of their genes.

21. True or False? Both prokaryotes and eukaryotes regulate transcription by using regulatory proteins that bind to <u>mRNA</u>.

22. Eukaryotic genes may be turned on when transcription factors bind to DNA sequences called ___________.

23. Repressor proteins may bind to DNA sequences called ___________, inhibiting the start of transcription.

Cell Signaling, DNA Microarrays: Visualizing Gene Expression

24. When using a microarray, a researcher begins by collecting ___________ from a particular type of cell.
- **A.** mRNA
- **B.** DNA
- **C.** proteins
- **D.** lipids
- **E.** ATP

25. True or False? A DNA microarray consists of a glass slide containing thousands of different single-stranded <u>mRNA</u> fragments arranged in a grid.

26. True or False? Cell-to-cell <u>signaling</u> is a key mechanism in development and in the coordination of cellular activities throughout an organism's life.

27. In cell-to-cell signaling, a signal molecule usually acts by binding to a receptor protein in the plasma membrane of the target cell and initiating a(n) ___________ pathway.

28. Researchers can use microarrays to learn what ___________ are active in different tissues.

Cloning Plants and Animals

The Genetic Potential of Cells, Reproductive Cloning of Animals

29. In the process of nuclear transplantation, the nucleus from a donor cell is transplanted into:
- **A.** an egg in which the nucleus has been removed.
- **B.** a normal egg, allowing the two nuclei to fuse.
- **C.** the nucleus of another adult cell.
- **D.** another adult cell in which the nucleus has been removed.
- **E.** a sperm, which is used to fertilize an egg.

30. Reproductive cloning can be used to:
- **A.** produce herds of farm animals with desired traits.
- **B.** restock populations of endangered animals.
- **C.** produce pigs for organ donation that lack a gene that produces a protein that can cause immune system rejection in humans.
- **D.** all of the above.
- **E.** none of the above.

31. True or False? Hundreds or thousands of genetically identical <u>clones</u> can be produced from the cells of a single plant.

32. True or False? The process of cloning shows that differentiation <u>does not</u> involve irreversible changes in the DNA.

33. True or False? Dolly, the first mammal to be cloned, genetically resembled the <u>egg</u> donor.

34. Salamanders are capable of ___________, the regrowth of lost body parts.

35. True or False? Animal cloning was first performed in the <u>1990s</u>.

Therapeutic Cloning and Stem Cells

36. Which one of the following statements is *false*?
- **A.** When grown in laboratory culture, embryonic stem cells can divide indefinitely.
- **B.** Adult stem cells are much more difficult than embryonic stem cells to grow in culture.
- **C.** If the right conditions are used, scientists can induce changes in gene expression that cause differentiation of embryonic stem cells into a particular cell type.
- **D.** In the future, embryos may be created using a cell nucleus from a patient so that ES cells can be harvested and induced to develop into replacement tissues or organs.
- **E.** Embryonic stem cells are partway along the road to differentiation and usually give rise to only a few related types of specialized cells.

37. True or False? <u>Embryonic</u> stem cells generate replacements for nondividing differentiated cells in adults.

38. The purpose of ___________ cloning is to produce embryonic stem cells.

The Genetic Basis of Cancer

Genes That Cause Cancer

39. Which one of the following does *not* typically promote cancer?
- **A.** bacteria transmitting tumor-suppressor genes
- **B.** mutations in proto-oncogenes that code for growth factors
- **C.** the inactivation of tumor-suppressor genes that inhibit cellular growth
- **D.** a mutation that causes the *ras* protein to be hyperactive

40. Cancers usually take a long time to develop because:
- **A.** oncogenes are rare.
- **B.** only old cells can become cancerous.
- **C.** several specific mutations must occur.
- **D.** cancer cells usually grow very slowly.

41. Finding a single cure for all cancer is unlikely because:
- **A.** we've made so little progress in recent years.
- **B.** we just don't understand the genetics of the disease.
- **C.** the rapidly dividing cells cannot be killed.
- **D.** cancer is caused by many different factors.
- **E.** cancer cells migrate throughout the body.

42. True or False? Some viruses carry <u>oncogenes</u>.

43. True or False? For a proto-oncogene to become an oncogene, a cell's <u>RNA</u> must become mutated.

44. True or False? Cancer <u>always</u> results from changes in DNA.

45. True or False? Most cases of breast cancer are <u>caused</u> by inherited mutations.

46. Many proto-oncogenes code for ___________, proteins that stimulate cell division.

Cancer Risk and Prevention

47. The one substance known to cause more types of cancer is:
- **A.** alcohol.
- **B.** asbestos.
- **C.** X-rays.
- **D.** table salt.
- **E.** tobacco.

48. Which one of the following is *not* a cancer risk factor?
- **A.** a diet high in fat
- **B.** a diet high in protein
- **C.** the use of tobacco
- **D.** exposure to ultraviolet light
- **E.** alcohol consumption

49. True or False? People can reduce their risks of developing colon cancer by consuming a diet high in <u>sugar</u>.

50. Cancer-causing compounds called ___________ include ultraviolet light and tobacco smoke.

Evolution Connection: Homeotic Genes

51. Homeoboxes, found in homeotic genes:
- **A.** are types of proto-oncogenes that are a common cause of breast cancer.
- **B.** promote cancer by increasing the rate of cellular division.
- **C.** are characteristic of only mammals and birds.
- **D.** appear to be of recent evolutionary origin, coding for many animal traits that have only recently evolved.
- **E.** are very similar in many diverse organisms, suggesting a common evolutionary heritage.

52. True or False? Homeoboxes containing homeotic genes have <u>different</u> developmental roles in mice and fruit flies.

53. Researchers studying homeotic genes found a common sequence of 180 ___________.

Word Roots

homeo = alike (homeobox: a 180-nucleotide sequence within a homeotic gene)
onkos = tumor (oncogene: a gene that causes cancer)
proto = first (proto-oncogene: a normal gene with the potential to become an oncogene)

Key Terms

activators
adult stem cells
alternative RNA splicing
carcinogens
complementary DNA (cDNA)
cellular differentiation
clones
DNA microarray
embryonic stem cells (ES cells)
enhancers
gene expression
gene regulation
growth factors
homeoboxes
homeotic genes
nuclear transplantation
oncogene
operator
operon
promoter
proto-oncogene
regeneration
repressor
reproductive cloning
silencers
therapeutic cloning
transcription factors
tumor-suppressor genes
X chromosome inactivation

Crossword Puzzle

Use the Key Terms list from this chapter to fill in the crossword puzzle.

ACROSS

3. cancer-causing agent
5. using a somatic cell to make one or more genetically identical individuals
6. a glass slide containing thousands of kinds of single-stranded DNA fragments
7. the overall process by which genetic information flows from genes to proteins
8. a cancer-causing gene
10. a site where the transcription enzyme RNA polymerase attaches and initiates transcription
11. undifferentiated cells in an embryo that undergo unlimited division and produce several different types of cells
13. proteins secreted by certain cells that stimulate other cells to divide
15. DNA sequences where eukaryotic activators bind
16. a DNA molecule made *in vitro* using mRNA as a template and reverse transcriptase
17. the replacement of body parts
18. genetically identical organisms
22. proteins that switch on a gene or group of genes
24. a master control gene that regulates batteries of other genes
25. a cluster of genes with related functions along with a promoter and an operator
26. a 180-nucleotide sequence within a homeotic gene

DOWN

1. eukaryotic gene regulatory proteins
2. a molecule that can turn off transcription
4. a way for an organism to generate more than one polypeptide from a single gene
6. the process of cells becoming specialized in structure and function
9. a type of switch between the promoter and the enzyme genes
12. DNA sequence where eukaryotic repressor proteins bind
13. the turning on and off of genes
14. the process by which one of two X chromosomes is inactivated at random
19. a normal gene with the potential to become an oncogene
20. the type of gene that codes for proteins that normally help prevent uncontrolled cell growth
21. the type of cloning that scientists use to help patients with irreversibly damaged tissues
23. type of adult cell that generates replacements for nondividing differentiated cells

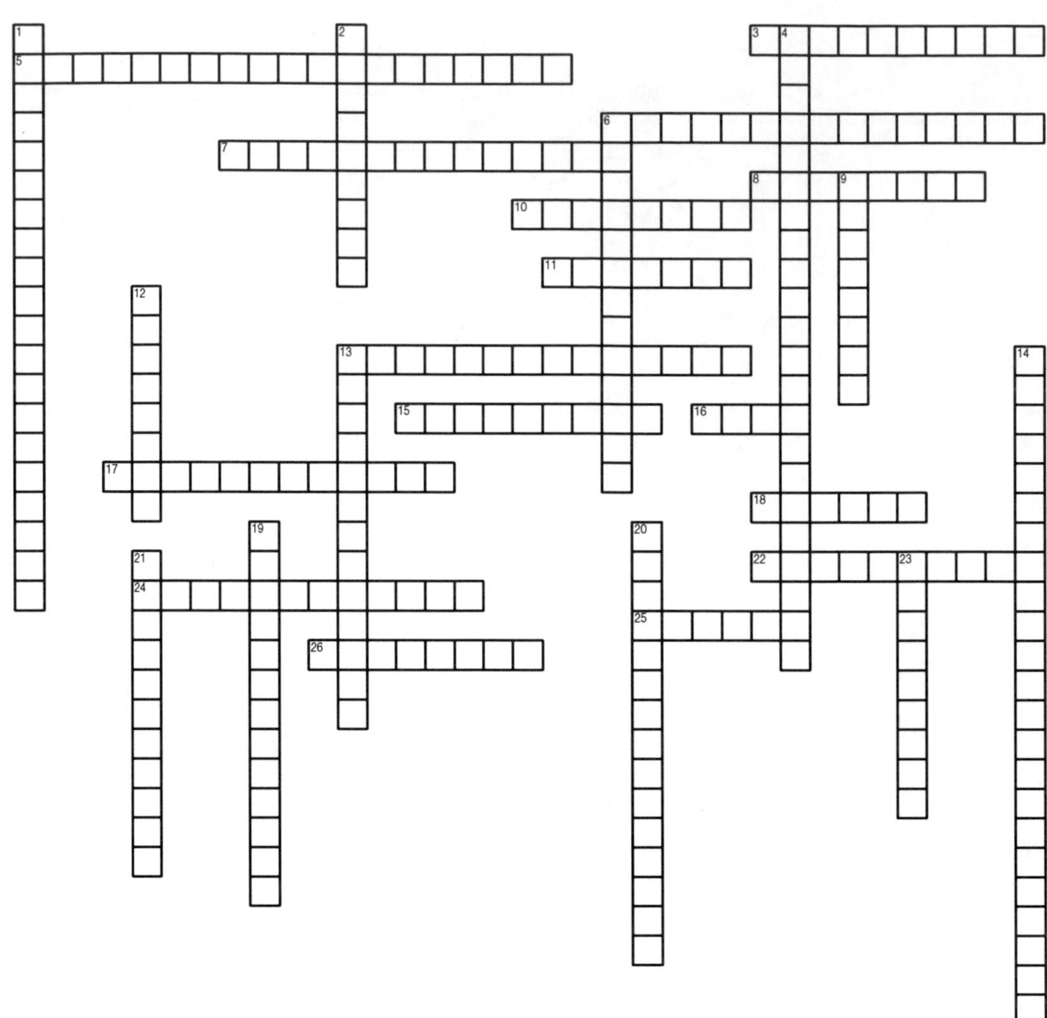

1
2
3
4
5
6
7
8
9
10
11
12
13
14
15
16
17
18
19
20
21
22
23
24
25
26

17 DNA Technology

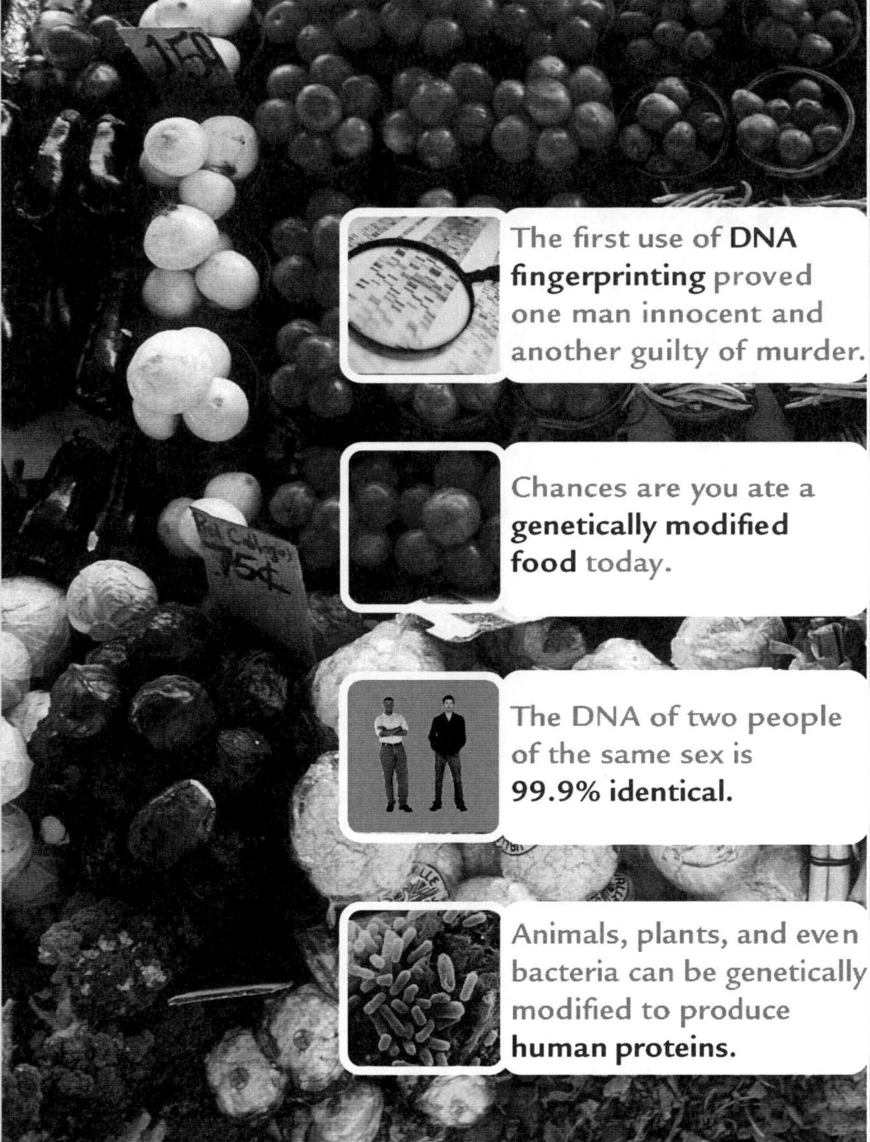

The first use of **DNA fingerprinting** proved one man innocent and another guilty of murder.
Chances are you ate a **genetically modified food** today.
The DNA of two people of the same sex is **99.9% identical.**
Animals, plants, and even bacteria can be genetically modified to produce **human proteins.**

LOOKING AHEAD

My Chemistry & Biology Portal

http://www.pearsoncustom.com/devry/mycbp

Chapter Review

Concept Map

DNA Technology
involves new
has many
techniques and tools
lead back and forth
applications
such as
restriction enzymes
gel electrophoresis
hybridization
polymerase chain reaction
gene cloning
recombinant DNA
DNA sequencing
RFLP analysis
DNA microarray assay
including
basic research
medicine
agriculture
forensic and environmental
as in
combine for
as in
as in
gene function and regulation, evolution, genomics, proteomics, systems biology
Human Genome Project
drugs, hormones, vaccines, diagnosis, gene therapy
productivity of crops and livestock, GM organisms

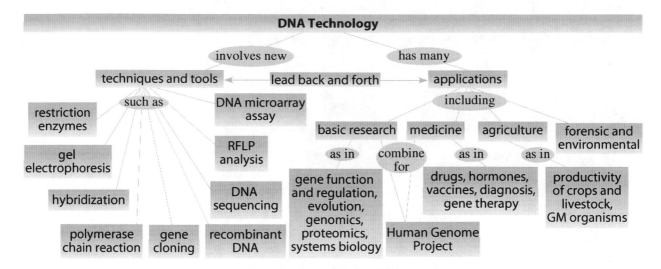

Chapter Concept Review

Biology and Society: Crime Scene Investigations: Murders in a Small Town

- Forensics, the scientific analysis of legal evidence, has been revolutionized by DNA technology.

Recombinant DNA Technology

- Recombinant DNA technology is a set of laboratory procedures for combining DNA from different sources—even different species—into a single DNA molecule.

Activity *Applications of DNA Technology*

- **From Humulin to Genetically Modified Foods** Recombinant DNA techniques have been used to create nonhuman cells that produce human proteins, genetically modified food crops, and transgenic farm animals.

Activity *DNA Technology and Golden Rice*

- **Recombinant DNA Techniques**

Case Study in the Process of Science *How Are Plasmids Introduced into Bacterial Cells?*

Activity *Cloning a Gene in Bacteria*

Activity *Restriction Enzymes*

DNA Fingerprinting and Forensic Science

- DNA fingerprinting is used to determine whether two DNA samples come from the same individual.

Activity *DNA Fingerprinting*

- **Murder, Paternity, and Ancient DNA** DNA fingerprinting can be used to establish innocence or guilt of a criminal suspect, identify victims, determine paternity, and contribute to basic research.
- **DNA Fingerprinting Techniques** Short tandem repeat (STR) analysis compares DNA fragments using PCR and gel electrophoresis.

Activity *Gel Electrophoresis of DNA*

Activity *Analyzing DNA Fragments Using Gel Electrophoresis*

Case Study in the Process of Science *How Can Gel Electrophoresis Be Used to Analyze DNA?*

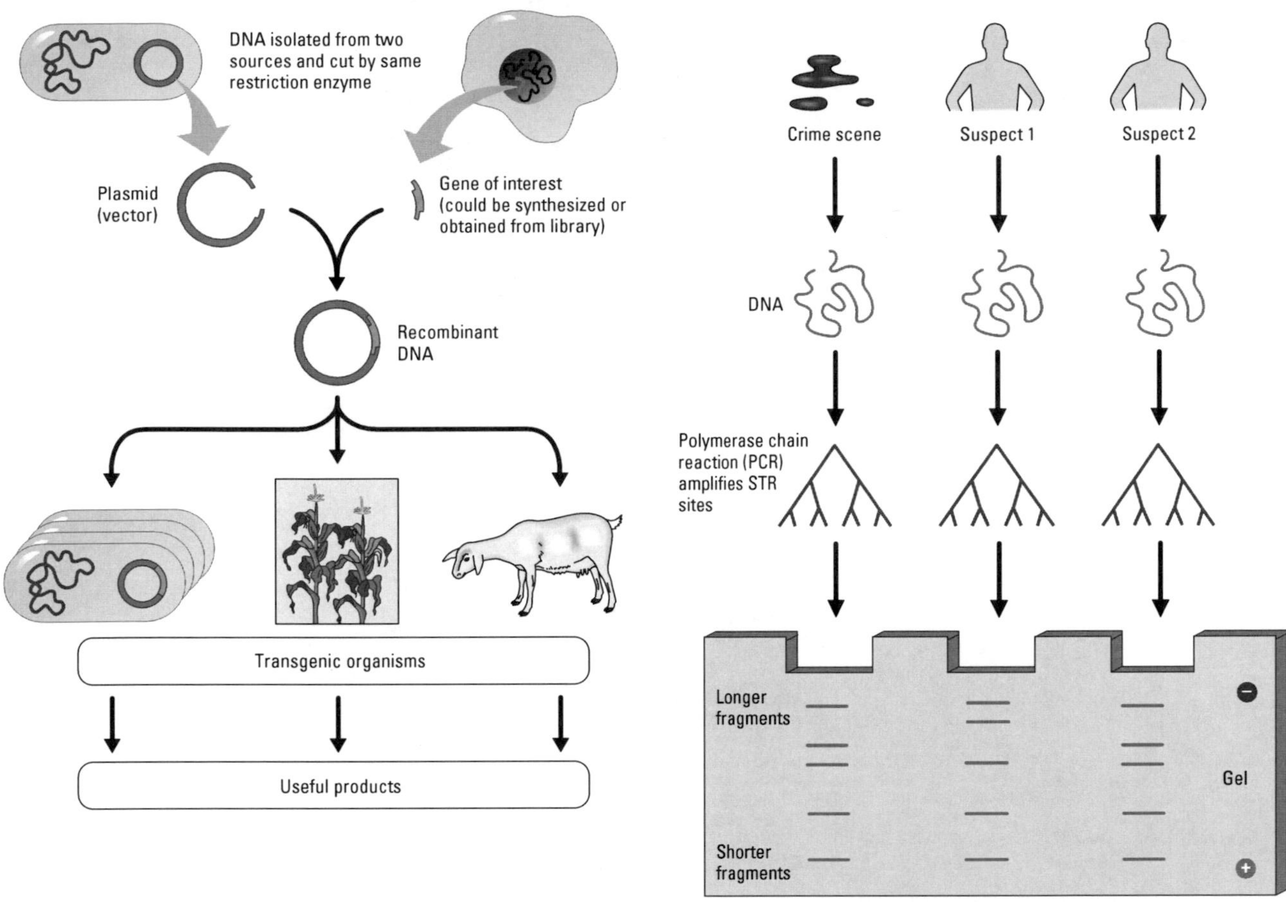

Genomics and Proteomics

- **The Human Genome Project** Started in 1990 and largely completed in 2003, the nucleotide sequence of the human genome is providing a wealth of useful data. The 24 different chromosomes of the human genome contain about 2.9 billion nucleotide pairs and 25,000 genes. The majority of the genome consists of noncoding DNA.

Activity *The Human Genome Project: Human Chromosome 17*

- **Tracking the Anthrax Killer** Comparing genomes can aid criminal investigations and basic research.
- **Genome-Mapping Techniques** The Human Genome Project proceeded through several stages during which preliminary maps were created and refined. The whole-genome shotgun method involves sequencing DNA fragments from an entire genome and reassembling them in a single stage.
- **Proteomics** Success in genomics has given rise to proteomics, the systematic study of the full set of proteins found in organisms.

Human Gene Therapy

- **Treating Severe Combined Immunodeficiency** Gene therapy trials have focused on SCID, an inherited immune disease, with some success and some setbacks.

Safety and Ethical Issues

- **The Controversy over Genetically Modified Foods** The debate about genetically modified crops centers on whether they might harm humans or damage the environment by transferring genes through cross-pollination with other species.

- **Ethical Questions Raised by DNA Technology** We as a society and as individuals must become educated about DNA technologies to address the ethical questions raised by their use.

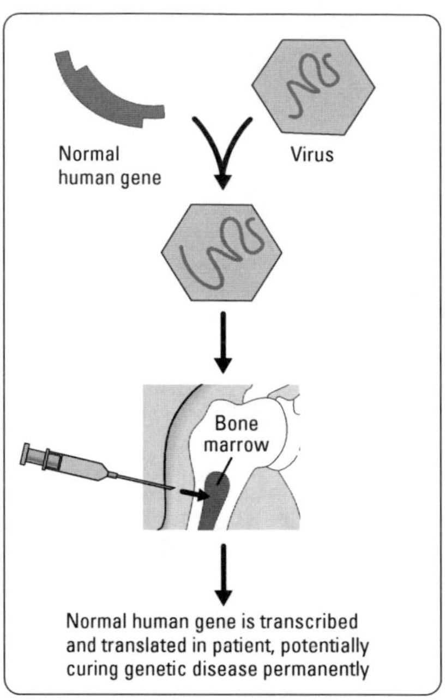
Normal
human gene
Virus
Bone
marrow
Normal human gene is transcribed
and translated in patient, potentially
curing genetic disease permanently

Organizing Tables

Indicate the starting materials and products of each of the procedures described in the text. To help you in this task, the "procedure" cells in the table are already completed.

TABLE 17.1

Process	Starting Materials	Procedure	Product
Cloning genes in a recombinant plasmid		1. Use the restriction enzyme to cleave the plasmid in only one place.	
		2. Use the same restriction enzyme to cleave the DNA into many pieces.	
Making pure genes using reverse transcriptase		1. Use reverse transcriptase to make a pure gene.	
		2. Insert the pure gene into a bacterium.	

Describe the function of each of the enzymes listed in the table below.

TABLE 17.2

Enzyme	Enzyme Function
DNA ligase	
DNA polymerase	
Restriction enzymes	
Reverse transcriptase	

Practice Test for Chapter 17

Directions: Identify the *one* best answer for the multiple-choice questions. For true/false questions, determine if the statement is true or false. If false, change the underlined word(s) to make the statement true. Finally, add the correct word(s) to the fill-in-the-blank questions to make the statements true.

Biology and Society: Crime Scene Investigations: Murders in a Small Town

1. The first legal use of DNA technology revealed that:
- **A.** one man was innocent and another was guilty.
- **B.** two men were guilty of rape.
- **C.** two men were innocent of rape.
- **D.** there are genetic differences between identical twins.
- **E.** DNA fingerprinting is not a reliable technique.

2. True or False? DNA technology is the study and manipulation of <u>protein</u> material.

3. The scientific analysis of evidence for legal investigations is called __________.

Recombinant DNA Technology

4. Recombinant DNA technology combines:
- **A.** genes from different sources.
- **B.** the nucleus of one cell with the cytoplasm of another.
- **C.** all of the genetic material of two cells.
- **D.** proteins from one cell and DNA from another.
- **E.** proteins from two different cells.

5. True or False? A host that carries <u>recombinant DNA</u> is called a transgenic or genetically modified organism.

6. True or False? Biotechnology was first used <u>hundreds</u> of years ago to make bread and wine.

7. Research on *E. coli* led to the development of __________, a set of laboratory techniques for combining genes from different sources into a single DNA molecule.

8. The use of organisms to perform practical tasks defines __________.

From Humulin to Genetically Modified Foods

9. Which one of the following, if any, is *not* produced by recombinant DNA technology?
A. humulin
B. human growth hormone
C. vaccines
D. insect-resistant plants
E. All of the above are produced by recombinant DNA technology.

10. True or False? Today, <u>about half</u> of all American corn crops are genetically modified.

11. Genetic engineering has produced rice that can help prevent __________ deficiency, a disease that often leads to vision impairment and increases susceptibility to disease.

12. Genetic engineering has now produced __________ that synthesize and secrete humulin.

13. Genetic engineering has produced potatoes that may help provide immunity against the disease __________.

14. For many viral diseases, prevention by __________ is the only medical way to fight the disease.

Recombinant DNA Techniques

Sequencing: Number the following seven steps in the order that they occur in the process of cloning genes in recombinant plasmids.

15. _____The recombinant DNA plasmids are mixed with bacteria. The bacteria take up the recombinant plasmids.

16. _____The plasmid and human DNA are cut.

17. _____The transgenic bacteria, with the desired gene, is grown in large tanks, producing large quantities of the desired protein.

18. _____A biologist isolates two kinds of DNA: many copies of a bacterial plasmid to serve as a vector and human DNA containing a gene of interest.

19. _____The bacterial clone with the specific gene of interest is identified.

20. _____The cut DNA is mixed. The human DNA and plasmids join together.

21. _____Each bacterium, with its recombinant plasmids, is allowed to reproduce.

22. When biologists want to customize bacteria to produce a specific protein, the gene for that protein is typically inserted into:
A. the chromosome of another bacterium.
B. the coat of a phage.
C. the DNA of a phage.
D. a plasmid.
E. the chromosome of the bacterium.

23. True or False? The DNA of a plasmid is <u>part of</u> the bacterial chromosome.

24. True or False? A nucleic acid probe <u>can be used</u> when only a part of the nucleotide sequence of a gene is already known.

25. True or False? In a genomic library, each cell within a clone carries <u>a different</u> recombinant plasmid.

26. True or False? A <u>nucleic acid probe</u> can be used to identify a bacterial clone carrying a particular gene of interest amongst the thousands of clones produced by shotgun cloning.

27. A(n) ___________ is a short, single-stranded molecule of radioactively labeled DNA whose nucleotide sequence is complementary to part of the gene or other DNA of interest.

28. The cutting tools for making recombinant DNA are bacterial enzymes called ___________.

29. The entire collection of cloned DNA fragments from a shotgun experiment, in which the starting material is bulk DNA from whole cells, is called a(n) ___________.

30. When plasmids function as DNA carriers, moving genes from one cell to another, they are acting as ___________.

31. The workhorses of modern biotechnology are ___________.

32. A recombinant DNA molecule is produced when DNA pieces are connected into a continuous strand by ___________, which forms covalent bonds between adjacent nucleotides.

DNA Fingerprinting and Forensic Science

Murder, Paternity, and Ancient DNA

33. Which one of the following, if any, is *not* a typical step in the DNA fingerprinting process?
- **A.** DNA samples are collected from different sources.
- **B.** When the genetic material is insufficient to analyze, DNA in the sample is amplified.
- **C.** Proteins are produced from the DNA.
- **D.** The DNA samples are compared to each other.
- **E.** All of the above steps are used in a typical DNA fingerprinting process.

34. True or False? DNA from semen can be compared to DNA <u>from blood</u> to help solve crimes.

35. Since its introduction in 1986, ___________ has become a standard part of law enforcement.

DNA Fingerprinting Techniques

36. Which one of the following techniques is used to sort macromolecules, primarily on the basis of their electric charge and length?
- **A.** gel electrophoresis
- **B.** RFLP analysis
- **C.** recombinant DNA technology
- **D.** gene cloning
- **E.** polymerase chain reaction

37. The ___________ is a technique by which any segment of DNA can be cloned.

38. Repetitive DNA sequences from different individuals can be compared using ___________ analysis.

39. The key to PCR is an unusual ___________ that can withstand the heat needed to separate DNA strands.

40. Much of the DNA between genes is ___________ DNA, which can be used in STR analysis.

Genomics and Proteomics

The Human Genome Project

41. The first targets of genomics research were:
- **A.** algae.
- **B.** human cells.
- **C.** eukaryotic disease-causing microbes.
- **D.** prokaryotic disease-causing microbes.
- **E.** viruses.

42. Which one of the following is *false*?
  A. The human genome carries between 2,000 and 3,000 genes.
  B. The human genome contains approximately 2.9 billion nucleotide pairs.
  C. Much of the DNA of humans consists of introns and repetitive DNA.
  D. The genomes of many multicellular organisms have been sequenced.
  E. About 97% of the entire human genome consists of DNA that does not code for proteins.

43. True or False? The human genome consists of 24 different types of <u>genes</u>.

44. The science of studying whole genomes is called __________.

45. Much of the DNA between genes consists of nucleotide sequences present in many copies, called __________.

Tracking the Anthrax Killer

46. When the genomes of the anthrax spores used in the 2001 bioterrorist attacks were compared, it was determined that the mailed spores:
  A. were not identical.
  B. came from different sources.
  C. were all a harmless veterinary vaccine strain.
  D. were all from the Ames strain.
  E. all came from one particular laboratory.

47. True or False? Comparative genomics has revealed that humans and chimpanzees share <u>about 65%</u> of their DNA.

Genome-Mapping Techniques

48. The stage of the human genome project that uses restriction enzymes to break the DNA of each chromosome into a number of identifiable fragments, which are then cloned, is the:
  A. genetic mapping stage.
  B. DNA-sequencing stage.
  C. physical mapping stage.
  D. whole-genome shotgun method.
  E. assembly stage.

49. Which one of the following did Celera Genomics pioneer as part of the Human Genome Project?
  A. genetic mapping stage
  B. DNA-sequencing stage
  C. physical mapping stage
  D. whole-genome shotgun method
  E. assembly stage

50. True or False? The functions of all human genes <u>have</u> been determined for the human genome.

51. True or False? The human genome project used DNA from <u>one human</u>.

52. Research on lung cancer has revealed that the treatment of some types of cancer may be tailored to the specific __________ of each patient.

Proteomics

53. To better understand the structures and functions of cells and organisms, scientists are also studying proteomics because in organisms:
  A. proteins outnumber genes and proteins carry out cell activities.
  B. proteins outnumber genes and genes carry out cell activities.
  C. genes outnumber proteins and proteins carry out cell activities.
  D. genes outnumber proteins and genes carry out cell activities.

54. True or False? The study of genes and <u>the proteins they encode</u> is helping biologists understand how all of these parts interact within an organism.

55. The systematic study of full protein sets that a genome encodes is called ___________.

Human Gene Therapy

Treating Severe Combined Immunodeficiency

56. Which one of the following statements is *false?*

A. The goal of gene therapy is to replace a mutant version of a gene with a properly functioning one within a living person.
B. It was not until 2000 that the first scientifically strong evidence of effective gene therapy was reported.
C. Safe and effective gene therapy is now widely used in medicine.
D. Severe combined immunodeficiency (SCID) is a fatal inherited disease caused by a single defective gene.

57. True or False? Human gene therapy is a recombinant DNA procedure that alters a living genome by introducing <u>natural</u> genetic material.

58. One of the prime targets for gene therapy are bone ___________ cells that give rise to all the cells of the blood and immune system.

Safety and Ethical Issues

The Controversy over Genetically Modified Foods

59. Which one of the following statements is *false?*

A. The European Union suspended the introduction of new GM crops.
B. GM strains account for a significant percentage of several agricultural crops.
C. In the United States, labeling of GM foods is now being debated but has not yet become law.
D. Lawn and crop grasses commonly exchange genes with wild relatives via pollen transfer.
E. In the United States today, most public concern centers not on genetically modified (GM) foods but on recombinant microbes.

60. True or False? The U.S. National Academy of Sciences released a study finding <u>no scientific evidence</u> that transgenic crops pose any special health or environmental risks.

Ethical Questions Raised by DNA Technology

61. With respect to the ethical issues raised by genetic engineering, the authors argue that:

A. there really isn't much to be concerned about.
B. the issues are so troubling that current research should be stopped.
C. there are serious societal issues that need to be addressed.
D. the scientific community will find answers to these concerns.
E. scientists have not been concerned about these issues.

62. True or False? Genetic engineering of gametes (sperm or ova) and zygotes in humans <u>has not</u> been attempted.

Evolution Connection: Genomes Hold Clues to Evolution

63. Research on the genetics of organisms at all levels of biological organization suggests that:

A. organisms are not as interrelated as we think.
B. life does not have unifying principles.
C. life at all levels is interrelated.
D. the genetics of yeast and humans are fundamentally different systems.
E. although primitive forms of life are similar, they share little with multicellular eukaryotes.

64. True or False? The DNA sequences determined to date do not confirm the evolutionary connections between distantly related organisms.

65. True or False? Some yeast genes can substitute for similar genes in human cells.

Word Roots

liga = tied (DNA ligase: the enzyme that permanently "pastes" together DNA fragments)
telo = an end (telomeres: the repetitive DNA at chromosome ends)

Key Terms

biotechnology
DNA fingerprinting
DNA ligase
DNA technology
forensics
gel electrophoresis
gene cloning
genetic marker
genetically modified (GM) organism
genomic library
genomics
human gene therapy
nucleic acid probe
plasmid
polymerase chain reaction (PCR)
proteomics
recombinant DNA
recombinant DNA technology
repetitive DNA
restriction enzyme
restriction fragments
STR analysis
transgenic organism
vaccine
vector

Crossword Puzzle

Use the Key Terms list from this chapter to fill in the crossword puzzle.

ACROSS

1. another term for a genetically modified organism
3. abbreviation for a technique that quickly and precisely copies a segment of DNA
4. the cutting tool for making recombinant DNA
6. much of the DNA between genes
7. a harmless variant or derivative of a pathogen used to prevent disease
9. the study of full protein sets encoded by genomes
10. the alternation of the genes of a person afflicted with a genetic disease
13. the entire collection of cloned DNA fragments from a shotgun experiment
15. methods for studying and manipulating genetic material
16. the production of multiple copies of a gene
17. pieces of DNA produced by restriction enzymes
18. the scientific analysis of evidence for legal investigations
19. the enzyme that permanently "pastes" together DNA fragments
20. a specific pattern of electrophoresis bands that are of forensic use
21. abbreviation for the type of analysis that compares repetitive DNA sequences
23. the study of whole sets of genes and their interactions
24. a type of technology that combines genes from different sources

DOWN

2. in DNA technology, a labeled single-stranded nucleic acid molecule used to find a specific gene
5. the role of a plasmid when it carries extra genes to another cell
8. a host that carries recombinant DNA
11. any DNA segment that varies from person to person
12. a method for sorting macromolecules primarily on the basis of their size and electrical charge
14. the use of organisms to perform practical tasks
22. a small ring of DNA separate from the chromosome(s)

1
2
3
4
5
6
7
8
9
10
11
12
13
14
15
16
17
18
19
20
21
22
23
24

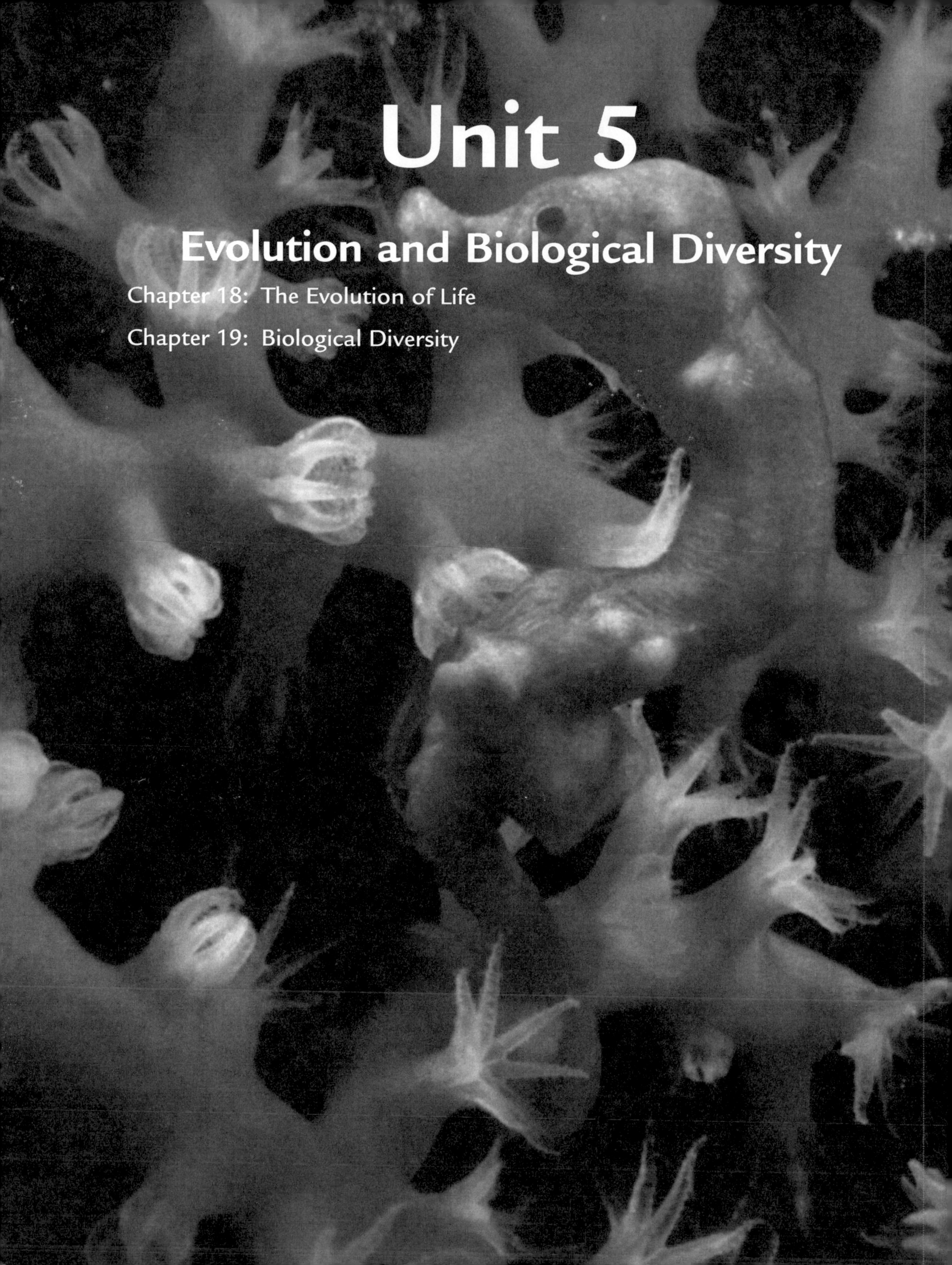

Unit 5

Evolution and Biological Diversity

18 The Evolution of Life

A longnose hawkfish is well hidden in its coral reef habitat off the Philippines.

LOOKING AHEAD

http://www.pearsoncustom.com/devry/mycbp

Study Goals

- Explain how pesticide-resistant insect populations evolve.
- Explain how evolution underlies the unity and diversity that defines modern biology.
- Compare the ideas of Lamarck, Darwin on the ability of species to change.
- Explain how Darwin's voyages on the Beagle influenced the development of his thoughts on evolution.
- Explain how Thomas Malthus' ideas impacted Darwin's thinking.
- Describe the circumstances that led to the presentation of Darwin's and Wallace's ideas in 1858 and the publication of Darwin's work, The Origin of Species.
- Describe Darwin's two main points in The Origin of Species.
- Explain how each of the following provides evidence that evolution occurs: the fossil record, biogeography, comparative anatomy, comparative embryology, and molecular biology.
- Describe Darwin's two main observations that led to the concept of natural selection.
- Explain how natural selection is more a process of editing than a creative mechanism.
- Explain what is meant by the phrases modern synthesis and population genetics. Further, define a population, describe its properties, and explain why a population is the smallest unit of evolution.
- Explain the relative importance of mutation and sexual recombination in the evolution of bacteria, animals, and plants.
- Explain how the Hardy-Weinberg formula can be used to determine the frequency of genotypes in a gene pool. Explain why this formula is a model for genetic equilibrium.
- Distinguish between the following concepts: genetic drift versus gene flow; the founder effect versus bottleneck effect; and directional selection, disruptive selection, and stabilizing selection.
- Explain why sickle-cell anemia is much more common in African Americans than in the general U.S. population.

Chapter Review

Concept map

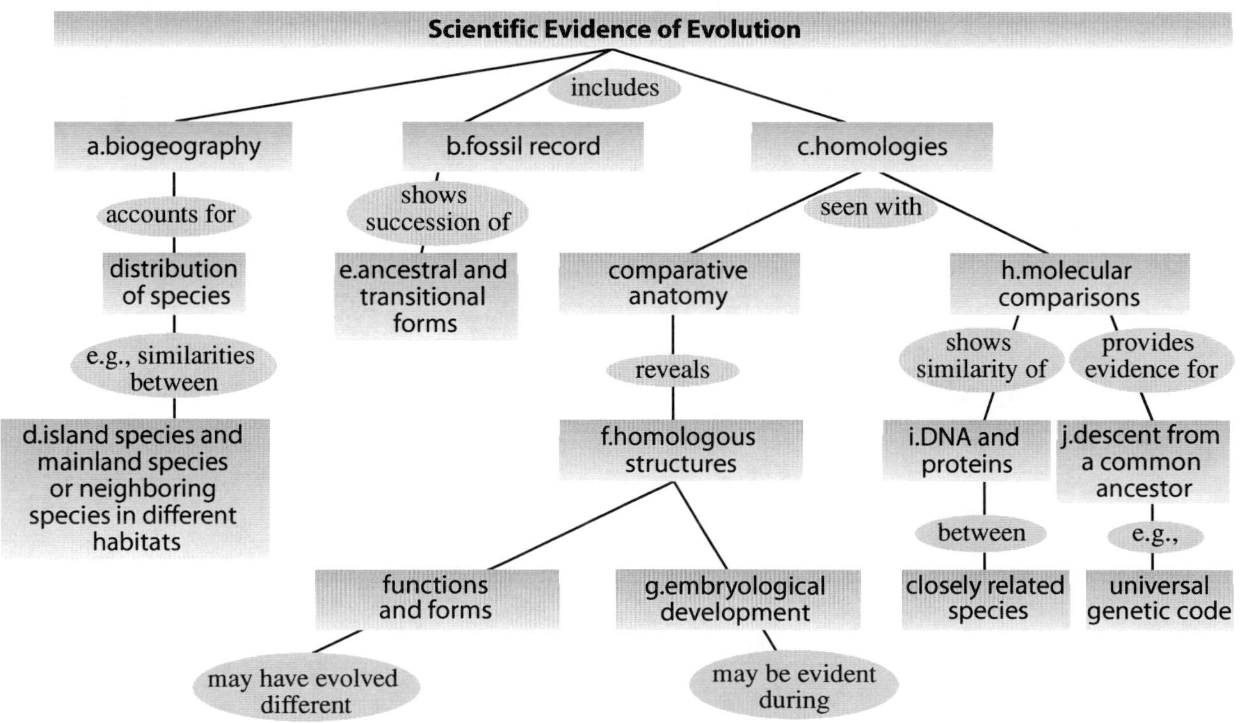

Chapter Concept Review

Charles Darwin and *The Origin of Species*

- Charles Darwin established the ideas of evolution and natural selection in his 1859 publication *On the Origin of Species by Means of Natural Selection.*
- **Darwin's Cultural and Scientific Context** During his around-the-world voyage on the *Beagle*, Darwin observed adaptations of organisms that inhabited diverse environments. In particular, Darwin was struck by the geographic distribution of organisms on the Galápagos Islands, off the South American coast. When Darwin considered his observations in light of new evidence for a very old Earth that changed slowly, he arrived at ideas that were at odds with the long-held notion of a young Earth populated by unrelated and unchanging species.
- **Descent with Modification** Darwin made two proposals in *The Origin of Species:* (1) Modern species descended from ancestral species, and (2) natural selection is the mechanism of evolution.

Evidence of Evolution

- **The Fossil Record** The fossil record shows that organisms have appeared in a historical sequence, and many fossils link ancestral species with those living today.
- **Biogeography** Biogeography, the study of the geographic distribution of species, suggests that species evolved from ancestors that inhabited the same region.
- **Comparative Anatomy** Homologous structures among species and vestigial organs provide evidence of evolutionary history.
- **Comparative Embryology** Closely related species often have similar stages in their embryonic development.
- **Molecular Biology** All species share a common genetic code, suggesting that all forms of life are related through branching evolution from the earliest organisms. Comparisons of DNA and proteins provide evidence of evolutionary relationships.

Natural Selection

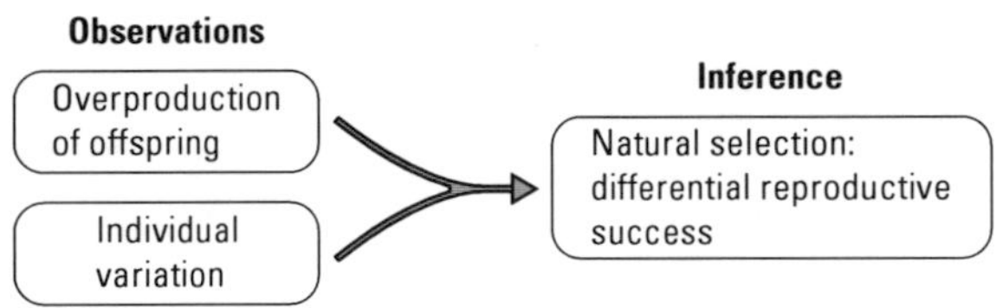

- **Darwin's Theory of Natural Selection** Individuals best suited for a particular environment are more likely to survive and reproduce than less fit individuals.
- **Natural Selection in Action** Natural selection can be observed in the evolution of pesticide-resistant insects, drug-resistant microbes, and horned lizards, among many other organisms.

The Modern Synthesis: Darwinism Meets Genetics

- The modern synthesis fused genetics (Mendelism) and evolutionary biology (Darwinism) in the mid-1900s.
- **Populations as the Units of Evolution** A population, members of the same species living in the same time and place, is the smallest biological unit that can evolve. Population genetics emphasizes the extensive genetic variation within populations and tracks the genetic makeup of populations over time.
- **Genetic Variation in Populations** Polygenic ("many gene") inheritance produces traits that vary continuously, whereas traits that are determined by one genetic locus may be polymorphic, with two or more distinct forms. Mutation and sexual recombination produce genetic variation.
- **Analyzing Gene Pools** The gene pool consists of all alleles in all the individuals making up a population. The Hardy-Weinberg formula can be used to calculate the frequencies of genotypes in a gene pool from the frequencies of alleles, and vice versa:

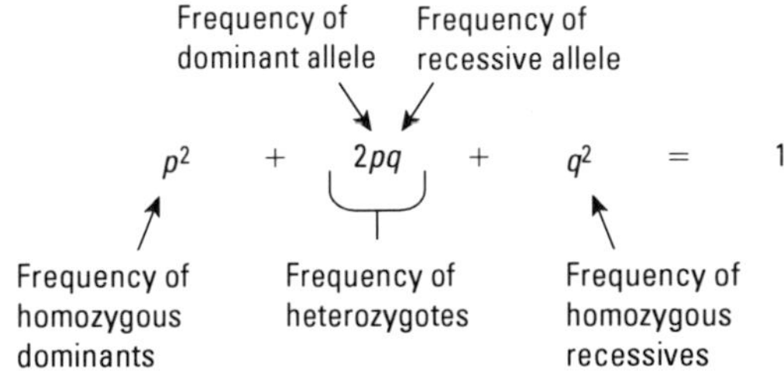

Case Study in the Process of Science *How Can Frequency of Alleles Be Calculated?*

- **Population Genetics and Health Science** The Hardy-Weinberg formula can be used to estimate the frequency of a harmful allele, which is useful information for public health programs dealing with genetic diseases.
- **Microevolution as Change in a Gene Pool** Microevolution is a generation-to-generation change in a population's frequencies of alleles.
- **Genetic Drift** Genetic drift is a change in the gene pool of a small population due to chance. Bottlenecking (a drastic reduction in population size) and the founder effect (a new population started by a few individuals) are two situations leading to genetic drift.
- **Gene Flow** A population may gain or lose alleles by gene flow, which is genetic exchange with another population.
- **Mutation** Individual mutations have relatively little short-term effect on a large gene pool. In the long term, mutation is the source of genetic variation.
- **Natural Selection: A Closer Look** Of all causes of microevolution, only natural selection promotes evolutionary adaptations. Darwinian fitness is the contribution an individual makes to the gene pool of the next generation relative to the contributions of other individuals. The outcome of natural selection may be directional, disruptive, or stabilizing.

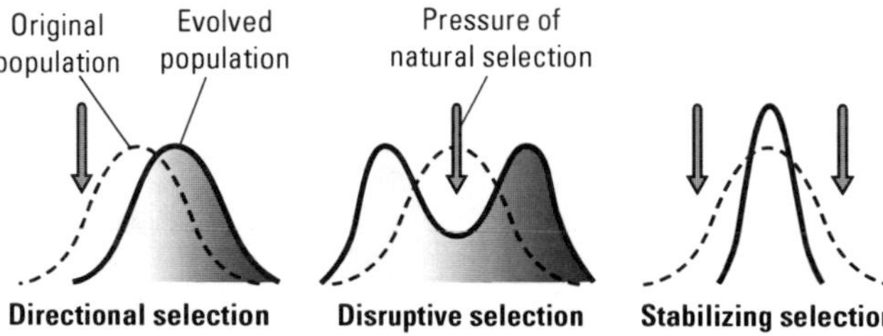

Key Terms

Adaptation An evolved trait that makes organisms more suited to living and reproducing in their environments.

Adaptive radiation The evolution of multiple species, each adapted to a distinct way of life, from a single ancestor.

Allopatric speciation Speciation that occurs after a geographic barrier divides a group of organisms into two isolated populations.

Artificial selection The selective breeding of organisms with desirable traits in order to produce offspring with the same traits.

Autotrophs Living organisms that make their own food and organic materials.

Chemoautotrophs Autotrophs that use energy from inorganic chemicals to make their food and organic materials.

Endosymbiotic theory The theory that the mitochondria and chloroplasts of eukaryotic cells evolved from prokaryotes living inside early eukaryotic cells.

Evolution Heritable changes in living organisms over time—or, as Darwin put it, "descent with modification."

Fitness The number of offspring an organism produces in its lifetime compared to other organisms in the population.

Heritable Traits that are passed from parents to offspring because they are at least partially determined by genes.

Heterotrophs Living organisms that obtain their energy and organic materials from other living organisms or other outside sources.

Natural selection Organisms with heritable, advantageous traits leave more offspring than organisms with other traits, causing advantageous traits to become more common in populations over time.

Postzygotic reproductive barrier A barrier that prevents members of different species from successfully reproducing because the hybrids produced are either unable to survive or sterile.

Prezygotic reproductive barrier A barrier that prevents members of different species from mating in the first place or that keeps fertilization from occurring if they do mate.

Punctuated equilibrium The theory that species do not change very much over long periods of time and then change a lot suddenly, during speciation.

Speciation The formation of new species.

Species A group of organisms whose members can inter-breed among themselves, but not with members of other species.

Sympatric speciation Speciation that occurs without the introduction of a geographic barrier.

Variation Differences in a trait from one individual to another.

Exercises in The Evolution of Life

Natural Selection

1. A. One of the best-documented instances of natural selection in the wild is the evolution of bird beak sizes during a severe drought on the Galápagos Islands in 1977. Before the drought, there was natural variation in beak size in a species of finch found on the islands. Draw a series of finches, showing this variation in beak size.

B. What happened was this: The drought made seeds scarce. Small seeds were quickly eaten up, leaving only larger, tougher seeds. Birds with larger, stronger beaks were better at cracking these larger seeds. Many birds died during the drought. Which were most likely to survive? Mark X's through some of the individuals in your drawing likely to have died, and circle individuals likely to have survived.

C. Beak size is a trait that is partly genetically determined, so parents with larger, stronger beaks tend to have offspring with larger, stronger beaks. Draw the offspring of the individuals you circled as surviving the drought.

Natural Selection—continued

D. How does the population you drew in part (c) compare with the population you drew in part (a)?

2. Of the human traits listed below, put a V by traits that are variable and put an H by traits that are heritable. Which traits have the potential of evolving via natural selection?

A. age
B. eye color
C. number of toes
D. curliness or straightness of hair
E. presence or absence of dimples
F. upright posture
G. owning versus not owning a dog
H. height

Adaptation

1. The imaginary mammal below occupies temperate forests in the Eastern United States.

If a population of these mammals moved to and successfully colonized an Arctic habitat, how might you predict that it would evolve? Draw the Arctic form below.

If a population of these mammals moved to and successfully colonized a desert habitat, how might you predict that it would evolve? Draw the desert form below.

Adaptation—continued

Explain your drawings.

____

____

____

____

____

____

____

____

____

____

____

____

2. You are studying peppered moth populations in various locales. In order to determine whether light moths or dark moths survive better in different habitats, you mark 500 light moths and 500 dark moths and release them in different places.

If light moths survive better, you expect to recapture more ______________________________.

Similarly, if dark moths survive better, you expect to recapture more ________________________.

Do you expect light moths or dark moths to survive better in the following habitats?

A. polluted areas
B. unpolluted areas
C. industrial centers before pollution laws were passed
D. industrial centers some time after pollution laws were passed
E. the countryside

Speciation

1. What's the difference between a prezygotic reproductive barrier and a postzygotic reproductive barrier?

2. Which of the following are prezygotic reproductive barriers and which are postzygotic reproductive barriers?
A. different courtship rituals in different bird species
B. incompatible anatomical structures that prevent copulation in insects
C. different-sounding calls by males in different frog species
D. sterility in offspring produced when members of two different species mate

Speciation—continued

E. two species that mate at different times of year
F. two species that use different mating sites
G. offspring that are unable to survive when members of two species mate

3. What's the difference between allopatric speciation and sympatric speciation?

4. Are the following examples of allopatric or sympatric speciation?
A. speciation after developing glaciers divide a population
B. speciation by hybridization
C. speciation after a river cuts through a population's habitat
D. speciation after plate tectonics causes a continent to split
E. speciation by polyploidy

Self-Quiz

1. Which of the following is *not* an observation or inference on which Darwin's theory of natural selection is based?
A. There is heritable variation among individuals.
B. Poorly adapted individuals never produce offspring.
C. Because excessive numbers of offspring are produced, there is a struggle for limited resources.
D. Individuals whose inherited characteristics best fit them to the environment will generally produce more offspring.

2. Which of the following is a true statement about Charles Darwin?
A. He was the first to discover that living things can change, or evolve.
B. He based his theory on the inheritance of acquired characteristics.
C. He proposed natural selection as the mechanism of evolution.
D. He was the first to realize that Earth is more than 6,000 years old.

3. In a population with two alleles for a particular genetic locus, *B* and *b*, the allele frequency of B is 0.7. If this population is in Hardy-Weinberg equilibrium, the frequency of heterozygotes is _____, the frequency of homozygous dominants is _____, and the frequency of homozygous recessives is _____.

4. Define fitness from an evolutionary perspective.

5. The processes of _____ and _____ generate variation, and _____ produces adaptation to the environment.
A. sexual recombination . . . natural selection . . . mutation
B. mutation . . . sexual recombination . . . genetic drift
C. genetic drift . . . mutation . . . sexual recombination
D. mutation . . . natural selection . . . sexual recombination
E. mutation . . . sexual recombination . . . natural selection

6. As a mechanism of microevolution, natural selection can be most closely equated with
A. random mating.
B. genetic drift.
C. unequal reproductive success.
D. gene flow.

7. Why does a founder event favor microevolution in the founding population?

8. In a particular bird species, individuals with average-sized wings survive severe storms more successfully than other birds in the same population with longer or shorter wings. Of the three general outcomes of natural selection (directional, disruptive, or stabilizing), this example illustrates _____.

9. Which of the following statements is (are) true about a population in Hardy-Weinberg equilibrium? (More than one may be true.)
A. The population is quite small.
B. The population is not evolving.
C. Gene flow between the population and surrounding populations does not occur.
D. Natural selection is not occurring.

10. What environmental factor accounts for the relatively high frequency of the sickle-cell allele in tropical Africa?

Practice Test for Chapter 18

Organizing Data

Define and distinguish between each pair of terms in the table below.

Pair Term	Definition and Differences
Postzygotic vs. Prezygotic reproductive barrier	
Punctuated equilibrium vs. Endosymbiotic theory	
Species vs. Speciation	
Variation vs. Adaptation	
Adaptive radiation vs. Allopatric speciation	
Autotrophs vs. Hetrotrophs	

Content Quiz

1. Spontaneous generation held that living things appeared fully formed from nonliving materials—for example, frogs appeared in mud after heavy rains. Spontaneous generation was dealt a fatal blow as a result of experiment done by:
A. Antony van Leeuwenhoek.
B. Louis Pasteur
C. Darwin
D. Stanley Miller
E. Thomas Austin

2. In 1953 two scientists were able to model the early Earth by mixing together an "atmosphere" of water vapor, ammonia, methane, and hydrogen and placing that atmosphere over a "sea" of water. They then shot electric sparks through the mixture to simulate lightning storms. The results were staggering—within a week, complex organic molecules had formed, including amino acids; the building blocks of proteins. These two scientists are:
A. Stanley Miller and Harold Urey
B. *Kenneth Kaneshiro and Linda Graham*
C. *Abour Cherif and Linda Michel*
D. Charles Lyell and Thomas Malthus.
E. Stephen Jay Gould and Niles Eldredge

3. True or False? Louis Pasteur found that life did not appear in a sterile broth if it was carefully isolated from airborne particles.

4. True or False? Further experiments showed that all the important organic molecules that make up life—not just amino acids, but sugars, lipids, even the nitrogenous bases found in RNA and DNA—can be generated in a similar way.

5. True or False? Earth was steadily bombarded by meteorites during its early history, and some of the meteorites that have been recovered here do in fact contain an impressive array of complex organic molecules, presumably formed in outer space. For example, the Murchison meteorite that fell in Australia in 1969 contained nearly a hundred different amino acids.

6. True or False? Another alternate hypothesis is that large numbers of organic molecules were synthesized in deep sea environments on Earth similar to the hydrothermal vent habitats of today. Chemical reactions in these habitats could have spontaneously produced large numbers of the organic molecules necessary for the evolution of life.

7. For several reasons, scientists now believe that the first genes were probably made of _____, not _____. Even without cells and enzymes, short strands of _____ can spontaneously assemble from individual nucleotides and even reproduce themselves.

8. The oldest known fossils date from 3.5 billion years ago and are of prokaryotes.
   A. Prokaryotes
   B. Eukaryotes
   C. All of the above
   D. None of the above

9. True or False? Astronomers have discovered that complex organic molecules called polyaromatic hydrocarbons (PAHs) existed when the universe was only 4 billion years old. These molecules are considered to be among the building blocks of life. Their presence in the young universe indicates that, at least in certain galaxies, life has had ample time to emerge.

10. True or False? Earth's early autotrophs included organisms that used sunlight energy to build molecules as well as chemoautotrophs that used energy from a variety of inorganic chemicals.

11. True or False? Although the large majority of autotrophs today photosynthesize, some living archaeans—prokaryotes of the domain Archaea—are chemoautotrophs.

12. True or False? The origin of autotrophic organisms was certainly a crucial event in Earth history—without autotrophs, heterotrophs would have eaten quickly through their food supply and died out.

13. As the number of heterotrophs increased through reproduction, the supply of organic molecules dwindled and competition set in. Organisms that were better at obtaining and using food were:
   A. favored
   B. not favored
   C. Neutral

14. The rise of the cyanobacteria (photosynthetic bacteria), some 2.7 billion years ago represented an important event in the history of life. This is because Cyanobacteria:
   A. release carbon dioxide as a by-product of photosynthesis, and it was their incredible success that first introduced carbon dioxide into Earth's atmosphere.
   B. release carbon dioxide as a by-product of photosynthesis, and it was their incredible success that first introduced oxygen into Earth's atmosphere.
   C. release oxygen as a by-product of photosynthesis, and it was their incredible success that first introduced carbon dioxide into Earth's atmosphere.
   D. release oxygen as a by-product of photosynthesis, and it was their incredible success that first introduced oxygen into Earth's atmosphere.

15. The earliest living organisms were:
- **A.** Marine prokaryotes living in a world with no free oxygen.
- **B.** Likely to have been heterotrophs that obtain energy and organic materials from outside sources, as humans and other animals do today.
- **C.** Used a ready found supply of food in the organic molecules that had accumulated in the oceans.
- **D.** Anaerobic processes to obtain energy.
- **E.** All of the above

16. As the number of heterotrophs increased through reproduction, the supply of organic molecules dwindled and competition set in. Organisms that were better at obtaining and using food were:
- **D.** favored
- **E.** not favored
- **F.** Neutral

17. True or False? Evidence of an oxygenated atmosphere comes from the presence of banded iron formations in old sedimentary rocks. These formations are produced when atmospheric oxygen combines with iron dissolved in Earth's oceans. Oxygen is now essential to the vast majority of living organisms for cellular respiration.

18. True or False? Stromatolites are among the oldest known fossils on Earth. They are formed by mats of photosynthetic cyanobacteria, the prokaryotes that changed the history of life on Earth by creating an atmosphere rich in oxygen.

19. True or False? Today, the cyanobacteria that produce stromatolites are nearly extinct, occurring in only a few places. These are in Shark Bay, Australia.

20. Atmospheric ______, another form of oxygen, shields the Earth from dangerous mutation causing ultraviolet radiation. Without this protective ozone layer, life might never have been able to move onto land!

21. The living organisms we are most familiar with—animals, plants, and fungi—are all:
- **A.** eukaryotes.
- **B.** Prokaryotes.
- **C.** Both eukaryotes and prokaryotes.

22. Eukaryotes first appeared on Earth:
- **A.** Only about 2 billion years ago.
- **B.** At least 3.5 billion years.
- **C.** More than 3.5 billion years ago
- **D.** Much less than 2 billion years ago.

23. Scientists believe mitochondria and chloroplasts, which have quite fascinating origin, evolved from:
- **A.** Eukaryotic living inside the earliest prokaryotes cells.
- **B.** Prokaryotes living inside the earliest eukaryotic cells.

24. Endosymbiotic theory (*endo* means "in" and *symbiotic* means "to live with") is supported by several observations:
- **A.** mitochondria and chloroplasts have their own membranes and their own DNA.
- **B.** DNA is in the form of a circular chromosome, just like prokaryotic DNA.
- **C.** Both mitochondria and chloroplasts also make their own proteins, using ribosomes that resemble those of prokaryotes.
- **D.** All of the above
- **E.** None of the above.

25. True or False? By studying their structures, scientists have concluded that mitochondria are most likely descended from a group of oxygen-breathing bacteria and that chloroplasts most likely originated from our old friends, the photosynthesizing cyanobacteria.

26. True or False? Given that mitochondria use oxygen to obtain energy for eukaryotic cells, and that chloroplasts perform photosynthesis in plant cells, these origins make good sense.

27. The Scientist who believed that organisms acquired new characteristics over a lifetime of activity and then passed these characteristics onto their offspring, is:
A. American Biologist Stephen Jay Gould
B. American Biologist Niles Eldredge
C. French naturalist Jean Baptiste Lamarck (1744–1829)
D. English naturalist Charles Darwin (1809–1882)

28. The book of *The Origin of Species by Means of Natural Selection* was published *by*:
A. French naturalist Jean Baptiste Lamarck (1744–1829)
B. English naturalist Charles Darwin (1809–1882)

29. __________ 's theory for how change occurs, called the *inheritance of. acquired characteristics*, proved to be incorrect—organisms cannot pass characteristics acquired during their lifetimes to their offspring because these acquired characteristics are not genetic.

30. Match the right term to its best deception in the left column.

Charles Lyell _____	**A.** Human populations grow much faster than available food supplies
Darwin _____	**B.** Evolution—heritable changes
Lamarck _____	**C.** *Evolution—inheritance of acquired characteristics.*
Darwin's finches _____	**D.** Galápagos Islands
Endosymbiotic _______	**E.** Released Rabbits in southern Victoria, Australia.
Thomas Austin ______	**F.** to live with"
Thomas Malthus _____	**G.** geological features of the Earth were created by gradual processes that produced their effects over long time periods.

31. ________ wrote, "Seeing this gradation and diversity of structure in one small, intimately related group of birds, one might really fancy that from an original paucity of birds in this archipelago, one species had been taken and modified for different ends."

32. Under ________ 's theory of evolution, offspring inherit the characteristics that their parents acquire over a lifetime of activity. He argued that ancestral giraffes stretched their necks after ever-higher leaves on trees and passed these longer necks to their offspring.

33. Under _________ 's theory of evolution by natural selection, organisms with advantageous traits leave more offspring than organisms with other traits, causing advantageous traits to become more common in a population. He argued that modern giraffes have long necks because ancestral giraffes with long necks left more offspring than ancestral giraffes with short necks.

34. In addition to his *Beagle* observations, Darwin was inspired by the work of two of his contemporaries:
A. Charles Lyell and Thomas Malthus.
B. Stanley Miller and Harold Urey
C. *Kenneth Kaneshiro and* Linda Graham
D. *Abour Cherif and Linda Michel*
E. Jean Lamarck and

35. The economist __________ was a second important influence for Darwin, and the one who led Darwin to his great idea on the cause of evolutionary change. He observed that human populations grow much faster than available food supplies and concluded, with despair, that famine was an inevitable feature of human existence.

36. True of False? Darwin argued that, because there are not enough resources for all organisms to survive and to reproduce as much as they can, living organisms are involved in an intense "struggle for existence." As a result, organisms with advantageous traits leave more offspring than organisms with other traits, causing populations to change over time.

37. True of False? If Lamarck were correct, the bodybuilder's children would inherit the increased muscle mass that the bodybuilder had acquired over a lifetime of weightlifting. However, because Lamarck's theory turned out to be incorrect, the children will have to do their own bodybuilding.

38. True of False? In Australia, the rabbit population had evolved disease resistance through the process of natural selection. Within the original rabbit population, a small number of individuals just happened to be resistant to myxoma virus. These resistant individuals survived the epidemics and reproduced, producing yet more disease resistant offspring.

39. True of False Disease resistance is just one example of natural selection at work. Natural selection occurs when organisms with certain advantageous traits leave more offspring than organisms with other traits, causing populations to change over time.

40. Which of the following is correct: In any population of organisms:
A. Individuals have traits, many of which show variation.
B. Many of these variable traits are determined by genes and therefore will be heritable passed from parents to offspring.
C. Some of these variable, heritable traits will be advantageous and allow the organisms possessing them to leave more offspring than other organisms.
D. Advantageous traits are "selected for" and become more common in a population.
E. All of the above.

41. True or False? The fitness of an organism describes the number of offspring it leaves over its lifetime compared to other individuals in the population. An organism that leaves more offspring than other individuals in the population is said to have greater fitness.

42. Natural selection can only act on traits where there is _________ among individuals of a given species.

43. True or False? Some traits are heritable—they are determined by genes and so are passed from parents to offspring. Organisms have lots of traits, many of which show variation.

44. True or False? Variation in heritable traits sometimes results in some organisms leaving more offspring than others—that is, in natural selection. Natural selection causes advantageous traits to become more common in a population, producing the adaptation of organisms to their environments.

45. True or False? Although natural selection acts on individuals within a population, allowing some individuals to leave more offspring than others, it is the population that evolves.

46. _____________ acts as the driving force behind evolution because it leads to the evolution of adaptations—traits that make organisms well suited to living and reproducing in their environments.

47. ____________ can relate to many different aspects of an organism's life. Many of the adaptations organisms evolve help them survive. Survival is, after all, usually a requirement for leaving offspring.

48. True or False? Butterflies have evolved a variety of ways to avoid predators. The Painted Lady flies in an erratic, unpredictable manner, making it hard to catch. The Monarch eats plants that are toxic to other animals so that its tissues become toxic. Birds that try to eat Monarchs vomit, and remember to avoid the striking black and orange pattern in the future. The Viceroy is not toxic but is a mimic of the toxic Monarch, resembling it closely in appearance. As a result, the Viceroy is also avoided by birds.

49. True or False? Nature does not plan ahead—it does not plan to make a falcon or a polar bear. Instead, adaptations are built step-by-step, through the never-ending selection of the most successful forms that arise from chance mutations.

50. Match the right term to its best deception in the left column.

Natural selection _______	**A.** Produced remarkable adaptations over time
Bergmann's Rule ______	**B.** Natural selection that is related to acquiring mates.
Sexual selection. _______	**C.** In animals, volume increases more quickly than surface area as organisms get bigger

51. True or False? Animals that live in extremely hot or extremely cold habitats need to be able to maintain appropriate body temperatures in those environments—to *thermoregulate*. These means, they have to evolve behavioral, physiological, and anatomical adaptations relating to heat balance.

52. A key factor in heat balance is an animal's surface area-to-volume ratio. The heat an animal generates is proportional to its:
A. volume.
B. surface area
C. volume and surface area
D. All of the above
E. None of the above.

53. A key factor in heat balance is an animal's surface area-to-volume ratio. The heat an animal dissipates is proportional to its:
A. volume.
B. surface area
C. volume and surface area
D. All of the above
E. None of the above.

54. Animals are better able to lose heat if they have a ________. This influences both the size and shape of animals that occupy extreme habitats.
A. high surface area-to-volume ratio.
B. low surface area-to-volume ratio.
C. None of the above

55. Animals are better able to retain heat if they a ________. This influences both the size and shape of animals that occupy extreme habitats.
A. high surface area-to-volume ratio.
B. low surface area-to-volume ratio.
C. None of the above

56. True or False? Larger organisms, whether they are cells or animals, tend to have smaller surface area-to-volume ratios. This is because volume increases more quickly than surface area as organisms get bigger.

57. True or False? Animals found in cold habitats are often larger than related forms in warm habitats. Also, living species in hot climates typically have long legs and large ears that increase the surface area available for heat dissipation than those live in cold ones.

58. True or False? Males are more brightly colored than females in many species of birds. Bright males are believed to result from a female preference for colorful mates. Females, not subject to these pressures, have been selected to be less bright because that makes them less conspicuous to predators.

59. ________ animals are better able to dissipate heat because of their large surface area-to-volume ratios. This is why the small sun bear is found in tropical forests in Southeast Asia.

60. _______ animals are better able to retain heat because of their small surface area-to-volume ratios. This is why the polar bear, the largest terrestrial carnivore in the world, is found throughout the Arctic.

61. True or Fales? Natural selection is sometimes classified into three different modes depending on how it affects populations. *directional selection, stabilizing selection, and diversifying selection*

62. In _________ *selection,* natural selection favors organisms with a trait that is different from the population average. Over time, ________ selection causes the population average to shift towards the favored trait.

63. In 1977. a severe drought took place Galápagos Islands. The drought made seeds scarce, with the result that small seeds were quickly eaten up, leaving only larger, tougher seeds. Birds with larger, stronger beaks were better at cracking these larger seeds and so were more likely to survive. As a result, the finch population shifted towards larger beak size. Is this:
A. *directional selection?*
B. *stabilizing selection?*
C. *diversifying selection?*
D. *different type of selection*?
E. Not an example of natural selection?

64. In ________ *selection,* natural selection favors organisms with the average trait in the population over organisms with traits that differ from it. Over time, _______ selection causes the distribution of traits in the population to become narrower.

65. Babies born at average weight survive better than either heavier or lighter babies. Over time, this type of selection causes human babies to be born within a narrower weight range. A birth weight in human babies is an example of __________.
A. *directional selection.*
B. *stabilizing selection*
C. *diversifying selection*
D. *different type of selection*
E. Not an example of natural selection

66. In ___________ *selection,* natural selection favors traits at two extremes on either side of the population average. Over time, ________ selection causes the population to diverge into two groups, clustered around the two optimum traits.

67. What type of selection occurs in the coloration of butterflies that mimic the appearance of two different toxic species; meaning natural selection favors individuals that closely resemble either of the two toxic species, but not individuals with an intermediate appearance—intermediate butterflies don't look toxic and so are eaten?
A. *directional selection.*
B. *stabilizing selection*
C. *diversifying selection*
D. *different type of selection*
E. Not an example of natural selection

68. The incorporation of modern genetics into Darwin's theory of evolution took place in the middle of the twentieth century and is known as the *Modern Synthesis*. The Modern Synthesis focuses on evolution *as changes in the* __________ *of genes over time.*

69. In the light of the *Modern Synthesis* natural selection can be re-described as:

A. first, there is variation in a gene when alternate alleles exist within a population.
B. second, a specific allele may give an organism some advantage that allows it to reproduce more than other organisms in the population.
C. third, as a result, more copies of the advantageous allele are passed to the next generation, causing the frequency of the allele to increase in the population.
D. all of the above
E. none of the above

70. Natural selection is not the only driving force behind evolution and the mechanism that causes populations to become adapted to their environments. Populations also change over time because of:

A. mutation pressure,
B. genetic drift
C. migration.
D. all of the above
E. none of the above

71. Match the right term to its best deception in the left column.

Term	**Discretion**
Directional selection. ___	**A.** Selection for organisms that have a trait at the population average. It causes the distribution of traits in the population to become narrower. An example of this type of selection is birth weight in humans.
Natural selection. ___	**B.** Produced remarkable adaptations over time. It is sometimes classified into different modes depending on the effect it has on populations.
Stabilizing selection. ____	**C.** Selects for organisms that differ from the population average. It causes the average trait in a population to shift. An example of this type of selection is the increase in beak size in a finch population on the Galápagos Islands following a drought.
Diversifying selection. _____	**D.** Exists if the alleles responsible for color are more likely to mutate in one direction than the other. For example, a brown allele may be more likely to mutate into a green allele than vice versa. This would cause the lizard population to evolve to a higher frequency of green alleles.
Mutation pressure. _____	**E.** Selection selects for traits at two extremes within a population. It causes the population to diverge in the trait. This type of selection occurs in the coloration of butterflies that mimic the appearance of two different toxic species.
Genetic drift. __________	**F.** Occurs when, by chance rather than because it confers greater fitness, more alleles of one color are transmitted to the next generation than alleles of the other color. For example, even if brown and green lizards have equal fitness, green lizards might just happen to leave more offspring (and therefore more green alleles) than brown lizards one year, causing the population to evolve to a greater frequency of green alleles.
Speciation ______	**G.** A group of organisms whose members can interbreed among themselves but not with members of other species.
Species ________	**H.** The formation of new species
Allopatric speciation ___	**I.** New species are formed after a geographic barrier divides a single population into two.

72. True or False? Genetic drift operates in a way that is similar to a coin flip—you are equally likely to get heads or tails when you flip a coin. However, if you flip a coin 100 times you won't necessarily get exactly 50 heads and exactly 50 tails. Similarly, of 100 baby lizards that hatch in the next generation, there won't necessarily be exactly 50 brown ones and 50 green ones.

73. Genetic drift is a particularly important mechanism of evolution in small populations. This is because chance is more likely to:
A. change allele frequencies significantly in small populations.
B. change allele frequencies significantly in large populations.
C. change allele frequencies less significantly in small populations.
E. change allele frequencies more significantly in large populations.
F. None of the above

74. To test the hypothesis that the shift in coloration in the peppered moth population was caused by natural selection, biologist _____________ performed a series of experiments showing that camouflage and bird predation were in fact crucial pieces to the peppered moth puzzle.

75. True or False? Diseases once easy to treat—tuberculosis, pneumonia, even common childhood ailments such as ear infections—are now often resistant to multiple antibiotics. And in some hospitals, there are infectious bacteria that are resistant to every antibiotic on the market. Because it results from natural selection, antibiotic resistance is inevitable—all antibiotic use contributes to resistance.

76. What needs to be done about antibiotic resistance is:
A. First, humans must learn to use antibiotics wisely, taking them only when they are needed—that is, for bacterial infections—and then taking the entire course of treatment.
B. Physicians and veterinarians can also promote a socially responsible approach to antibiotics by educating patients and agriculturalists on the proper application of these drugs.
C. Finally, since many antibiotics are less effective now because of resistance, scientists must continue to search for new antibiotics that will take the place of those that no longer do the job, crucial genetic characteristics of the 1918 virus.
D. All of the above.

77. True of False? Speciation—the formation of new species—is the evolution of *reproductive barrier*s that prevent two groups of organisms from interbreeding.

78. Match the right term to its best deception in the left column.

Adaptive radiation_____	**A.** Chromosomal change in which two species interbred and produce fertile offspring.
Sympatric speciation ______	**B.** The evolution of a large number of new species, each adapted to a distinct way of life, from a single ancestor.
Humans __________	**C.** Speciation occurs without the introduction of a geographic barrier. It is much less common than other type of speciation.
Hybridization _________	**D.** *Primates* and also *hominids.*
Artificial selection	**E.** Punctuated equilibrium
Gould and Eldredge _____	**F.** Selective breeding of organisms with desirable traits in order to produce offspring with the same traits.

79. The productive barrier that prevent members of different species from mating in the first place or prevent fertilization from occurring if they do mate is known as:
A. prezygotic reproductive barriers.
B. postzygotic reproductive barriers.
C. poutzygotic reproductive barriers.
D. interzygotic reproductive barriers.

80. The productive barrier that act after fertilization has taken place; meaning occurs when mating produces hybrids that either don't survive or are sterile—unable to breed themselves, is known as:
A. prezygotic reproductive barriers.
B. postzygotic reproductive barriers.
C. outzygotic reproductive barriers.
D. interzygotic reproductive barriers.

81. There are many types of _________ organisms may differ in when they breed, where they breed, or in the details of their courtship rituals. Their sex organs may not fit together properly, preventing successful sperm transfer, or other factors may prevent fertilization even if sperm is transferred.

82. The mule, the offspring of a horse and a donkey, is sterile and cannot reproduce. Likewise, a liger the product of the mating of a lion and a tiger, is sterile. This is example of _____________.

83. When new species are formed after a geographic barrier divides a single population into two, is known as __________. The two populations, now that they are isolated from one another, begin to evolve independently, accumulating differences due to natural selection (which is likely to differ in the two environments) as well as genetic drift. Over time, the populations will have evolved key differences that prevent organisms from interbreeding.

84. Differing courtship rituals prevent individuals of different species from mating. In the red-crowned cranes courtship involves an 85. elaborate display—birds dance around each other, bob their heads, stretch their necks, extend their wings, and leap straight into the air, singing in unison. Unless you can do all that just right, you have little hope of convincing a red-crowned crane to mate with you. This type of reproductive barriers is known as:
A. prezygotic reproductive barriers.
B. postzygotic reproductive barriers.
C. outzygotic reproductive barriers.
D. interzygotic reproductive barriers.

85. The flowers of most primrose species open at different times of day. In One primrose species, flowers open in the late afternoon. In the other species, flowers open in the morning. So, even though the two species occupy, for example, the same western North American deserts and both are pollinated by bees, hybrids are rarely produced. This type of reproductive barriers is known as:
A. prezygotic reproductive barriers.
B. postzygotic reproductive barriers.
C. outzygotic reproductive barriers.
D. interzygotic reproductive barriers

86. The evolution of a large number of new species, each adapted to a distinct way of life, from a single ancestor is known as ___________. They are most often seen after a few members of a species colonize a new habitat.

87. Speciation is much less common than the other type of speciation and that occurs without the introduction of a geographic barrier, is know as ____________.

88. The professor that was interviewed for the Evolutionary History of Biological Diversity in unit 5 of this textbook is:
A. Professor *Kenneth Kaneshiro*
B. Professor Linda Graham
C. *Professor Abour Cherif*
D. *Professor* Thomas Malthus.

89. In plants, __________ is often the result of sudden chromosomal changes. One such chromosomal change is *polyploidy*, which occurs when organisms inherit more than the usual two sets of chromosomes, usually as a result of improper meiosis.

90. True or False? Geographic barriers isolate populations and allow them to evolve independently. Sometimes, a reproductive barrier will evolve, producing allopatric speciation.

91. True or False? Another instance of sympatric speciation through chromosomal change is *hybridization*, which occurs when two species interbreed and produce fertile offspring.

92. True or False? In both polyploidy and hybridization, chromosomal differences between the new species and the parent species prevent interbreeding. These types of speciation are much more rare in animals than in plants but are not unheard of.

93. True or False? Humans may vary in significant ways from one part of the world to another, but we all belong to the same species—all humans are able to interbreed!

94. The theory of evolution is a theory in the way that Sir Isaac Newton's law of universal gravitation is a theory and that Albert Einstein's theory of relativity is a theory. That is, the theory of evolution has been tested repeatedly against observations of the natural world, and the evidence for evolution has met the most rigorous standards of the scientific community.

95. Many lines of evidence support the argument that Earth's diversity of life is the result of evolution. Evolution is also evident in living creatures themselves, in the form of:
A. shared anatomy,
B. shared patterns of development
C. shared DNA sequences.
D. all of the above

96. There is plentiful evidence of natural selection in action. This includes for example;
A. coloration evolution in peppered moths.
B. resistance to myxoma virus in Australian rabbits.
C. break size increase in a Galápagos finch.
D. antibiotic resistance in bacteria.
E. all of the above.

97. True or False? Artificial selection is the selective breeding of organisms with desirable traits in order to produce offspring with the same traits. Through artificial selection, humans have brought about dramatic evolutionary changes in these organisms.

98. True or False? In fact, artificial selection has produced countless forms of domestic animals and crops, all with traits valued by humans.

99. True or False? In many cases, the evolutionary histories of species are preserved in the structures of their bodies. For example, some snakes actually retain tiny, incomplete hind legs, evidence of their evolution from legged vertebrates.

100. True or False? Whenever we compare the bodies of related species. we can easily see evidence of shared ancestry. For example, the limbs of mammals are used by different mammals for different purposes—humans walk, bats fly, whales swim, and moles dig, just to name a few. If each of these mammals had originated independently, we would expect their limbs to look completely different. Yet, in fact, all mammalian limbs resemble each other and are made up of the same set of bones.

101. True or False? The macromolecules of organisms retain evidence of their shared evolutionary history. For example, the DNA of related species have similar ACGT sequences. This is true not only for sequences in the DNA molecule that tell cells how to build proteins but even for sequences that have no obvious function. This sequence similarity, and the fact that DNA sequences tend to be more similar in more closely related species, is logically explained by shared evolutionary history.

102. True or False? Similarly, almost all organisms on Earth share the same genetic code, the rules for translating codons into amino acids during the construction of proteins. The universality of the genetic code suggests that it arose early in the evolution of life and was then passed on to all living species.

103. True or False? Related species also develop in similar ways. For example, human embryological development resembles that of other vertebrates in that we go through a stage where we have gill slits and a tail even though these structures aren't actually present in humans. If each species on Earth had originated independently, we wouldn't expect these similarities in development.

104. True or False? Many early relatives of horses have been preserved as fossils. Over time, species grew larger in size, their legs became specialized for running (the lower leg bones fused, and the number of toes was reduced), and their teeth became specialized for grinding tough grasses rather than browsing on soft leaves.

105. True or False? The Arctic and Antarctic, which have similar habitats, are occupied by very different species. Polar bears are found in the Arctic but not the Antarctic, penguins in the Antarctic but not the Arctic.

106. The idea that evolution does not occur gradually, but in spurts is proposed in 1977 biologists by:
- **A.** Stanley Miller and Harold Urey
- **B.** Kenneth Kaneshiro and Linda Graham
- **C.** Abour Cherif and Linda Michel
- **D.** Charles Lyell and Thomas Malthus.
- **E.** Stephen Jay Gould and Niles Eldredge

107. The punctuated equilibrium theory hypothesizes that species maintain *equilibrium*, or stability, for long periods of time. These periods of equilibrium, in which species do not change very much, are *punctuated* by bouts of rapid change. Moreover, the rapid change occurs during speciation. This theory was proposed biologists by:
- **A.** Stanley Miller and Harold Urey
- **B.** Kenneth Kaneshiro and Linda Graham
- **C.** Abour Cherif and Linda Michel
- **D.** Charles Lyell and Thomas Malthus.
- **E.** Stephen Jay Gould and Niles Eldredge

108. The professor that was interviewed for the mechanisms of evolution in unit 5 of this textbook is:
- **A.** Professor Kenneth Kaneshiro
- **B.** Professor Linda Graham
- **C.** rofessor Abour Cherif
- **D.** Professor Charles Lyell.

Critical Thinking Questions

1. Miller and Urey found that organic molecules are easily formed in large quantities from nonorganic materials. But Pasteur had already shown that life does not come from nonlife. Why aren't these results contradictory?
2. What evidence is there that life on Earth could have originated on Mars?
3. What is the primary objection to this hypothesis?
4. When people live at high altitude, where oxygen is scarce, their red blood cell count increases. Is this an example of evolution?

5. If Lamarck had been correct and evolutionary change occurred through the inheritance of acquired characteristics, what trait might a bodybuilder pass to his offspring?
6. Which of the following traits are variable in cats? Fur color. Tail length. Number of eyes.
7. Are these cat traits heritable?
8. In elephant seals, males fight to control and mate with large "harems" of female seals. The outcome of such a fight usually depends on factors such as, size and strength. Could this lead to natural selection among elephant seals? If what evolutionary change might be seen in the elephant seal population?
9. If natural selection led to the evolution of light colors in many desert species, why doesn't it appear to have selected for dark colors in many Arctic species? Why are polar bears, Arctic hares, and Arctic foxes all white during the winter?
10. On cold days, people often bundle up babies and small children carefully. Are babies more likely to need the extra bundling than adults? Why or why not?
11. If genetic drift caused our lizard population to evolve towards a greater frequency of brown alleles one year, would it have the same effect the following year?
12. If 20 brown lizards migrated into our lizard population, and 30 green lizard migrated out, what would be the net effect of migration on allele frequencies?
13. A small river forms, dividing a group of moles into two isolated populations. After many years, a biologist puts moles from opposite sides of the river together and finds that they will not mate. Has speciation occurred? If so, what type of speciation is it?
14. Do you think the same river would cause birds to speciate?
15. Two species of frogs do not interbreed because one species breeds in the spring and the other breeds in the fall. Is this a prezygotic or postzygotic reproductive barrier?
16. Why is the fact that many species found on islands resemble species found on nearby mainlands evidence for evolution?
17. Match the right term to its best deception in the left column.

Term	**Discretion**
Heterotrophs	Living organisms that obtain their energy and organic materials from other living organisms or other outside sources.
Natural selection	Organisms with heritable, advantageous traits leave more offspring than organisms with other traits, causing advantageous traits to become more common in populations over time.
Postzygotic reproductive barrier	A barrier that prevents members of different species from successfully reproducing because the hybrids produced are either unable to survive or sterile.
Prezygotic reproductive barrier	A barrier that prevents members of different species from mating in the first place or that keeps fertilization from occurring if they do mate.
Punctuated equilibrium	The theory that species do not change very much over long periods of time and then change a lot suddenly, during speciation.
Speciation	The formation of new species.
Species	A group of organisms whose members can interbreed among themselves, but not with members of other species.
Sympatric speciation	Speciation that occurs without the introduction of a geographic barrier
Variation	Differences in a trait from one individual to another
Adaptation	An evolved trait that makes organisms more suited to living and reproducing in their environments.
Adaptive radiation	The evolution of multiple species, each adapted to a distinct way of life, from a single ancestor.
Allopatric speciation	Speciation that occurs after a geographic barrier divides a group of organisms into two isolated populations.

Artificial selection	The selective breeding of organisms with desirable traits in order to produce offspring with the same traits.
Autotrophs	Living organisms that make their own food and organic materials
Chemoautotrophs	Autotrophs that use energy from inorganic chemicals to make their food and organic materials.
Endosymbiotic theory	The theory that the mitochondria and chloroplasts of eukaryotic cells evolved from prokaryotes living inside early eukaryotic cells.
Evolution	Heritable changes in living organisms over time—or, as Darwin put it, "descent with modification."
Fitness	The number of offspring an organism produces in its lifetime compared to other organisms in the population.
Heritable	Traits that are passed from parents to offspring because they are at least partially determined by genes.

Word Roots

bio = life; **geo** = the earth (biogeography: the geographic distribution of species)
homo = alike (homology: traits that appear similar due to common ancestry)
micro = small (microevolution: evolution at its smallest scale)
poly = many; **morph** = form (polymorphic: a characteristic of a population in which two or more forms are clearly present)

Key Terms

adaptation
biogeography
bottleneck effect
comparative anatomy
comparative embryology
directional selection
disruptive selection
evolution
fitness
fossil record
founder effect
gene flow
gene pool
genetic drift
Hardy-Weinberg equilibrium
Hardy-Weinberg formula
homology
microevolution
modern synthesis
natural selection
polymorphic
population
population genetics
stabilizing selection
vestigial organs

Crossword Puzzle

Use the Key Terms list from this chapter to fill in the crossword puzzle.

ACROSS

3. a population in which two or more morphs are clearly present
4. the type of selection that maintains variation for a particular trait within a narrow range
5. remnants of structures that served important functions in an organism's ancestors
6. the mechanism for descent with modification
7. the geographic distribution of species
10. the type of selection that shifts the phenotypic curve of a population in favor of some extreme phenotype
12. genetic exchange with another population
13. a population's increase in the frequency of traits suited to the environment
14. all of the alleles in all of the individuals in a population
15. the contribution an individual makes to the gene pool of the next generation relative to the contributions of other individuals
16. a trait that appears similar due to common ancestry
17. genetic change in a population or species over generations
18. the comparison of body structures between different species

19. the type of selection that can lead to a balance of two or more different morphs
20. the fusion of genetics with evolutionary biology
21. the ordered sequence of fossils as they appear in rock layers, marking the passage of geologic time
22. genetic drift in a new colony
23. the name of the formula and type of equilibrium that describes a population's gene pool

DOWN

1. evolution at its smallest scale
2. a group of interacting individuals belonging to one species and living in the same geographic area
7. genetic drift due to a drastic reduction in population size
8. the study of genetic variation within a population and over time
9. the comparison of structures that appear during the development of different organisms
11. a change in a gene pool of a small population due to chance

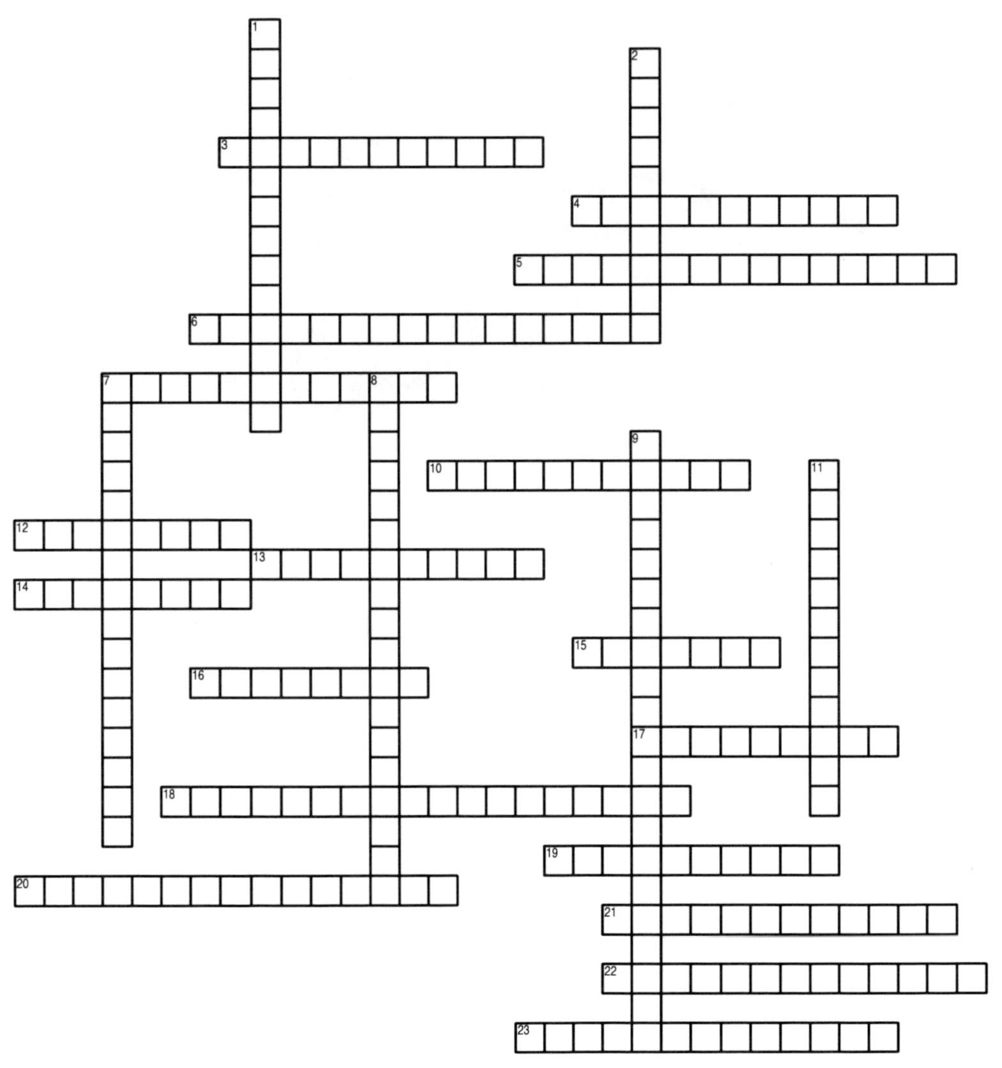

19 Biological Diversity

Life on Earth has evolved into countless forms. Clockwise from the upper right, these are seeds from tropical legume plants, euphorbia flowers, jewel beetles, cockle shells, foliose lichen, a fossilized fish, tropical butterflies, sprats, and pheasant feathers.

Globally, however, the rate of spcies loss may be 50 times higher now than at any time in the past 100,000 years.

LOOKING AHEAD

http://www.pearsoncustom.com/devry/myc

Exercises in Biological Diversity

Classification

1. Linnaean classification groups species together based on ______.

2. Fill in the levels of Linnaean classification from the largest group to the smallest group below.
Domain

_____

_____

_____

_____

_____

_____

Species

3. A species' scientific name consists of its ______ name and its ______ name.

4. Cladistic classification groups species together based on their ____.

5. The following cladogram shows evolutionary relationships between the rufous hummingbird, the honey mushroom, and the bristlecone pine.

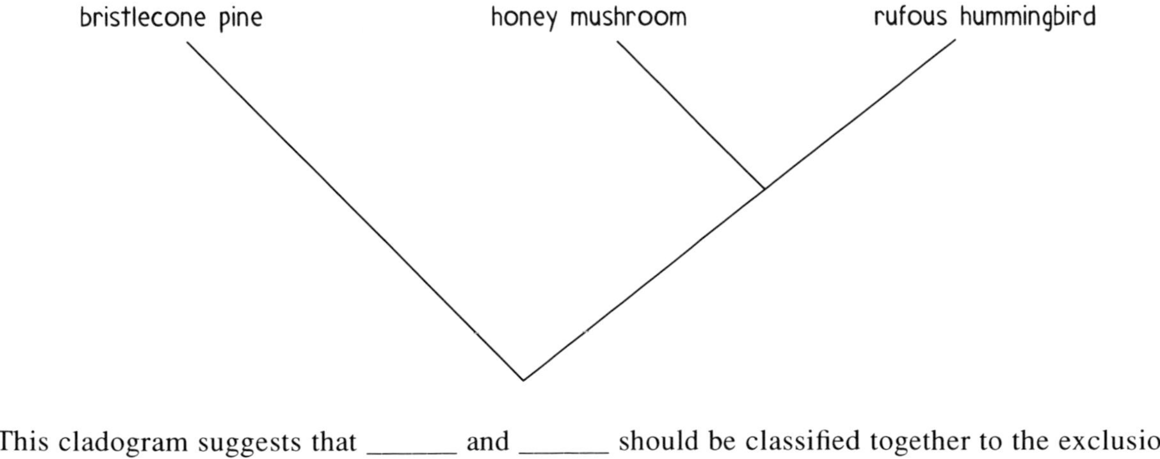

This cladogram suggests that ______ and ______ should be classified together to the exclusion of ________.

Biological Diversity I: Bacteria, Archaea, Protists

1. What are the three domains of life?

____

Of the three domains, ______ and ______ consist of prokaryotes and ______ consists of eukaryotes.

____

2. The four kingdoms that make up Eukarya are:

____

3. Are there any bacteria that can photosynthesize? Are there any heterotrophic bacteria?

____

4. How do bacteria typically reproduce?

____

5. Can bacteria exchange genetic material? If so, how?

____

____

____

6. Do the many bacteria that live in and on our bodies benefit us in any way?

____

7. Are archaea more closely related to bacteria or to eukaryotes? What evidence supports this?

____

____

____

Biological Diversity I: Bacteria, Archaea, Protists—continued

8. What's an extremophile? Are all archaea extremophiles?

____

____

____

9. What is a chemoautotroph?

____

____

10. Are each of the following groups of protists autotrophs or heterotrophs?
    - **A.** diatoms
    - **B.** amoebas
    - **C.** kelp
    - **D.** dinoflagellates
    - **E.** *PLASMODIUM* (the protist that causes malaria)

Biological Diversity II: Plants, Fungi, Animals

1. Match the following plant structures with their function:

stomata	**A.**	move water and nutrients up from the roots
roots	**B.**	take in carbon dioxide
shoots	**C.**	conduct photosynthesis
xylem	**D.**	move sugars produced during photosynthesis
phloem	**E.**	transport resources to different parts of plant
vascular system	**F.**	absorb water and nutrients from soil

2. The life history of plants involves a(n) ______ in which plants move between a haploid _______ stage and a diploid ______ stage.

3. Mosses are unique among plants in that the ______ is much larger than the ______. When you see a moss in the forest, you are looking at a(n) ______. The sperm are released by the male ______ directly into the environment, where they use their flagella to swim through a film of water to eggs in the female gametophyte. Sperm and egg then fuse and grow into a tiny (haploid/diploid) ______ that is completely dependent on the female gametophyte for nutrients and water. Eventually, cells in the sporophyte undergo meiosis to produce (haploid/diploid) spores that scatter and grow into new ______ (moss plants).

Biological Diversity II: Plants, Fungi, Animals—continued

4. Why are ferns less tied to a moist environment than mosses? Why are they more tied to a moist environment than seed plants?

____

____

____

____

5. What is pollen? What is a seed? What is a fruit? In what groups of plants are each of these structures found?

____

____

____

____

6. Fungi are autotrophs/heterotrophs/both. Fungi are unicellular/multicellular/both. Fungi reproduce sexually/asexually/both.

____

Biological Diversity II: Plants, Fungi, Animals

7. Match the following animal groups with the list of features. Some groups may have more than one feature.

sponges
cnidarians
flatworms
roundworms
arthropods
mollusks
annelids
echinoderms
chordates
catilaginous fishes
ray-finned fishes
amphibians
reptiles

A. muscular foot responsible for locomotion
B. swim bladder
C. the only animals that lack tissues
D. adaptations for subduing large prey and swallowing them whole
E. muscles all run longitudinally—from head to tail—down the body, resulting in a flailing whiplike motion
F. polyp stage and medusa stage alternate
G. leeches
H. segmented worms
I. segmented bodies and jointed legs
J. terrestrial vertebrates restricted to moist environments because their skins are composed of living cells that are vulnerable to drying out, and lay eggs without shells
K maintain a constant flow of water in through numerous pores, into the central cavity, and out the top, whose purpose is for food capture

Biological Diversity II: Plants, Fungi, Animals—continued

turtles	**L.** birds and crocodiles
snakes	**M.** tube feet
birds	**N.** tentacles armed with barbed stinging cells
mammals	**O.** hollow bones, air sacs in the body, and a four-chambered heart
	P. includes the most diverse group of living things on Earth, the insects
	Q. a notochord, gill slits, and a tail that extends beyond the anus
	R. starfish
	S. have a skeleton made of cartilage
	T. have hair and feed their young milk
	U. tapeworms
	V. platypus
	W. squeezes its entire body inside its ribcage
	X. flying endotherms
	Y. frogs

Chapter Review: Summary of Terms

Alternation of generations The plant life cycle, which alternates between a haploid gametophyte stage and a diploid sporophyte stage.

Animals A clade of multicellular heterotrophic eukaryotes that take food into their bodies for digestion.

Archaea One of the three domains of life, consisting of prokaryotic organisms, many of which are adapted to extreme environments.

Bacteria One of the three domains of life, consisting of a wide range of generally single-celled prokaryotic organisms.

Clade A group of species that includes an ancestor and all its descendants.

Cladogram A diagram that shows the history of speciation events among a group of organisms.

Ectotherms Organisms that regulate their body temperature behaviorally, by seeking either warm or cool areas—their body temperature tends to fluctuate depending on environmental conditions.

Endoskeleton An internal skeleton, such as that found in echinoderms and chordates.

Endotherms Organisms that rely on food metabolism to maintain a relatively constant and relatively high body temperature.

Exoskeleton An external skeleton, such as that found in arthropods.

Flower The reproductive structure of flowering plants, which may include stamens (male reproductive structures) and/or carpels (female reproductive structures), as well as petals.

Fruit In flowering plants, a structure surrounding the seeds that typically contributes to seed dispersal.

Fungi A clade of heterotrophic eukaryotes that obtain food by secreting digestive enzymes over organic matter and then absorbing the nutrients.

Larva A stage in the growth and development of animals that is distinct from the adult in form and ecology.

Mycorrhizae Close associations between fungi and the roots of plants in which the fungi obtain nutrients from the plant while helping the roots absorb water and minerals from the soil.

Plants A clade of autotrophic, multicellular, terrestrial eukaryotes that obtain energy through photosynthesis.
Pollen In seed plants, immature male gametophytes wrapped in protective coatings.
Protists Eukaryotic organisms that are not plants, animals, or fungi.
Seed In seed plants, a structure consisting of a sporophyte plant embryo, a food supply, and a tough outer coating.
Viruses Small pieces of genetic material wrapped in protein coats that infect and reproduce within host cells.

Practice Test for Chapter 19

Organizing Data

Define and distinguish between each pair of terms in the table below.

Pair of Terms	Definition and Differences
Endoskeleton vs. Exoskeleton	
Ectotherms vs. Endotherms	
Kingdom vs. Phylum	
Fruit vs. Seed	
Staman vs. Carpel	
Gametophyte vs. Sporophyte	
Xylem vs. Phloem	
Genus vs. Species	
Viruses vs. *Prions*	

Content Quiz

1. Early classifications of living organisms placed them in a hierarchy from simple to complex. For example, thousands of years ago, living organisms were arranged in a "Chain of Being" that proceeded from minerals to plants, animals, man, and God by:
   A. Aristotle
   B. Carolus Linnaeus
   C. Derek Lovley

2. Building on previous ideas and thinking, in the eighteenth century, Swedish naturalist __________ developed a new system of classification that emphasized the shared similarities of organisms. This system of classification makes use of multiple levels, which from largest to smallest are the domain, kingdom, phylum, class, order, family, genus, and species.
   A. Aristotle
   B. Carolus Linnaeus
   C. Derek Lovley

3. True or False? Each domain contains one or more kingdoms, each kingdom contains one or more phyla, each phylum contains one or more classes, and so on until you get to each genus containing one or more species.

4. True or False? Every living species belongs to one domain, one kingdom, one phylum, one class, one order, one family, one genus, and one species. You can think of each successive Linnaean level as allowing you to "home in" on a particular species, much the way successive geographical levels allow you to home in on a particular house and human resident.

5. At Linnaean system,
A. species are grouped together based on shared similarities.
B. all species have a two-part scientific name consisting of the genus name and species name.
C. genus and species names are always Latinized and italicized, with the genus capitalized.
D. sometimes the genus name is abbreviated as a single letter, as in *E. coli* for the human gut bacterium *Escherichia coli.*
E. all of the above.

6. At every level in the Linnaean system, species are grouped together based on ___________. For example, species in the class Mammalia (all mammals) are grouped together based on shared features such as their possession of hair and their production of milk.

7. Each specie has a scientific name. Each scientific name has a two-parts consisting of the _____ name and _______ name. Some examples of scientific names include *Homo sapiens* ("wise man") for humans and *Canis familiaris* ("intimate dog").

8. As seen in the following two examples, *Homo sapiens* ("wise man") and *Canis familiaris* ("intimate dog"), genus and species names are always ______ and _________ , with the genus _______.

9. Instead of Linnaean classification, biologists now aim to classify living organisms based on this evolutionary history because:
A. a classification based on evolutionary history is not at all arbitrary.
B. classifying organisms based on their evolutionary history allows biologists to make predictions about the characteristics of organisms that are unstudied or poorly known.
C. a classification system based on evolutionary history allows biologists to study more effectively how specific features of organisms evolved.
D. all of the above
E. none of the above.

10. True or False? In order to actually accomplish the goal of classifying organisms based on evolutionary history, biologists have to reconstruct the history of speciation events among a group of organisms using DNA sequences, fossils as well as information on the anatomical, behavioral, and molecular traits of existing organisms.

11. True or False? Interestingly, DNA can also provide evidence for how long it has been since particular speciation events occurred. This gives scientists an estimate for when particular groups of organisms diverged evolutionarily from one another.

12. The accumulating changes in the DNA sequence of a given species at a fairly constant rate over time is known as _____________.

13. True or False? By looking at the *molecular clocks* and how much the DNA sequence of a gene differs between two organisms, scientists can estimate how long ago the organisms diverged. Multiple genes, as well as information from the fossil record, are usually used to estimate divergence times.

14. Once biologists have a hypothesis for how speciation occurred within a group of organisms, this can be diagrammed in:
A. cladogram
B. *volutionary tre e*
C. *molecular clocks*
D. a and b
E. a and c
F. b and c

15. Biological groups that are constructed based on evolutionary history are called _______. It is a group that includes an ancestral species and all of its descendants. It can be small groups, such as the genus *Homo* or the species *Homo sapiens*, or broad groups, such as mammals or animals or eukaryotes

A. cladogram
B. *volutionary tre e*
C. *molecular clocks*
D. clade(s)

16. True or False? The cladistic classification relates to the Linnaean system of kingdoms, classes, orders, and families. For example, the Linnaean kingdom Animalia—all animals—is a clade. The Linnaean kingdoms Plantae and Fungi are also clades. Mammals, amphibians, primates, rodents, birds, frogs—these familiar Linnaean groups are all clades.

17. True or False? This means that all Linnaean groups are clades.

18. True or False? Cladograms are used to diagram the evolutionary relationships among species or other biological groups. The cladogram for humans, elephants, and daisies shows that humans and elephants are more closely related to each other than either is to daisies.

19. True or False? Under the Linnaean system, species are grouped together based on shared similarities. Turtles, lizards, snakes, and crocodiles had been grouped together based on shared features such as "coldbloodedness" and the possession of scales. Under the cladistic classifica-tion, species are grouped together based on their evolutionary relationships. Birds, because they are "warm-blooded" and have feathers, were placed in a different group; squarely among the reptiles.

20. The scientific name of the endangered orangutan of Sumatra is *Pongo abelii*. This means that its genus name is ________, and its species name is ________?

21. True or False? Life is classified into three domains—Bacteria, Archaea, and Eukarya. Of the three domains, Bacteria and Archaea consist of prokaryotic organisms. Eukarya includes all organisms with nucleated cells. The domain Eukarya is further divided into four kingdoms—Protists. Plants, Fungi, and Animals.

22. True or False? The Protist kingdom is problematic because it includes all eukaryotes that aren't plants, animals, or fungi—in other words, it's a hodgepodge of species that don't represent a clade. Amoebas, kelp, and diatoms are all protists, although they have little in common other than the fact that they are eukaryotes. Until a more accurate classification emerges, however, we are stuck with the term Protists.

23. True or False? Birds aren't only reptiles—they're dinosaurs! This is because birds are descended from the last common ancestor of all the dinosaurs, too. So dinosaurs didn't all go extinct—birds survived, and they are certainly alive and well today, with nearly 10,000 described species.

24. True or False? According to the cladogram of the evolutionary relationships, birds *are not* descended from the last common ancestor of reptiles, and so are crocodiles.

25. The domain of life that is the most ancient lineages on Earth, occupies habitats where no other organisms can survive, and life on Earth would quickly end without them is _________.

26. __________ are prokaryotes so diverse that it is hard to make generalizations about them. Some are autotrophs, make their own food through photosynthesis. Others are heterotrophs that obtain food from other organisms. Most bacteria are single-celled, but others gather in multicellular clusters.

27. True or False? Under favorable conditions, reptiles can divide very quickly, as often as every 20 minutes. This allows reptile populations to grow rapidly when resources are plentiful. In poor conditions, many reptiles form hardy spores that remain dormant until conditions improve.

28. True or False? Bacteria can live in habitats where no other organisms can survive. These bacteria were found thriving in Antarctica's Lake Vostok, which is thousands of meters below the ice sheet.

29. True or False? **Archaea** which are now recognized as a distinct domain of prokaryotic organisms, are more closely related to eukaryotes than to bacteria. Many features of archaean genetics in particular link archaea to eukaryotes—their ribosomes and tRNA resemble those of eukaryotes, their genes contain introns like those of eukaryotes, and their DNA is associated with histone proteins, like that of eukaryotes.

30. True or False? Many archaea are adapted to extreme environments, such as very salty ponds or the scalding waters of hot springs and hydrothermal vents. These archaea are called "extremophiles"—lovers of the extreme—and are of particular interest to biologists because they live in conditions thought to be similar to those found on the early Earth.

31. True or False? When resources are plentiful, bacterial populations grow exponentially. (This is true for populations of other organisms as well, but bacteria more commonly encounter such favorable conditions.).

32. True or False? Most bacteria are very small because they rely on diffusion to obtain nutrients. However, a few are big enough to be seen with the naked eye! The largest bacteria known belong to the species *Thiomargarita namibiensis*, which means "Sulfur Pearls of Namibia." These giant bacteria measure of a millimeter across, or about the size of the period at the end of this sentence. If a typical bacterium were the size of a mouse, scientists say, these bacteria would be as big as blue whales!

33. Mud-dwelling bacteria of the genus *Geobacter* directly release electrons as they consume organic pollutants and decaying plant and animal matter. Team led by biologist from University of Massachusetts, Amherst, designed a battery (simple system) for catching these electrons, and run the battery on pure bacteria power. The next challenge will be to make *Geobacter* energy generation more efficient. This biologist is
A. Carolus Linnaeus.
B. Darwin.
C. Derek Lovley.
E. Abour Cherif.

34. True or False? *Geobacter* is already making itself useful running weather sensors and deep-sea mapping instruments, devices that require only 1 watt of power. A series of *Geobacter* "batteries" (the tubes in the background) are powering this calculator.

35. Some archaea are *chemoautotrophs* that are able to make food using ________ energy rather than energy from sunlight. Archaea in hydrothermal vent habitats, for example, obtain energy from a _________ abundant there, hydrogen sulfide. These archaea form the basis of remarkable biological vent communities that are entirely independent of sunlight.

36. Eukaryotes that are not plants, animals, or fungi are
A. Archaea
B. Protists.
C. Both, a and b
D. None of the above.

37. True or False? Protests includes autotrophs, heterotrophs, and even species that use both strategies to obtain nutrition. They may be single-celled or multicellular.

38. True or False? Certain protists, the slime molds, actually hover somewhere between single-celled and multicellular—they go from one condition to the other during the course of their lives. By studying this process, scientists have obtained clues about how multicellularity might have evolved in other biological groups.

39. True or False? Diatoms are bacteria that float in the open ocean and have elaborate, often very beautiful shells made of silica. These shells are sometimes used in manmade products—for example, they provide the gritty texture of toothpaste.

40. True or False? The singlecelled *dinoflagellates* are important oceanic photosynthesizers. Dinoflagellate population explosions are responsible for the "red tides" that occur when sunlight and nutrients are plentiful. The discoloration that gives red tides their name is caused, believe it or not, by the sheer number of dinoflagellates in the water!

41. Most heterotrophic protists are mobile, active hunters, and all have special cell vacuoles for digesting prey. They include:
A. amoebas.
B. ciliates.
C. flagellates.
D. a and b.
E. a, b, and c.

42. ________ move by extending part of their body forward as a pseudopodium, a temporary protrusion of the cell, and then pulling the rest of the body behind. They surround and engulf prey.

43. _________ move by beating numerous hairlike projections called cilia.

44. __________ move by whipping long flagella. Both ciliates and flagellates have openings that function as "mouths."

45. True or False? Protists are responsible for a number of serious human diseases, including malaria, African sleeping sickness, and amoebic dysentery.

46. _________ is caused by *Plasmodium* protists that divide their life cycle between mosquitoes and humans. Humans contract the disease when they are bitten by infected mosquitoes.

47. True or False? In amoebic dysentery Plasmodium protists infect human red blood cells where they reproduce in huge numbers. The synchronized emergence of protists from host red blood cells causes periodic bouts of chills, fever, and vomiting.

48. True or False? Red tides aren't always red—the color of the water may also be pink, purple, green, orange, brown, or blue, depending on the dinoflagellate responsible and which pigment it uses for photosynthesis.

49. True or False? In almost every natural terrestrial environment, the majority of life forms you come across are plants. **Plants** are autotrophic, multicellular, terrestrial eukaryotes that obtain energy through photosynthesis.

50. True or False? Plants have a variety of adaptations that make them well suited to their terrestrial environments. Roots anchor them to the ground and absorb water and nutrients from the soil. Shoots, which include stems and leaves, are a plant's aboveground structures and conduct photosynthesis. Leaves are the site of the bulk of photosynthesis. Most plants also have a vascular system, a sort of plant "circulatory system" that distributes water and other resources.

51. True or False? In photosynthesis, sunlight is caught on the surfaces of the stems and the roots, and carbon dioxide is taken in through small pores known as *stomata*.

52. The plant vascular system consists of two types of tissues: the _________ is made up of dead, tube-shaped cells through which water and nutrients move up from the roots. The ________ consists of living cells that pass the sugars produced during photosynthesis down from the leaves.

53. True or False? Maple syrup is a liquid that flows in a plant's vascular system. It is made by boiling down liquid called sap that collected from the vascular systems of maple trees.

54. The three major groups of plants are ________, __________, and __________ seed.

55. True or False? While the details of the life cycle vary among the major groups of plants, plant reproduction occurs through an **alternation of generations**, in which the life cycle alternates between a haploid stage called a *gametophyte* and a diploid stage called a *sporophyte*.

56. True or False? *Mosses* are small, seedless plants that have no vascular systems. Instead, every part of a moss plant receives water directly from the environment through diffusion. As a result, mosses can live only in moist habitats such as bogs or the shady parts of forests.

57. True or False? In most mosses, there are separate male and female gametophytes that produce sperm and eggs, respectively. The sperm are released by the male gametophyte directly into the environment, where they use their flagella to swim through a film of water to eggs in the female gametophyte.

58. Mosses are unique among plants. When you see a moss in the forest, you are looking at a haploid gametophyte. This is because in mosses,
A. the gametophyte is much larger than the sporophyte.
B. the sporophyte is much larger than the gametophyte.
C. the sporophyte is always in the gametophyte.
D. the gametophyte is always in the sporophyte.
E. you can not distinguish between the gametophyte and the sporophyte.

59. Stomata are tiny pores in plant leaves used to take in carbon dioxide. Most stomata are found on the shaded undersides of leaves, again to help reduce water loss To prevent too much water loss, the size of stomata is controlled by:
A. flanking "xylem" cells.
B. flanking "phloem" cells.
C. flanking "guard" cells.
D. flanking "stem" cells.

60. True or False? In mosses, sperm and egg fuse and grow into a tiny diploid sporophyte that is completely dependent on the female gametophyte for nutrients and water. Eventually, cells in the sporophyte undergo meiosis to produce haploid spores that scatter and grow into new gametophytes—new moss plants.

61. True or False? *Ferns* are seed plants with distinctive feathery leaves. They are often found in the forest understory, where they thrive in the shade of large trees. Even though ferns have a vascular system for transporting water and nutrients, they still require moist habitats because, as with mosses, the sperm of ferns must swim through the environment to fertilize eggs.

62. In like in the Mosses, when you see a fern in the forest, you are looking at a diploid sporophyte. This is because in ferns,
A. the haploid gametophyte is much larger than the diploid sporophyte.
B. the diploid sporophyte is much larger than the haploid gametophyte.
C. the sporophyte is always in the gametophyte.
D. the gametophyte is always in the sporophyte.
E. you can not distinguish between the gametophyte and the sporophyte.

63. True or False? A mature fern sporophyte forms haploid spores on the underside of special leaves. These spores are scattered and grow into tiny, but independent, haploid gametophytes. The gametophytes then form eggs and sperm, which fuse and grow into new sporophytes.

64. *Seed plants* which are the largest group of plants, have two key features that have made them successful in a wide variety of land habitats:
A. Pollen and seeds.
B. Leaves and flowers.
C. Roots and stems.
D. Branches and leaves.

65. True or False? Pollen which can be transported to female gametophytes by wind or by animals, consists of numerous tiny grains, each of which is an immature male gametophyte wrapped in a protective coating.

66. True or False? Seed plants do not require the swimming sperm that limit mosses and ferns to moist habitats. The fertilized eggs of seed plants grow into small embryonic sporophytes that are then encased in a tough outer coating along with a food supply—this entire structure is called a **seed**.

67. In seed plants,
A. the haploid gametophyte is much larger than the diploid sporophyte.
B. the diploid sporophyte is much larger than the haploid gametophyte.
C. the sporophyte is always in the gametophyte.
D. the gametophyte is always in the sporophyte.
E. you can not distinguish between the gametophyte and the sporophyte.

68. True or False? In the alternation of generation in ferns, the sporophyte stage is much larger than the gametophyte stage. The gametophyte is very small, but independent.

69. The two major groups of seed plants are conifers and flowering plants. The _______ are the largest and most successful group of seed plants.

70. The ___________ include well-known species such as redwoods, pines, cedars, spruces, and firs. Conifers have waxy, needlelike leaves and reproductive structures called *cones*.

71. Flowering plants have two important features absent in other seed plants________ and ________.

72. The ________ of a flower is the male reproductive structure. It consists of a stalk capped with an *anther* where pollen develops. The ________ is the female reproductive structure. It includes an *ovary* where eggs develop and a stalk capped by the *stigma*, a sticky structure that traps pollen.

73. After studying a species of night-blooming orchid in Madagascar, for example, _________ predicted the existence of a nocturnal moth with a tongue 30 centimeters long. Forty years later, the moth was discovered!

74. True or False? Flowering plants surround their seeds with a structure called a **fruit**. Fruits help spread seeds around—when fruits are eaten by birds or mammals, for example, the seeds pass unharmed through the digestive tract and eventually emerge far from the parent plants.

75. True or False? Tasty fruits evolved in certain plants because they were more likely to be eaten by animals and so were more likely to be dispersed. Seeds themselves, on the other hand, often taste bad, discouraging animals from eating them.

76. Some fruits help plants spread their seeds using other strategies—the burrs that catch on your socks during a hike are also _______. These hitch a ride until you pull them off and drop them on the ground, where the seeds inside them may just grow and take root.

77. True or False? All plant flowers smell sweet, Including flowers of the dead horse arum lily mimic the smell of rotting flesh to attract certain flies that normally lay their eggs in carrion.

78. When you keep a loaf of bread too long, or leave a lemon in the fruit bowl for weeks, you often end up with some fuzzy stuff called mold. This mold is a
A. fungus.
B. fern.
C. moss.
D. protist.
E. archaea.

79. _________, the first antimalarial drug, comes from the bark of cinchona trees, long used in native Peruvian medicine to treat fever, digestive ailments, and malaria.

80. ___________ originally came from willow bark, which has been used for thousands of years to relieve pain.

81. Madagascar _______, a plant used by several native peoples for diabetes and other conditions, provided two new cancer drugs.

82. ________ are heterotrophs, some are single-celled, but most species are multicellular. Multicellular that are composed of masses of small threadlike filaments. They obtain food by secreting digestive enzymes over organic matter and then absorbing the nutrients.

83. Fungi are essential to the survival and growth of many, perhaps most, plants. This is because in most plant species, roots form close associations with fungi known as ____________. The fungus receives nutrients from the plant while helping roots absorb water and minerals from soil.

84. True or False? Fungi important to humans include yeast, which is used in baking and brewing, and edible mushrooms and truffles. Fungi are also used to make blue cheeses such as Roquefort and gorgonzola (the blue stuff is actually a colossal number of minuscule fungal spores—enjoy!). Penicillin, the first antibiotic, was originally isolated from a fungus in 1928.

85. True or False? Yeast infections, ringworm, and athlete's foot, dutch elm, are all examples of disease caused by a fungus.

86. True or False? Unlike fungi secrete digestive enzymes *out over* their food, animals which obtain nutrients by eating other organisms, *ingest* food, taking it into their bodies for digestion.

87. Most animals reproduce ________ and are diploid during most of their life cycle, with the gametes—sperm and eggs—being the only haploid stage.

88. True or False? Many animals go through a juvenile period as a **larva** that is markedly different from adults in form and ecology. Also, most of them have muscles for moving, sense organs for taking in information from their environments, and nervous systems for controlling their actions.

89. True or False? *Sponges* are sedentary marine animals that posses a tubelike structure with a large central cavity, most likely are sponges.

90. True or False? The largest living organism in the world is a fungus—an underground honey mushroom in Oregon's Blue Mountains that measures 5.6 kilometers (3.5 miles) across! Scientists have collected DNA from different parts of this organism to confirm that it is all one individual.

91. The only animals that lack tissues, groups of similar cells that perform a certain function, are the ________.

92. If you separate a sponge's cells by passing it through a sieve, the cells will reassemble on the other side, forming a new sponge. No other animal can do that. The sponge's ability to reassemble is possible because:
A. sponges lack reproductive system.
B. sponges lack digestive system.
C. sponges lack skeleton system.
D. sponges lack tissues systems.

93. Jellyfish, sea anemones, corals, and hydras are examples of
A. arthropods
B. sponges
C. *cnidarians*
D. mycorrhizae

94. Unlike sponges, _________ have two distinct tissue layers—an outer layer that protects the body and an inner layer that digests food. These are separated by a jellylike middle layer.

95. True or False? In Cnidarians, prey are digested in a *gastrovascular cavity* that has a single opening that serves as both mouth and anus. Also, many cnidarians alternate between a sedentary polyp stage and a mobile, bell-shaped, medusa stage.

96. True or False? Coral reefs occur in tropical oceans, where they are found in clear, shallow waters with temperatures between 20 and 28°C (68 and 82°F). They are among the most diverse, and most important, ecosystems in the world. Numerous marine species, including commercially important fish, spend all or part of their life cycles in coral reefs.

97. True or False? Corals are cnidarians that form colonies of tiny polyps encased in calcium carbonate skeletons. They are found in shallow, warm, tropical waters. Most occur between 30 degrees north latitude and 30 degrees south latitude.

98. Coral bleaching occurs when corals evict their dinoflagellates. The corals quite literally turn white since it is the dinoflagellates that give them their colors. Coral bleaching is most often triggered by:
A. Increases in seawater temperature.
B. Decreases in seawater temperature.
C. Increases in seawater pH.
D. Decreases in seawater pH.

99. True or False? A rise of as little as a few degrees Celsius can start bleaching. However, only extended periods of warming—not rapid temperature fluctuations—produce bleaching.

100. True or False? Scientists have shown that elevated temperatures interfere with dinoflagellate photosynthesis, damaging certain proteins that help convert carbon dioxide to glucose. The inability to complete photosynthesis causes toxins to build up in the dinoflagellates' bodies, which causes the corals to eject them. Corals can survive for a short time without their dinoflagellates. However, if warm temperatures or other stressful conditions continue for too long, the corals starve to death.

101. True or False? Mass coral bleaching events have become common in recent years, almost certainly due to the higher water temperatures that have resulted from global warming. In 2002, high ocean temperatures affected coral reefs worldwide, killing more than 90 percent of corals in some places.

102. _________ have distinct "head" and "tail" ends, "back" and "belly" sides, a single body opening serves as both mouth and anus, and an elaborately branched digestive tract transports nutrients to the entire body. The flat shape of body allows oxygen to be absorbed efficiently across the skin via diffusion.

103. True or False? In humans, earthworms cause the disease schistosomiasis, which is characterized by diarrhea and intense abdominal pain.

104. True or False? Roundworms which are different earthworms, occupy almost every conceivable habitat, and often in staggering numbers—thousands of individuals can sometimes be found in a single handful of soil.

105. Several human diseases, including hookworm, pinworm, elephantitis, and trichinosis are caused by:
A. arthropods
B. roundworms
C. flatworms
D. earthworms

106. True or False? Roundworm *Caenorhabditis elegans* is very significant to biologists because it the first species to have its entire genome sequenced.

107. ____________*which* are found in just about every known habitat on Earth, include species as diverse as lobsters, barnacles, spiders, scorpions, ticks, centipedes, and insects.

108. The living organisms that have an external **exoskeleton** made of chitin that protects and supports the body, as well as have segmented bodies and jointed legs, are:
A. arthropods
B. roundworms
C. flatworms
D. earthworms

109. True of False? In most species of Antropods, some segments of the body are fused and some legs have been modified during the course of evolution to form mouthparts, antennae, or reproductive structures. Arthropods also have a brain and a number of highly developed sense organs.

110. The major groups of arthropods are the crustaceans, the chelicerates, and the uniramians. The __________ include centipedes, millipedes, and insects. Insects are noteworthy as the most diverse group of living organisms on Earth—there are over a million known species and perhaps as many as ten times that number waiting to be discovered.

111. The major groups of arthropods are the crustaceans, the chelicerates, and the uniramians. The ________________ include horseshoe crabs, spiders, scorpions, ticks, and mites.They have four pairs of legs and one pair of mouthparts.

112. The major groups of arthropods are the crustaceans, the chelicerates, and the uniramians. The ____________ include lobsters, crabs, shrimp, krill, and barnacles.

113. True or False? All insects have three body parts—a head, thorax, and abdomen—and three pairs of legs. Most also have two pairs of wings. Many insects are important to humans as plant pollinators. Others impact humans as disease carriers (mosquitoes carry malaria and West Nile virus) or as agricultural pests.

114. Living organisms that are soft-bodied animals, most have a protective shell, have a muscular "foot" responsible for locomotion, a visceral mass holds the digestive and reproductive organs, and a mantle that secretes the shell, and include organisms such as clams, oysters, squids, octopuses, snails, and slugs, are:
A. Arthropods
B. Mollusks
C. Annelids
D. Echinoderm
E. Chordates

115. True or False? The earliest flying insects weren't able to fold their wings back on their bodies. That evolutionary innovation came later in insect history. Dragonflies are an example of a group that still retains the old trait—have you noticed how their wings always stick straight out?

116. *Bivalves Cephalopods and, Gastropods are* There are three main groups of:
A. Antropods
B. Mollusks
C. Annelids
D. Echinoderms
E. Chordates

117. There are three main groups of mollusks. _____________ such as squids and octopuses are active predators that use arms (eight in octopuses and ten in squids) to capture prey. They also have well-developed brains and eyes.

118. There are three main groups of mollusks. __________ have two hinged shells and include species such as clams, oysters, mussels, and scallops. Most of them are sedentary and feed by filtering small particles from the water.

119. There are three main groups of mollusks. __________ have a single, spiral shell and include species such as snails, abalone, and limpets. Most gastropods are herbivores.

120. The segmented worms which have muscles are arranged in both circular (around the body) and longitudinal (head-to-tail) orientations, and included worms such as earthworms, leeches, and the less familiar marine bristleworms, are known as:
A. antropods.
B. mollusks.
C. annelids.
D. echinoderms.
E. chordates.

121. True or False? The flatworms feed by passing large amounts of soil through their digestive tracts and absorbing the available nutrients. They play an essential role in decomposing organic materials, and their burrowing activity helps to aerate soil, supplying it with oxygen.

122. ___________ are external parasites that feed off the blood of their hosts. They usually cut through skin using their bladelike teeth and secrete anticoagulants to keep blood from clotting while they feed.

123. The living organisms with spiny surfaces, have internal skeletons, or **endoskeletons**, made of small interlocking plates, use small, suckerlike appendages called tube feet to move, and include marine animals such as the sea stars, sea urchins, and sea cucumbers, are:
A. antropods
B. mollusks
C. annelids
D. echinoderms
E. chordates

124. The living organisms that share four key features: a brain and a spinal cord that runs along the back of the body; a *notochord*—a stiff but bendable rod that supports the back; gill slits; and a tail that extends beyond the anus, are all belong to:
A. antropods
B. mollusks
C. annelids
D. echinoderms
E. chordates

125. The _______ include tunicates, lancelets, and vertebrates, that includes humans.

126. ___________ are sedentary marine species also known as sea squirts. They feed by filtering small particles from the water. ___________ are small, swimming, bladeshaped marine species that live buried in sand. Like tunicates, _________ filter food from the water. __________ are animals with backbones. They include several groups of fishes as well as amphibians, reptiles, and mammals.

127. True or False? The earliest vertebrates had mouths lacking hinged jaws. However, the only jawless vertebrates still in existence are hagfishes, slimy marine species that eat marine worms and other animals, and lampreys, parasites that suck blood from ray-finned fishes.

128. True or False? At one time, "bleeding" a patient with leeches was standard medical treatment for a wide variety of ailments. Then this practice was viewed as medical quackery. Now, the leech is back! Leeches release powerful anticoagulants—substances that keep blood from clotting—when they feast on their hosts. And leech anticoagulants, it turns out, are still better than anything in the arsenal of modern medicine.

129. Cartilaginous fishes which include sharks, skates, and rays, have skeletons made of:
A. cartilage
B. bone.
C. hybrid of bone and cartilage
D. hybrid of sponge and cartilage

130. The type of fish that have a gas-containing sac called a *swim bladder* use to adjust their buoyancy, and include fishes such as tuna, salmon, perch, bass, and so forth, are called:
A. ray-finned
B. cartilaginous fish
C. boned fish

131. The swim bladder is filled with just enough gas that the overall density (mass/volume) of the fish is the __________ the density of water—because of this, a ray-finned fish neither sinks nor floats, allowing it great flexibility of motion in the water.

132. True or False? Cartilaginous fishes, which do not have swim bladders, sink if they stop swimming.

133. True or False? *Lungfishes* and *coelacanths* resemble ray-finned fishes superficially, but they are actually more closely related to terrestrial vertebrates such as amphibians, reptiles, and mammals.

134. True or False? Although there are only a few species, lungfishes and coelacanths are of particular interest to evolutionary biologists because they provide clues about how the limbs of terrestrial vertebrates evolved.

135. *Amphibians* include salamanders, frogs, and caecilians. ___________ have compact bodies suited to jumping, ___________ have elongated bodies and tails, and __________, the least familiar group, are limbless amphibians that live primarily as burrowers.

136. The name "amphibian" refers to the fact that many species make use
A. aquatic habitats.
B. terrestrial habitats
C. aquatic and terrestrial habitats.

137. Although, some amphibians are entirely aquatic and many are entirely terrestrial, all amphibians are restricted to _______ environments because their skins are composed of living cells that are vulnerable to drying out.

138. True or False? The earliest vertebrates did not have hinged jaws. However, only modern lampreys retain this condition.

139. True or False? Lungfishes may look like other ray-finned fishes, but they are more closely related to terrestrial vertebrates.

140. Living organisms that have skin that is made of dead cells to prevent water loss and have shelled eggs that are not vulnerable to drying out, belong to:
A. *amniotes*
B. antropods
C. mollusks
D. annelids
E. echinoderms
F. chordates

141. Reptiles (including the feathered ones—birds) and mammals are *Amniotes.* __________ include turtles, lizards (including snakes), crocodilians, and birds.

142. True or False? Birds are reptiles (a group of dinosaurs, in fact) that have evolved the ability to fly Flight in birds is associated with a suite of adaptations including wings, feathers, hollow bones, air sacs in the body, and a four-chambered heart. Birds and crocodiles are each other's closest living relatives. Both show parental care of young in addition to sharing skeletal features.

143. During metabolism, when organic molecules are broken down to make ATP, energy is lost to the environment as heat—this energy helps warm the body. Because of this, endotherms have to eat:
A. much less food than equivalently sized ectotherms.
B. much more food than equivalently sized ectotherms.
C. the same amount of food that is equivalently sized ectotherms.

144. Amphibians have long been favorite organisms for studies of animal development because:
A. the embryos in the eggs develop very fast.
B. the development stages are very distinguished and easy to recognize.
C. the eggs have no shells and thus are transparent.
D. all of the above.
E. none of the above.

145. True or False? Hundreds of species of salamanders, found in the family Plethodontidae, have neither lungs nor gills. Instead, they get all their oxygen through their skins. Scientists hypothesize that munglessness originally evolved in fast-flowing mountain streams where lungs—more or less big bags of air—made animals too buoyant to swim effectively.

146. _________ are amniotes that have hair and feed their young milk. All mammals are endotherms. The majority of them live on the ground, but bats fly and two groups, seals and whales, are partly or fully aquatic.

147. There are three major groups of mammals:

148. ____________ such as the platypus and spiny echidna differ from other mammals in that they lay eggs. They feed their young milk but do not have nipples. Instead, milk is secreted over the skin and lapped up by the young.

149. __________ such as possums, koalas, and kangaroos give birth to live young at a very early developmental stage. Upon birth, the young crawl up to the mother's pouch and attach to a nipple where they feed and continue development.

150. ___________, which include the vast majority of living mammal species, also give birth to live young, but these are born at a more advanced stage of development than in marsupials.

151. True or False? Today, the platypus, which is an egg-laying mammal, is classified in the mammalian clade Monotremata, which means "one hole" and refers to the animals' single exit for reproductive, excretory, and digestive systems. Only one other creature—the spiny echidna, the platypus's closest relative left on Earth—belongs to the group.

152. Bird wings function as airfoils. Lift is produced by:
A. the difference in air pressure above and below the wing.
B. the high air pressure above the wing.
C. the high air pressure below the wing.
D. the low air pressure above the wing.
E. the low air pressure below the wing.

153. True or False? The rapid mutation of viral genomes explains why there's never a shortage of colds to catch and why the flu comes back, in a different form, year after year.

154. *Prions* are unique among infectious agents in that they lack:
A. protein materials.
B. amio acids.
C. genetic material.
D. all of the above.

155. True or False? Prions are misfolded proteins, have no genetic materials, believed to cause mad cow disease and the related Creutzfeldt-Jakob disease in humans. Both of these conditions are characterized by fatal brain degeneration. Prions infect cells, where they "reproduce" by converting normal proteins to the misfolded, prion variety.

156. True or False? Disease causing prions are most likely transmitted through the consumption of infected animal products. Cooking, which destroys the nucleic acids found in all other types of infectious agents, has no effect on prions.

157. True or False? In recent years, scientists have manipulated the genomes of certain human cold viruses to make them preferentially attack cancer cells in the body. These viruses are known as oncolytic viruses (*onco* means "cancer" and *lytic* means "killing"). Where radiation and chemotherapy generally kill many normal cells in addition to tumor cells, oncolytic viruses have been designed to target cancer cells specifically. As a result, treatment with oncolytic viruses has fewer negative side effects than traditional therapies. A number of oncolytic viruses are now in clinical trials.

158. Which of the following is true?
A. All viruses have DNA.
B. A few viruses have evolved the ability to reproduce outside a host cell.
C. Viruses infect all other forms of life, from bacteria to plants and animals.
D. Viroids are circular proteins that infect plants.

159. Match each term in the right to its best discretion on the left column

Cladogram, ____	**A.** Accumulating changes in their DNA sequence at a fairly constant rate over time.
Bacteria _____	**B.** Small, seedless plants that have no vascular systems.
Molecular clocks. ____	**C.** Evolutionary tree
Mosses ____	**D.** Reproduce asexually by dividing, and most exchange genetic material at least occasionally—when they take up small pieces of naked DNA from the environment
Ethnobotany _____	**E.** Focus on plant use in prehistoric times by examining seeds, pollen, wood, and other plant remains found at archaeological sites.
Paleoethnobotanists ____	**F.** The study of how people use plants, generally by interviewing local peoples and studying their traditions and habits.
Exoskeleton ____	**G.** It is incapable of growth and must be shed periodically as animals grow.
Dragonflies ___	**H.** Have electroreceptive organs that are able to detect the electric currents given off by the muscles and nerves of nearby prey.
Annelids ____	**I.** Animals that regulate their body temperature behaviorally by seeking sunlight when they need to warm up and shade when they need to cool down.
Sharks ____	**J.** Their wings always stick straight out. They still retains the old trait.
Endotherms ____	**K.** Circular molecules of RNA, lack a protein coat and infect plants
Viroids ____	**L.** Animals that maintain a relatively constant and relatively high body temperature by metabolizing large amounts of food.
Ectotherms ____	**M.** Able to contract one part of the body while keeping the rest of the body still.

Critical Thinking Questions

1. Why is a cladistic classification, the classification of life by evolutionary history, more useful for biologists studying the evolution of traits than the Linnaean classification system?
2. Are humans more closely related to button mushrooms or to celery?
3. Some people contract yeast infections after taking a course of antibiotics. Why?
4. How does the alternation of generations differ among mosses, ferns, and seed plants?
5. Why don't mosses and ferns need pollinators?
6. Fruits evolved to help flowering plants disperse their seeds. How is dispersal adaptive?
7. The temperature increases associated with global warming devastate coral reefs through bleaching. A second effect of global warming is rising sea levels (due primarily to the expansion of seawater as its temperature. How would rising sea levels affect corals?
8. If global warming continues, how might the species composition of coral reefs change over time?
9. For all their success, the one thing insects don't seem to have is size—why are there no giant insects?

10. Dispersal is important for most living organisms. How do animals disperse? How do animal dispersal strategies compare with those of plants?

11. Does an eagle or a sparrow produce more lift as it flies?

12. Given the way lift is produced, do you think it is a greater challenge for large birds or small birds to keep themselves aloft?

13. Check whether or not the matching definition is correct for each term.

Alternation of generations.	The plant life cycle, which alternates between a haploid gametophyte stage and a diploid sporophyte stage
Animals	A clade of multicellular heterotrophic eukaryotes that take food into their bodies for digestion.
Archaea	One of the three domains of life, consisting of prokaryotic organisms, many of which are adapted to extreme environments.
Bacteria.	One of the three domains of life, consisting of a wide range of generally single-celled prokaryotic organisms
Clade	A group of species that includes an ancestor and all its descendants.
Cladogram	A diagram that shows the history of speciation events among a group of organisms.
Ectotherms	Organisms that regulate their body temperature behaviorally, by seeking either warm or cool areas—their body temperature tends to fluctuate depending on environmental conditions.
Endoskeleton	An internal skeleton, such as that found in echinoderms and chordates.
Endotherms	Organisms that rely on food metabolism to maintain a relatively constant and relatively high body temperature.
Exoskeleton	An external skeleton, such as that found in arthropods.
Flower	The reproductive structure of flowering plants, which may include stamens (male reproductive structures) and/or carpels (female reproductive structures), as well as petals.
Fruit	In flowering plants, a structure surrounding the seeds that typically contributes to seed dispersal.
Fungi	A clade of heterotrophic eukaryotes that obtain food by secreting digestive enzymes over organic matter and then absorbing the nutrients.
Larva	A stage in the growth and development of animals that is distinct from the adult in form and ecology.
Mycorrhizae	Close associations between fungi and the roots of plants in which the fungi obtain nutrients from the plant while helping the roots absorb water and minerals from the soil.
Plants	A clade of autotrophic, multicellular, terrestrial eukaryotes that obtain energy through photosynthesis.
Pollen	In seed plants, immature male gametophytes wrapped in protective coatings.
Protists	Eukaryotic organisms that are not plants, animals, or fungi.
Seed	In seed plants, a structure consisting of a sporophyte plant embryo, a food supply, and a tough outer coating.
Viruses	Small pieces of genetic material wrapped in protein coats that infect and reproduce within host cells.

Key Terms

allopatric speciation
analogy
binomial
biological species concept
clade
cladistics
class
convergent evolution
domain
exaptation
family
genus
geologic time scale
kingdom
macroevolution
order
paedomorphosis
phyla
phylogenetic tree
phylogeny
postzygotic barriers
prezygotic barriers
punctuated equilibrium
radiometric dating
speciation
species
sympatric speciation
systematics
taxonomy
three-domain system

Crossword Puzzle

Use the Key Terms list from this chapter to fill in the crossword puzzle.

ACROSS

5. a group of classes
7. the study of the diversity and relationships of organisms, past and present
8. the system of classification that divides all life into three groups
9. the origin of new species
11. the type of systematics that uses computers and homologous structures
14. the evolution of a structure in one context that becomes adapted for other functions
17. the type of concept that defines a species
18. the identification, naming, and classification of species
19. anatomical similarity due to convergent evolution
22. a branching diagram that represents a hypothesis about evolutionary relationships among organisms
24. in classification, the taxonomic category just below genus
25. the first part of a binomial
27. the type of barriers that prevent development of a zygote that is a hybrid between species
28. the broadest category of classification that contains kingdoms
29. a table of historical periods grouped into four eras

DOWN

1. the process by which new species form in spurts of rapid change followed by periods of slow speciation
2. major biological changes evident in the fossil record
3. the retention of juvenile body features in the adult stage
4. the type of barriers that prevent the fertilization of the egg of different species
6. the use of half-lives to identify the age of fossils
10. a two-part, Latinized name of a species; for example, *Homo sapiens*
12. a group of orders
13. a group of genera
15. the type of evolution in which unrelated organisms evolve structures with similar functions
16. the evolutionary history of a species
19. the type of speciation in which a new species forms by geographical isolation
20. a group of families
21. the type of speciation in which a new species forms without geographic isolation
23. a group of phyla
26. an ancestral species and all of its descendants

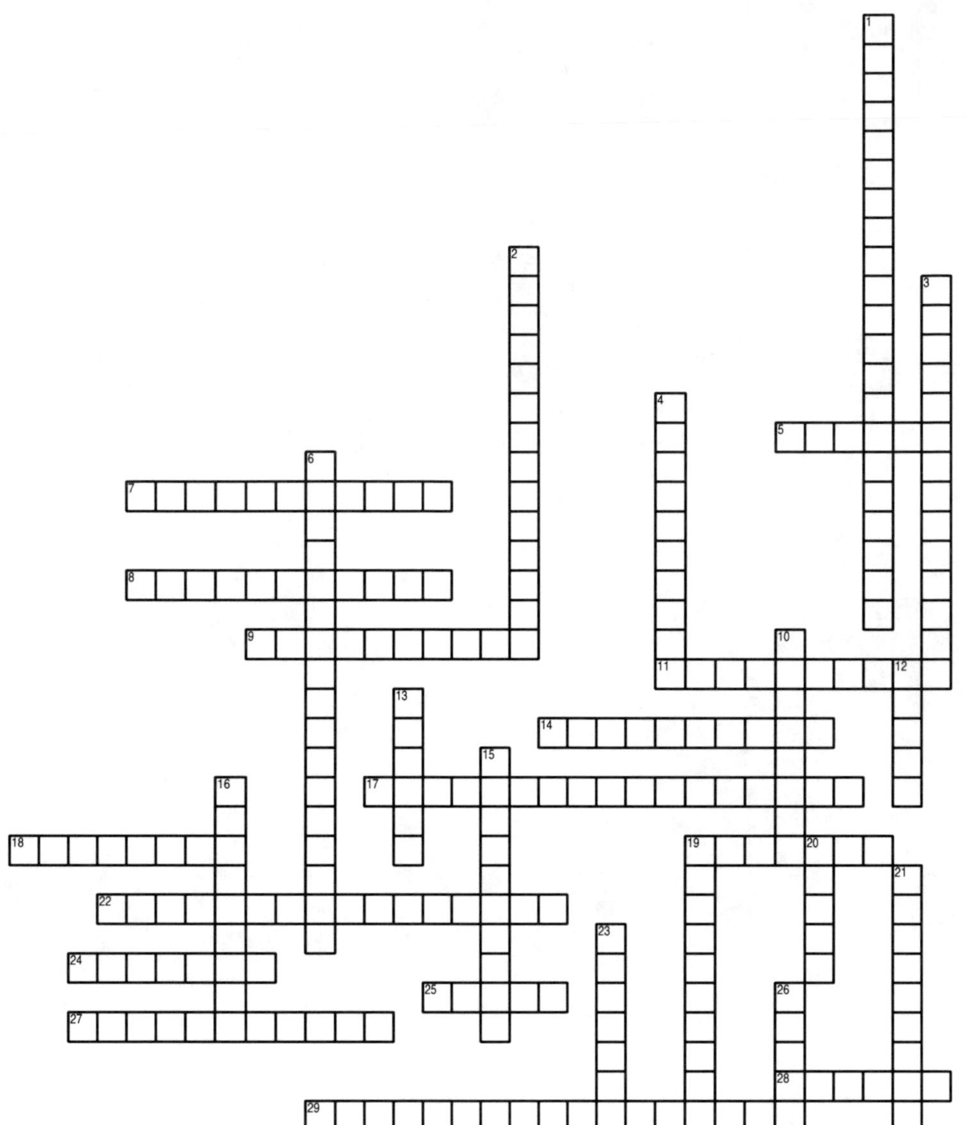
1
2
3
4
5
6
7
8
9
10
11
12
13
14
15
16
17
18
19
20
21
22
23
24
25
26
27
28
29

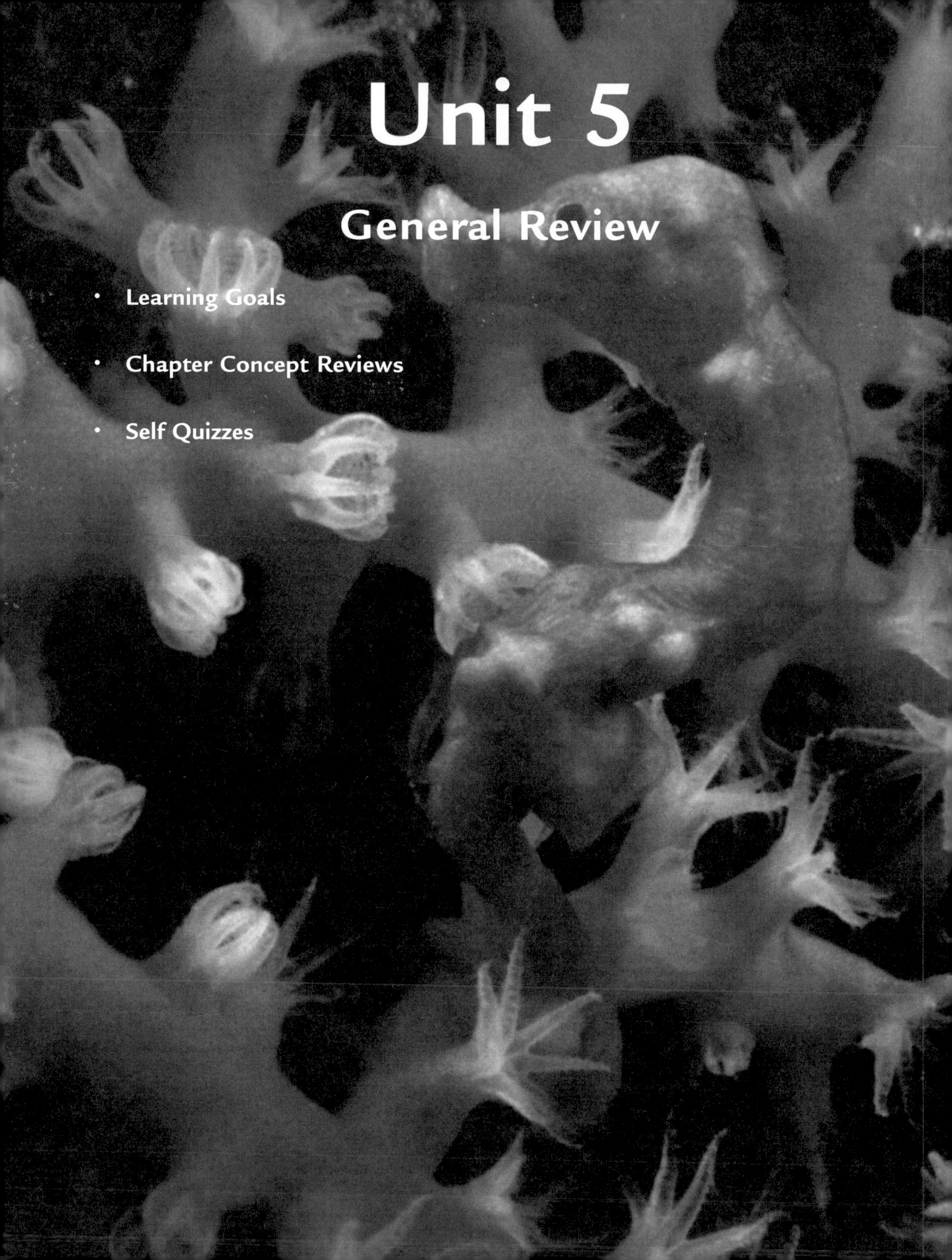

Unit 5

General Review

- Learning Goals
- Chapter Concept Reviews
- Self Quizzes

Learning Goals

1. Define the biological species concept. Explain its limitations when applied to all types of Living organisms.

2. Describe the different types of prezygotic and postzygotic reproductive isolating mechanisms noting examples of each.

3. Distinguish between allopatric and sympatric speciation, noting examples of each.

4. Describe the punctuated equilibrium model of evolution. Relate a "sudden" geological appearance to our "human" sense of time.

5. List, in order, the four distinct ages in the history of life on Earth. Explain how the boundaries of each division are defined.

6. Explain how analyzing sedimentary rock layers and radiometric dating help us understand the fossil history of life on Earth.

7. Distinguish between taxonomy and systematics. Explain how the binomial system is used to identify species. Finally, list the levels of taxonomic groups in order, beginning with species and ending at domain.

8. Explain how homologies are used to create classification systems. Distinguish between homologous and analogous structures. Explain how convergent evolution can make interpreting homologies difficult.

9. Distinguish between the two-kingdom, five-kingdom, and three-domain systems of classification. Explain why classification systems are revised.

10. Explain why it is misleading to label Darwin's ideas as "just a theory."

Chapter Concept Review

Diversity of Life

- Whereas microevolution is a change in the gene pool of a population, macroevolution comprises changes at the species level, often evident in the fossil record. Macroevolution includes the appearance of new species, the origins of evolutionary novelties, and the explosive diversification that follows some evolutionary breakthroughs and mass extinctions.

The Origin of Species

- **What Is a Species?** According to one definition of a species, the biological species concept, a species is a population or group of populations whose members have the potential to interbreed with one another in nature to produce fertile offspring.
- **Reproductive Barriers between Species**

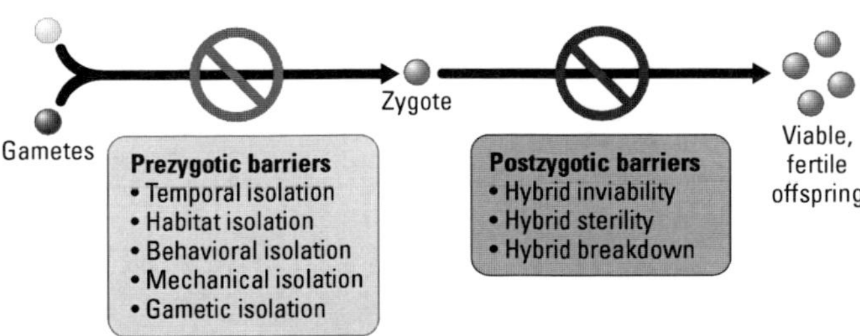

- **Mechanisms of Speciation** When the gene pool of a population is severed from other populations of the parent species, the splinter population can follow its own evolutionary course.

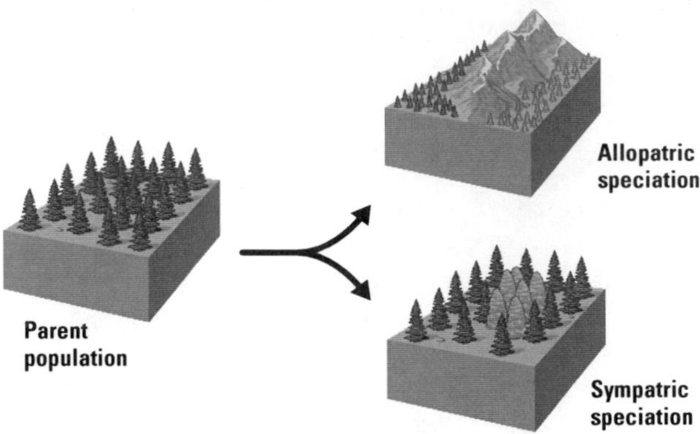

Hybridization leading to polyploids is a common mechanism of sympatric speciation in plants.

- **What Is the Tempo of Speciation?** According to the punctuated equilibrium model, the time required for speciation in most cases is relatively short compared with the overall duration of the species' existence. This accounts for the relative rarity of transitional fossils linking newer species to older ones.

The Evolution of Biological Novelty

- **Adaptation of Old Structures for New Functions** An exaptation is a structure that evolves in one context and gradually becomes adapted for other functions.
- **"Evo-Devo": Development and Evolutionary Novelty** A subtle change in the genes that control a species' development can have profound effects. In paedomorphosis, for example, the adult retains juvenile body features.

Earth History and Macroevolution

- **Geologic Time and the Fossil Record** Geologists have established a geologic time scale with four broad divisions: Precambrian, Paleozoic, Mesozoic, and Cenozoic. The most common method for determining the ages of fossils is radiometric dating.
- **Plate Tectonics and Macroevolution** About 250 million years ago, plate movements brought all the landmasses together into the supercontinent Pangaea, causing extinctions and providing new opportunities for the survivors to diversify. About 180 million years ago, Pangaea began to break up, causing geographic isolation.
- **Mass Extinctions and Explosive Diversifications of Life** The fossil record reveals long, relatively stable periods punctuated by mass extinctions followed by explosive diversification of certain survivors. For example, during the Cretaceous extinctions, about 65 million years ago, the world lost an enormous number of species, including dinosaurs. Mammals greatly increased in diversity after the Cretaceous.

Classifying the Diversity of Life

- Systematics, the study of biological diversity, includes taxonomy, which is the identification, naming, and classification of species.
- **Some Basics of Taxonomy** Each species is assigned a two-part name consisting of the genus and the species. In the taxonomic hierarchy, domain > kingdom > phylum > class > order > family > genus > species.
- **Classification and Phylogeny** The goal of classification is to reflect phylogeny, which is the evolutionary history of a species. Classification is based on the fossil record, homologous structures, and comparisons of DNA and amino acid sequences. Cladistics uses shared characteristics to group related organisms into clades.

- **Arranging Life into Kingdoms: A Work in Progress** Biologists currently classify life into a three-domain system:

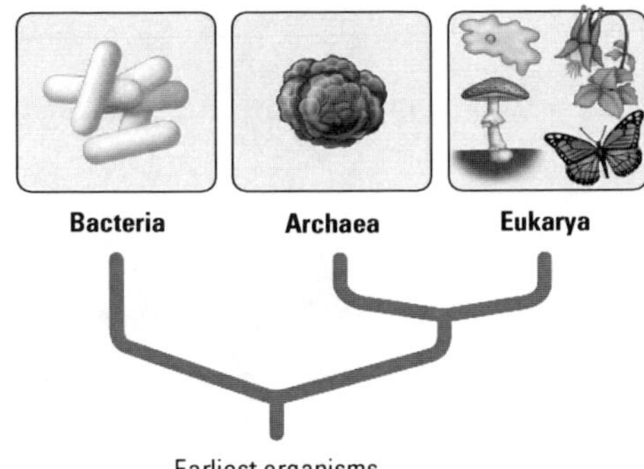

Self-Quiz

1. Bird guides once listed the myrtle warbler and Audubon's warbler as distinct species that lived side by side in parts of their ranges. However, recent books show them as eastern and western forms of a single species, the yellow-rumped warbler. Apparently, it has been found that the two kinds of warblers
   A. live in the same areas.
   B. successfully interbreed.
   C. are almost identical in appearance.
   D. are merging to form a single species.

2. Label each of the following reproductive barriers as prezygotic or postzygotic:
   A. One lilac species lives on acid soil, another on basic soil.
   B. Mallard and pintail ducks mate at different times of year.
   C. Two species of leopard frogs have different mating calls.
   D. Hybrid offspring of two species of jimsonweed always die before reproducing.
   E. Pollen of one kind of tobacco cannot fertilize another kind.

3. Why is a small, isolated population more likely to undergo speciation than a large one?

4. Many species of plants and animals adapted to desert conditions probably did not arise there. Their success in living in deserts could be due to ___________, structures that evolved in one context but became adapted for different functions.

5. Mass extinctions that occurred in the past
   A. cut the number of species to the few survivors left today.
   B. resulted mainly from the separation of the continents.
   C. occurred regularly, about every million years.
   D. were followed by diversification of the survivors.

6. The animals and plants of India are almost completely different from the species in nearby Southeast Asia. Why might this be true?
   A. They have become separated by convergent evolution.
   B. The climates of the two regions are completely different.
   C. India is in the process of separating from the rest of Asia.
   D. India was a separate continent until relatively recently.

7. Place these levels of classification in order from least inclusive to most inclusive: class, domain, family, genus, kingdom, order, phylum, species.

8. A paleontologist estimates that when a particular rock formed, it contained 12 mg of the radioactive isotope potassium-40. The rock now contains 3 mg of potassium-40. The half-life of potassium-40 is 1.3 billion years. From this information, you can conclude that the rock is approximately __________ billion years old.

9. In the three-domain system, which two domains contain prokaryotic organisms?

Major Episodes in the History of Life

Millions of years ago	Major episode
475	Plants and fungi colonize land
530	All major animal phyla established
1,000	First multicellular organisms
2,200	Oldest eukaryotic fossils
2,700	Accumulation of atmospheric O_2
3,500	Oldest prokaryotic fossils
4,600	Origin of Earth

Activity *The History of Life*

The Origin of Life

- **Resolving the Biogenesis Paradox** All life today arises only by the reproduction of preexisting life. However, most biologists think it possible that chemical and physical processes in Earth's primordial environment produced the first cells through a series of stages.
- **A Four-Stage Hypothesis for the Origin of Life** One scenario suggests that the first organisms were products of chemical evolution in four stages:

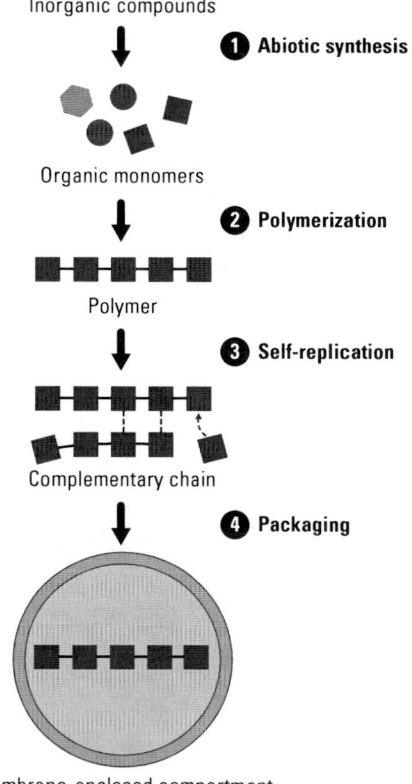

- **From Chemical Evolution to Darwinian Evolution** Over millions of years, natural selection favored the most efficient pre-cells, which evolved into the first prokaryotic cells.

Prokaryotes

- **They're Everywhere!** Prokaryotes are found wherever there is life and greatly outnumber eukaryotes. Prokaryotes thrive in habitats where eukaryotes cannot live. A few prokaryotic species cause serious diseases, but most are either benign or beneficial to other forms of life.
- **The Two Main Branches of Prokaryotic Evolution:** Bacteria and Archaea

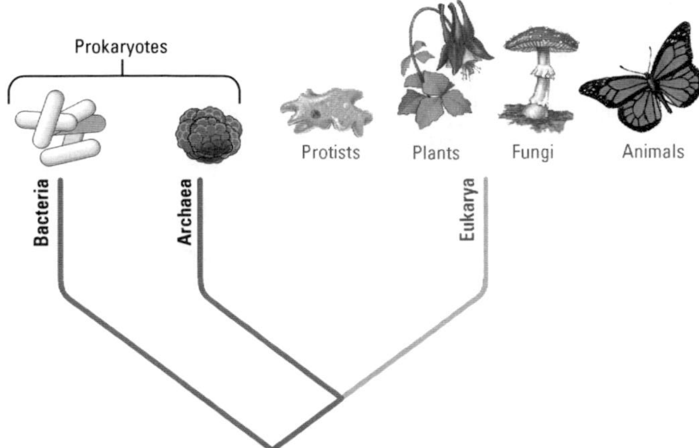

- **The Structure, Function, and Reproduction of Prokaryotes** Prokaryotic cells lack nuclei and other membrane-enclosed organelles. Most have cell walls. Some of the most common shapes of prokaryotes are:

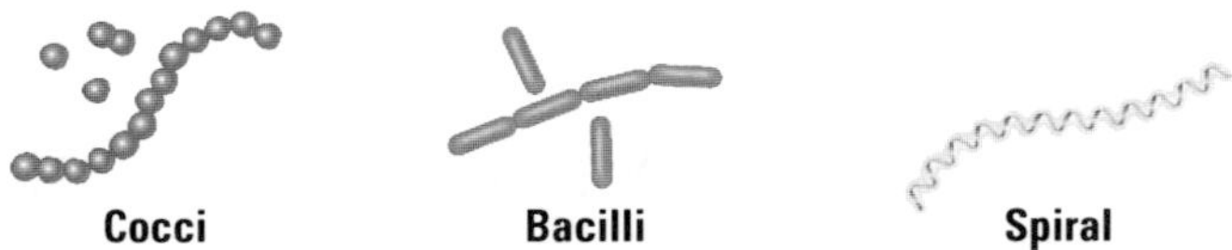

About half of all prokaryotic species are mobile, most of these using flagella to move. Some prokaryotes can survive extended periods of harsh conditions by forming endospores. Many prokaryotes can reproduce by binary fission at high rates if conditions are favorable, but growth is usually restricted by limited resources.

Activity *Prokaryotic Cell Structure and Function*

- **The Nutritional Diversity of Prokaryotes** Prokaryotes exhibit four major modes of nutrition:

Nutritional Mode	Energy Source	Carbon Source
Photoautotroph	Sunlight	CO_2
Chemoautotroph	Inorganic chemicals	
Photoheterotroph	Sunlight	Organic compounds
Chemoheterotroph	Organic compounds	

- **The Ecological Impact of Prokaryotes** Most pathogenic bacteria cause disease by producing exotoxins or endotoxins. Sanitation, antibiotics, and education are the best defenses against bacterial disease. Prokaryotes help recycle chemical elements between the biological and physical components of ecosystems. Humans can use prokaryotes to remove pollutants from water, air, and soil in the process called bioremediation.

Activity *Diversity of Prokaryotes*

Protists

- **The Origin of Eukaryotic Cells** The nucleus and endomembrane system of eukaryotes probably evolved from infoldings of the plasma membrane of ancestral prokaryotes. Mitochondria and chloroplasts probably evolved from symbiotic prokaryotes that took up residence inside larger cells.
- **The Diversity of Protists** Protists are unicellular eukaryotes and their closest multicellular relatives.
  - Protozoans (including flagellates, amoebas, apicomplexans, and ciliates) primarily live in aquatic environments and ingest their food.
  - Slime molds (including plasmodial slime molds and cellular slime molds) resemble fungi in appearance and lifestyle as decomposers, but are not at all closely related.
  - Unicellular algae (including dinoflagellates, diatoms, and unicellular green algae) are photosynthetic protists that support food chains in freshwater and marine ecosystems.
  - Seaweeds—which include green, red, and brown algae—are large, multicellular marine algae that grow on and near rocky shores.

Case Study in the Process of Science *What Kinds of Protists Are Found in Various Habitats?*

Self-Quiz

1. Place these events in the history of life on Earth in the order that they occurred.
A. origin of multicellular organisms
B. colonization of land by plants and fungi
C. origin of eukaryotes
D. origin of prokaryotes
E. colonization of land by animals

2. Place the following steps in the origin of life in the order that they are hypothesized to have occurred.
A. integration of self-replicating molecules into membrane-enclosed pre-cells
B. origin of the first molecules capable of self-replication
C. abiotic joining of organic monomers into polymers
D. abiotic synthesis of organic monomers
E. natural selection among pre-cells

3. DNA replication relies on the enzyme DNA polymerase. Why does this suggest that the earliest genes were made from RNA?

4. The two main evolutionary branches of prokaryotic life are ___________ and ___________. Which is more likely to be found on your table top?

5. Why do penicillins kill certain bacteria but not the human host?

6. Contrast exotoxins with endotoxins.

7. What is the difference between autotrophs and heterotrophs in terms of the source of their organic compounds?

8. The bacteria that cause tetanus can be killed only by prolonged heating at temperatures considerably above boiling. What does this suggest about tetanus bacteria?

9. To what nutritional classification do you belong?

10. Of the following, which describes protists most inclusively?
- **A.** multicellular eukaryotes
- **B.** protozoans
- **C.** eukaryotes that are not plants, fungi, or animals
- **D.** single-celled organisms closely related to bacteria

11. Which algal group is most closely related to plants?
- **A.** diatoms
- **B.** green algae
- **C.** dinoflagellates
- **D.** seaweeds

Unit 6

Ecology

Chapter 20: Ecosystems and Environment

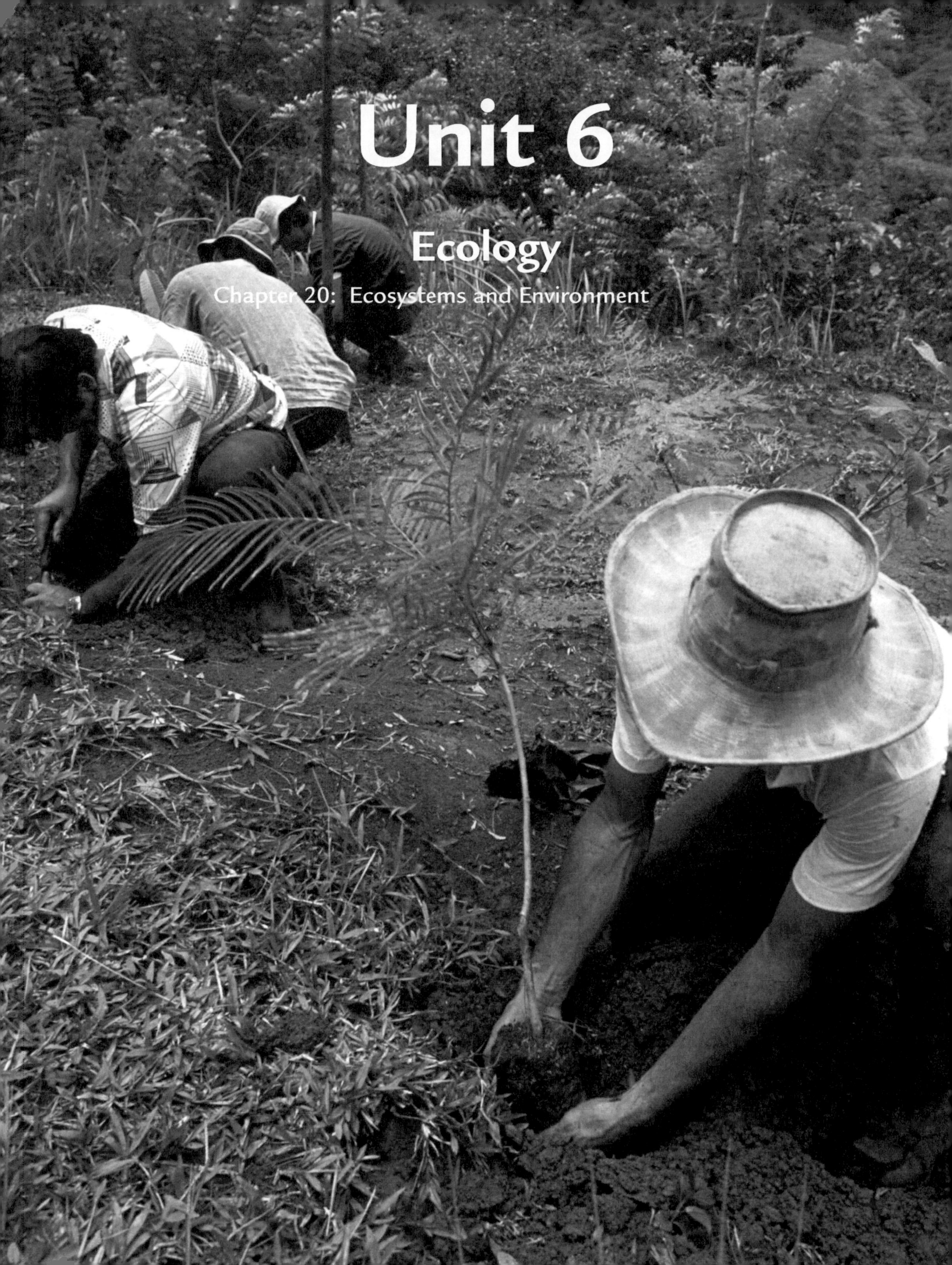

20 Ecosystems and Environment

Two lionesses watch a herd of nervous zebras in the Masai Mara Reserve, Kenya.

LOOKING AHEAD

http://www.pearsoncustom.com/devry/mycbp

Chapter Concept Review

An Overview of Ecology

- Ecology is the scientific study of interactions between organisms and their environments. The environment includes abiotic (nonliving) and biotic (living) components.
- **Ecology as Scientific Study** Ecologists use observation, experiments, and computer models to test hypothetical explanations of these interactions.
- **A Hierarchy of Interactions** Ecologists study interactions at four increasingly complex levels.

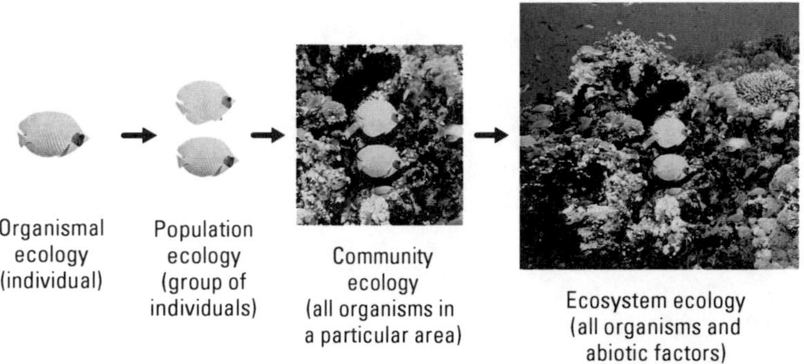

- **Ecology and Environmentalism** Human activities have had an impact on all parts of the biosphere. Ecology provides the basis for understanding and addressing these environmental problems.

Activity *DDT and the Environment*

The Evolutionary Adaptations of Organisms

- **Abiotic Factors of the Biosphere** The biosphere is an environmental patchwork in which abiotic factors affect the distribution and abundance of organisms. These include the availability of sunlight and water, temperature, wind, rock and soil characteristics, and catastrophic disturbances such as fires, hurricanes, tornadoes, and volcanic eruptions.

Case Study in the Process of Science *Do Pillbugs Prefer Wet or Dry Environments?*

Case Study in the Process of Science *How Do Abiotic Factors Affect the Distribution of Organisms?*

- **Physiological Responses** Most organisms adjust their physiological conditions in response to changes in the environment. Acclimation is a longer-term response that can take days or weeks. The ability to acclimate is generally related to the range of environmental conditions that a species naturally experiences.
- **Anatomical Responses** Many organisms respond to environmental change with reversible or irreversible changes in anatomy. Unable to move to a better location, plants are generally more anatomically plastic than animals.
- **Behavioral Responses** Able to travel about, animals frequently adjust to poor environmental conditions by moving to a new location. These may be small adjustments such as shuttling between sun and shade or seasonal migrations to new regions.

Activity *Evolutionary Adaptations*

What Is Population Ecology?

- Population ecology focuses on the factors that influence a population's size, growth rate, density, and structure. A population consists of members of a species living in the same place at the same time.
- **Population Density** Population density, the number of individuals of a species per unit area or volume, can be estimated by a variety of sampling techniques. These include counting the number of individuals in sample plots and the mark-recapture method.

Activity *Techniques for Estimating Population Density and Size*

- **Patterns of Dispersion** Dispersion patterns of a population are determined by various environmental or social factors.

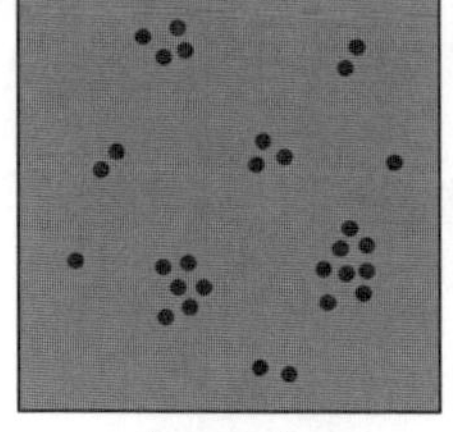
Clumped

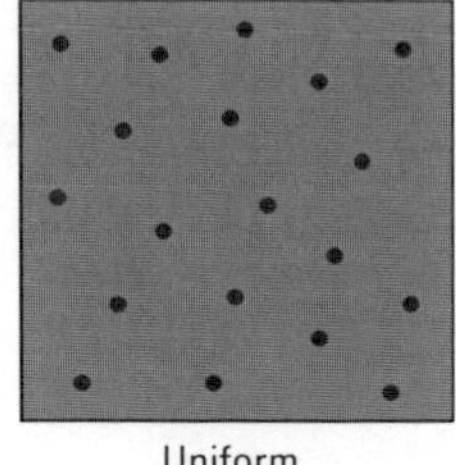
Uniform

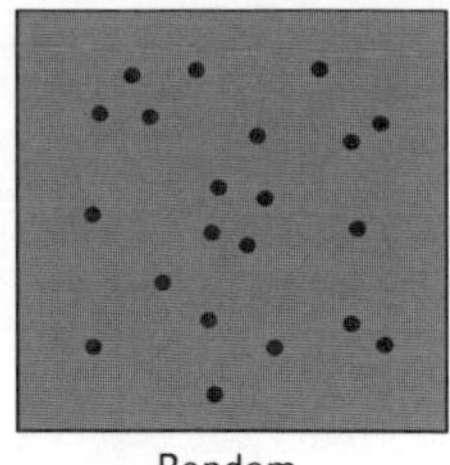
Random

- **Population Growth Models**

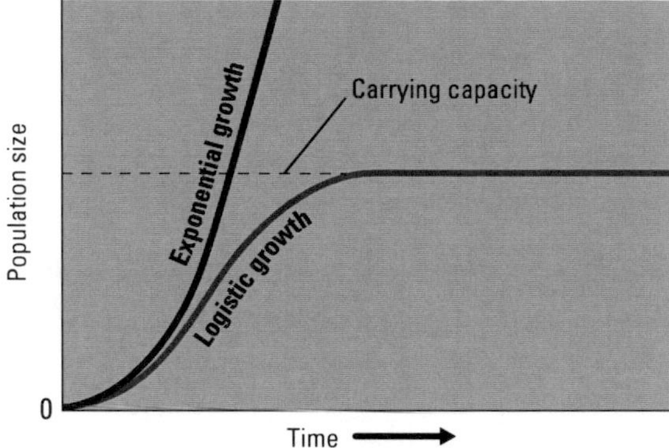

The exponential model of population growth describes an idealized population in an unlimited environment. This model predicts that the larger a population becomes, the faster it grows. Exponential growth in nature is generally a short-lived consequence of organisms being introduced to a new or underexploited environment. The logistic model of population growth describes an idealized population that is slowed by limiting factors. This model predicts that a population's growth rate will be small when the population size is either small or large, and highest when the population is at an intermediate level relative to the carrying capacity.

- **Regulation of Population Growth** Over the long term, most population growth is limited by a mixture of density-independent and density-dependent factors. Density-dependent factors intensify as a population increases in density, increasing the death rate, decreasing the birth rate, or both. Density-independent factors affect the same percentage of individuals regardless of population size. Some populations have regular boom-and-bust cycles.
- **Human Population Growth** The human population has been growing almost exponentially for centuries. Human population growth is based on the same two general parameters that affect other animal and plant populations: birth rates and death rates. Birth rates increased and death rates decreased when agricultural societies replaced a lifestyle of hunting and gathering. The age structure of the population is a major factor in the different growth rates of different countries. Population researchers predict that the U.S. population will continue to grow well into the 21st century. Age-structure diagrams also predict social predicaments. Predictions of future trends in global human population growth vary widely. The human species is unique in having the ability to consciously control its own population growth, the fate of our species, and the fate of the rest of the biosphere.

Life Histories and Their Evolution

- **Life Tables and Survivorship Curves** A population's pattern of mortality is a key feature of life history. A life table tracks survivorship and mortality in a population. Survivorship curves can be classified into three general types, depending on the rate of mortality over the entire life span.
- **Life History Traits as Evolutionary Adaptations** Life history traits are shaped by evolutionary adaptation; they may vary within a species and may change as the environmental context changes. Most populations probably fall between the extreme opportunistic strategies of many insects and equilibrial strategies of many larger-bodied species.

Key Properties of Communities

- **Diversity** Community diversity includes the species richness and relative abundance of different species.

Case Study in the Process of Science *How Are Impacts on Community Diversity Measured?*

- **Prevalent Form of Vegetation** The types and structural features of plants largely determine the kinds of animals that live in a community.
- **Stability** A community's stability is its ability to resist change and return to its original species composition after being disturbed. Stability depends on the type of community and the nature of the disturbances.
- **Trophic Structure** Trophic structure consists of the feeding relationships among the various species making up a community.

Interspecific Interactions in Communities

- **Competition Between Species** When populations of two or more species in a community rely on similar limiting resources, they may be subject to interspecific competition. Two species cannot coexist in a community if their niches are identical. Resource partitioning is the differentiation of niches that enables similar species to coexist in a local community.
- **Predation** Natural selection refines the adaptations of both predators and prey. Most predators have acute senses that enable them to locate and identify potential prey. Plants mainly use chemical toxins, spines, and thorns to defend against predators. Animals may defend themselves by using passive defenses, such as cryptic coloration (camouflage), or active defenses, such as escaping, alarm calls, mobbing, or distraction displays. Animals with chemical defenses are often brightly colored, a warning to potential predators. A species of prey may also gain protection through mimicry. In Batesian mimicry, a palatable species mimics an unpalatable model. In Müllerian mimicry, two or more unpalatable species resemble each other. Predator-prey relationships can preserve diversity. A keystone predator is a species that reduces the density of the strongest competitors in a community. This predator helps maintain species diversity by preventing competitive exclusion of weaker competitors.
- **Symbiotic Relationships** A symbiotic relationship is an interspecific interaction in which two species live in direct contact. Parasitism is a one-sided relationship in which the parasite benefits at the expense of the host. Natural selection has refined the relationships between parasites and their hosts. Mutualism is a symbiosis that benefits both partners. Many mutualistic relationships may have evolved from predator-prey or host-parasite interactions.
- **The Complexity of Community Networks** The branching of interactions between species makes communities complex.

Disturbance of Communities

- Disturbances are episodes that damage biological communities, at least temporarily, by destroying organisms and altering the availability of resources such as mineral nutrients and water. Most communities spend much of their time in various stages of recovery from disturbances.
- **Ecological Succession** The sequence of changes in a community after a disturbance is called ecological succession. Primary succession occurs where a community arises in a virtually lifeless area with no soil. Secondary succession occurs where a disturbance has destroyed an existing community but left the soil intact.
- **A Dynamic View of Community Structure** In general, disturbances keep communities in a continual flux, making them mosaics of patches at various successional stages and preventing them from reaching a completely stable state. Small-scale disturbances often have positive effects, such as creating new opportunities for species. Species diversity may be greatest in places where disturbances are moderate in severity and frequency.

An Overview of Ecosystem Dynamics

- An ecosystem is a biological community and the abiotic factors with which the community interacts. Energy must flow continuously through an ecosystem, from producers to consumers and decomposers. Chemical elements can be recycled between an ecosystem's living community and the abiotic environment.

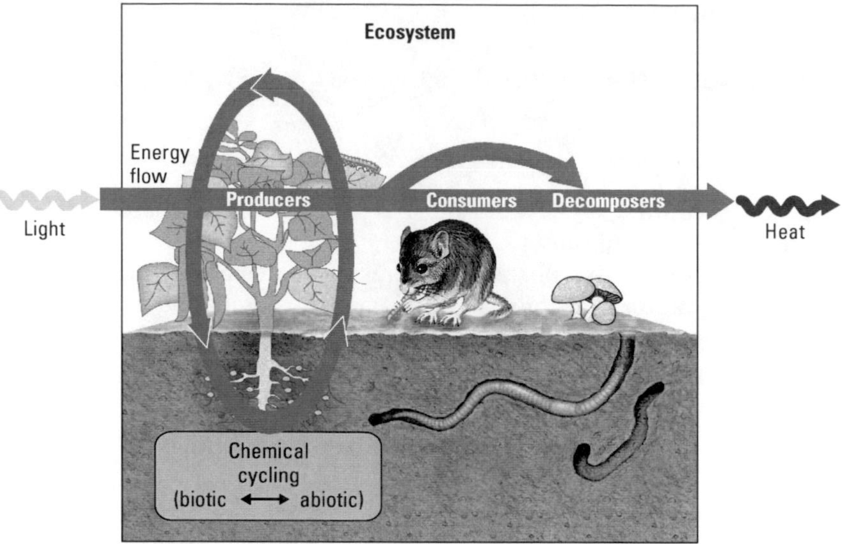

Activity *Energy Flow and Chemical Cycling*

- **Trophic Levels and Food Chains** Trophic relationships determine an ecosystem's routes of energy flow and chemical cycling.

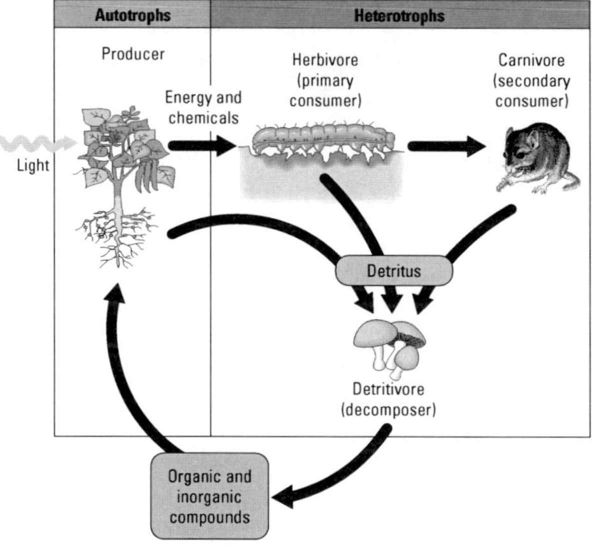

- **Food Webs** The feeding relationships in an ecosystem are usually woven into elaborate food webs.

Energy Flow in Ecosystems

- **Productivity and the Energy Budgets of Ecosystems** The rate at which plants and other producers build biomass is the ecosystem's primary productivity. Ecosystems vary considerably in their productivity. Primary productivity sets the spending limit for the energy budget of the entire ecosystem because consumers must acquire their organic fuels from producers.

Case Study in the Process of Science *How Does Light Affect Primary Productivity?*

- **Energy Pyramids** In a food chain, only about 10% of the biomass at one trophic level is available to the next:
- **Ecosystem Energetics and Human Nutrition** Eating producers instead of consumers requires less photosynthetic productivity and reduces the impact to the environment.

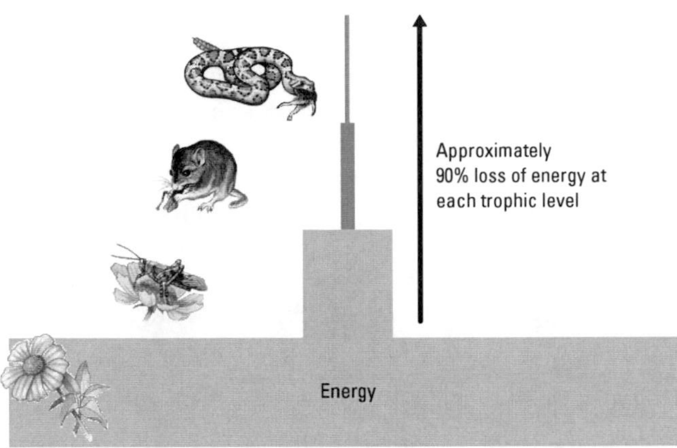

Activity *Energy Pyramids*

Chemical Cycling in Ecosystems

- **The General Scheme of Chemical Cycling** Biogeochemical cycles involve biotic and abiotic components. Each circuit has an abiotic reservoir through which the chemical cycles. Some chemical elements require "processing" by certain microorganisms before they are available to plants as inorganic nutrients.
- **Examples of Biogeochemical Cycles** A chemical's specific route through an ecosystem varies with the element and the trophic structure of the ecosystem. Phosphorus is not very mobile and is cycled locally. Carbon, nitrogen, and water spend part of their time in gaseous form and are cycled globally.

Biomes

- **How Climate Affects Biome Distribution** The geographic distribution of terrestrial biomes is based mainly on regional variations in climate. Climate is largely determined by the uneven distribution of solar energy on Earth. Proximity to large bodies of water and the presence of landforms such as mountains also affect climate.
- **Terrestrial Biomes** If the climate in two geographically separate areas is similar, the same type of biome may occur in both. Most biomes are named for major physical or climatic features and for their predominant vegetation. The major terrestrial biomes include tropical forest, savanna, desert, chaparral, temperate grassland, temperate deciduous forest, coniferous forest, and tundra.
- **Freshwater Biomes** Freshwater biomes include lakes, ponds, rivers, streams, and wetlands. Lakes vary, depending on depth, with regard to light penetration, temperature, nutrients, oxygen levels, and community structure. Rivers change greatly from their source to the point at which they empty into a lake or an ocean.
- **Marine Biomes** Estuaries, located where a freshwater river or stream merges with the ocean, are one of the most biologically productive environments on Earth. As in freshwater environments, marine life is distributed into distinct zones (intertidal, pelagic, and benthic) according to the depth of the water, degree of light penetration, distance from shore, and open water versus bottom. Hydrothermal vent communities are a marine deepwater biome powered by chemical energy from Earth's interior instead of by sunlight.

Evolution Connection: Coevolution in Biological Communities

- The interaction of *Passiflora* passionflowers and *Heliconius* butterflies is an example of coevolution, when an adaptation in one species leads to a counteradaptation in a second species.

Self-Quiz

1. Place these levels of ecological study in order, from the least to the most comprehensive: community ecology, ecosystem ecology, organismal ecology, population ecology.

2. Name several abiotic factors that might affect the community of organisms living inside a home fish tank.

3. The formation of goose bumps on your skin in cold weather is an example of a (an) ___________ response, while seasonal migration is an example of a (an) ___________ response.

4. What two values would you need to know to figure out the human population density of your community?

5. Pine trees in a forest tend to shade and kill pine seedlings that sprout nearby. What pattern of growth will this produce?

6. A uniform dispersion pattern for a population may indicate that
   a. the population is spreading out and increasing its range.
   b. resources are heterogeneously distributed.
   c. individuals of the population are competing for some resource, such as water and minerals for plants or nesting sites for animals.
   d. there is an absence of strong attractions or repulsions among individuals.

7. With regard to its percent increase, a population that is growing logistically grows fastest when its density is ____________ compared to the carrying capacity.
   a. low **b.** intermediate **c.** high

8. Which of the following shows the effects of a density-dependent limiting factor?
   a. A forest fire kills all the pine trees in a patch of forest.
   b. Early rainfall triggers the explosion of a locust population.
   c. Drought decimates a wheat crop.
   d. Rabbits multiply, and their food supply begins to dwindle.

9. Skyrocketing growth of the human population since the beginning of the Industrial Revolution appears to be mainly a result of
   a. migration to thinly settled regions of the globe.
   b. better nutrition boosting the birth rate.
   c. a drop in the death rate due to better nutrition and health care.
   d. the concentration of humans in cities.

10. If members of a species produce a large number of offspring but provide minimal parent care, then a Type ___________ survivorship curve is expected. In contrast, if members of a species produce few offspring and provide them with long-standing care, then a Type ___________ survivorship curve is expected.

Answers to the Self-Quiz questions can be found in Appendix A.

Self-Quiz

1. The concept of trophic structure of a community emphasizes the
   A. prevalent form of vegetation.
   B. keystone predator.
   C. feeding relationships within a community.
   D. species richness of the community.

2. Match each organism with its trophic level (you may choose a level more than once).

A. alga	**1.** detritivore
B. grasshopper	**2.** producer
C. zooplankton	**3.** tertiary consumer
D. eagle	**4.** secondary consumer
E. fungi	**5.** primary consumer

3. According to the concept of competitive exclusion,
 A. two species cannot coexist in the same habitat.
 B. extinction or emigration is the only possible result of competitive interactions.
 C. intraspecific competition results in the success of the best-adapted individuals.
 D. two species cannot share the same niche in a community.

4. How can a keystone predator help maintain species diversity within a community?

5. Match the defense mechanism with the term that describes it.

A. a harmless beetle that resembles a scorpion	**1.** camouflage coloration
B. the bright markings of a poisonous tropical frog	**2.** warning coloration
C. the mottled coloring of moths that rest on lichens	**3.** Batesian mimicry
D. two poisonous frogs that resemble each other in coloration	**4.** Müllerian mimicry

6. Over a period of many years, grass grows on a sand dune, then shrubs grow, and then eventually trees grow. This is an example of ecological __________.

7. According to the energy pyramid model, why is eating grain-fed beef a relatively inefficient means of obtaining the energy trapped by photosynthesis?

8. Local conditions, such as heavy rainfall or the removal of plants, may limit the amount of nitrogen, phosphorus, or calcium available to a particular ecosystem, but the amount of carbon available to the system is seldom a problem. Why?

9. We are on a coastal hillside on a hot, dry summer day among evergreen shrubs that are adapted to fire. We are most likely standing in a __________ biome.

10. In volume, which biome is largest?
 A. deserts
 B. the intertidal zone
 C. the photic zone of the oceans
 D. the pelagic zone of the oceans

Ecosystems and Environment

Species Interactions

Define the following terms.

1. A population is ______.

A community is ______.

An ecosystem is ______.

Species Interactions—continued

2. Look at the food chain below:

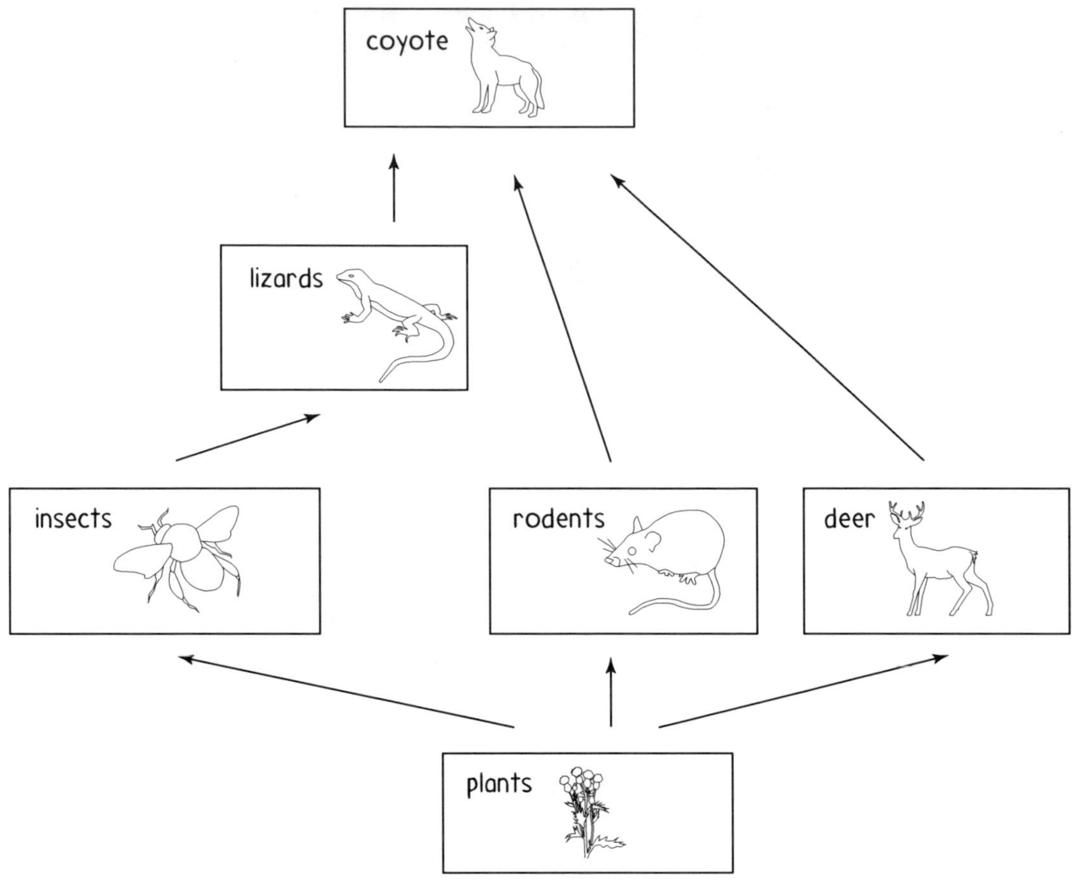

A. Who are the producers in this community?

____

B. Who are the primary consumers?

____

C. Who are the secondary consumers?

____

D. Who are the tertiary consumers?

____

E. Who is the top predator?

____

3. What is a species's niche?

____

4. What is symbiosis?

____

Of the three types of symbiosis, _________ benefits one member of the interaction and harms the other, _________ benefits one species of the interaction while having no effect on the other, and _________ benefits both species.

Ecosystems

1. Match each of the following features with the appropriate biome or aquatic life zone:

tropical forest
temperate forest
coniferous forest
tundra
savanna
temperate grassland
desert
littoral zone
limnetic zone
profundal zone
estuary
pelagic zone
benthic zone
intertidal zone
neritic zone
oceanic zone

A. tropical grassland
B. habitats that receive very little precipitation, may be cold or hot
C. permafrost
D. plants that are adapted to surviving in changing salinity conditions
E. in the water column
F. evergreen trees with needlelike leaves
G. inhabitants have adaptations that allow them to deal with exposure, temperature fluctuations, and the action of waves
H. deep water habitats in ponds and lakes
I. more species are found in this biome than in all other biomes combined
J. grassland with fertile soil, in areas with four distinct seasons
K. lake habitat close to the water surface and to shore
L. trees drop their leaves in the autumn
M. lake and pond habitats that are close to the water surface, but far from shore
N. on the ocean bottom
O. marine habitats far from coasts
P. underwater marine habitats near the coasts

2. Carbon is an essential component of all organic molecules. Most of the inorganic carbon on Earth exists as ___________ and is found either in the ___________ or dissolved in ___________. Carbon moves into the biotic world when ____ _________________________. This carbon becomes available to other organisms as it passes up the food chain. Carbon is returned to the environment by living organisms as ___________ during the process of ___________. An important part of Earth's carbon supply is also found in fossil fuels such as ___________. Human burning of fossil fuels has released so much carbon dioxide that atmospheric carbon dioxide levels are now higher than they have been for 420,000 years. Because atmospheric carbon dioxide traps heat on the planet, this has resulted in ___________.

3. How do living things obtain water?

____

How do living things return water to the abiotic world?

____

____

4. The difference between primary succession and secondary succession is that

____

____

Ecosystems—continued

During ecological succession, the total biomass of the ecosystem typically___________, and the number of species present in the habitat typically ___________.
Ecological succession ends with the ___________.

5. What does the intermediate disturbance hypothesis state?

____

____

____

Populations

1. Which of the following graphs shows exponential growth and which shows logistic growth?

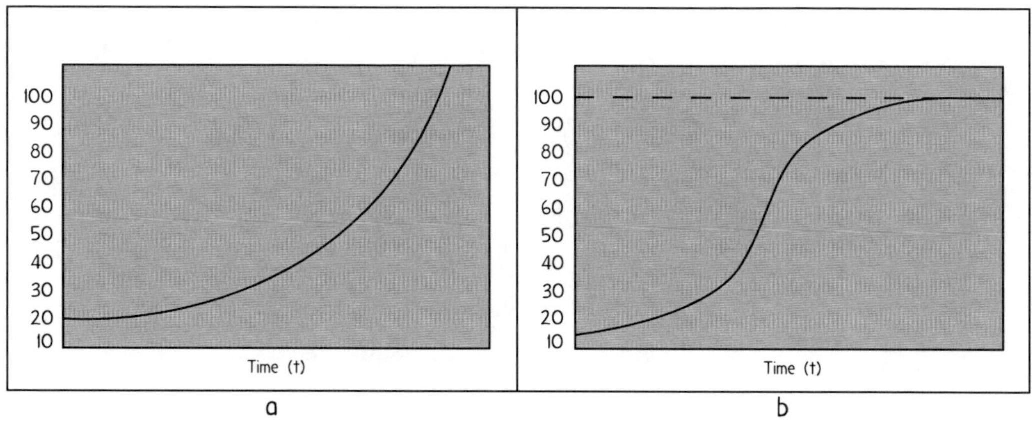

Using words, describe the difference between exponential growth and logistic growth.

____

____

____

What is the carrying capacity in the graph on the right?

____

2. Label the three survivorship curves shown below. Indicate which organisms at right correspond to which survivorship curve.

____

Populations—continued

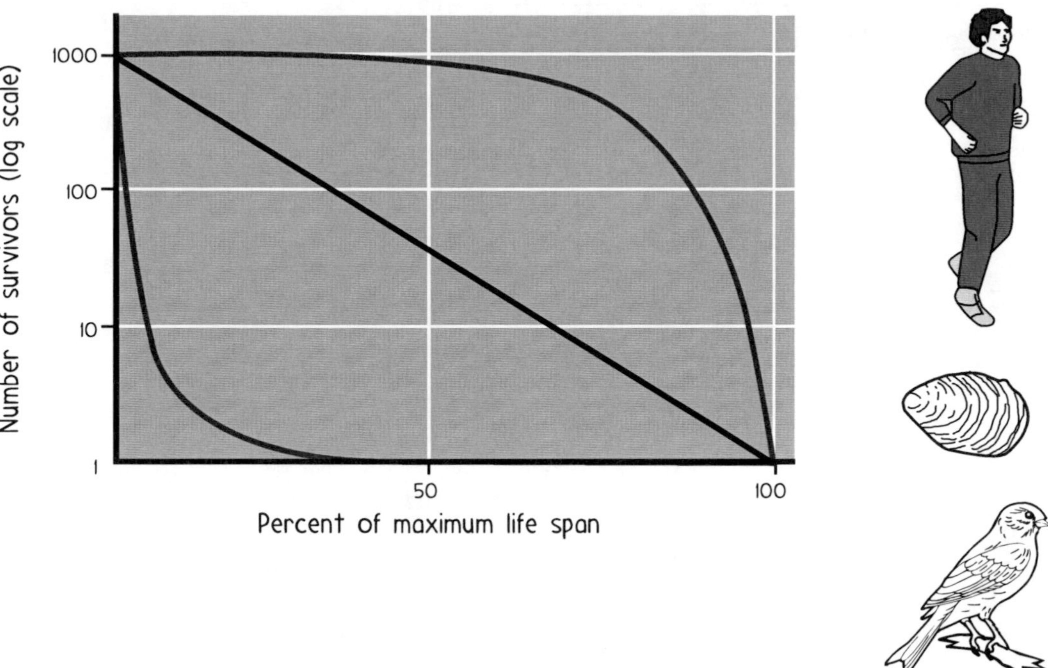

Using words, describe Type I, Type II, and Type III survivorship.

____

____

____

3. Of the following traits, indicate which are associated with K-selected populations and which are associated with r-selected populations.
unstable environment
large body size
few offspring
no parental care
reach sexual maturity slowly
long life expectancy
exponential population growth
Type III survivorship
parental care
stable environment
short life expectancy
small body size
Type I survivorship

Practice Test for Chapter 20: Part I

Organizing Tables

Define each of the following terms and concepts using the textbook. These definitions will be a helpful reference as you read and review the chapter.

TABLE 20.1

Terms and Concepts	Textbook Definition
Ecology	
Abiotic	
Biotic C	
Organismal	
Population	
ommunity	
Ecosystem	

Content Quiz

Directions: Identify the *one* best answer for the multiple-choice questions. For true/false questions, determine if the statement is true or false. If false, change the underlined word(s) to make the statement true. Finally, add the correct word(s) to the fill-in-the-blank questions to make the statements true.

1. The continued increase of the human population in the face of limited resources has led to:
A. global warming.
B. civil strife aggravated by depressed economics.
C. conflicts over oil.
D. declining health of the oceans.
E. toxic waste.
F. all of the above.

2. True or False? The human population on Earth is approaching 7 billion people.

3. Earth's most significant biological phenomenon is now the __________

4. Ecology is the scientific study of interactions between:
A. organisms and their environment.
B. different types of animals.
C. animals and plants.
D. abiotic factors and the environment.
E. plants and the organisms that pollinate them.

5. True or False? Many ecologists are able to conduct experiments in the field of ecology.

6. The nonliving chemical and physical factors of the environment are the __________ component.

7. Matching: Match the level of ecology on the left to its best description on the right.

Level of Ecology	Best Description
Organismal Ecology _____	**A.** the study of all the interactions between the abiotic factors and the environment of species that exists in a certain area.
Community Ecology _____	**B.** the study of the evolutionary adaptations species that exists in a certain area that enable individual organisms to meet the abiotic factors and the community of the challenges posed by their abiotic environments.
Ecosystem Ecology _____	**C.** the study of the factors that affect population size, growth, and composition.
Population Ecology _____	**D.** the study of all the organisms that inhabit a particular area.

8. Which one of the following correctly lists the levels of ecology in order of increasingly comprehensive levels?
A. Organismal ecology, community ecology, population ecology, ecosystem ecology
B. Population ecology, organismal ecology, community ecology, ecosystem ecology
C. Ecosystem ecology, community ecology, organismal ecology, population ecology
D. Organismal ecology, community ecology, ecosystem ecology, population ecology
E. Organismal ecology, population ecology, community ecology, ecosystem ecology

9. True or False? The distribution of organisms is limited by the abiotic conditions they can tolerate.

10. The __________ is the sum of all the planet's ecosystems, or all of life and where it lives.

11. A basic understanding of the field of __________ is required to analyze environmental issues and plan for better practices.

12. The patchy nature of the biosphere exists mainly because of:
A. the types of predatory animals that live in a particular region.
B. differences in climate and other abiotic factors.
C. random events due to the chance evolution of a new species in a particular region.
D. the types of plants that grow in a particular region.

13. Which one of the following is *not* an adaptation to conserve water?
A. a waxy coating on the leaves and other aerial parts of most plants
B. a dead layer of outer animal skin containing a water-proofing protein
C. the ability of human kidneys to excrete a very concentrated urine
D. All of the above are adaptations to conserve water.

14. Which one of the following is *not* an abiotic factor?
A. wind
B. fires, hurricanes, tornadoes, and volcanic eruptions
C. temperature
D. predation
E. water
F. sunlight

15. True or False? Most organisms cannot maintain a sufficiently active metabolism at temperatures close to 0°C.

16. True or False? Birds and mammals can remain considerably warmer than their surroundings.

17. True or False? Most photosynthesis occurs near the bottom of a body of water.

18. True or False? In some communities, catastrophic disturbances such as fires are necessary to maintain a community.

19. Pollen dispersal, openings in forests, and increased loss of water by evaporation are all consequences of high __________.

20. True or False? Ectotherms are better able to tolerate the greatest temperature extremes.

21. True or False? In general, animals are more anatomically plastic than plants.

22. Matching: Match the term on the left to its best description on the right.

Level of Ecology	Best Description
Population Ecology ___	**A.** a group of individuals of the same species living in a given area at a given time
Population density ___	**B.** the field that examines the factors that influence a population's size, density, and characteristics
Mark recapture method ___	**A.** a sampling technique used to estimate wildlife populations
Population __	**C.** the number of individuals of a species per unit area or volume

23. A biologist is trying to determine the number of carp in a pond. She uses a net to capture 100 carp, marks each fish with a tag, and returns them to the pond. A week later she nets out 100 more carp and finds that 50 of them had a tag and were caught the week before. How many carp does she estimate are in the pond?
A. 100
B. 150
C. 200
D. 250
E. 300

24. True or False? When estimating populations, the larger the number and size of sample plots, the more accurate the estimates of population size.

25. Organisms that exhibit a(n) __________ life history tend to grow exponentially when conditions are favorable.

26. Exponential growth typically produces a curve shaped like the letter whereas logistic growth typically produces a curve shaped most like the letter
A. S . . . J
B. J . . . S
C. L . . . S
D. U . . . J
E. S . . . L

27. True or False? Growth rate is greatest in the logistic model at the highest population level.

28. True or False? Growth rate during exponential growth is greatest at the highest population level.

29. The rate of expansion of a population under ideal conditions is called __________

30. A description of idealized population growth that is slowed by limiting factors is the __________ model.

31. Environmental factors that restrict population growth are called __________ factors.

32. Which one of the following is most likely a density-dependent factor?
A. hurricane damage to the nesting sites of birds
B. a long, very cold winter that kills many bison
C. a shortage of good browsing vegetation because of overeating.
D. a limited number of nesting sites for birds because of forest fires.

33. When deer populations are low,
A. density-dependent factors have their greatest impact.
B. many twins are produced.
C. food quality is poor.
D. many females fail to reproduce.
E. density-independent factors have their greatest intensity.

34. A population that grows exponentially, but is eventually limited by density- dependent factors, will have a growth chart most similar to the shape of the letter:
A. J.
B. U.
C. L.
D. S.
E. V.

35. True or False? A density-dependent factor intensifies as the population <u>decreases</u> in size.

36. True or False? Density-independent factors are unrelated to population density.

37. True or False? In many populations, <u>density-independent factors</u> limit population size before density-dependent factors have their greatest impact.

38. A population that remains near its carrying capacity for a long period of time is most likely limited by __________ factors.

39. Human population growth:
A. is closest to the model for exponential growth.
B. is closest to the model for logistic growth.
C. has remained steady over the course of human history.
D. is now on the decline, due to density-dependent factors.
E. has experienced a pattern of boom and bust.

40. A unique feature of human population growth is:
A. the independence of factors affecting the birth rates.
B. the independence of factors affecting the death rates.
C. our ability to voluntarily control it.
D. that it cannot be limited by density-dependent factors.
E. that it cannot be limited by density-independent factors.

41. True or False? Since the Industrial Revolution, exponential growth of the human population has resulted mainly from <u>an increase</u> in death rates.

42. True or False? The population of the United States continues to <u>increase</u>.

43. True or False? Delayed reproduction dramatically <u>decreases</u> population growth rates.

44. True or False? Carrying capacity <u>has changed</u> with human cultural evolution.

45. Human population growth is based on the same two general parameters that affect other animal and plant populations: __________ rates and __________ rates.

46. The survivorship curve for humans has:
A. the highest mortality later in life.
B. the highest mortality in the middle of the potential life span.
C. the highest mortality earliest in life.
D. an even mortality rate throughout the life span.
E. high rates of mortality early and late in life and low mortality in the middle of the life span.

47. A plot of the number of people still alive at each age in a life table is called a(n) __________.

48. Populations that exhibit an equilibrial life history:
- **A.** have a Type III survivorship curve.
- **B.** are mostly smaller-bodied species such as insects.
- **C.** mature later.
- **D.** produce many offspring.
- **E.** do not care for their young.

49. True or False? Life history traits, like anatomical features, are shaped by adaptive evolution.

Practice Test for Chapter 20: Part II

Organizing Tables

1. Describe each of the four properties of a community in Table 20.2 below.

TABLE 20.2

	Description
Diversity	
Stability	
Trophic structure	

2. Distinguish between the pairs of terms in Table 20.3 below.

TABLE 20.3

Biotic vs. Abiotic	
Native species vs. Invasive species	
Batesian mimicry vs. Mullerian mimicry	
Parasitism vs. mutualism	
Primary succession vs. secondary succession	

3. Define and give an example of each of the four trophic levels noted in Table 20.4 below. Try to use examples that could all be found in one food chain.

TABLE 20.4

	Definition	Example
Producer		
Primary consumer		
Secondary consumer		
Tertiary consumer		
Detritivore (decomposer)		

4. Define, give example, location, and Special Characteristics of each of the terrestrial biomes in Table 20.5 below.

TABLE 20.5

	Definition	Location and Examples	Special Characteristics
Tropical forest			
Temperate forests			
Coniferous forests			
Tundra			
Savannas			
Temperate grasslands			
Chaparral			
Deserts			

5. Define and compare the following parts of freshwater biomes in table 20.6 below, using information from textbook. Also indicate examples of organisms that live in each zone. One cell in the table is already filled in to help you.

Table 20.6

	Definition	Example of Organisms that Live in This Zone
Freshwater zone		
Photic zone		
Aphotic zone		No plants, Fish and other swimming animals may pass through
Benthic zone		

6. In Table 20.7 below, compare the lakes and ponds zones and habitats

Table 20.7

	Location	Special Characteristics
Littoral zone		
Limnetic zone		
Profundal zone		

7. In Table 20.8 below, compare the marine biomes and habitats.

Table 20.8

	Location	Special Characteristics
Estuaries		
Interidal zone		
Benthic zone		
Hydrothermal vent communities		
Coral reefs		
Photic zone		
Aphotic zone		
Neritic zone		

Content Quiz Part II

Directions: Identify the *one* best answer for the multiple-choice questions. For true/false questions, determine if the statement is true or false. If false, change the underlined word(s) to make the statement true. Finally, add the correct word(s) to the fill-in-the-blank questions to make the statements true.

1. Which one of the following statements about corals is *false?*
A. Corals dominate coral reef systems.
B. Corals secrete soft external skeletons made of sodium chloride.
C. Corals feed on microscopic organisms and particles of organic debris.
D. Corals obtain organic molecules from the photosynthesis of symbiotic algae that live in their tissues.

2. True or False? Some coral reefs cover enormous expanses of <u>deep</u> ocean.

3. Corals are also subject to damage from native and introduced __________.

4. Coral reefs are distinctive and complex __________.

5. What property of a community determines the passage of energy and nutrients from plants and other photosynthetic organisms to herbivores and then to carnivores?
A. Stability
B. Trophic structure
C. Diversity
D. Prevalent form of vegetation

6. True or False? A forest dominated by cedar and hemlock trees is a <u>highly stable</u> community because these trees can withstand most natural disturbances, including lightning-caused fires.

7. The term __________ as used by ecologists, considers *both* diversity factors: richness and relative abundance.

8. An organism's __________ includes abiotic factors and other individuals in its population and populations of other species living in the same area.

9. An assemblage of species living close enough together for potential interaction is called a(n) __________.

10. What will happen if two species in an ecosystem have identical niches?
A. Both species will be driven to local extinction.
B. One species will be driven to local extinction.
C. One species will be driven to local extinction, or one of the species may evolve enough to use a different set of resources.
D. Both species will evolve enough to use a different set of resources.
E. Both species will be driven to local extinction, or both species will evolve enough to use a different set of resources.

11. Which one of the following typically results when population density increases and nears carrying capacity?
A. Population growth increases.
B. Birth rates increase.
C. Mortality increases.
D. Individuals have access to a larger share of some limiting resource.

12. According to the competitive exclusion principle:
A. as the number of species in a community increases, interspecific competition decreases.
B. species will share the community resources to decrease interspecific competition.
C. when interspecific competition increases, population densities decrease.
D. if two species compete for the same limiting resources they cannot coexist in the same place.

13. True or False? The population growth of a species <u>may be limited</u> by the density of competing species.

14. Interactions between species are called __________ interactions.

15. When populations of two or more species in a community rely on similar limiting resources, they may be subject to __________

16. An organism's ecological role is the same as its ecological __________

17. The differentiation of niches that enables similar species to coexist in a community is called __________

18. Which one of the following statements about predation, according to this chapter, is *false?*
A. In a predator-prey relationship, the consumer is the predator.
B. In a predator-prey relationship, the food species is the prey.
C. In herbivory, the prey is an animal.
D. Predation is a form of interspecific competition.
E. Natural selection refines the adaptations of predators and prey.

19. Which one of the following is characteristic of predators?
A. Acute senses
B. Thorns
C. Poisons such as strychnine, mescaline, and tannins
D. Alarm calls
E. Mobbing behavior

20. True or False? Predator-prey relationships can preserve species diversity

21. A toxic animal will often have __________ coloration to caution predators.

22. A species that reduces the density of the strongest competitors in a community is called a(n) __________ predator.

23. Which one of the following is *not* an example of a parasitic relationship?
A. Mosquitoes and people
B. Aphids and plants
C. Root-fungus associations called mycorrhizae
D. A leech and a fish
E. Tapeworms and cattle

24. Which one of the following is most like a parasitic relationship?
A. A person shopping for groceries
B. A student writing a paper for a course
C. A sailor using wind to propel a sailboat
D. A student stealing a book from another student
E. A physician treating the wound of a patient

25. Which one of the following is most like a mutualistic relationship?
A. A person collecting and eating nuts that have fallen from the trees
B. Giving someone $20 to help you change a flat tire
C. A person moving from one apartment to another
D. A cow eating grass
E. Bird migrations over great distances

26. True or False? In the symbiotic relationship termed <u>mutualism,</u> one organism benefits at the expense of the other.

27. True or False? Many <u>mutualistic</u> relationships may have evolved from predator-prey or host-parasite interactions.

28. In humans and other vertebrates, an elaborate system helps defend the body against parasites.

29. Which one of the following is the most common sequence of appearance of organisms during primary succession?
A. Lichens and mosses, grasses, autotrophic microorganisms, shrubs, and trees
B. Lichens and mosses, grasses, shrubs, and trees, autotrophic microorganisms
C. Autotrophic microorganisms, lichens and mosses, grasses, shrubs, and trees
D. Autotrophic microorganisms, grasses, shrubs, and trees, lichens and mosses

30. Which of the following might happen to a community to cause secondary succession? A disturbance has:
A. destroyed most of the shrubs and trees but left most microorganisms, lichens, and grasses intact.
B. destroyed an existing community but left the soil intact.
C. completely eliminated one level of a community and the soil.
D. completely destroyed a community and all the components of its environment.
E. eliminated the abiotic components of a community.

31. The process of community change is called __________

32. Species diversity appears to be greatest in communities with __________ amounts of disturbance.
A. virtually no
B. very small
C. intermediate
D. very large
E. continual

33. True or False? Most communities experience a regular change in <u>species diversity</u>.

34. The two key processes of ecosystem dynamics are:
A. energy flow and chemical recycling.
B. energy flow and phase changes.
C. photosynthesis and metabolism.
D. phase changes and chemical recycling.

35. True or False? Energy reaches most ecosystems in the form of heat.

36. True or False? Unlike matter, energy cannot be recycled.

37. The highest level of biological organization is a(n) __________

38. Chemical elements can be recycled between an ecosystem's living community and the __________ environment.

39. Plants and other producers acquire their carbon, nitrogen, and other chemical elements in inorganic form from the ________ and ________

40. Energy flow and chemical recycling in an ecosystem depend on the transfer of substances in the __________ structure, or feeding relationships.

41. Matching: Match the term on the left to its best description on the right.

	Best Description
Detritivore _____	**A.** an organism that uses photosynthesis.
Primary consumer _____	**B.** an animal that eats herbivores
Producer _____	**C.** decomposer
Secondary consumer ____	**D.** herbivore

42. Which of the following *never* function as producers in an ecosystem?
A. Terrestrial plants
B. Fungi
C. Phytoplankton
D. Multicellular algae and aquatic plants

43. All organisms in trophic levels above the producers are:
A. autotrophic producers.
B. autotrophic consumers.
C. heterotrophic producers.
D. heterotrophic consumers.

44. Examine the food web in Figure 19.23. Which one of the following changes would likely decrease the number of hawks?
A. An increase in the mouse population
B. An increase in the snake population
C. An increase in the owl population
D. An increase in the lizard population

45. True or False? The trophic level that supports all others is the consumer.

46. Ecologists divide the species of an ecosystem into different __________ based on their main sources of nutrition.

47. The sequence of food transfer from trophic level to trophic level is called a(n) __________.

48. An ecosystem's main detritivores are __________ and __________.

49. The feeding relationships in an ecosystem are usually woven into elaborate food __________.

50. Which one of the following statements about energy pyramids is true?
A. Primary consumers form the lowest level of an energy pyramid.
B. The highest level of an energy pyramid represents the producers.
C. Most energy pyramids have 10–15 levels.
D. Herbivores usually appear in the second level of an energy pyramid.

51. True or False? Only about 1% of the visible light that reaches producers is converted to chemical energy by photosynthesis.

52. True or False? On average, only about 10% of the energy in the form of organic matter at each trophic level is stored as biomass in the next level of the food chain.

53. When we eat beef, we are:
A. producers.
B. herbivores.
C. primary consumers.
D. secondary consumers.

54. True or False? It takes about the same amount of photosynthetic productivity to produce 10 pounds of corn or one pound of hamburger.

55. In many developing countries, people primarily eat __________ because they cannot afford more energy-expensive foods.

56. A chemical's specific route through an ecosystem depends upon the:
A. particular element and the trophic structure of the ecosystem.
B. amount of rainfall and the variation of the seasons.
C. number of producers and consumers.
D. amount of carbon and nitrogen in the atmosphere.

57. Which one of the following nutrients is not very mobile and is mostly cycled locally?
A. Carbon
B. Nitrogen
C. Phosphorus
D. Water

58. True or False? Plants get most of their nitrogen from the air.

59. True or False? Some water can bypass the biotic components of an ecosystem and rely completely on geologic processes.

60. True or False? Each chemical that moves through an ecosystem cycles through an abiotic reservoir.

61. Chemical cycles in an ecosystem are also called __________ cycles because they include biotic and abiotic components.

62. The two main factors that determine the type of biome in a particular region are:
A. temperature and rainfall.
B. wind patterns and light intensity.
C. periodic disturbances and soil quality.
D. predation and proximity to large bodies of water.

63. Most biomes are named:
  A. according to the type of wind and type of soil that are predominant in the region.
  B. for major physical or climatic features and for their predominant vegetation.
  C. after the largest geological feature that is near them, such as a lake, mountain, or ocean.
  D. based upon their physical position on Earth.

64. True or False? If the climates in two geographically separate areas are similar, the same type of biome may occur in them.

65. Which one of the following types of biomes occupies the largest part of the biosphere?
  A. Savannas
  B. Estuaries
  C. Aquatic biomes
  D. Grasslands temperate deciduous forest.

66. Which one of the following statements about marine biomes is *false?*
  A. Evaporation from the oceans provides most of Earth's rainfall.
  B. Life originated in the sea.
  C. Photosynthesis by zooplankton supplies a substantial portion of the biosphere's oxygen.
  D. Ocean temperatures have a major effect on climate and wind patterns.
  E. Aquatic biomes occupy the largest part of the biosphere.

67. Which one of the following is *not* characteristic of intertidal zones?
  A. Twice-daily alternations of submergence in seawater and exposure to air
  B. Relatively even temperatures
  C. Strong wave action
  D. Wide fluctuations in the availability of nutrients
  E. Organisms that can burrow or that can cling to rocks or vegetation

Word Roots

a = without; **bio** = life (abiotic component: the nonliving chemical and physical factors in an environment)
bio = life; **sphere** = a ball (biosphere: the sum of all of Earth's ecosystems)
eco = house (ecology: the scientific study of the interactions between organisms and their environments)
intra = within (intraspecific competition: the reliance of individuals of the same species on the same limited resources)

Key Terms 1

abiotic component
acclimation
age structure
biosphere
biotic component
carrying capacity
clumped
community
community ecology
density-dependent factor
density-independent factor
dispersion pattern
ecology
ecosystem
ecosystem ecology
exponential growth model
growth rate
habitats
intraspecific competition
life history
life table
logistic growth model
mark-recapture method
organismal ecology
population
population density
population ecology
population-limiting factors
random
survivorship curve
uniform

Chapter Review: Key Terms

Abiotic Nonliving.
Biogeochemical cycles The movement of substances such as water, carbon, and nitrogen between the tissues of living organisms and the abiotic world, particularly Earth's atmosphere, crust, and waters.
Biomass The amount of organic matter present in an ecosystem.
Biomes Major types of terrestrial ecosystems, as classified by their plant life, including tropical forest, temperate forest, coniferous forest, tundra, savanna, temperate grassland, chaparral, and desert.
Biotic Pertaining to living organisms.
Carrying capacity A maximum number of individuals or maximum population density that a habitat can support.
Community All the organisms that live within a given area.
Consumer An organism that obtains food from other living organisms.
Ecological succession Changes in the species composition of an ecosystem following a disturbance.
Ecology The study of how organisms interact with their environments.
Ecosystem All the organisms that live within a given area and all the abiotic features of their environment.
Exponential growth A model of population growth in which a population grows at a rate proportional to its size.
Life history strategy The position a population of organisms occupies on the continuum between producing a large number of "inexpensive" offspring and a small number of "expensive" offspring.
Logistic growth A model of population growth in which growth slows as the population approaches the carrying capacity of its habitat.
Niche The total set of biotic and abiotic resources a species uses within a community.
Population A group of individuals of a single species that occupies a given area.
Producer An organism that makes organic molecules from inorganic materials and energy.
Symbiosis A situation in which individuals of two species live in close association with one another.
Trophic level One of the feeding levels in a food chain, including producers, primary consumers, secondary consumers, tertiary consumers, and so forth.

Crossword Puzzle 1

Use the Key Terms list from this chapter to fill in the crossword puzzle.

ACROSS

6. the study of how members of a population interact with their environment
9. a group of individuals of the same species living in a particular geographic area
11. all the organisms in a given area, along with the nonliving factors with which they interact
12. the type of mathematical model of idealized population growth that is restricted by limiting factors
14. the study of interactions between organisms and their environments
15. the rate of expansion of a population under ideal conditions
16. the type of pattern in which individuals in a population are spaced in a patternless, unpredictable way
17. a type of population-limiting factor whose intensity is unrelated to population size
18. the type of pattern that often results from interactions among individuals of a population
19. the change in population size per time interval
20. the type of ecology concerned with evolutionary adaptations of individual organisms
22. the type of ecology concerned with energy flow and the cycling of chemicals among the various biotic and abiotic factors
23. the global ecosystem
24. the number of individuals in a population that an environment can sustain
26. reversible, long-term physiological responses to the environment
28. all the organisms living together and potentially interacting in a particular area
29. environmental situations in which organisms live
30. a type of population-limiting factor that intensifies as the population increases in size

DOWN

1. the type of competition between individuals of the same species for a limited resource
2. a type of sampling method used to estimate wildlife populations
3. a plot of the number of people still alive at each age
4. the type of component in the environment that is not alive
5. the number of individuals of a species per unit area or volume
7. the traits that effect an organism's schedule of reproduction and death
8. the way individuals are spaced within their area
10. a listing of survival and death in a population in a particular time period
13. a type of environmental factor that restricts population growth
21. a characteristic of a population referring to the proportion of individuals in different age groups
24. the type of ecology concerned with interactions between species
25. the type of component in the environment that is alive
27. describing a dispersion pattern in which individuals are aggregated in patches

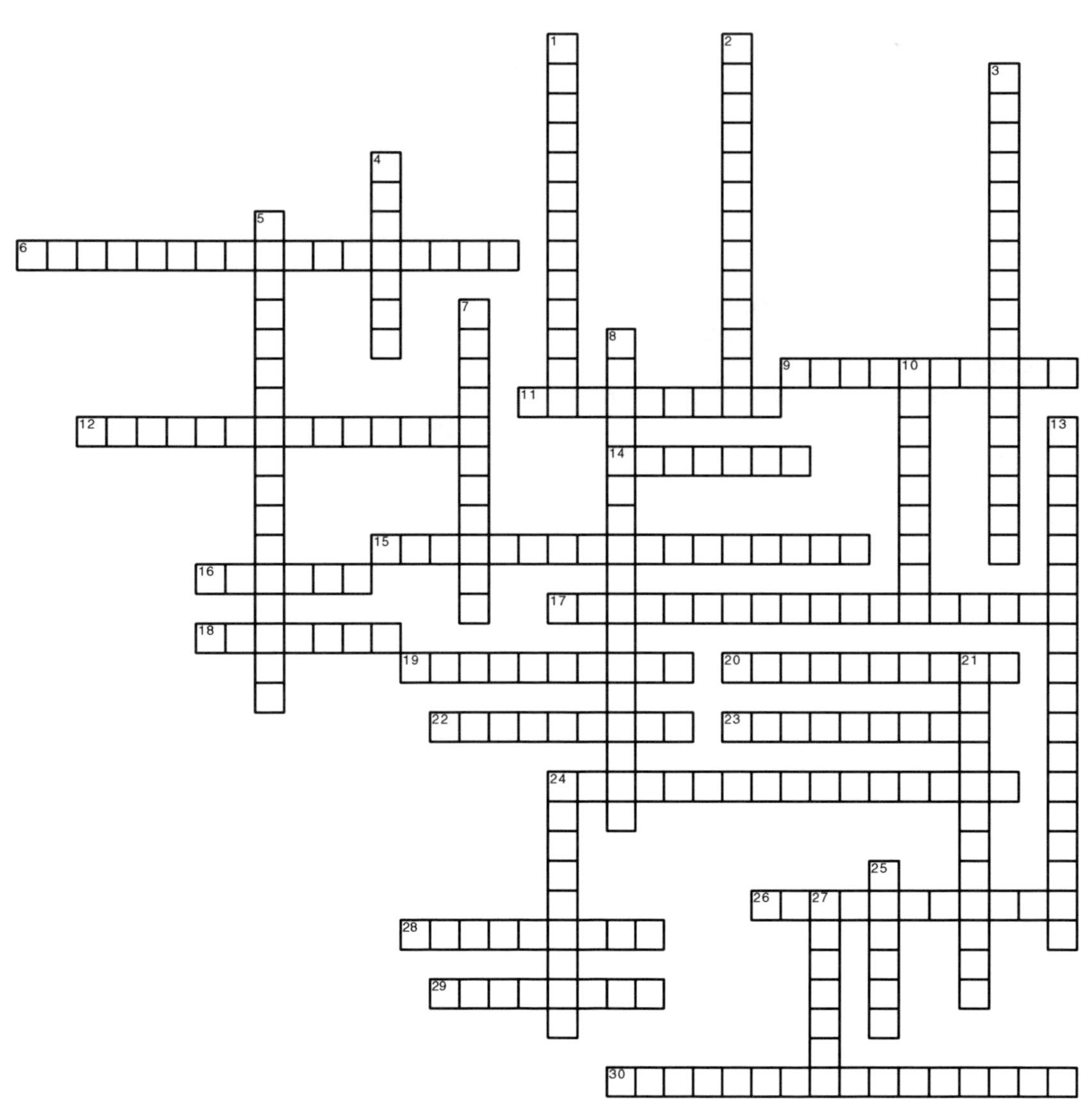

Key Terms 2

abiotic reservoir
aphotic zone
Batesian mimicry
benthic zone
biogeochemical cycles
biomass
biomes
carnivores
chemical cycling
coevolution
community
competitive exclusion principle
cryptic coloration
decomposers
detritivores
detritus
disturbances
ecological succession
ecosystem
energy flow
energy pyramid
estuary
food chain
food webs
herbivores
host
hydrothermal vent communities
interspecific competition
interspecific interactions
intertidal zone
keystone predator
Müllerian mimicry
mutualism
niche
omnivores
parasite
parasitism
pelagic zone
photic zone
phytoplankton
predation
predator
prey
primary consumers
primary productivity
primary succession
producers
quaternary consumers
resource partitioning
secondary consumers
secondary succession
species diversity
species richness
stability
symbiotic relationship
temperate zones
tertiary consumers
trophic levels
trophic structure
tropics
warning coloration
zooplankton

Crossword Puzzle 2

Use the Key Terms list from this chapter to fill in the crossword puzzle.

ACROSS

2. the rate at which an ecosystem's plants and other producers build biomass, or organic matter
4. an organism eaten by a predator
6. a type of consumer that eats plants, algae, or autotrophic bacteria
7. a type of consumer that eats secondary consumers
8. a type of ecological succession in which a biological community arises in an area without soil
10. the diverse algae and cyanobacteria that drift passively in the pelagic zone
11. the tendency of a biological community to resist change and return to its original species composition after being disturbed
12. a symbiotic relationship in which the symbiont benefits at the expense of the host
14. a type of ecological succession in which a disturbance has destroyed an existing biological community but left the soil intact
15. a type of consumer that eats tertiary consumers
16. the type of zone that includes the open ocean
20. the type of often bright coloration of animals possessing chemical defenses
21. a type of mimicry that is mutual by two species, both of which are harmful to a predator
23. a type of predator species that reduces the density of the strongest competitors in a community
25. the total number of different species in a community
27. the types of interactions between species
28. the region from the Tropic of Cancer to the Tropic of Capricorn
29. an animal that eats both plants and animals
30. animals that drift in the pelagic zone of an aquatic environment
32. a population's role in its community
36. the reciprocal evolutionary influence between two species
39. all the abiotic factors in addition to the community of species that exist in a certain area
40. a major type of ecosystem that covers a large geographic region
42. a type of chemical cycling occurring in an ecosystem, involving both biotic and abiotic components
45. a type of coloration that is a form of camouflage
46. an animal that eats plants, algae, or autotrophic bacteria
47. nonliving organic matter
50. the nonbiological location where components of biogeochemical cycles are stored
51. the larger participant in a symbiotic relationship, serving as home and feeding ground to the symbiont

52. an animal that eats other animals
53. a force that changes a biological community and usually removes organisms from it
54. organisms that promote the breakdown of organic materials into inorganic ones
55. a type of consumer that eats primary consumers
56. the sequence of food transfer from producers through several levels of consumers in an ecosystem

DOWN

1. the number and relative abundance of species in a biological community
3. an interaction between species in which one species, the predator, eats the other, the prey
5. a type of interspecific relationship in which one species lives in or on another species
9. the type of zone that includes water near shore and at the surface exposed to light
12. an organism that makes organic food molecules from carbon dioxide and water and other inorganic molecules
13. a type of symbiosis that benefits both species
17. a type of principle that states that populations of two species cannot coexist in a community if their niches are nearly identical
18. the feeding relationships in an ecosystem
19. the type of competition between populations of two or more species that require similar limited resources
22. the type of community found on a seafloor and powered by chemical energy
24. latitudes between the tropics and the Arctic Circle or the tropics and the Antarctic Circle
26. the type of zone where land meets the sea
31. the process of biological community change resulting from disturbance
33. the division of environmental resources by coexisting species populations
34. a network of interconnecting food chains
35. all the organisms living together and potentially interacting in a particular area
36. a type of cycling that reuses chemical elements
37. a diagram depicting the cumulative loss of energy from a food chain
38. the amount of organic material in an ecosystem
41. an organism that derives its energy from organic wastes and dead organisms; also called decomposer
42. the type of zone that includes the substrate of a lake, pond, or seafloor
43. the passage of energy through the components of an ecosystem
44. the type of zone which includes water that does not get exposed to light
48. an area where fresh water merges with seawater
49. the type of mimicry in which a species that a predator can eat looks like a species that is harmful

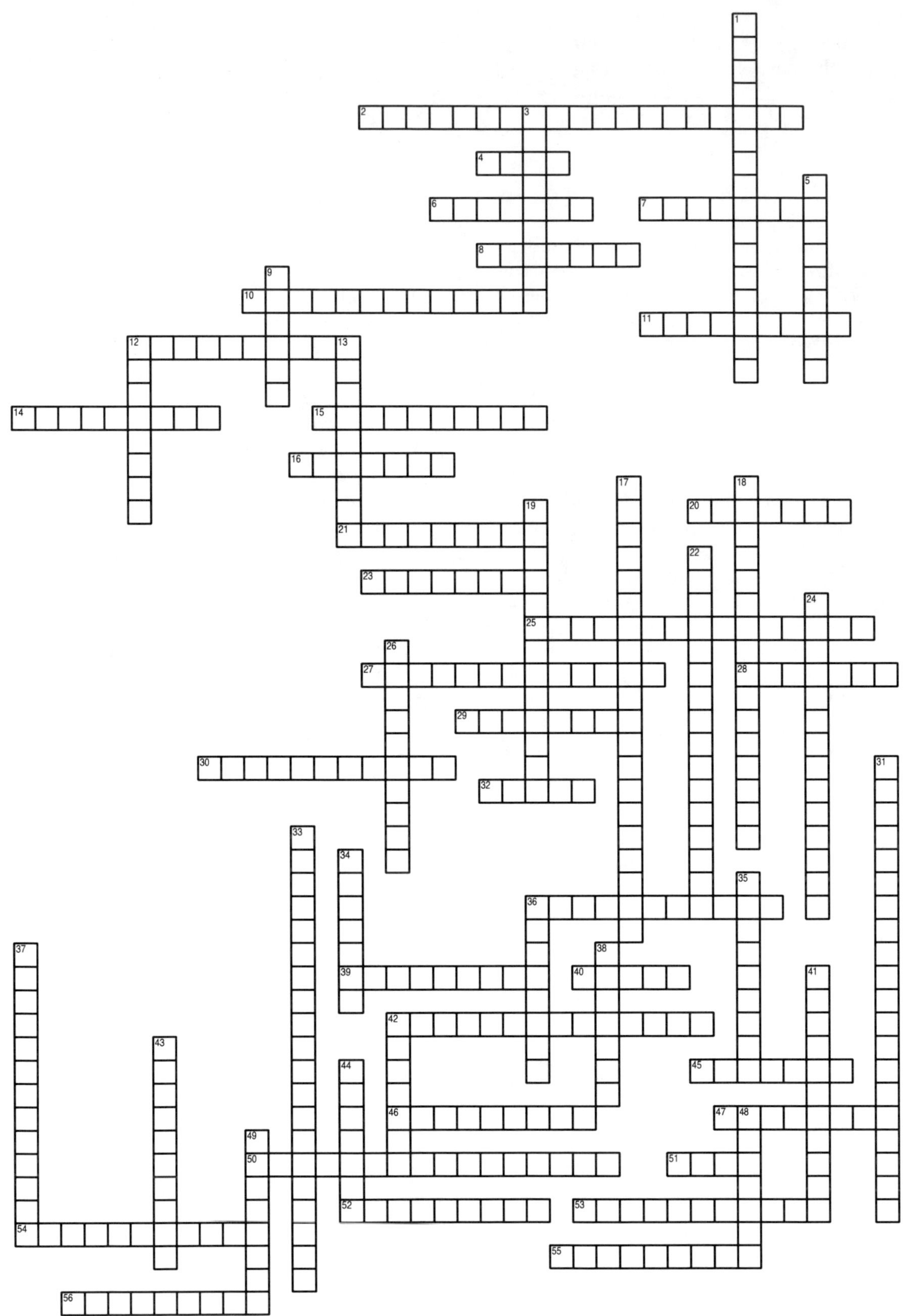
1
2
3
4
5
6
7
8
9
10
11
12
13
14
15
16
17
18
19
20
21
22
23
24
25
26
27
28
29
30
31
32
33
34
35
36
37
38
39
40
41
42
43
44
45
46
47
48
49
50
51
52
53
54
55
56

Key Terms 3

biodiversity
biodiversity crisis
biodiversity hot spot
biological magnification
biophilia
conservation biology
endangered species
endemic species
eutrophication
greenhouse effect
introduced species
landscape
landscape ecology
monocultures
movement corridor
ozone layer
population fragmentation
sink habitat
source habitat
sustainable development
threatened species
zoned reserve

Crossword Puzzle 3

Use the Key Terms list from this chapter to fill in the crossword puzzle.

ACROSS

4. a small geographic area with an exceptional concentration of species
6. process of atmospheric carbon dioxide trapping heat
7. a human desire to affiliate with other life in its many forms
8. the type of species that is in danger of extinction throughout all or a significant portion of its range
10. the current rapid decline in the variety of life on Earth, largely due to the effects of human culture
11. the accumulation of persistent chemicals in the living tissues of consumers in food chains
12. the type of ecology that examines the application of ecological principles to the study of land-use patterns
13. a species that has a distribution limited to a specific geographic area
16. the type of fragmentation in which populations are split and isolated
17. the band of O_3 in the upper atmosphere that protects life on Earth from the harmful ultraviolet rays in sunlight
18. a type of species likely to become endangered in the foreseeable future throughout all or a significant portion of its geographic range
19. a type of habitat where a species' reproductive success exceeds its death rate and from which new individuals often disperse to other areas
20. a series of small clumps or a narrow strip of quality habitat that connects otherwise isolated patches of quality habitat
21. an extensive region of land that includes one or more areas undisturbed by humans
22. a type of habitat where a species' death rate exceeds its reproductive success

DOWN

1. Earth's great variety of life
2. an increase in productivity of an aquatic ecosystem
3. the type of biology that studies ways to counter the loss of biodiversity
5. the type of species that is moved from its native location to a new geographic region
9. a regional assemblage of interacting ecosystems
14. intensive cultivation of a single plant variety over large areas
15. the type of development that produces long-term prosperity of human societies and the ecosystems that support them

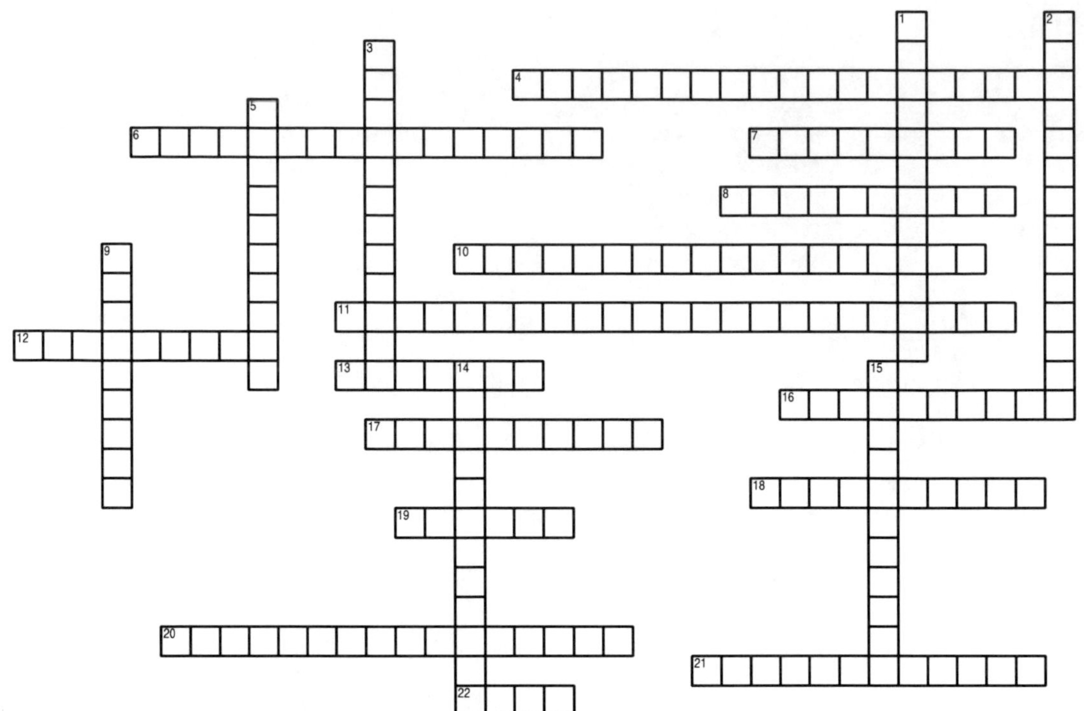
1
2
3
4
5
6
7
8
9
10
11
12
13
14
15
16
17
18
19
20
21
22

Unit 7

Reading Supplements

Supplement 1: Measurements

Supplement 2: Microscopy

Supplement 3: The Earth's Waters

Supplement 4: Household Chemicals

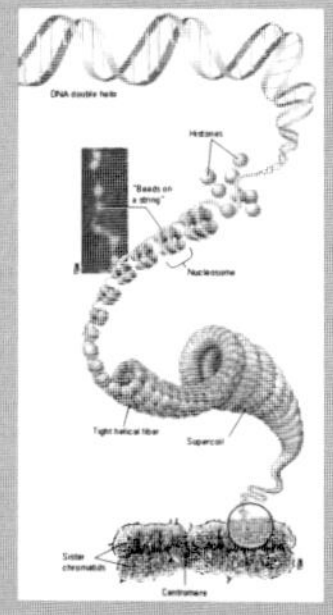

Supplement 5: Chromosomes: Structure, Organization, and Replication

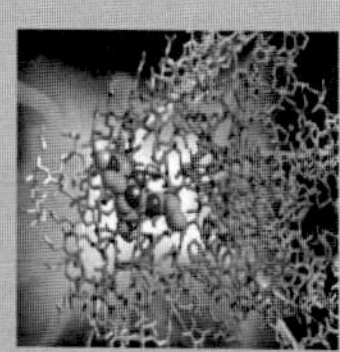

Supplement 6: Signaling and Cell Communication

Supplement 1

Measurements

1 Measurements

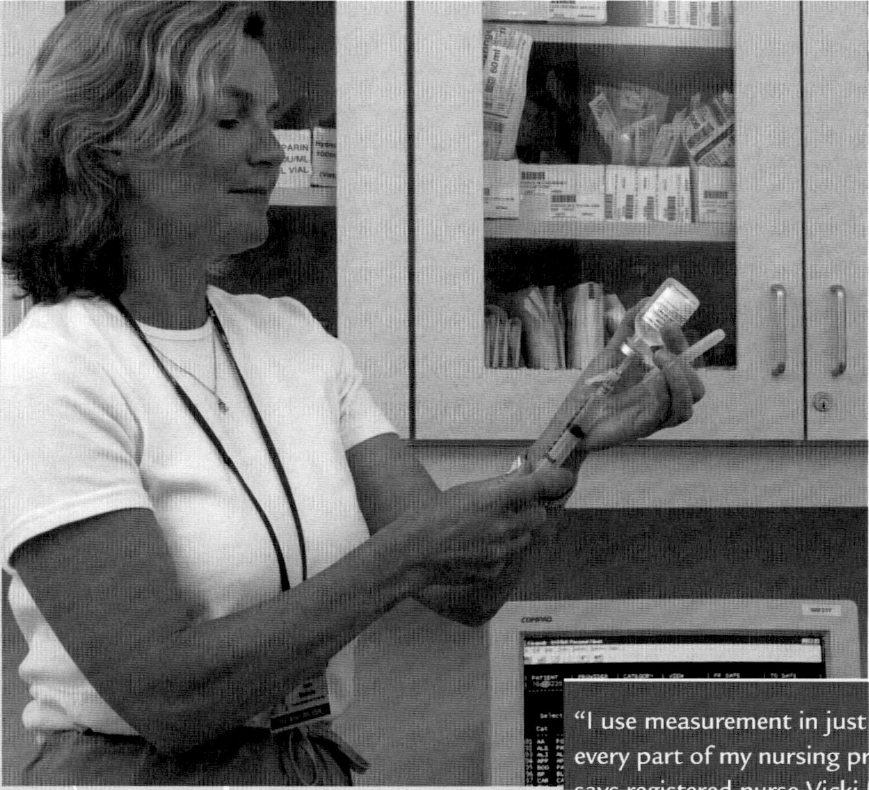

LOOKING AHEAD

"I use measurement in just about every part of my nursing practice," says registered nurse Vicki Miller. "When I receive a doctor's order for a medication, I have to verify that order. Then I draw a carefully measured volume from an IV or a vial to create that particular dose. Some dosage orders are specific to the size of the patient. I measure the patient's weight and calculate the dosage required for the weight of that patient."

Nurses use measurement each time they take a patient's temperature, height, weight, or blood pressure. Measurement is used to obtain the correct amounts for injections and medications and to determine the volumes of fluid intake and output. For each measurement, the amounts and units are recorded in the patient's records.

Study Goals

- Learn the units and abbreviations for the metric (SI) system.
- Distinguish between measured numbers and exact numbers.
- Determine the number of significant figures in a measurement.
- Use prefixes to change base units to larger or smaller units.
- Write conversion factors from the units in an equality.
- In problem solving, convert the initial unit of a measurement to another unit.
- Round off a calculator answer to report an answer with the correct number of significant figures.
- Calculate the density of a substance; use density to convert between mass and volume.

Chapter Review

Concept Map

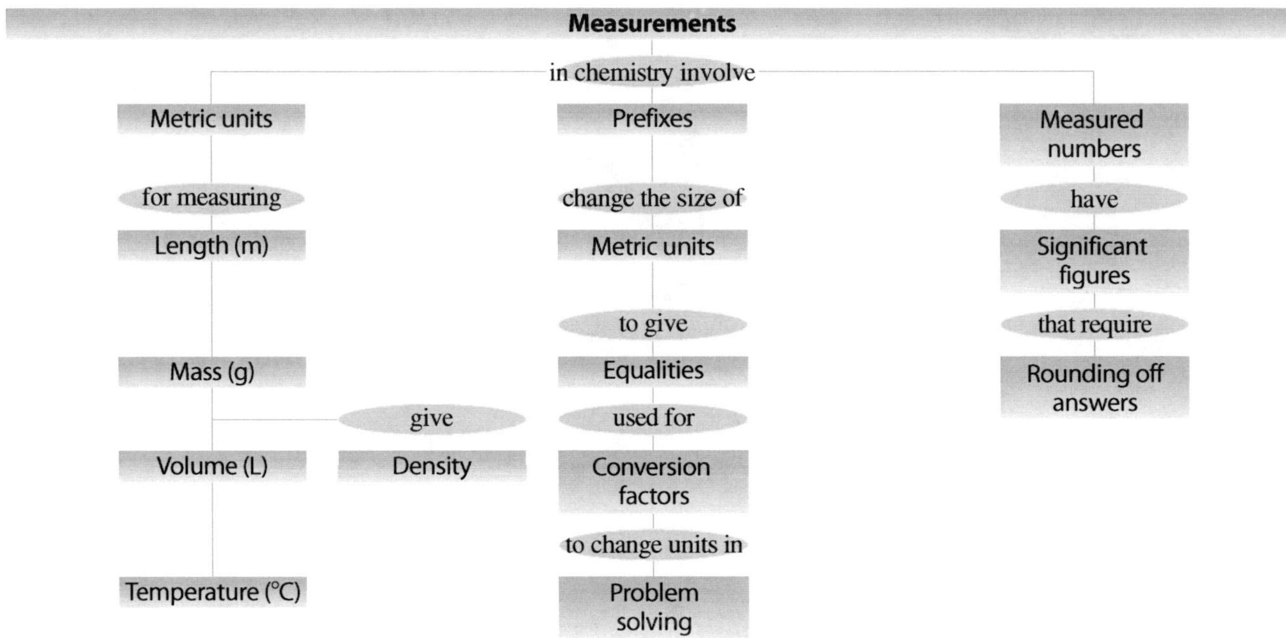

Chapter Concept Review

1.1 Units of Measurement

In science, physical quantities are described in units of the metric or International System (SI). Some important units are meter (m) for length, liter (L) for volume, gram (g) and kilogram (kg) for mass, and Celsius (°C) for temperature. Large and small numbers can be written using scientific notation in which the decimal point is moved to give a coefficient between 1 and 10 and the number of decimal places moved shown as a power of 10. A large number will have a positive power of 10, while a small number will have a negative power of 10.

1.2 Measured Numbers and Significant Figures

A measured number is any number obtained by using a measuring device. An exact number is obtained by counting items or from a definition; no measuring device is used. Significant figures are the numbers reported in a measurement including the last estimated digit. Zeros in front of a decimal number or at the end of a large number are not significant.

1.3 Significant Figures in Calculations

In multiplication or division, the final answer is written so it has the same number of significant figures as the measurement with the fewest significant figures. In addition or subtraction, the final answer is written so it has the same number of decimal places as the measurement with the fewest decimal places.

1.4 Prefixes and Equalities
Prefixes placed in front of a unit change the size of the unit by factors of 10. Prefixes such as *centi, milli,* and *micro* provide smaller units; prefixes such as *kilo* provide larger units. An equality relates two metric units that measure the same quantity of length, volume, or mass. Examples of metric equalities are 1 m = 100 cm; 1 L = 1000 mL; 1 kg = 1000 g.

1.5 Writing Conversion Factors
Conversion factors are used to express a relationship in the form of a fraction. Two factors can be written for any relationship in the metric or U.S. system.

1.6 Problem Solving
Conversion factors are useful when changing a quantity expressed in one unit to a quantity expressed in another unit. In the process, a given unit is multiplied by one or more conversion factors that cancel units until the desired answer is obtained.

1.7 Density
The density of a substance is a ratio of its mass to its volume, usually g/mL or g/cm^3. The units of density can be used as a factor to convert between the mass and volume of a substance. Specific gravity (sp gr) compares the density of a substance to the density of water, 1.00 g/mL.

Think About It

1. What kind of device would you use to measure each of the following: your height, your weight, and the quantity of water to make soup?

2. How do you determine the amount of money in your wallet?

3. When you do a measurement, why should you write down a number and a unit?

4. Why does oil float on water?

Key Terms

Match each of the following key terms with the correct definition.

a. metric system **b.** exact number **c.** significant figures
d. conversion factor **e.** density

1. _____ All the numbers recorded in a measurement including the estimated digit.
2. _____ A fraction that gives the equal quantities of a relationship in the numerator and denominator.
3. _____ The relationship of the mass of an object to its volume usually expressed as g/mL.
4. _____ A number obtained by counting items or from a definition.
5. _____ A decimal system of measurement used throughout the world.

1.1 Units of Measurement

- In the sciences, physical quantities are described in units of the metric or International System (SI).
- Length or distance is measured in meters (m), volume in liters (L), mass in grams (g), and temperature in Celsius (°C) or kelvin (K).
- A number written in scientific notation has two parts: a coefficient between 1 and 10 followed by a power of 10.

- For large numbers greater than 10, the decimal point is moved to the left to give a positive power of ten. For small numbers less than 1, the decimal point is moved to the right to give a negative power of ten.

◆ Learning Exercise 1.1A

Indicate the type of measurement in each of the following:

1. length **2.** mass **3.** volume **4.** temperature

a. _____ 45 g **c.** _____ 215°C **e.** _____ 825 K

b. _____ 8.2 m **d.** _____ 45 L **f.** _____ 8.8 kg

◆ Learning Exercise 1.1B

Study Note

1. The number 2.5×10^3 means that 2.5 is multiplied by 10^3 (1000).

$$2.5 \times 1000 = 2500$$

The number 8.2×10^{-2} means that 8.2 is multiplied by 10^{-2} (0.01).

$$8.2 \times 0.01 = 0.082$$

2. For a number greater than 10, the decimal point is moved to the left to give a number between 1 and 10 and a positive power of ten. For small numbers less than 1, the decimal point is moved to the right to give a number between 1 and 10 and a negative power of ten.

Write the following measurements in scientific notation:

a. 240 000 cm ____________ **e.** 0.002 m ____________

b. 800 m ____________ **f.** 0.000 001 5 g ____________

c. 230 000 kg ____________ **g.** 0.08 kg ____________

d. 50 000 years ____________ **h.** 0.0001 sec ____________

1.2 Measured Numbers and Significant Figures

Significant Figures

- A measured number is obtained when a measuring device is used to determine an amount of some item.
- An exact number is obtained by counting items or from a definition that relates units in the same measuring system.
- There is uncertainty in every measured number, but not in exact numbers.
- Significant figures in a measured number are all the reported figures including the estimated digit.
- Zeros written in front of a nonzero number or zeros used as placeholders in a large number are not significant digits.

◆ Learning Exercise 1.2A

Are the numbers in each of the following statements measured (M) or exact (E)?

a. _____ There are 7 days in one week.

b. _____ A concert lasts for 73 minutes.

c. _____ There are 1000 g in 1 kg.

d. _____ The potatoes have a mass of 2.5 kg.

e. _____ A student has 26 CDs.

f. _____ The snake is 1.2 m long.

◆ Learning Exercise 1.2B

Study Note

Significant figures are all the numbers reported in a measurement including the estimated digit. Zeros are significant unless they are placeholders appearing at the beginning of a decimal number or in a large number without a decimal point.

4.255 g (four sig figs) 0.0042 (two sig figs) 46 500 (three sig figs)

State the number of significant figures in the following measured numbers:

a. 35.24 g ____________ **e.** 5.025 L ____________

b. 0.000 080 m ____________ **f.** 0.006 kg ____________

c. 55 000 m ____________ **g.** 268 200 mm ____________

d. 805 mL ____________ **h.** 25.0°C ____________

1.3 Significant Figures in Calculations

- In a calculation with measured numbers, the number of significant digits given in the answer must match the number of significant figures in the measurement with the fewest significant figures.
- When evaluating a calculator answer, it is important to count the significant figures in the measurements, and round off the calculator answer properly.
- Answers in chemical calculations rarely use all the numbers that appear in the calculator. Exact numbers are not included in the determination of the number of significant figures in an answer.

◆ Learning Exercise 1.3A

Study Note

1. To round off a number less than 5, keep the digits you need and drop all the digits that follow.

Round 42.8254 to three significant figures → 42.8 (drop 254)

2. If the first number dropped is 5 or greater, keep the proper number of digits and increase the last retained digit by 1.

Round 8.4882 to two significant figures → 8.5

3. In large numbers, maintain the value of the answer by adding nonsignificant zeros.

Round 356 835 to three significant figures → 357 000

Round off each of the following to give **two** significant figures:

a. 88.75 m ____________ **d.** 1.6726 m ____________

b. 0.002 923 g ____________ **e.** 0.001 0558 kg ____________

c. 50.525 g ____________ **f.** 82.08 L ____________

◆ Learning Exercise 1.3B

Study Note

1. An answer from multiplying and dividing has the same number of significant figures as the measurement that has the smallest number of significant figures.

$$1.5 \times 32.546 = 48.819 \rightarrow 49$$ ***Answer rounded to 2 significant figures.***

two sig figs *five sig figs*

2. An answer from adding or subtracting has the same number of decimal places as the initial number with the fewest decimal places.

$$82.223 + 4.1 = 86.323 \rightarrow 86.3$$ ***Answer rounded to one decimal place.***

Solve each problem and give the answer with the correct number of significant figures:

a. $1.3 \times 71.5 =$ **b.** $\frac{8.00}{4.00} =$

c. $\frac{0.082 \times 25.4}{0.116 \times 3.4} =$ **d.** $\frac{3.05 \times 1.86}{118.5} =$

e. $\frac{376}{0.0073} =$ **f.** $38.520 - 11.4 =$

g. $4.2 + 8.15 =$ **h.** $102.56 + 8.325 - 0.8825 =$

1.4 Prefixes and Equalities

The Metric System

- In the metric system, larger and smaller units use prefixes to change the size of the unit by factors of 10. For example, a prefix such as *centi* or *milli* preceding the unit meter gives a smaller length than a meter. A prefix such as *kilo* added to gram gives a unit that measures a mass that is 1000 times greater than a gram.
- Some of the most common metric (SI) prefixes are shown below:

Prefix	Symbol	Meaning	Numerical	Value
giga	G	one billion	1 000 000 000	10^9
mega	M	one million	1 000 000	10^6
kilo	k	one thousand	1 000	10^3
deci	d	one-tenth	0.1	10^{-1}
centi	c	one-hundredth	0.01	10^{-2}
milli	m	one-thousandth	0.001	10^{-3}
micro	μ	one-millionth	0.000 001	10^{-6}
nano	n	one billionth	0.000 000 001	10^{-9}

- An equality contains two units that measure the *same* length, volume, or mass.
- Some common metric equalities are: 1 m = 100 cm; 1 L = 1000 mL; 1 kg = 1000 g.
- Some useful metric-American equalities are:
  2.54 cm = 1 inch 1 kg = 2.20 lb 946 mL = 1 quart

◆ Learning Exercise 1.4A

Match the items in column **A** with those from column **B.**

	A		B
1. _____	kilo-	**a.**	millimeter
2. _____	one thousand liters	**b.**	0.1 L
3. _____	deciliter	**c.**	one-millionth of a liter
4. _____	milliliter	**d.**	kiloliter
5. _____	centimeter	**e.**	0.01 m
6. _____	one-tenth centimeter	**f.**	1000 g
7. _____	microliter	**g.**	one-thousandth of a liter
8. _____	kilogram	**h.**	one thousand times

◆ Learning Exercise 1.4B

Place the following units in order from smallest to largest.

a.	kilogram	milligram	gram	____________________
b.	centimeter	kilometer	millimeter	____________________
c.	dL	mL	L	____________________
d.	kg	mg	μg	____________________

◆ Learning Exercise 1.4C

Complete the following metric relationships:

a.	1 L =	__________	mL	**f.**	1 cm =	__________	mm
b.	1 L =	__________	dL	**g.**	1 mg =	__________	μg
c.	1 m =	__________	cm	**h.**	1 dL =	__________	L
d.	1 dL =	__________	mL	**i.**	1 m =	__________	mm
e.	1 kg =	__________	g	**j.**	1 cm =	__________	m

1.5 Writing Conversion Factors

- Conversion factors are used in a chemical calculation to change from one unit to another. Each factor represents an equality that is expressed in the form of a fraction.
- Two forms of a conversion factor can be written for any equality. For example, the metric-U.S. equality 2.54 cm = 1 inch can be written as follows:

$$\frac{2.54\text{ cm}}{1\text{ inch}} \quad \text{and} \quad \frac{1\text{ inch}}{2.54\text{ cm}}$$

◆ Learning Exercise 1.5

Study Note

Metric conversion factors are obtained from metric prefixes. For example, the metric equality 1 m = 100 cm gives the factors

$$\frac{1\text{m}}{100\text{ cm}} \quad \text{and} \quad \frac{100\text{ cm}}{1\text{m}}$$

Write two conversion factors for each of the following pairs of units:

a. millimeters and meters

b. kilogram and grams

c. kilograms and pounds

d. inches and centimeters

e. centimeters and meters

f. milliliters and quarts

g. deciliters and liters

h. millimeters and centimeters

1.6 Problem Solving

- Conversion factors from metric and/or U.S. relationships, percent, and density are used to change a quantity expressed in one unit to a quantity expressed in another unit.

◆ Learning Exercise 1.6A

Study Note
To problem solve, identify the given quantity, write a unit plan, and select the appropriate conversion factors. Arrange the factors in a setup to cancel the starting unit and provide the desired unit.

Use metric-metric conversion factors to solve the following problems:

a. 189 mL = ____________ L

Example: Unit plan: mL → L Setup: $189\ \cancel{\text{mL}} \times \dfrac{1\ \text{L}}{1000\ \cancel{\text{mL}}} = 0.189\ \text{L}$

b. 2.7 cm = ____________ mm

c. 0.0025 L = ____________ mL

d. 76 mg = ____________ g

e. How many meters tall is a person whose height is 175 cm?

f. There are 285 mL in a cup of tea. How many liters is that?

g. The recommended daily value for calcium is 200 mg. How many g are recommended?

h. You walked 1.5 km on the treadmill at the gym. How many meters did you walk?

◆ Learning Exercise 1.6B

Use metric-U.S. conversion factors to solve the following problems:

a. 18 inches = __________ cm

b. 4.0 qts = __________ L

c. 275 mL = __________ qt

d. 1300 mg = __________ lb

e. 150 lb = __________ kg

f. 840 g = __________ lb

g. 15 ft = __________ cm

h. 8.50 oz = __________ g

◆ Learning Exercise 1.6C

Study Note

1. For setups that require a series of conversion factors, it is helpful to write out the unit plan first. Work from the starting unit to the final unit. Then use a conversion factor for each unit change.

$$\text{Starting unit} \rightarrow \text{unit (1)} \rightarrow \text{unit (2)} = \text{final unit}$$

2. To convert from unit to another, select conversion factors that cancel the given unit and provide a unit or the final unit for the problem. Several factors may be needed to work the units toward the final unit.

$$\cancel{\text{Starting unit}} \times \frac{\cancel{\text{unit (1)}}}{\cancel{\text{Starting unit}}} \times \frac{\text{unit (2)}}{\cancel{\text{unit (1)}}} = \text{final unit}$$

Use conversion factors to solve the following problems:

a. A piece of plastic tubing measures 120 mm. What is the length of the tubing in inches?

b. A statue weighs 240 pounds. What is the mass of the statue in kilograms?

c. Your friend has a height of 6 feet 3 inches. What is your friend's height in meters?

d. In a triple-bypass surgery, a patient requires 3.00 pints of whole blood. How many mL of blood were given if 1 quart = 2 pints?

e. A doctor orders 0.450 g of a sulfa drug. On hand are 150-mg tablets. How many tablets are needed?

1.7 Density

- The density of a substance is a ratio of its mass to its volume, usually in units of g/mL or g/cm^3 (1 mL is equal to 1 cm^3). For example, the density of sugar is 1.59 g/mL and silver is 10.5 g/mL.

$$\text{Density} = \frac{\text{mass of substance}}{\text{volume of substance}}$$

- Specific gravity (sp gr) is a unitless relationship of the density of a substance divided by the density of water, 1.00 g/mL. We can calculate the specific gravity of sugar as

$$\frac{1.59\ \cancel{\text{g/mL}}\ \text{(density of sugar)}}{1.00\ \cancel{\text{g/mL}}\ \text{(density of water)}} = 1.59\ \text{(sp gr of sugar)}$$

Study Note

Density can be used as a factor to convert between the mass (g) and volume (mL) of a substance. The density of silver is 10.5 g/mL. What is the mass of 6.0 mL of silver?

$$6.0\ \cancel{\text{mL silver}} \times \frac{10.5\ \text{g silver}}{1\ \cancel{\text{mL silver}}} = 63\ \text{g silver}$$

Density

What is the volume of 25 g of olive oil (D = 0.92 g/mL)?

$$25\ \cancel{\text{g olive oil}} \times \frac{1\ \text{mL olive oil}}{0.92\ \cancel{\text{g olive oil}}} = 27\ \text{mL olive oil}$$

Density

◆ Learning Exercise 1.7

Calculate the density or specific gravity, or use density as a conversion factor to solve each of the following:

a. What is the density (g/mL) of glycerol if a 200. mL sample has a mass of 252 g?

b. A person with diabetes may produce 5 to 12 liters of urine per day. Calculate the specific gravity of a 100.0 mL sample that has a mass of 100.2 g.

c. A small solid has a mass of 5.5 oz. When placed in a graduated cylinder with a water level of 25.2 mL, the object causes the water level to rise to 43.8 mL. What is the density of the object in g/mL?

d. A sugar solution has a density of 1.20 g/mL. What is the mass in grams of 0.250 L of the solution?

e. A piece of pure gold weighs 0.26 pound. If gold has a density of 19.3 g/mL, what is the volume in mL of the piece of gold?

f. Diamond has a density of 3.52 g/mL. What is the specific gravity of diamond?

g. A salt solution has a specific gravity of 1.15 and a volume of 425 mL. What is the mass in grams of the solution?

h. A 50.0-g sample of a glucose solution has a density of 1.28 g/mL. What is the volume in liters of the sample?

Check List for Supplement 1

You are ready to take the practice test for Supplement 1. Be sure that you have accomplished the following learning goals for this supplement. If you are not sure, review the section listed at the end of the goal. Then apply your new skills and understanding to the practice test.
After studying Supplement 1, I can successfully:

_____ Write the names and abbreviations for the metric (SI) units of measurement (1.1).

_____ Write large or small numbers using scientific notation (1.1).

_____ Identify a number as a measured number or an exact number (1.2).

_____ Count the number of significant figures in measured numbers (1.2).

_____ Report an answer with the correct number of significant figures (1.3).

_____ Write a metric equality from the numerical values of metric prefixes (1.4).

_____ Use conversion factors to change from one unit to another (1.5).

_____ Calculate the density of a substance, or use the density to calculate the mass or volume (1.6).

Practice Test for Supplement 1

Instructions: Select the letter preceding the word or phrase that best answers the question.

1. Which of the following is a metric measurement of volume?
A. kilogram **B.** kilowatt **C.** kiloliter **D.** kilometer **E.** kiloquart

2. The measurement 24 000 g written in scientific notation is
A. 24 g **B.** 24×10^3 g **C.** 2.4×10^3 g **D.** 2.4×10^{-3} g **E.** 2.4×10^4 g

3. The measurement 0.005 m written in scientific notation is
A. 5 m **B.** 5×10^{-3} m **C.** 5×10^{-2} m **D.** 0.5×10^{-4} m **E.** 5×10^3 m

4. The measured number in the following is
A. 1 book **B.** 2 cars **C.** 4 flowers **D.** 5 rings **E.** 45 g

5. The number of significant figures in 105.4 m is
A. 1 **B.** 2 **C.** 3 **D.** 4 **E.** 5

6. The number of significant figures in 0.00082 g is
A. 1 **B.** 2 **C.** 3 **D.** 4 **E.** 5

7. The calculator answer 5.78052 rounded to two significant figures is
A. 5 **B.** 5.7 **C.** 5.8 **D.** 5.78 **E.** 6.0

8. The calculator answer 3486.512 rounded to three significant figures is
A. 4000 **B.** 3500 **C.** 349 **D.** 3487 **E.** 3490

9. The reported answer for the problem $16.0 \div 8.0$ is
A. 2 **B.** 2.0 **C.** 2.00 **D.** 0.2 **E.** 5.0

10. The reported answer for the problem $58.5 + 9.158$ is
A. 67 **B.** 67.6 **C.** 67.7 **D.** 67.66 **E.** 67.658

11. The reported answer for the problem $\frac{2.5 \times 3.12}{4.6}$ is
A. 0.54 **B.** 7.8 **C.** 0.85 **D.** 1.7 **E.** 1.69

12. Which of these prefixes has the largest value?
A. centi **B.** deci **C.** milli **D.** kilo **E.** micro

13. What is the decimal equivalent of the prefix *centi?*
A. one-thousandth **B.** one-hundredth **C.** one-tenth **D.** ten **E.** one hundred

14. Which of the following is the smallest unit of measurement?
A. gram **B.** milligram **C.** kilogram **D.** decigram **E.** centigram

15. Which volume is the largest?
A. mL **B.** dL **C.** cm^3 **D.** L **E.** kL

16. Which of the following is a conversion factor?
A. 12 inches **B.** 3 feet **C.** 20 meters **D.** $\frac{1000\text{ g}}{1\text{ kg}}$ **E.** 2 cubic centimeters

17. Which is a conversion factor that relates milliliters to liters?
A. $\frac{1000\text{ mL}}{1\text{ L}}$ **B.** $\frac{100\text{ mL}}{1\text{ L}}$ **C.** $\frac{10\text{ mL}}{1\text{ L}}$ **D.** $\frac{0.01\text{ mL}}{1\text{ L}}$ **E.** $\frac{0.001\text{ mL}}{1\text{ L}}$

18. Which is a conversion factor for millimeters and centimeters?
A. $\frac{1\text{ mm}}{1\text{ cm}}$ **B.** $\frac{10\text{ mm}}{1\text{ cm}}$ **C.** $\frac{100\text{ cm}}{1\text{ mm}}$ **D.** $\frac{100\text{ mm}}{1\text{ cm}}$ **E.** $\frac{10\text{ cm}}{1\text{ mm}}$

19. 294 mm is equal to
A. 2940 m **B.** 29.4 m **C.** 2.94 m **D.** 0.294 m **E.** 0.0294 m

20. The handle on a tennis racket measures 4.5 inches. What is that size in centimeters?
A. 11 cm **B.** 1.8 cm **C.** 0.56 cm **D.** 450 cm **E.** 15 cm

21. What is the volume of 65 mL in liters?
A. 650 L **B.** 65 L **C.** 6.5 L **D.** 0.65 L **E.** 0.065 L

22. What is the mass in kg of a 22-lb turkey?
A. 10. kg **B.** 48 kg **C.** 10 000 kg **D.** 0.048 kg **E.** 22 000 kg

23. The number of milliliters in 2 deciliters is
A. 20 mL **B.** 200 mL **C.** 2000 mL **D.** 20 000 mL **E.** 500 000 mL

24. A person who is 5 feet 4 inches tall would be
A. 64 m **B.** 25 m **C.** 14 m **D.** 1.6 m **E.** 1.3 m

25. How many ounces are in 1 500 grams? (1 lb = 16 oz)
A. 94 oz **B.** 53 oz **C.** 24 000 oz **D.** 33 oz **E.** 3.3 oz

26. How many quarts of orange juice are in 255 mL of juice?
A. 0.255 qt **B.** 270 qt **C.** 236 qt **D.** 0.270 qt **E.** 0.400 qt

27. An order for a patient calls for 0.020 gram of medication. On hand are 4-mg tablets. What dose is needed for the patient?
A. 2 tablets **B.** 4 tablets **C.** 5 tablets **D.** 8 tablets **E.** 200 tablets

28. A doctor orders 1500 mg of a sulfa drug.Tablets in stock are 0.500 g. How many tablets are needed?
A. 1 tablet **B.** 1½ tablets **C.** ⅓ tablet **D.** 2½ tablets **E.** 3 tablets

29. What is the density of a bone with a mass of 192 g and a volume of 120 cm^3?
A. 0.63 g/mL **B.** 1.4 g/cm^3 **C.** 1.6 g/cm^3 **D.** 1.9 g/cm^3 **E.** 2.8 g/cm^3

30. How many milliliters of a salt solution with a density of 1.8 g/mL are needed to provide 400 g of salt solution?
A. 220 mL **B.** 22 mL **C.** 720 mL **D.** 400 mL **E.** 4.5 mL

31. The density of a solution is 0.85 g/mL. Its specific gravity is
A. 222 mL **B.** 8.5 **C.** 0.85 mL **D.** 1.2 **E.** 0.85

32. Three liquids have densities of 1.15 g/mL, 0.79 g/mL and 0.95 g/mL. When the liquids, which do not mix, are poured into a graduated cylinder, the liquid at the top is the one with a density of
A. 1.15 g/mL **B.** 1.00 g/mL **C.** 0.95 g/mL **D.** 0.79 g/mL **E.** 0.16 g/mL

33. A sample of oil has a mass of 65 g and a volume of 80.0 mL. What is the specific gravity of the oil?
A. 1.5 **B.** 1.4 **C.** 1.2 **D.** 0.90 **E.** 0.81

34. What is the mass of a 10.0 mL sample of urine with a specific gravity of 1.04?
A. 104 g **B.** 10.4 g **C.** 1.04 g **D.** 1.40 g **E.** 9.62 g

35. Ethyl alcohol has a density of 0.790 g/mL. What is the mass of 0.250 L of the alcohol?
A. 198 g **B.** 158 g **C.** 3.95 g **D.** 0.253 g **E.** 0.160 g

Key Terms

Celsius (°C) temperature scale A temperature scale on which water has a freezing point of 0°C and a boiling point of 100°C.

centimeter (cm) A unit of length in the metric system; there are 2.54 cm in 1 in.

conversion factor A ratio in which the numerator and denominator are quantities from an equality or given relationship. For example, the conversion factors for the relationship 1 kg = 2.20 lb are written as the following:

$$\frac{2.20\ \text{lb}}{1\ \text{kg}} \quad \text{and} \quad \frac{1\ \text{kg}}{2.20\ \text{lb}}$$

cubic centimeter (cm^3, cc) The volume of a cube that has 1-cm sides, equal to 1 mL.

density The relationship of the mass of an object to its volume expressed as grams per cubic centimeter (g/cm^3), grams per milliliter (g/mL), or grams per liter (g/L).

equality A relationship between two units that measure the same quantity.

exact number A number obtained by counting or definition.

gram (g) The metric unit used in measurements of mass.

Kelvin (K) temperature scale A temperature scale on which the lowest possible temperature is 0 K.

kilogram (kg) A metric mass of 1000 g, equal to 2.20 lb. The kilogram is the SI standard unit of mass.

liter (L) The metric unit for volume that is slightly larger than a quart.

mass A measure of the quantity of material in an object.

measured number A number obtained when a quantity is determined by using a measuring device.

meter (m) The metric unit for length that is slightly longer than a yard. The meter is the SI standard unit of length.

metric system A system of measurement used by scientists and in most countries of the world.

milliliter (mL) A metric unit of volume equal to one-thousandth of a L (0.001 L).

prefix The part of the name of a metric unit that precedes the base unit and specifies the size of the measurement. All prefixes are related on a decimal scale.

scientific notation A form of writing large and small numbers using a coefficient between 1 and 10, followed by a power of 10.

significant figures The numbers recorded in a measurement.

SI units The International System of units that modifies the metric system.

specific gravity (sp gr) A relationship between the density of a substance and the density of water:

$$\text{sp gr} = \frac{\text{density of sample}}{\text{density of water}}$$

temperature An indicator of the hotness or coldness of an object.

volume The amount of space occupied by a substance.

Supplement 2

Microscopy

2 Microscopy

LOOKING AHEAD

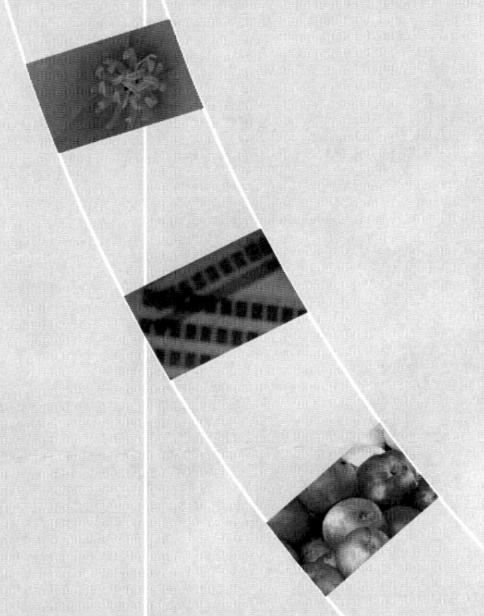

http://www.pearsoncustom.com/devry/mycbp

Study Goals

- Review Table 2.2 in your text

Chapter Review

Chapter Concept Review

Microscopy

1. **Microscopy** refers to the passage of light or electrons of various **wavelengths** through lenses to **magnify** objects and provide **resolution** and contrast so that those objects can be viewed and studied.

2. **Immersion oil** is used to fill the space between the specimen and a lens to reduce light refraction and thus increase the **numerical aperture** and resolution.

3. Staining techniques and polarized light may be used to enhance **contrast** between the object and its background.

4. **Simple microscopes** contain a single magnifying lens, whereas **compound microscopes** use a series of lenses for magnification.

5. The lens closest to the object being magnified is the **objective lens**, several of which are mounted on a **revolving nosepiece**. The lenses closest to the eyes are **ocular lenses**. **Condenser lenses** lie beneath the stage and direct light though the slide.

6. The magnifications of the objective lens and the ocular lens are multiplied together to give **total magnification**.

7. A photograph of a microscopic image is a **micrograph**.

8. **Dark-field microscopes** provide a dark background for small or colorless specimens.

9. **Phase microscopes**, such as **phase-contrast** and **differential interference contrast microscopes**, cause light rays that pass through a specimen to be out of phase with light rays that pass through the field, producing contrast.

10. **Fluorescent microscopes** use ultraviolet light and fluorescent dyes to fluoresce specimens and enhance contrast.

11. A **confocal microscope** uses fluorescent dyes in conjunction with computers to provide three-dimensional images of a specimen.

12. A **transmission electron microscope (TEM)** provides an image produced by the transmission of electrons through a thinly sliced, dehydrated specimen.

13. A **scanning electron microscope (SEM)** provides a three-dimensional image by scattering electrons from the surface of a specimen.

14. Minuscule electronic probes are used in **scanning tunneling microscopes (STM)** and in **atomic force microscopes (AFM)** to reveal details at the atomic level.

Chapter Summary

Microscopy
Microscopy refers to the use of light or electrons to magnify objects.

General Principles of Microscopy
The same general principles guide both light and electron microscopy.

Wavelength of Radiation

Various forms of radiation differ in **wavelength**, which is the distance between two corresponding parts of a wave. The human eye distinguishes different wavelengths of light as different colors.

In addition to light, moving electrons act as waves with wavelengths dependent upon the voltage of an electron beam. Electron wavelengths are much smaller than those of visible light, and thus their use results in enhanced microscopy.

Magnification

Magnification is the apparent increase in size of an object and is indicated by a number followed by an "×," which is read "times." Magnification results when a beam of radiation *refracts* (bends) as it passes through a lens.

Resolution

Resolution (also called *resolving power*) is the ability to distinguish between objects that are close together. The closer together two objects are and yet still distinguishable as separate objects, the better the resolution. Modern microscopes can distinguish between objects as close together as 0.2 μm. A principle of microscopy is that resolution distance is dependent on (1) the wavelength of the light or electron beam and (2) the **numerical aperture** of the lens, which is its ability to gather light. **Immersion oil** is used to fill the space between the specimen and a lens to reduce light refraction and thus increase the numerical aperture and resolution.

Contrast

Contrast refers to differences in intensity between two objects, or between an object and its background. Since most microorganisms are colorless, they are stained to increase contrast. Polarized light may also be used to enhance contrast.

Light Microscopy

Several classes of microscopes use various types of light to examine specimens.

Bright-Field Microscopes

The most common microscopes are *bright-field microscopes*, in which the background (or *field*) is illuminated. There are two basic types: **Simple microscopes**, which contain a single magnifying lens and are similar to a magnifying glass, and **compound microscopes**, which use a series of lenses for magnification. Light rays pass through a specimen and into an **objective lens** immediately above the object being magnified. The objective lens is really a series of lenses, and several objective lenses are mounted on a **revolving nosepiece**. The lenses closest to the eyes are **ocular lenses**, whereas **condenser lenses** lie beneath the stage of the microscope and direct light through the slide. The **total magnification** of a compound microscope is determined by multiplying the magnification of the objective lens by that of the ocular lens. The limit of useful magnification for light microscopes is 2000× because they are restricted by the wavelength of visible light. A photograph of a microscopic image is a **micrograph**.

Dark-Field Microscopes

Pale objects are best observed with **dark-field microscopes**, which utilize a dark-field stop in the condenser that prevents light from directly entering the objective lens. Instead, light passes into the slide at an oblique angle. Only light rays scattered by the specimen enter the objective lens and are seen, so the specimen appears light against a dark background.

Phase Microscopes

Phase microscopes use a *phase plate* to retard light rays passing through the specimen so that they are ½ wavelength out of phase with neighboring light waves, thereby producing contrast. **Phase-contrast microscopes** produce sharply defined images in which fine structures can be seen. **Differential interference contrast microscopes** create phase interference patterns and use prisms to split light beams into their component colors, giving images a dramatic three-dimensional or shadowed appearance.

Fluorescent Microscopes

Fluorescent microscopes use an ultraviolet (UV) light source to fluoresce objects. Since UV light has a shorter wavelength than visible light, resolution is increased. Contrast is improved because fluorescing structures are visible against a black background.

Confocal Microscopes

Confocal microscopes use fluorescent dyes in conjunction with UV lasers to illuminate the fluorescent chemicals in only one thin plane of a specimen at a time. Several images are taken and digitized, and then computers construct three-dimensional images of the entire specimen.

Electron Microscopy

Because the shortest wavelength of visible light is about 400 nm, structures closer together than about 200 nm cannot be distinguished using light microscopy. By contrast, electrons traveling as waves have wavelengths between 0.01 nm and 0.001 nm; thus, their resolving power is much greater, and they typically magnify objects 10,000× to 100,000×. There are two general types.

Transmission Electron Microscopes

A **transmission electron microscope (TEM)** generates a beam of electrons that passes through a thinly-sliced, dehydrated specimen, through magnetic fields that manipulate and focus the beam, and then onto a fluorescent screen that changes the electrons' energy into visible light.

Scanning Electron Microscopes

In a **scanning electron microscope (SEM)**, the surface of the specimen is first coated with a metal such as platinum or gold. The SEM then focuses the beam of electrons back and forth across the surface of the specimen, scanning it rather than penetrating it. Electrons scattered off the surface of the specimen pass through a detector and a photomultiplier, producing a signal that is displayed on a monitor.

Probe Microscopy

Probe microscopes use miniscule electronic probes to magnify specimens more than 100,000,000×. There are two types. **Scanning tunneling microscopes** pass a pointed tungsten probe across and above the surface of a specimen and measure the amount of electron flow. They can reveal details on a specimen surface at the atomic level. **Atomic force microscopes** traverse the tip of the probe lightly on the surface of the specimen. Deflection of a laser beam aimed at the probe's tip measures vertical movements that are translated by computer to reveal the specimen's atomic topography.

Practice Test for Supplement 2

Multiple Choice

1. Magnification makes an object:
A. Larger
B. Appear larger
C. Does not change the size of the object
D. Both b and c

2. Which of the following could have been the most precisely resolved object seen using a Leeuwenhoek microscope?
A. Mitochondrion
B. Protein
C. Red blood cell
D. Virus

3. Most microbes have poor contrast because:
A. They are small
B. They are colorless
C. They don't let light pass through them
D. All of the above

4. Oil immersion lenses help microscopists increase:
A. Contrast
B. Magnification
C. Resolution
D. Both b and c

5. For a light microscope, the limit of resolution is determined by:
A. The quality of the lenses
B. The magnification of the lenses
C. Contrast
D. The wavelength of visible light

6. Living microbes can best be viewed using which type of microscopy?
   A. Bright-field microscopy C. Phase contrast microscopy
   B. Dark-field microscopy D. Scanning electron microscopy

7. The resolving limit of the best light microscope under the best of conditions is __________ while that of a scanning electron microscope is __________.
   A. 200 μm, 0.001 μm C. 200 μm, 0.001 nm
   B. 200 nm, 0.001 nm D. 200 nm, 0.001 μm

8. The major difference between SEM and TEM is:
   A. SEM doesn't view specimens under a vacuum
   B. SEM requires specimens to be coated with metal "stains"
   C. SEM produces a three-dimensional image
   D. SEM allows visualization of living organisms

Fill in the Blanks

1. Empty magnification produces images that are faint and blurry because the image lacks sufficient ____________________ and ____________________.

2. Fluorescent microscopes have ______________________ (better/worse) resolution than standard bright-field microscopes because UV light has a ______________________ (longer/shorter) wavelength than visible light.

3. The two types of microscopy that produce direct three-dimensional images for viewing are ______________________ and ______________________.

4. Electron microscopy is most useful for viewing a cell's ______________________, those parts of the cell that can't be seen any other way.

5. Staining is useful because it increases ______________________ between structures or a specimen and its background; this, in turn allows for better ______________________.

Critical Thinking

1. Objective lenses on a compound light microscope come in several magnifications, usually 4×, 10×, 40×, and 100× (oil immersion). When you first put a slide on the microscope stage to locate your specimen, which lens should you use and why?

Supplement 3

The Earth's Waters

3 The Earth's Waters

LOOKING AHEAD

http://www.pearsoncustom.com/devry/mycbp

Earth's Surface—Land and Water

Groundwater Flow and Contaminant Transport

The occupants of Houses 1, 2, and 3 wish to drill wells for domestic water supply. Note that the locations of all houses are between Lakes A and B, at different elevations.

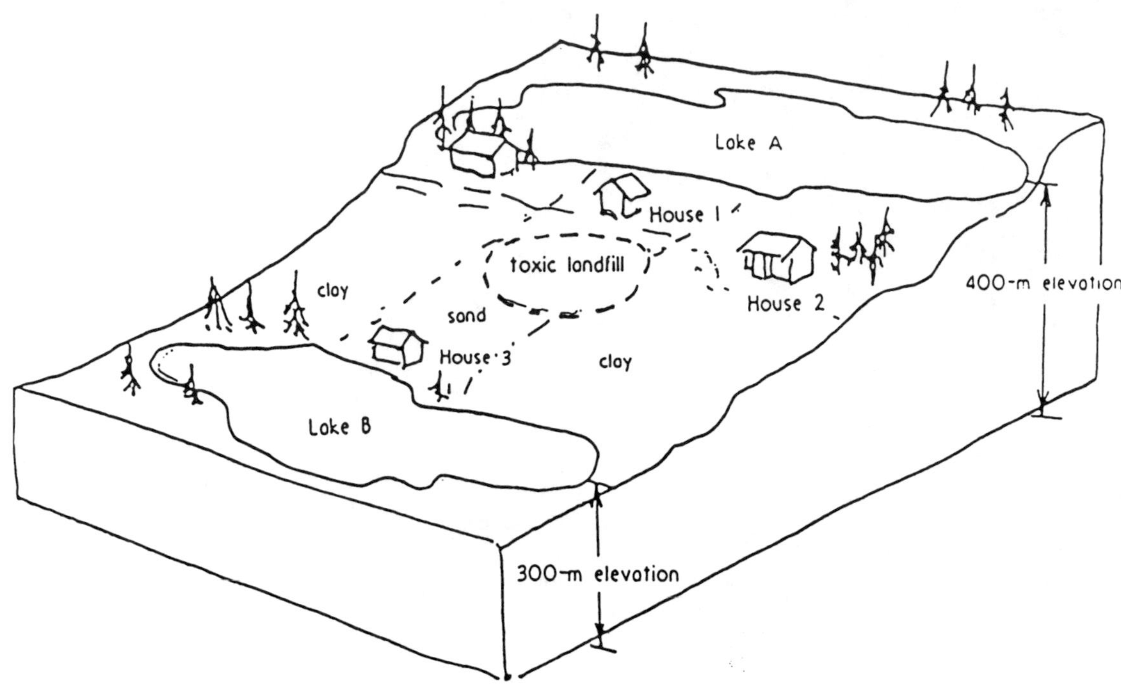

1. Show by sketching dashed lines on the drawing, the likely direction of groundwater flow beneath all the houses.

2. Which of the wells drilled beside Houses 1, 2, and 3 are likely to yield an abundant water supply?

3. Do any of the three need to worry about the toxic landfill contaminating their water supply? Explain.

4. Why don't the homeowners simply take water directly from the lakes?

5. Suggest a potentially better location for the landfill. Defend your choice.

Stream Velocity

Let's explore how the average velocity of streams and rivers can change. The volume of water that flows past a given location over any given length of time depends both on the stream velocity and the cross-sectional area of the stream. We say

$$Q = A \times V$$

where Q is the volumetric flow rate (a measure of the volume passing a point per unit time). Also, A is the cross-sectional area of the stream, and V its average velocity.

Consider the stream shown below, with rectangular cross-sectional areas

$$A = \text{width} \times \text{depth}$$

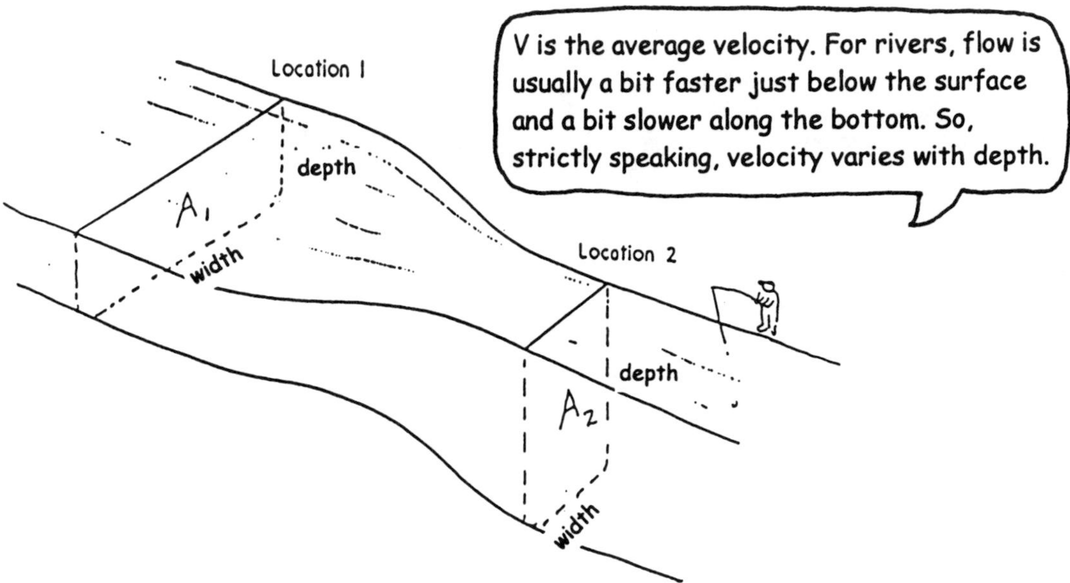
V is the average velocity. For rivers, flow is usually a bit faster just below the surface and a bit slower along the bottom. So, strictly speaking, velocity varies with depth.
Location 1
depth
A1
width
Location 2
depth
A2
width

1. The two locations shown have no stream inlets or outlets between them, so Q remains constant. Suppose the cross-sectional areas are also constant ($A_1 = A_2$), with Location 2 deeper but narrower than Location 1. What change, if any, occurs for the stream velocity?

____

2. If Q remains constant, what happens to stream velocity at Location 2 if A_2 is less than A_1?

____

3. If Q remains constant, what happens to stream velocity at Location 2 if A_2 is greater than A_1?

____

4. What happens to stream velocity at Location 2 if area A_2 remains the same, but Q increases (perhaps by an inlet along the way?)

___

5. What happens to stream velocity at Location 2 if both A_2 and Q increase?

___

Supplement 3 Review: Summary of Terms

Glacier A mass of dense ice that forms when snow on land is subjected to pressure from overlying snow, so that it is compacted and recrystallized.
Groundwater The water that resides in a saturation zone.
Hot spot A stationary, exceptionally hot region deep in Earth's interior, usually near the mantle–core boundary.
Hydrologic cycle The cycle of evaporation and precipitation that controls the distribution of Earth's water.
Infiltration Absorption of water by the ground.
Permeability The ease with which fluids flow through porous sediment and rock.
Porosity The proportion of open space in a rock or sediment.
Runoff Precipitation not absorbed by the ground that moves over Earth's surface.
Seamount An undersea volcanic peak.
Upwarped mountain A dome-shaped mountain produced by a broad arching of the Earth's crust.
Volcano A hill or mountain formed by the extrusion of lava, ash, and rock fragments.
Watershed The area of land that drains into a stream.
Water table The upper boundary of the saturated zone.

Supplement 4

Household Chemicals

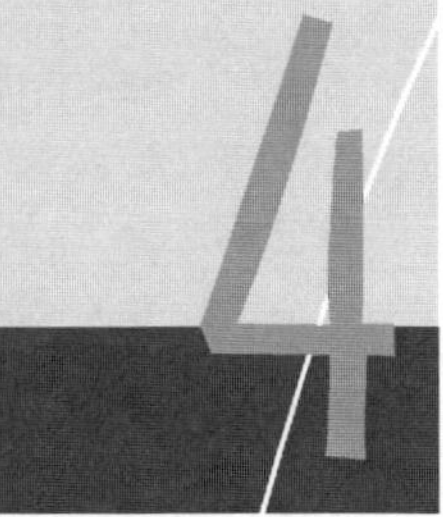

4 Household Chemicals

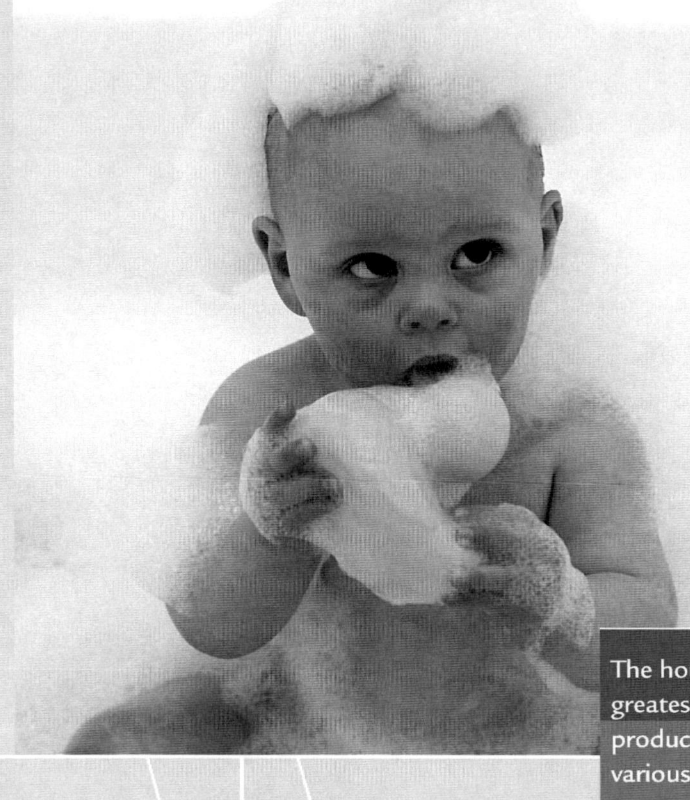

The household chemicals sold in greatest volume are cleaning products—soaps, detergents, and various special-purpose and multi-purpose cleaning mixtures.

LOOKING AHEAD

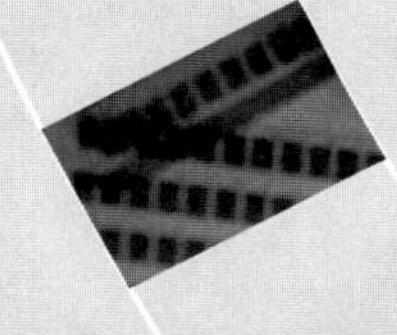

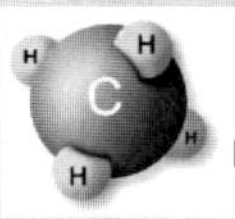

http://www.pearsoncustom.com/devry/mycbp

Study Goals

(You should know that...)

1. We use many chemicals in the home, and some of them are hazardous.

2. Cleaning with soap is a modern development.

3. Animal fat treated with NaOH forms natural soap. This is a long hydrocarbon chain that dissolves oils and is a water-soluble salt of a carboxylic acid.

4. Sodium salt soaps are precipitated by hard water; potassium salt soaps are softer and are used as liquid soaps; ammonium salt soaps are used in shampoos.

5. Water softeners remove Ca, Mg, and Fe ions.

6. Synthetic detergents were developed after World War II to avoid the problems of hard water. The ABS detergents were nonbiodegradable and discontinued because of ecological problems and were replaced with LAS detergents.

7. Laundry detergents have several components: builders that improve their cleaning ability and brighteners that absorb UV light and reemit in the visible range, making clothes look cleaner.

8. Liquid detergents are not as effective cleaners as solid detergents but more convenient. These are mostly anionic surfactants: the polar end is negative.

9. Quaternary ammonium salts are cationic surfactants (the polar end is positive) and are useful in killing germs.

10. Bleaches are oxidizing agents and include NaOCl (a chlorine bleach) and borax.

11. Some general purpose cleaners are ammonia (good for baked-on food and grease but hard on aluminum materials) baking soda (a good mild abrasive and odor absorber), and vinegar (good for grease but hard on marble).

12. Special-purpose cleaners include toilet bowl cleaners (dissolvers of limestone or $CaCO_3$ deposits such as HCl or sodium bisulfate) scouring powder (silica), glass cleaners (isopropyl alcohol or ammonia), drain cleaners (grease-active chemicals such as NaOH), and oven cleaners (NaOH to dissolve the grease).

13. There are a number of organic solvents (gasoline) that are highly flammable, toxic when swallowed, and narcotic at high concentrations, causing abuse potential and death when "sniffed."

14. Paints are composed of a pigment, a binder, and a solvent.

15. Waxes are esters of long-chain organic acids and long-chain alcohols. They are used to form protective coatings.

16. A variety of cosmetic products are defined legally as articles "for cleansing, beautifying, promoting attractiveness or altering the appearance...," but soaps are specifically excluded.

17. Cosmetic products include, skin creams and lotions (can form a protective coating, soften skin, hold in moisture or block UV radiation); lipstick (a dye with some protective properties); eye makeup (pigments with a wax base); and deodorants and antiperspirants (perfume to mask body odor and germicide to kill bacteria).

18. Toothpastes contain soaps and abrasives. Stannous fluoride is sometimes added to make the enamel stronger and more resistant to decay.

19. Perfumes, colognes, and aftershaves are complex compounds with attractive smells dissolved in alcohol and water.

20. Hair is primarily fibrous keratin, a protein, but with many more disulfide linkages than the keratin of skin.

21. Shampoos use a synthetic detergent as a cleansing agent; many shampoos have additives such as proteins that give more body; conditioners that soften the hair like fabric softeners; different ratios of cleansers for oily, normal, and dry hair; and "natural" additives such as honey, herbs, and the like, which display no evidence of effectiveness.

22. The amount of melanin (brown-black pigment) and phaemelanin determines the color of hair. Bleaches oxidize these pigments and hair colorants can be added. Hair treatments which are used to remove "grayness" use lead compounds to form lead sulfide with the hair.

23. Permanents break and reform the hydrogen bonds in the proteins of hair.

24. Hair sprays are solid or semisolid organic compounds that form a sticky layer on the hair.

25. Hair removers (depilatories) are strong bases that destroy the peptides in hair so that they can be washed off.

26. Hair restorers, such as (Rogaine®), dilate blood vessels in the scalp.

Chapter Review

Chapter Concept Review

Sections 4.1–4.2

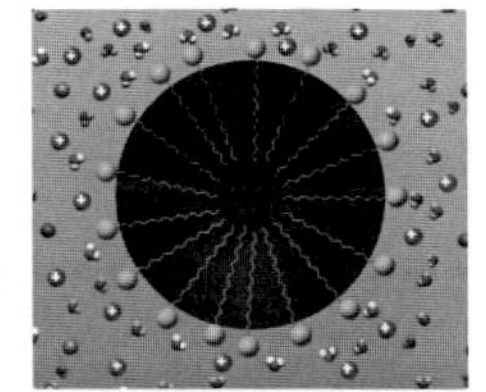

Some plants contain saponins, which produce lather. Plant ashes contain K_2CO_3 and Na_2CO_3, which are alkaline and have detergent properties. A **soap** is a salt of a long-chain carboxylic acid. Traditionally, soap was made from fat by a reaction with NaOH. Soap has been known for centuries, but has only come into common use since the mid-1800s. A soap molecule has a **hydrophobic** hydrocarbon tail (soluble in oil or grease) and a **hydrophilic** polar head (soluble in water). Soap molecules disperse oil or grease in water by forming **micelles**, tiny oil droplets surrounded by soap molecules. Agents that stabilize suspensions in this way are called **surface-active agents** (**surfactants**). Soaps do not work well in hard water (water containing Ca^{2+}, Fe^{2+}, or Mg^{2+} ions) because they form insoluble salts. Carbonates and phosphates act as water softeners, removing as insoluble salts the ions that otherwise cause water to be hard. Home water softeners remove the unwanted ions by replacing them with sodium or potassium ions (Na^+, K^+).

Sections 4.3–4.5

A synthetic detergent usually has a large hydrocarbon tail and a polar or ionic head. ABS detergents have branched-chain structures and are not easily biodegraded. LAS detergents have linear chains that can be broken down by microorganisms. Soap, ABS detergents, and LAS detergents are **anionic surfactants** that have negative charges on the active part. A **nonionic surfactant** has no charge. A **cationic surfactant** such as a quaternary ammonium salt has a positive charge. An **amphoteric surfactant** carries both positive and negative charges. Detergent formulations often include **builders** such as complex phosphates to increase detergency. **Optical brighteners**, which are fluorescent whitening agents, are often added to make whites "whiter." Other components such as bleaches, fragrances, and fabric softeners may be included. Hand-dishwashing detergents contain mainly surfactants as the active ingredients. Automatic dishwasher detergents are often strongly alkaline and are not to be used for hand dishwashing.

Sections 4.6–4.7

Cationic surfactants (alkylammonium salts) are useful as disinfectants. Those with two long hydrocarbon chains are used as fabric softeners. **Bleaches** are oxidizing agents. Hypochlorite bleaches release chlorine. Oxygen-releasing bleaches usually contain perborates or percarbonates. Bleaches act by oxidizing chromophores (colored compounds) to colorless fragments.

Sections 4.8–4.9

All-purpose cleaners may contain surfactants, ammonia, disinfectants, and other ingredients. Reading the label is imperative, so that the cleaner may be used properly and safely. Household ammonia, sodium bicarbonate (baking soda), and vinegar are good cleaners for many purposes. Special-purpose cleaners each have a specific purpose. Toilet bowl cleaners usually contain an acid. Scouring powders contain abrasives. Glass cleaners contain ammonia. Drain cleaners contain NaOH or bleach. Oven cleaners contain NaOH.

Sections 4.10–4.12

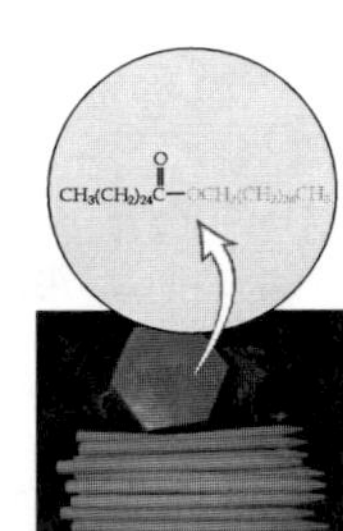

Solvents are used to remove paint and other materials. Many organic solvents are volatile and flammable. **Paint** contains a pigment, a binder, and a solvent. Titanium dioxide is the most common pigment. Water-based paints often use a polymer binder; oil-based paints use tung oil or linseed oil. A **wax** is an ester of a fatty acid with a long-chain alcohol. Beeswax and carnauba wax are commonly used waxes. **Lanolin**, from sheep's wool, is also a wax, useful for skin creams and lotions.

Section 4.13

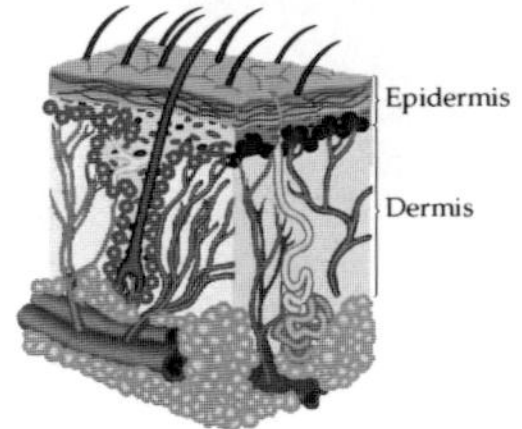

A **cosmetic** is something applied to the body for cleansing, promoting attractiveness or for similar purposes, but cosmetics do not have to be proven safe and effective like drugs. Toothpaste and soaps legally are not cosmetics. Skin is made of a tough, fibrous protein called **keratin. Sebum**, an oily secretion, protects skin from loss of moisture. A **lotion** is an emulsion of oil droplets in water; a **cream** is an emulsion of water droplets in oil. Each is a **moisturizer** that forms a protective physical barrier over the skin to hold in moisture. Creams and lotions also soften skin; such skin softeners are called **emollients**. Humectants such as glycerol hydrogen bond to water and hold it to the skin. Ultraviolet rays trigger the production of the pigment **melanin**, which darkens the skin. Most **sunscreen lotions** block shorter wavelength UV-B while letting through the longer wavelength, less-energetic

UV-A rays that promote tanning. PABA and OMC are the most common ingredients in sunscreens. The **skin protection factor (SPF)** is the factor by which the UV light is reduced. Eye makeup and lipstick are mainly blends of oil, waxes, and pigments. **Deodorants** mask body odor and kill odor-causing bacteria. **Antiperspirants** also retard perspiration. The most common antiperspirants act as **astringents**, constricting the openings of the sweat glands.

Sections 4.14–4.15

Toothpaste contains a detergent, an abrasive, a thickener, flavoring, and often an added fluoride compound. The fragrance of a **perfume** can usually be split into three basic fractions: the **top note** (which is the most volatile), the **middle note** (of intermediate volatility), and the **end note** (of lowest volatility). **Colognes** are diluted perfumes. **Hypoallergenic cosmetics** purport to cause fewer allergic reactions than regular products, but the term has no legal meaning.

Section 4.16–4.17

Shampoos are synthetic detergents blended with perfume ingredients and sometimes mixed with protein or other conditioners to give the hair more body. Dark hair contains the pigment melanin, red hair contains phaeomelanin, and blonde hair contains very little of either pigment. Many hair dyes are based on *para*-phenylenediamine.

Permanent waving of the hair uses a reducing agent to break the disulfide linkages and then an oxidizing neutralizer to reform the disulfide bonds in different places. Hair sprays contain **resins**, organic materials that leave a sticky film on the hair. Such resins are also available in foam form as **mousses**. Chemicals that remove hair are called **depilatories**, and most such chemicals can also damage the skin. The most expensive brand of a given product is not necessarily the best.

Chapter Summary

4.1 A History of Cleaning

- **A.** Saponins are soapy compounds found in the leaves of certain plants that were used by some primitive peoples for washing clothes.
- **B.** Plant ashes contain potassium carbonate; these alkaline ashes were used by Babylonians 4,000 years ago.
- **C.** Most people in the Western world seldom, if ever, bathed using soap until the nineteenth century.

4.2 Fat + Lye → Soap

- **A.** Soaps are salts of long-chain carboxylic acids.
    - **1.** Soaps are made by reacting animal fats or vegetable oils with sodium hydroxide (lye).
    - **2.** Early soaps often contained unreacted lye.
    - **3.** Toilet soaps contain additives, dyes, perfumes, creams, and oils.
    - **4.** Scouring soaps contain abrasives.
    - **5.** Few, if any, deodorant soaps contain an active deodorant.
    - **6.** Floating soaps are formed with air to lower their density.
    - **7.** Potassium soaps (used in shaving creams) are softer and produce a finer lather than sodium soaps.
    - **8.** Triethanolamine soaps are used in shampoos and other cosmetics.
- **B.** How soap works.
    - **1.** Oil and greases hold dirt to skin and fabrics.
    - **2.** Soap has an ionic (water-soluble) end and a hydrocarbon (oil-soluble) end.
        - **a.** Soap molecules break oils into tiny globules by sticking their hydrocarbon tails into the oil while the ionic heads remain in the aqueous phase.
        - **b.** The oil droplets don't coalesce owing to the repulsion of the charged groups.
- **C.** Disadvantages of soaps.
    - **1.** Under acidic conditions, natural soaps are converted to insoluble fatty acids that precipitate as greasy scum.
    - **2.** "Hard" water contains calcium, magnesium, or iron ions, which form insoluble salts with the fatty acid anions that precipitate as "bathtub ring."
- **D.** Water softeners.
    - **1.** Sodium carbonate (washing soda) acts in two ways.
        - **a.** It makes the water basic so that the fatty acids won't precipitate.
        - **b.** The carbonate ions precipitate the hard-water ions and keep them from forming soap scum.
    - **2.** Trisodium phosphate acts similarly.
        - **a.** It makes the water basic.
        - **b.** The phosphate ions precipitate calcium and magnesium ions.
    - **3.** Water softening tanks absorb the calcium, magnesium, and iron ions on polymeric materials, thus softening the water.

4.3 Synthetic Detergents

- **A.** ABS detergents: nondegradable.
    - **1.** Alkylbenzenesulfonate (ABS) detergents were derived from propylene, benzene, and sulfuric acid, followed by neutralization.
        - **a.** ABS detergents worked well in acidic and hard waters but were not degraded in nature.
        - **b.** Foaming rivers led to their ban in the 1960s.

B. LAS detergents: biodegradable.
   1. Linear alkylsulfonates (LAS) are derived from ethylene, benzene, and sulfuric acid, followed by neutralization.
      a. LAS detergents are biodegradable.

4.4 Laundry Detergent Formulations
A. Surface-active agents (surfactants) are substances that stabilize the suspension of nonpolar substances in water.
B. In addition to surfactants, modern detergent formulations contain
   1. Builders: substances such as phosphates and sodium carbonate that increase the detergency of phosphates.
      a. Many locales have banned the use of phosphates.
      b. Other builders include zeolites, complex aluminosilicates that tie up the hard-water ions.
C. Brighteners.
   1. Optical brighteners (blancophors, or colorless dyes) make clothes appear brighter by absorbing ultraviolet light (invisible) and reemitting it as blue light (visible).
   2. Brighteners cause mutations in microorganisms, but their only known effect on humans is skin rashes.

4.5 Dishwashing Detergents
A. Soap, LAS, and ABS are all anionic detergents.
   1. In anionics the nonpolar part is joined to an ionic end.
B. Liquid laundry detergents make heavy use of nonionic surfactants:
   1. In nonionics, the part that contains oxygen atoms is water soluble. There is no ionic charge on the molecule.
   2. Nonionic detergents readily remove oily dirt but can't keep it suspended as well as anionic surfactants.
   3. Unlike most substances, nonionic detergents are more soluble in cold than in hot water.
C. Dishwashing Detergents.
   1. Liquid dishwashing detergents for hand dishwashing generally contain anionic or nonionic surfactants as the only active ingredients.
      a. They differ mainly in the concentration of the surfactant.
      b. Other ingredients-perfumes, colors, substances purporting to soften hands, are there mainly as a basis for advertising claims.
   2. Detergents for automatic dishwashers are highly alkaline and should never be used for hand dishwashing.

4.6 Fabric Softeners: Quaternary Ammonium Salts
A. The working part of a cationic surfactant is a positive ion.
   1. Most cationics are quaternary ammonium salts; they have four alkyl groups attached to a nitrogen atom that has a positive charge.
   2. Cationic detergents are not very good for cleaning.
   3. They do have germicidal action.
      a. When combined with nonionic detergents, they are used for cleaning in the food and dairy industries.
B. Molecules with two long hydrocarbon tails (and two smaller groups on nitrogen) act as fabric softeners.
   1. They form a film on fibers, lubricating them for flexibility and softness.

4.7 Laundry Bleaches: Whiter Whites
A. Bleaches are oxidizing agents.
   1. Liquid laundry bleaches ("chlorine bleaches") are all 5.25% solutions of sodium hypochlorite. These solutions release chlorine rapidly and can damage fabrics.
   2. Solid chlorine bleaches (e.g., Symclosene, a cyanurate-type bleach) release chlorine slowly and are less damaging to fabrics.

3. Oxygen-releasing bleaches contain sodium perborate. They operate well only above 65°C.
   a. They are especially effective on resin-treated polyester cotton fabrics.

B. Mixing household chemicals can produce toxic substances.

4.8 All-Purpose Cleaning Products

A. All-purpose products for use in water may include
   1. surfactants.
   2. sodium carbonate (washing soda).
   3. ammonia.
   4. solvents (to dissolve grease).
   5. disinfectants, deodorants, etc.

B. Household ammonia has many uses.
   1. Undiluted it loosens baked-on grease, burned-on food.
   2. Diluted it cleans glass.
   3. Mixed with detergent it removes wax from linoleum.

C. Baking soda is
   1. a mild abrasive cleaner.
   2. an absorbent of odors in the refrigerator.

D. Vinegar is a good grease cutter.

4.9 Special-Purpose Cleaners

A. Toilet bowl cleaners.
   1. These are usually acidic to dissolve calcium carbonate buildup and fungal growth.

B. Scouring powder.
   1. Contains abrasives and surfactants
      a. Can scratch surfaces.

C. Glass cleaners.
   1. Volatile liquids that evaporate without leaving a residue

D. Drain cleaners contain.
   1. Sodium hydroxide, which reacts with water to generate heat.
      a. Heat melts the grease that was clogging the pipes.

E. Oven cleaners.
   1. Sodium hydroxide converts greasy deposits to soap.

4.10 Organic Solvents in the Home

A. Solvents are used to remove paint, varnish, adhesives, waxes, etc.

B. Solvents are also used in all-purpose cleansers.
   1. Pine oil terpenes dissolve grease and have a mild disinfectant action.
   2. Petroleum distillates dissolve grease.

C. Most of the solvents are volatile and flammable.
   1. They cause chemical pneumonia when swallowed.
   2. They cause narcosis when inhaled at high concentrations.

4.11 Paints

A. Paints contain pigment, binder, and solvent.
   1. Titanium oxide is used as the pigment.
   2. Binders are usually tung oil or linseed oil (oil-based paints) and polymers (water-based paints).
   3. Solvents are usually alcohol, a hydrocarbon, an ester, or water.

4.12 Waxes

A. Esters of long-chain, organic (fatty) acids with long-chain alcohols are called waxes.
   1. Beeswax, carnauba wax, spermaceti wax, and lanolin are some examples.

4.13 Cosmetics: Personal-Care Chemicals

A. Cosmetics are defined as articles intended to be rubbed, poured, sprinkled, or sprayed on, introduced into or otherwise applied to the human body or any part thereof, for cleansing, beautifying, promoting attractiveness, or altering appearance.
   1. Soap, antiperspirants, and antidandruff shampoos are excluded from this definition.

B. Skin creams and lotions
   1. The outer layer of skin is the epidermis. The corneal layer of the epidermis is composed of dead cells.
   2. The corneal layer is mainly keratin, a tough, fibrous protein with a moisture content of about 10%.
      a. Below 10% moisture, skin is dry and flaky.
      b. Above 10% moisture, microorganisms flourish.
      c. Sebum (skin oils) protects the skin from loss of moisture.
   3. Wind and water (especially with soap) remove sebum, leaving the skin dry. Dry skin can be treated with
      a. Lotions: emulsions of oil in water (feel cool).
         i. Typical oils include mineral oil, petroleum jelly, and natural fats and oils.
      b. Creams: emulsions of water in oil (feel greasy).
      c. Emollients provide a protective coating on the skin to prevent loss of moisture.
      d. Moisturizers that hold moisture in skin usually contain lanolin or collagen.
   4. Sunscreen lotions protect the skin from harmful ultraviolet radiation. The most common ingredient is *para*-aminobenzoic acid.
      a. Skin protection factors (SPF) indicate how long a person can remain in the sun without burning.
      b. Melanin is a dark skin pigment; its formation during tanning is stimulated by long-wave ultraviolet radiation.
         i. Short-wave ultraviolet radiation can cause skin cancer.
      c. Excessive sunbathing causes premature aging of the skin and can lead to skin cancer.
         i. Cigarette smoking causes premature wrinkling of the skin.

C. Lipsticks.
   1. Lipsticks are composed of an oil (often castor oil) and a wax: the wax makes lipsticks firmer than creams.

D. Eye makeup.
   1. Mascara, composed of a base of fats and waxes, is used to darken eyelashes.
      a. It is colored by mineral pigments.
   2. Eye shadow is composed of a base of petroleum jelly and fats, oils, and waxes.
      a. It is colored by dyes and pigments.

E. Deodorants and antiperspirants.
   1. Deodorants are perfumed products designed to mask body odor.
   2. Antiperspirants retard perspiration and therefore are classified as a drug.
      a. Nearly all antiperspirants have aluminum chlorohydrate as the only active ingredient.
      b. Aluminum chlorohydrate is an astringent; it constricts the openings of sweat glands.

4.14 Toothpaste: Soap with Grit and Flavor

A. Toothpastes have two essential ingredients, a detergent and an abrasive.

B. Sodium lauryl sulfate is a typical detergent used in toothpastes, but any pharmaceutical-grade soap or detergent would do.

C. Other ingredients include flavors, colors, and sweeteners.

D. Tooth decay is caused by bacteria that convert sugars to
   1. Dextrans (plaque).
   2. Acids (such as lactic acid) that dissolve tooth enamel.

E. Fluorides harden tooth enamel, reducing the incidence of decay.
   1. Fluorides convert hydroxyapatite to fluorapatite, a harder material.
   2. According to the law, fluoride toothpastes are drugs, not cosmetics.

F. Hydrogen peroxide and baking soda are used to prevent gum disease, the major cause of adult tooth loss.

4.15 Perfumes, Colognes, and Aftershaves

A. Perfumes are extracts from natural materials or similar materials put together by chemists.

B. Perfumes are characterized by notes (components with differing volatility).

1. *Top note*: the most volatile fraction; the first aroma detected when applied
2. *Middle note*: intermediate in volatility; responsible for the lingering aroma after the top note is gone
3. *End note*: low in volatility

C. Several fruity or flowery compounds are synthesized in large quantities for use in perfumes and as fragrances for commercial products.

D. Musks are added to counteract sweet, flowery odors.

E. Andron by Jovan claims to contain a human sex attractant.

F. Colognes are diluted perfumes.

G. Aftershave lotions are colognes, sometimes with menthol for a cooling effect or an emollient for soothing the scraped skin.

H. Many people have allergic reactions to perfumes.

1. Hypoallergenic cosmetics often omit perfumes.

4.16 Some Hairy Chemistry

A. Hair is composed of the fibrous protein keratin.

B. Protein molecules in hair are strongly held together by four types of forces.

1. *Hydrogen bonds*—disrupted by water
2. *Salt bridges*—destroyed by changes in pH
3. *Disulfide linkages*—broken and destroyed by permanent wave and hair straightening treatments.
4. *Hydrophobic interactions*

C. Shampoo.

1. When hair is washed, the keratin absorbs water. The water disrupts hydrogen bonds and some salt bridges.
   - **a.** The hair is softened and made more stretchable.
2. Hair shafts are dead; only the root is alive. The hair is lubricated by sebum.
   - **a.** Sebum adheres dirt to hair.
   - **b.** Washing hair removes the oil and dirt.
3. Shampoo for adults usually has an anionic surfactant, such as sodium dodecyl sulfate, as the principal active ingredient.
4. Baby shampoos have an amphoteric surfactant with both a negatively charged oxygen and a positively charged nitrogen.
5. Most components other than a detergent are in a shampoo only as the basis for advertising claims.
6. Hair is protein with both acidic and basic groups.
   - **a.** Most shampoos have a pH between 5 and 8, which does not damage hair or scalp.
   - **b.** Protein shampoos condition hair by coating the hair shaft with protein (glue).
   - **c.** Shampoos for dry or oily hair differ only in the relative amounts of detergent.

D. Hair coloring.

1. Hair (and skin) are colored by pigments.
   - **a.** Melanin is responsible for brown and black colors.
   - **b.** Phaeomelanin is the pigment in red hair.
   - **c.** Blondes have little of either pigment; brunettes can become blondes by oxidizing the pigments with hydrogen peroxide.
2. Permanent hair dyes often are derivatives of *p*-phenylenediamine. These compounds penetrate the hair shaft and are oxidized to colored products (presumably quinones).
   - **a.** P-phenylenediamine produces a black color.
   - **b.** P-aminodiphenylamine sulfonic acid is used for blondes.
   - **c.** Intermediate colors use other derivatives.
   - **d.** Several of the hair-coloring diamines have been shown to be carcinogenic or mutagenic.
3. Hair treatments that restore color gradually use lead acetate solutions.
   - **a.** The lead ions penetrate the hair and react with sulfur to form black, insoluble lead sulfide.

E. Permanent waving: chemistry to curl your hair
- **1.** Adjacent protein molecules in hair are cross-linked by disulfide groups. To put curl in hair
  - **a.** A reducing agent is used to rupture the disulfide linkages.
  - **b.** The hair is set on curlers; the protein chains slide in relation to one another.
  - **c.** Disulfide linkages are formed in new positions.
  - **d.** The same chemical process can be used to straighten hair.

F. Hair sprays.
- **1.** Hair can be held in place by resins (often polyvinylpyrrolidone or its copolymers).
  - **a.** The resin can be dissolved in a solvent and applied as a spray.
- **2.** Holding resins can also be formulated as mousses (foams or froths).

G. Hair removers (depilatories).
- **1.** These are strongly basic sulfur compounds that destroy peptide bonds.
- **2.** They can damage skin.

H. Hair restorers
- **1.** Minoxidil dilates blood vessels and produces growth of fine hair on skin containing hair follicles.

4.17 Well-informed consumer

A. Most cosmetics are formulated from inexpensive ingredients.

B. You don't have to pay a lot for extra ingredients that contribute little to the performance of the product.

Discussion

In this supplement we apply some of the principles learned earlier to a study of some of the chemicals used in and around the home. Our main focus is on chemicals used in cleaning, for these are among the most common-and often the most dangerous-of the household chemicals. Others are discussed elsewhere. Pesticides, fertilizers, and other "farm" chemicals are also used on lawns, on gardens, and on household plants.

In this supplement we also apply our knowledge of chemistry to the substances we put on our skin and hair to make us look or smell better. Some of the properties are desirable; often some are not. The properties are independent of our wishes. Often they fall far short of extravagant advertising claims. With the introduction to cosmetics, you will be better equipped to judge for yourself the validity of some of the assertions of advertisers.

Practice Test for Supplement 4

Multiple Choice

1. The salts of long-chain carboxylic acids are called

A. soaps **B.** synthetic detergents
C. fabric softeners **D.** bleaches

2. Which of these is true of soap?

A. soaps that are biodegradable increase the BOD of water
B. soap is an excellent cleanser in soft water
C. soap works poorly in hard water
D. all the above are true

3. Soap was made in the second century by which of these processes?

A. boiling saponins with potassium carbonate
B. boiling animal fats with lye
C. boiling potassium carbonate and oils
D. mixing oils and acids

4. Which of these is true of the action of soap in removing dirt?
   A. the hydrocarbon end of soap is soluble in water
   B. the ionic end is soluble in oils
   C. one end of soap is soluble in water and the other in oil
   D. all the above

5. Water alone is not as effective as it is with soap because
   A. oil and dirt are not soluble in water
   B. water and oil are both quite polar
   C. soap is soluble in water and oil at the same time
   D. all the above

6. Which compound would not be expected to exhibit detergent action?
   A. $CH_3CH_2CH_2CH_2CH_2CH_2CH_2CH_2CH_2CH_2CH_2CH_2CH_2CH_2CH_2COO^-Na^+$
   B. $CH_3CH_2CH_2CH_2CH_2CH_2CH_2CH_2CH_2CH_2CH_2CH_2CH_2CH_2CH_2COOH$
   C. $CH_3CH_2CH_2CH_2CH_2CH_2CH_2CH_2CH_2CH_2CH_2CH_2CH_2CH_2CH_2OSO_3^-Na^+$
   D. $CH_3CH_2CH_2CH_2CH_2CH_2CH_2CH_2CH_2CH_2CH_2CH_2N^+Me_3Cl^-$

7. Bathtub ring results from the presence in water of
   A. Na^+ **B.** Ca^{2+}
   C. grease **D.** phosphates

8. Increased interest in cleanliness resulted from the discovery of
   A. soap **B.** phosphates
   C. disease-causing microorganisms **D.** America

9. Floating soaps differ from other soaps in that they contain
   A. air **B.** oil
   C. potassium **D.** helium

10. In acidic solutions, soaps are converted into
    A. bases **B.** phenols
    C. esters **D.** carboxylic acids

11. Synthetic detergents, called ABS, replaced soaps in the early 1960s. The biggest disadvantage of ABS was that they
    A. failed to work in hard water
    B. precipitated under acidic conditions
    C. were not broken down by microorganisms
    D. did not work in alkaline water

12. The foaming rivers of the early 1960s resulted from
    A. synthetic detergents
    B. an increased population of soap users
    C. an increased BOD from biodegradable soaps
    D. the use of NTA

13. Most bleaches contain the element
    A. phosphorus **B.** nitrogen
    C. potassium **D.** chlorine

14. Oxygen-releasing bleaches usually contain
    A. NaOCl **B.** cyanurates
    C. phosphates **D.** sodium perborate

15. The only active ingredient in most household liquid bleaches is
A. sodium hydroxide
B. sodium bicarbonate
C. sodium hypochlorite
D. chlorine

16. Of the following, which substance is not used as a water-softening agent?
A. sodium carbonate
B. sodium hydroxide
C. sodium zeolites
D. trisodium phosphate

17. Ions of which element do not cause hard water?
A. calcium
B. iron
C. magnesium
D. potassium

18. Which carboxylic acid salt is insoluble in water? (R stands for a long-chain alkyl group.)
A. $(RCOO)_2Ca$
B. RCOOK
C. RCOONa
D. all are soluble

19. Substances that absorb ultraviolet light and re-emit it as visible light are called
A. bleaches
B. fabric softeners
C. optical brighteners
D. water softeners

20. Petroleum distillates are
A. flammable
B. grease cutters
C. narcotic at high concentrations
D. all of these

Matching

Caution: More than one response may be needed for some of the items.

21. _____ NaOCl

22. _____ $CH_3(CH_2)_{14}CH_2-N^+(CH_3)_2-CH_3 \quad Cl^-$

23. _____ $CH_3(CH_2)_8-C_6H_4-O(CH_2CH_2O)_7H$

24. _____ $CH_3(CH_2)_{16}COO^-Na^+$

25. _____ $CH_3CH(CH_3)(CH_2CH(CH_3))_3-C_6H_4-SO_3^-Na^+$

26. _____ $CH_3(CH_2)_{11}CH(CH_3)-C_6H_4-SO_3^-Na^+$

$NaBO_2 \cdot H_2O_2$

27. _____ $NaBO_2 \cdot H_2O_2$

28. _____

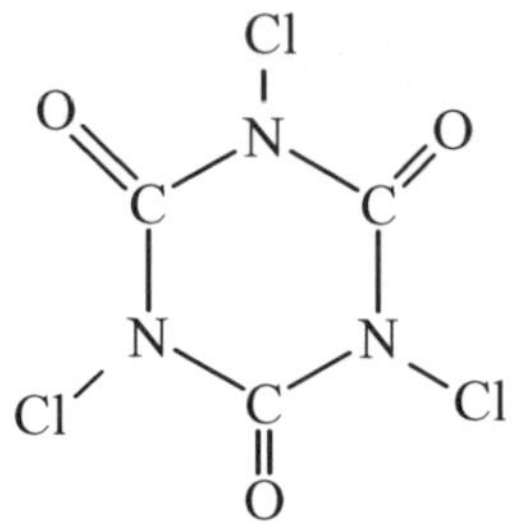

```
        Cl
        |
  O     N     O
   \\ /   \ //
     C     C
     |     |
     N     N
    / \   / \
  Cl    C    Cl
        ||
        O
```

29. _____ $CH_3(CH_2)_{16}CH_2 - \overset{\displaystyle CH_3}{\underset{\displaystyle CH_3}{N^+}} - CH_2(CH_2)_{16}CH_3Cl^-$

- **a.** cyanurate-type bleach
- **b.** germicide
- **c.** soap
- **d.** fabric softner
- **e.** oxygen-releasing bleach
- **f.** nonionic detergent
- **g.** ABS
- **h.** active ingredient in liquid bleaches
- **i.** cationic detergent
- **k.** LAS
- **l.** nonbiodegradable detergent

Multiple Choice

30. Under U.S. law, which is not a cosmetic?
- **A.** cologne
- **B.** lipstick
- **C.** shampoo
- **D.** soap

31. The two main ingredients in most brands of toothpaste are detergent and a(n)
- **A.** buffer for pH balance
- **B.** sweetener
- **C.** fruit flavor
- **D.** abrasive

32. Fluoride in drinking water or toothpaste retards tooth decay by
- **A.** killing decay-causing bacteria
- **B.** strengthening tooth enamel
- **C.** deactivating salivary enzymes
- **D.** stopping carbohydrate metabolism

33. The main cause of tooth loss in adults in the United States is
- **A.** accidents
- **B.** fluorides
- **C.** gum disease
- **D.** sugars

34. Which is a likely major ingredient of lotions and creams?
- **A.** an abrasive
- **B.** a detergent
- **C.** petroleum jelly or mineral oil
- **D.** aluminum chlorohydrate

35. Emollients act
A. by releasing water to keep the skin wet
B. as detergents
C. by forming a protective layer on the skin
D. by retarding perspiration

36. An emulsion of water in oil is called a
A. cream **B.** lipstick
C. lotion **D.** moisturizer

37. The two main ingredients in most lipsticks are a wax and
A. aluminum chlorohydrate **B.** castor oil
C. lanolin **D.** a detergent

38. For a long time *p*-aminobenzoic acid (PABA) was the main ingredient in
A. face creams **B.** mascara
C. sunscreen lotions **D.** toothpastes

39. In suntanning, long-wave ultraviolet rays promote the formation of
A. collagen **B.** keratin
C. melanin **D.** sebum

40. Lanolin is
A. a hydrocarbon oil **B.** a hydrocarbon wax
C. a plant wax **D.** wax from sheep's wool

41. Aftershave lotions are 60 to 75% aqueous
A. acetic acid **B.** alcohol
C. mineral oil **D.** castor oil

42. The cooling effect of some aftershave lotions is provided by
A. ice crystals **B.** ether
C. menthol **D.** cologne

43. The most volatile components of a perfume are called
A. the end note **B.** colognes
C. musks **D.** the top note

44. Antiperspirants are drugs because they
A. change a normal body function **B.** contain narcotic propellants
C. contain perfume **D.** contain oxidizing agents

45. Aluminum chlorohydrate is the active ingredient in nearly all
A. antiperspirants **B.** lipsticks
C. skin lotions **D.** deodorants

46. Herbal essence, added to shampoo,
A. gives it pH balance **B.** feeds hair roots
C. gives hair body **D.** attracts insects

47. Which of the following is a drug?
A. deodorant **B.** antidandruff shampoo
C. baby shampoo **D.** lanolin

48. Strawberry essence, added to shampoo,
A. gives it pH balance
B. feeds hair roots
C. gives hair body
D. attracts insects

49. Hair is
A. protein
B. carbohydrate
C. fat
D. cellulose

50. The principal ingredient of any shampoo is
A. a detergent
B. protein
C. an oil
D. a buffer to balance pH

51. Which of the following can nourish hair?
A. beer
B. wheat germ
C. vitamins
D. none of these

52. What type of detergent is found in nearly all baby shampoos?
A. cationic
B. nonionic
C. amphoteric
D. none of these

53. Shampoos for adults usually employ
A. soap
B. anionic detergents
C. cationic detergents
D. nonionic detergents

54. In shampoos, pH balance means
A. equal amounts of phosphorus and hydrogen
B. equal numbers of protons and hydrogen ions
C. a pH of exactly 7
D. a pH range that will not harm eyes or skin

55. Most conditioners for hair are
A. detergents
B. resins
C. proteins
D. herbal essences

56. Bleaches for hair oxidize colored pigments to
A. carbon dioxide and water
B. hydrogen peroxide
C. disulfide linkages
D. colorless compounds

57. Most hair dyes are colorless compounds that are absorbed into hair and then oxidized to
A. carbon dioxide and water
B. hydrogen peroxide
C. para-phenylenediamine
D. colored compounds

58. Curling or straightening of hair involves breaking and re-forming of
A. protein chains
B. hair fibers
C. disulfide linkages
D. diamine bonds

59. Hair sprays are principally
A. oils
B. waxes
C. synthetic resins
D. proteins

60. The color of hair that is treated to establish color gradually is due to
A. diamines
B. lead sulfide
C. peroxides
D. quinones

Key Terms

anionic surfactants
antiperspirants
astringent
bleaches
builder
cationic surfactants
colognes
cosmetics
cream
deodorants
depilatories
emollients
end note
eye shadow
hydrophilic
hydrophobic
hypoallergenic cosmetics
Keratin
lanolin
lotion
mascara
melanin
micelle
middle note
moisturizers
mousse
nonionic surfactants
optical brighteners
paint
perfumes
resins
sebum
skin protection factor (SPF)
soap
sunscreen lotions
surfactant
surface-active agent (surfactant)
synthetic detergents
top note
wax

Supplement 5

Chromosomes: Structure, Organization, and Replication

5 Chromosomes: Structure, Organization, and Replication

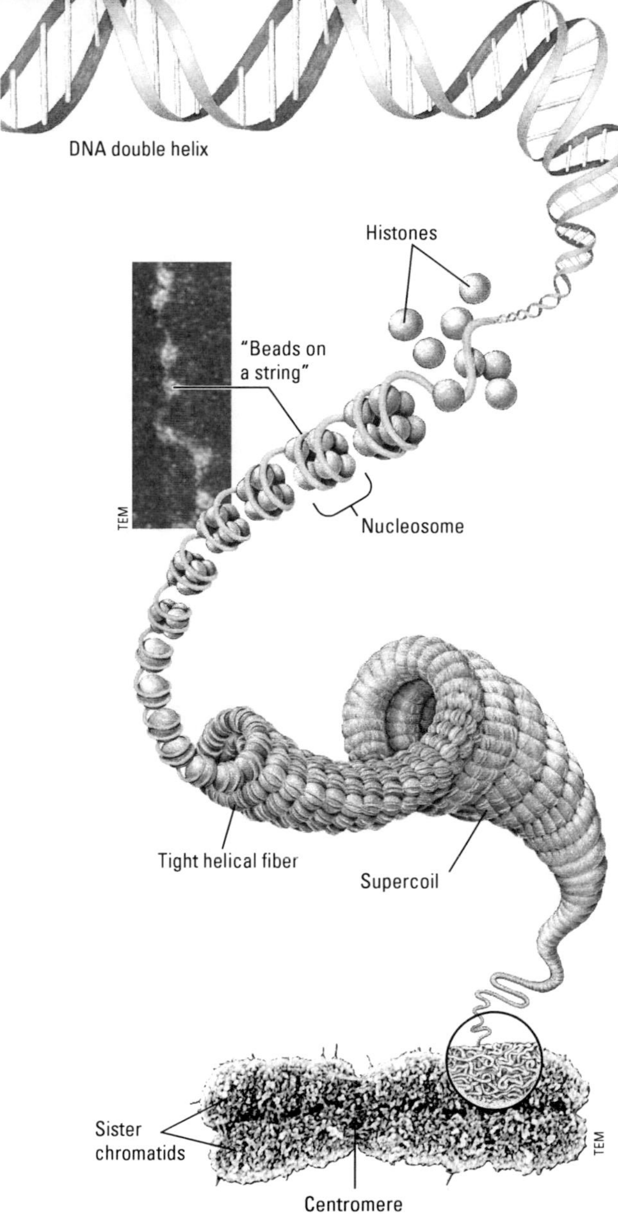

DNA packing in a eukaryotic chromosome. Successive levels of coiling of DNA and associated proteins ultimately results in highly condensed chromosomes. When not dividing, the DNA of active genes is only lightly packed, in the "beads on a string" arrangement. At the bottom of the figure, you can see a highly compacted chromo-some from a cell preparing to divide. The constricted region is the centromere. The fuzzy appearance comes from the intricate twists and folds of the chromatin fibers.

LOOKING AHEAD

http://www.pearsoncustom.com/devry/mycbp

Organizing Data

Define and distinguish between each pair of terms in the table below.

Heterochromatin vs. Euchromatin
Theophilus Painter vs. Joe Hin Tjio and Albert Levan
Centromeres vs. Satellite.
Polymerase vs. Telomerase
Nucleosome vs. *Nucleotides*
Haploid vs. Diploid
homologous chromosomes vs. Non-homologous chromosomes
Deletion vs. Duplication:
Inversion vs. Translocation

Practice Test for Supplement 5

1. Your body is composed of trillions of cells. These cells can be divided into two major categories: somatic (body) cells and sex cells (sperm or ova). With the exception of ________, all of these cells have a nucleus that contains DNA.

2. The DNA present in a cell is often referred to as its **genome**. The genome of eukaryotic cells usually consists of a number of _____________ made up of DNA molecules that are associated with proteins.

3. True or False? In humans as in most eukaryotes, chromosomes come in pairs. During cell division, the chromosomes are duplicated, separated from each other, and than shared between the resulting daughter cells.

4. Human chromosomes were first studied by:
   A. Joe Hin Tjio
   B. Theophilus Painter
   C. Albert Levan
   D. Theodor Boveri
   E. Walter S. Sutton

5. True or False? The number of chromosomes (with rare exceptions) is characteristic of the Genus.

6. True or False? Each human somatic cell has 23 single chromosomes while each human **gamete** (sex) cell has 23 pairs of chromosomes.

7. True or False? When human chromosomes were first studied by Theophilus Painter in 1921, he claimed that there were **24** unpaired chromosomes in the sex cells of human testes and therefore **48** total chromosomes in somatic cells. This number was not disputed and was even confirmed by other researchers for many years.

8. True or False? It was only in 1955 when Joe Hin Tjio and Albert Levan used better microscopic and staining techniques to clearly count 23 pairs of chromosomes in somatic tissues. These two researchers also recounted the chromosomes in Painter's earlier photos and counted 23 chromosomes in the gametic tissues rather than 24.

9. True or False? When a cell is not undergoing division, its chromosomes occur in the form of thin, loosely-packed chromatin fibers that are very hard to see with a light microscope. During cell division however, the chromatin fibers are condensed and, with special staining, are visible with a microscope as chromosomes.

10. True or False? Various characteristics such as size, length, and shape can be used to distinguish between chromosomes within and between species.

11. A typical human chromosome is found in the nucleus of the cell and is composed of __________, __________ and _______________ centromeres. In some chromosomes, a chromosomal segment branches off from the rest of the chromosome, but it is still connected by a thin filament or stalk. This type of segment is called a _________.

12. The arm or the rod-like structure of the chromosome is called
- **A.** telomeres
- **B.** centromeres
- **C.** chromatid.
- **D.** satellite.

13. Before duplication, each chromosome consists of a single chromatid. Once duplicated, a chromosome consists of two identical chromatids attached to each other through a single point called __________.

14. Each individual chromatid is formed by a single long double-stranded DNA molecule complexed with proteins known as ____________. The chromatids cannot be easily seen except when they are condensed and appear as chromosomes during cell division.

15. In addition to DNA and histone proteins, chromosomes also contain a small amount of RNA and the enzymes necessary for DNA and RNA synthesis. This entire complex (DNA and its associate proteins) is called ___________.

16. Using stains and dyes, two types of shaded areas can be seen along the chromosomes under the microscope. The dark areas are called _____________ and consist mainly of repetitive DNA sequences. The lighter areas are called ___________ and contain mainly genes that encode proteins.

17. The specialized section of the chromosome that holds the two chromatids together is called:
- **A.** telomere
- **B.** centromere
- **C.** chromatid.
- **D.** satellite.

18. Centromeres are important in identifying and classifying chromosomes. Eukaryotic chromosomes are distinguished by and classified based on the location of their _______________ along the chromosomes.

19. Each chromosome has two arms, the shorter arm is called *p* arm and the longer one is called *q* arm. Based on the centromere location on these arms, four specific types of chromosomes can be identified. They are ________________, ______________________, ______________, and ___________________ chromosomes.

20. ____________ chromosomes have a centrally located centromere and two approximately equal arms (approximately 1:1 ratio). They include human chromosomes number 1, 2, 3,19, and 20.

21. ____________ chromosomes have a centromere located off-center resulting in unequal arm length (approximately a 1:2 ratio). They include human chromosomes number 4, 5, 6–12, 16, 17, 18, and X chromosome.

22. _____________ chromosomes have the centromere located at one end with no second arm (1:0 ratio). None of the human chromosmes are telocentic.

23. ________________ chromosomes have the centromere located very close to one end making second arm much shorter (approximately 1:3 ratio). They include human chromosomes number 13–15, 21, 22, and Y chromosome.

24. Remember, a satellite is a chromosomal segment that branches off from the rest of the chromosome, but it is still connected by a thin filament or stalk is known as:
A. telomere
B. centromere
C. chromatid
D. satellite

25. The terminal tip or end of the eukaryotic chromosome that is made of a tightly wound and highly repetitive heterochromatin, each with about 100 to 1000 repetitions of a short nucleotide sequence, TTAGGG in humans, is called:
A. telomere
B. centromere
C. chromatid
D. satellite

26. True or False? Telomerase is an enzyme capable of directing the replication of telomeres to maintain their length. Without this enzyme, the chromosomes of germ cells become shorter in every cell cycle. The germ cells would eventually die, causing a species to go extinct.

27. True or False? DNA polymerase is unable to replicate chromosomal DNA all the way to the ends of the chromosome so every time a chromosome is replicated, a portion of the telomere DNA near the end is lost. If not for telomeres, some genes would be lost during each replication cycle.

28. Every time a cell divides, the telomere shortens. When they get too short, the cell can no longer divide and dies. Some cells, such as germ cells (egg and sperm) and cancer cells are able to avoid having their telomeres shortened by producing an enzyme called ____________.

29. On the other hand, cancer cells can escape death through their production of:
A. polymerase
B. telomerase
C. chromatase
D. satellite

30. In the table below, match each term on the right to its best description and or definition on the left.

Term	Its Best Description
Associated proteins ____	**A.** Consists of chromatin (a complex of DNA and associated proteins), a centromere, and telomeres.
Centromeres ____	**B.** Carries the genetic information (the instructions the cell uses to construct itself, tissue, and the organism of which it is part), and associated proteins.
Telomeres __	**C.** Organize the chromosome physically and regulate the DNA activities.
Chromosome __	**D.** A specialized region along the chromosome to which spindle fibers are attached during cell division.
DNA ___	**E.** Involved in the replication and stability of linear DNA molecules.
Klinefelter's syndrome ___	**F.** A species-specific photographic inventory of an individual's (cell's) chromosomes as viewed with light microscope.
Down syndrome ______.	**G.** An individual with (Trisomy 21) possesses 3 copies of chromosome 21.
karyotype ___	**H.** A male possesses an extra X chromosome resulting in a genotype of XXY.

31. True or False? Today, many geneticists believe that telomeres define the molecular and the genetic limits of chromosomes and in turn the life span of a given cell and or organism.

32. True or False? Today, we use the term chromosome to depict the condensed structures of chromosomal materials that are visible during cell division and the term chromatin to describe the decondensed, threadlike fibers of the chromosomal materials of the non-dividing cells.

33. Under the electron microscope DNA and histone proteins of chromosomes can be seen. The proteins appear as tiny beads and the DNA as a thin thread that surrounds and connect the beads. Each bead is made up of double loop of DNA around a core of eight histone proteins and is called a:

A. nucleosome
B. nucleozone
C. nucleotone
D. ***nucleotides***

34. True or False? There are five types of nitrogenous base nitrogen bases found in nucleic acids, but only four types of bases found in DNA: Adenine (A), Thymine (T), Guanine (G), and Cytosine (C).

35. As you have learned, DNA strands are composed of linked building-block molecules called ____________. Each one is made up of three main components, a five-carbon sugar (deoxyribose), a phosphate group, and a ringed nitrogen-containing molecule known as a base or a nitrogenous base.

36. The nucleotides are linked together by ___________ bonds between the sugar and phosphate group to form a long chain of nucleotides. Two of these long nucleotide strands are held together in a double helix by ___________ bonds between the nitrogenous bases of opposite strands.

37. True or False? In other word, nucleotides of one strand are linked to their complementary nucleotide on the opposite strand by covalent bonds between the nitrogen bases, thus forming a pair of nucleotides, known as a base pair (bp), or nucleotide base.

38. True or False? The nucleotide bases always pair in the following a specific order, adenine with cytosine and guanine with thymine. Cytogeneticists have estimated that 24 types of human chromosomes range in size from 50 to 250 millions of bases (megabases).

39. True or False? Today, we use the term chromosome to describe the condensed structures of chromosomal materials that are visible during cell division and the term chromatin to describe the threadlike fibers of the chromosomal materials of the non-dividing cells.

40. Chromosomes replicate during the S stage of interphase producing sister chromatids that are joined together at the centromere. However, before a given cell starts dividing, the genetic information (DNA) in chromosomes must be _____________ so that each daughter cell will receive the same amount of DNA.

41. All human cells are diploid (2N) cells except for _______ (eggs and sperm) that are haploid (N) cells. The haploid __________ fuse to form diploid offspring.

42. All the chromosomes in diploid cells exist in matched, **homologous** pairs. The members of each chromosome pair contain the same **genes** on the same locations along the chromosomes and are able to pair during ________ cell division. Each member of a pair of homologous chromosomes is called a __________.

43. True or False? The two chromosomes of a given homologous pair have important genetic similarities. They are identical in their morphological appearance and carry the same genes at the same sites (**loci**) along their length. These unique characteristics make the two chromosomes of a given homologous pair identical in their genetic potential.

44. True or False? Homologous chromosomes ***are not*** responsible for the genetic variation in eukaryotes that occurs during Meiosis. Because, one way genetic variation occurs is through the independent assortment of chromosomes.

45. True or False? The number of combinations possible when chromosomes assort independently into gametes during meiosis cell division is 2^n, where n is the haploid number. For humans ($n = 23$), there are more than 8 million (2^{23}) possible combinations of chromosomes!

46. Genetic variability greatly increases as a result of the:
A. independent assortment.
B. crossing over.
C. fertilization.
D. all of the above.
E. a and b.
F. b and c.

47. Additionally, An ordered photographic display of the pairs of chromosomes from a cell, often at metaphase stage of cell division when chromosomes are condensed and easier to see, is called:
A. nucelotypes
B. phototypes
C. chromotypes
D. karyotypes

48. True or False? Karyotypes are useful for identifying characteristics such as the loss of all or part of a chromosome and or the addition of extra chromosomes or chromosome fragments. But they are not useful in identifying mutations in single genes.

49. True or False? It is worth to mention however that, while in mammals, males are (ZZ) and female are (ZW), birds and snakes are the opposite, males are (XY) while females are(XX).

50. True or False? A gene is a section of DNA that contains instructions for making a specific molecule, usually a protein. In human, both the sex chromosomes and the autosomes carry genes that control inherited traits.

51. True or False? A given pair of genes ***can not*** affect a single trait, several traits or can share in the controlling of a given trait with other pairs of genes.

52. True or False? Humans have about 30,000–35,000 genes that are distributed on the 24 chromosomes. In a given chromosome, the genes are arranged one after the other, in linear sequence along the chromosomes.

53. Genes that are located on the same chromosome and are often inherited together. The closer two genes are to each other on a single chromosome, the lower the probability that they will be separated by recombination, and thus the more likely they are to be inherited together. This type of genes are called:
A. linked genes
B. unlinked genes
C. recombinant genes
D. non-recombinant genes

54. True or False? The closer two genes are to each other, the higher the probability that a crossing-over will occur between the members of the chromosomal pair, and therefore the higher the recombination frequency and the lower the probability that they will be inherited together.

55. True or False? In addition to their role in determining sex (male and female), the sex chromosomes (X and Y), also have genes for a number of characteristics unrelated to sex. Genes that are located on either sex chromosome (X or Y) are called **sex-linked genes** and follow specific patterns of inheritance.

56. The majority of sex-linked genes are on the X chromosome. This means that men, who only have one copy of the X chromosome, are more likely than women, who have two copies of the X chromosome, to exhibit recessive sex-linked traits such as red–green color-blindness, Duchenne muscular dystrophy, and hemophilia. This is because:
A. Y chromosome is smaller and carries less genetic information
B. Y chromosome is bigger and carries more genetic information
C. Y chromosome has mechanisms to illuminate unwanted genes
D. X chromosome is smaller and carries less genetic information

57. True or False? Sex-linked genes on the Y chromosome are transmitted from male to male only with no affect on females.

58. True or False? The end result of meiosis is generally a total of a four daughter cells, each with half the number of the chromosomes as the mother cell. However, accidents, errors, and/or abnormal chromosome movement during meiosis can lead to the inheritance of an abnormal number of autosomes or sex chromosomes and lead to genetic disorders.

59. True or False? Fetuses with abnormalities in autosomal chromosomes are often spontaneously aborted. Furthermore, Abnormal numbers of sex chromosomes do not usually affect survival of individuals but they can lead to sterility.

60. True or False? Inheriting the right number of chromosomes always ensure that a person also inherited the right genes with their genetic information. Breaks or other changes in chromosomal structure cannot cause genes to be deleted or moved to another location. The structure cannot even be changed by transposable genetic elements or "jumping genes" that insert themselves into various places in the DNA of a chromosome.

61. Mammalian females have two X chromosomes in their normal autosome cells. However in each cell, only one of these two X chromosomes is active. The other chromosome becomes almost completely inactive during fetal development. The inactive X chromosome in each of a female condenses into a compact object called X chromatinor a:

A. barr body
B. satellite
C. linked gene
D. sex-gene

62. The chromosomal theory of inheritance is one of the cornerstones of the modern understanding of genetics and biological evolution. It was first formulated by the American scientist:

A. Theophilus Painter
B. Albert Levan
C. Theodor Boveri
D. Walter Sutton
E. Thomas Hunt Morgan

63. The scientist who provided the first evidence to support the chromosome theory of heredity by showing that genes determining Mendelian traits reside on chromosomes, was:

A. Theophilus Painter
B. Albert Levan
C. Theodor Boveri
D. Walter Sutton

Supplement 6

Signaling and Cell Communication

6 Signaling and Cell Communication

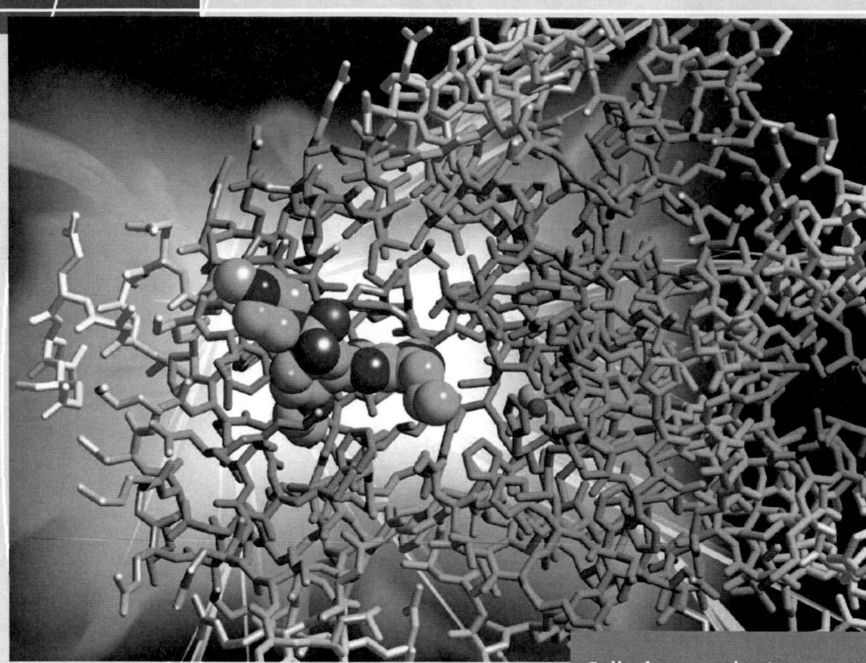

LOOKING AHEAD

6.1 External Signals are Converted into Responses Within the Cell

6.2 Reception: A signal molecule binds to a receptor protein, causing it to change shape

6.3 Transduction: Pathways of molecular interactions relay signals from receptors to target molecules in the cell

6.4 Response: Cell signaling leads to regulation of cell activites

Cell phones, the Internet, e-mail, instant messaging—no one would deny the importance of communication in our lives. The role of communication in living things at the cellular level is equally critical. Cell-to-cell communication is absolutely essential for multicellular organisms such as humans and oak trees.

http://www.pearsoncustom.com/devry/mycbp

Chapter Review

Key Concepts

6.1 External signals are converted into responses within the cell

6.2 Reception: A signal molecule binds to a receptor protein, causing it to change shape

6.3 Transduction: Cascades of molecular interactions relay signals from receptors to target molecules in the cell

6.4 Response: Cell signaling leads to regulation of cytoplasmic activities or transcription

Concept Map

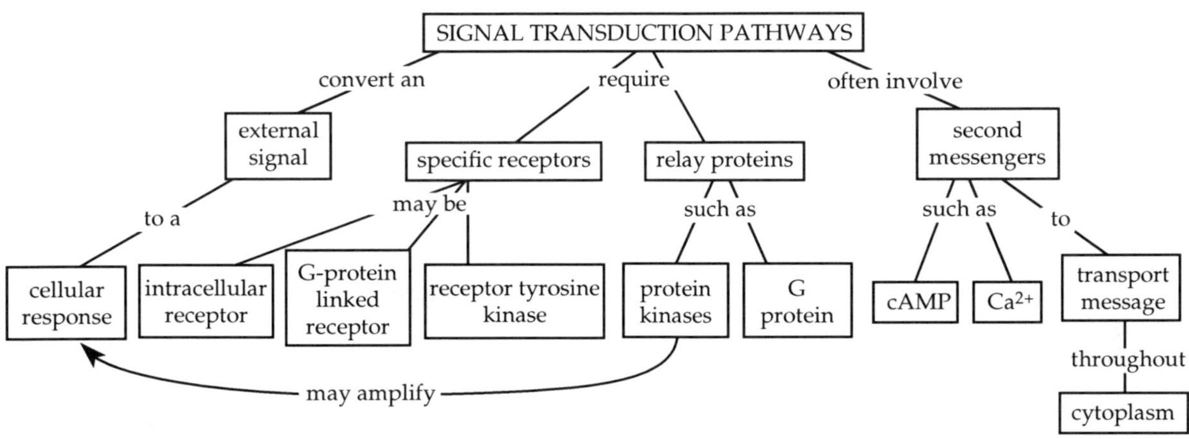

Chapter Concept Review

Cell-to-cell communication is critical to the development and functioning of multicellular organisms and also to communication between unicellular organisms. Some universal mechanisms of cellular interaction provide evidence for the evolutionary relatedness of all life.

6.1 External signals are converted into responses within the cell

Evolution of Cell Signaling The two mating types of yeast secrete chemical factors that bind to receptors on the other cell type, initiating fusion (mating) of the cells. The series of steps involved in the conversion of a cell surface signal to a cellular response is called a **signal transduction pathway.** Similarities among these pathways in bacteria, yeast, plants, and animals suggest an early evolution of cell-signaling mechanisms.

Local and Long-Distance Signaling Chemical signals may be communicated between cells through direct cytoplasmic connections (gap junctions or plasmodesmata) or through contact of surface molecules (cell-cell recognition in animal cells).

In *paracrine signaling* in animals, a signaling cell releases messenger molecules into the extracellular fluid, and these **local regulators** influence nearby cells. In another type of local signaling called *synaptic signaling*, a nerve cell releases neurotransmitter molecules into the narrow synapse separating it from its target cell.

Hormones are chemical signals that travel to more distant cells. In hormonal or endocrine signaling in animals, the circulatory system transports hormones throughout the body to reach target cells with appropriate receptors.

Transmission of signals through the nervous system is also a type of long-distance signaling.

> **Interactive Question 6.1**
>
> **a.** Do plant cells communicate using hormones?
> **b.** If so, how do those hormones travel between secreting cells and target cells?

The Three Stages of Cell Signaling: A Preview
E. W. Sutherland's work studying epinephrine's effect on the hydrolysis of glycogen in liver cells established that cell signaling involves three stages: **reception** of a chemical signal by binding to a receptor protein either inside the cell or on its surface; **transduction** of the signal, often by a signal transduction pathway—a sequence of changes in relay molecules; and the final **response** of the cell.

6.2 Reception: A Signal Molecule Binds to a Receptor Protein, Causing it to Change Shape

A signal molecule acts as a **ligand,** which specifically binds to a receptor protein and usually induces a change in the receptor's conformation.

Intracellular Receptors
Hydrophobic (hot water-soluble) chemical messengers may cross a cell's plasma membrane and bind to receptors in the cytoplasm or nucleus of target cell. An example of this is the steroid hormone testosterone.

Receptors in the Plasma Membrane Membrane receptors bind with water-soluble signal molecules and transmit information into the cell.

Interactive Question 6.2

a. What determines whether a cell is a target cell for a particular signal molecule?
b. What determines whether a signal molecule binds to a membrane-surface receptor or an intracellular receptor?

6.3 Transduction: Cascades of Molecular Interactions Relay Signals from Receptors to Target Molecules in the Cell

Multistep signal pathways allow a small number of extracellular signal molecules to be amplified to produce a large cellular response.

Signal Transduction Pathways
The relay molecules in a signal transduction pathway are usually proteins, which interact as they pass the message from the extracellular signal to the protein that produces the cellular response.

Protein Phosphorylation and Dephosphorylation
Protein kinases are enzymes that transfer phosphate groups from ATP to proteins, often to the amino acid serine or threonine. Relay molecules in signal transduction pathways are often protein kinases, which are sequentially phosphorylated, producing a conformational change that activates each enzyme. Hundreds of different kinds of protein kinases regulate the activity of a cell's proteins.

Protein phosphatases are enzymes that remove phosphate groups from proteins. They effectively shut down signaling pathways when the extracellular signal is no longer present.

Interactive Question 6.3

a. What does a protein kinase do?
b. What does a protein phosphatase do?
c. What is a phosphorylation cascade?

Small Molecules and Ions as Second Messengers
Small, water-soluble molecules or ions such as cAMP or Ca^{2+} often function as **second messengers,** which rapidly relay the signal from the membrane-receptor-bound "first messenger" into a cell's interior.

6.4 Response: Cell Signaling Leads to Regulation of Cytoplasmic Activities or Transcription

Cytoplasmic and Nuclear Responses

Signal transduction pathways may lead to the activation of cytoplasmic enzymes or other proteins, or may lead to the synthesis of such proteins by affecting gene expression. Growth factors and certain animal and plant hormones may initiate pathways that ultimately activate transcription factors, which regulate the transcription of mRNA from specific genes.

Fine-Tuning of the Response

A signal transduction pathway can amplify a signal in an enzyme cascade, as each successive enzyme in the pathway can process multiple molecules that then activate the next step.

As a result of their particular set of receptor proteins, relay proteins, and effector proteins, different cells can respond to different signals or can exhibit different responses to the same molecular signal. Pathways may branch to produce multiple responses, or two pathways may interact ("cross-talk") to mediate a single response.

Scaffolding proteins are large relay proteins to which other relay proteins attach, increasing the efficiency of signal transduction in a pathway.

Inactivation mechanisms that discontinue a cell's response to a signal are essential in keeping a cell responsive to regulation.

Interactive Question 6.4

How do the following mechanisms or molecules maintain a cell's ability to respond to fresh signals?

a. reversible binding of signal molecules
b. protein phosphatases

Word Roots

liga- = bound or tied (*ligand:* a small molecule that specifically binds to a larger one)
trans- = across (*signal transduction pathway:* the process by which a signal on a cell's surface is converted into a specific cellular response inside the cell)
-yl = substance or matter (*adenylyl cyclase:* an enzyme built into the plasma membrane that converts ATP to cAMP)

Structure Your Knowledge

1. Why is cell signaling such an important component of a cell's life?
2. Briefly describe the three stages of cell signaling.
3. Some signal pathways alter a protein's activity; others may result in the production of new proteins. Explain the mechanisms for these two different responses.
4. How does an enzyme cascade produce an amplified response to a signal molecule?

Test Your Knowledge

Multiple Choice

1. When epinephrine binds to cardiac (heart) muscle cells, it speeds their contraction. When it binds to muscle cells of the small intestine, it inhibits their contraction. How can the same hormone have different effects on muscle cells?
   A. Cardiac cells have more receptors for epinephrine than do intestinal cells.
   B. Epinephrine circulates to the heart first and thus is in higher concentration around cardiac cells.
   C. The two types of muscle cells have different signal transduction pathways for epinephrine and thus have different cellular responses.
   D. Cardiac muscle is stronger than intestinal muscle and thus has a stronger response to epinephrine.
   E. Epinephrine binds to G-protein-linked receptors in cardiac cells, and these receptors always increase a response to the signal. Epinephrine binds to receptor tyrosine kinases in intestinal cells, and these receptors always inhibit a response to the signal.

2. Which of the following would be used in the type of local signaling called paracrine signaling in animals?
   A. the neurotransmitter acetylcholine
   B. the hormone epinephrine
   C. the neurotransmitter norepinephrine
   D. a local regulator such as a growth factor
   E. Both a and c are correct.

3. A signal molecule that binds to a plasma-membrane protein functions as a
   A. ligand.
   B. second messenger.
   C. protein phosphatase.
   D. protein kinase.
   E. receptor protein.

4. Which of the following can activate a protein by transferring a phosphate group to it?
   A. cAMP
   B. G protein
   C. phosphodiesterase
   D. protein kinase
   E. protein phosphatase

5. Many signal transduction pathways use second messengers to
   A. transport a signal through the lipid bilayer portion of the plasma membrane.
   B. relay a signal from the outside to the inside of the cell.
   C. relay the message from the inside of the membrane throughout the cytoplasm.
   D. amplify the message by phosphorylating proteins.
   E. dampen the message once the signal molecule has left the receptor.

6. Signal amplification is most often achieved by
   A. an enzyme cascade involving multiple protein kinases.
   B. the binding of multiple signal molecules.
   C. branching pathways that produce multiple cellular responses.
   D. activating transcription factors that affect gene expression.
   E. the action of adenylyl cyclase in converting ATP to ADP.

7. Which of the following is a similarity between G-protein-linked receptors and receptor tyrosine kinases?
   A. signal-binding sites specific for steroid hormones
   B. formation of a dimer following binding of a signal molecule
   C. activation that results from binding of GTP
   D. phosphorylation of specific amino acids in direct response to signal binding
   E. α-helix regions of the receptor that span the plasma membrane

8. Which of the following is *incorrectly* matched with its description?
   A. scaffolding protein—large relay protein that may bind with several other relay proteins to increase the efficiency of a signaling pathway
   B. protein phosphatase—enzyme that transfers a phosphate group from ATP to a protein, causing a conformational change that usually activates that protein

9. Which of the following signal molecules pass through the plasma membrane and bind to intracellular receptors that move into the nucleus and function as transcription factors to regulate gene expression?
   A. epinephrine
   B. growth factors
   C. yeast mating factors α and a
   D. testosterone, a steroid hormone
   E. neurotransmitter released into synapse between nerve cells

Cell Communication: Part B
Practice Test for Supplement 6

1. True or False? The cells of yeast *Saccharomyces cerevisiae*, which people have used for millennia to make bread, wine, and beer, identify their mates by chemical signaling yeasts of opposite mating types.

2. True or False? The universal mechanisms of cellular regulation, is possible additional evidence for the evolutionary relatedness of all life.

3. The series of steps involved in converting a cell surface signal to a cellular response in bacteria, yeast, plants and animals is called: a **signal transduction pathway**.

4. True or False? Scientists think that signaling mechanisms evolved at the same time in bacteria, yeast, plants and animals.

5. True or False? Like yeast cells, cells in a multicellular organism communicate with each other via chemical messengers. These chemical messengers can pass freely through adjacent cells via direct cytoplasmic connections like gap junctions or plasmodesmota. Moreover, animal cells may communicate via direct contact between membrane–bound cell surface molecules.

6. True or False? In many other cases, messenger molecules such as growth factors are released outside of the cell, and travel only short distances. These **local regulators** influence only nearby cells.

7. True or False? Both animals and plants use chemicals called *hormones* for long–distance signaling. In animals, specialized cells release hormone molecules into blood vessels and they travel to target cells in other parts of the body.

8. True or False? Plant hormones (often called growth regulators) usually reach their targets by moving through cells or by diffusion through the air as a gas. The plant hormone *ethylene* is a gas that promotes fruit ripening and helps regulate growth.

9. True or False? When a cell encounters a signal, the signal must be *recognized* by a specific receptor molecule, and the information it carries must be changed or *transduced* into another form inside the cell before the cell can respond.

10. Our current understanding of how chemical messengers act via signal transduction pathways had its origins in the pioneering work of: a. Earl W. Sutherland

11. The three stages of cell signaling are ______________, ________________ , and ______________.

12. ______________ Reception is the target cell's detection of a signal molecule coming from outside the cell. A chemical signal is "detected" when it binds to a receptor protein usually located at the cell's surface.

13. _______________ The binding of the signal molecule changes the receptor protein in some way. The signal is converted to a form that can bring about a specific cellular response. It usually requires a sequence of changes—a signal transduction pathway.

14. _________ In the third stage of cell signaling, the transduced (changed) signal finally triggers a specific cellular response, such as the breaking down of glycogen.

15. True or False causing it to change? A signal molecule binds to a receptor protein, causing it to resist change in shape and form.

16. True or False? Receptor proteins may be located inside the cell or in the cell membrane. A receptor protein on or in the target cell allows the cell to "hear" the signal and respond to it.

17. True or False? Intracellular receptor proteins are found in either the cytoplasm or nucleus of target cells. To reach such a receptor, a chemical signal passes through the target cell's membrane.

18. True or False? The receptor protein for testosterone is an intracellular receptor. Testosterone is secreted by cells of the testis and then travels through the blood and enters cells all over the body. The hormone binds to the receptor protein in target cells and activates it. With the hormone attached, the active form of the receptor protein then enters the nucleus and turns on specific genes that control male sex characteristics.

19. True or False? Receptors in the Plasma Membrane transmit information from the extracellular environment to the inside of the cell by changing shape or clumping together when a signal binds to it.

20. True or False? Nerve growth factor (NGF) is a water-soluble signal molecule. The receptor for NGF is:
A. intracellular or in the membrane.
B. extracellular environment.
C. both Intracellular and then Extracellular.
D. both Extracellular and then intracellular.

21. When signal receptors are membrane proteins the transduction stage of cell signaling is usually:
A. singlestep pathways.
B. doublestep pathways.
C. multistep pathway.

22. One benefit of such __________ pathways is the possibility of greatly amplifying a signal, similar to how the ear amplifies sound. If some of the molecules in a pathway transmit the signal to multiple molecules of the next component in the series, the end result is a small number of extracellular signal molecules producing a large cellular response.

23. True or False? Like falling dominoes, signal transduction pathway (activated receptor) activates another protein, which activates another molecule, and so on, until the protein that produces the final cellular response is activated. The molecules that relay a signal from receptor to response are mostly proteins.

24. True or False? In signal transduction pathway the original signal molecule is not physically passed along a signaling pathway; in most cases, it never even enters the cell. When we say that the signal is relayed along a pathway, we mean that certain information is passed on. At each step, the signal is transduced (changed) into a different form, commonly a shape change in a protein.

25. The phosphorylation (adding phosphate groups) and dephosphorylation (removing phosphate groups) of proteins is a widespread mechanism for:
A. regulating protein activity.
B. transmitting protein.
C. regulating genetic materials.
D. regulating cell production.

26. __________ is an enzyme that transfers phosphate groups from ATP to a protein. Many of the molecules in signal transduction pathways are this type of enzymes, and they often act on other protein kinases in the pathway.

27. True or False? The importance of protein kinases can hardly be overstated. About 2% of our own genes are thought to code for protein kinases. A single cell may have hundreds of different kinds, each specific for a different substrate protein. Abnormal activity of such a kinase can cause abnormal cell growth and contribute to the development of cancer.

28. __________, enzymes that remove phosphate groups from proteins, a process called dephosphorylation. They provide the mechanism for turning off the signal transduction pathway.

29. True or False? Not all components of signal transduction pathways are proteins. Many signaling pathways also involve small, nonprotein molecules or ions called **second messengers**. The two most widely used second messengers are cyclic AMP (made from ATP) and calcium ions, Ca^{2+}.

30. Ultimately, a signal transduction pathway leads to the regulation of one or more cellular activities. The response may occur in the ________ or the ___________.

31. True or False? In the cytoplasm of a liver cell, for example, a signal may activate the enzyme that causes the breakdown of glycogen. **In every** step of the process of the pathways, the response is amplified and the number of molecules involved increases.

32. Many other signaling pathways regulate not the *activity* of enzymes but their ___________, usually by turning specific genes on or off in the nucleus.

33. The multiplicity of steps between a signaling event at the cell surface and the cell's response have two important benefits:
A. They amplify the signal (and thus the response).
B. They contribute to the specificity of response.
C. They prevent intervenes form other cells.
D. They store information just in case something goes wrong.

Appendix A

Answers to Chapter Questions and Exercises

Chapter 1

Practice Test for Chapter 1

Answers & Feedback

1. **e.** A supernatural force cannot be predicted or tested using our current understanding of the natural world.
2. **b.** A prediction, in the form of an "if . . . then" statement, is the expected result from a particular test of the hypothesis. The prediction in this statement is based on Susan's first observation, which was that vegetarians experience fewer colds than nonvegetarians.
3. **d.** There is no way to experimentally test what occurred in the past; scientists must rely on observations of the natural world in the form of the fossil record.
4. **b.** The control is treated in every way similarly to the experimental, except that the control is not exposed to the treatment. This control would rule out any effects that might be due to the solution in which the drug was dissolved.
5. **a.** Random assignment of individuals to the experimental and control groups minimizes the possibility that the individuals involved in the experiment may bias its results and thus reduces the likelihood of alternative hypotheses for the experimental results.
6. **e.** Fred may underreport his weight changes if he thinks he is in the control group; this phenomenon is called subject expectation, which must be minimized to produce objective results in an experiment.
7. **e.** A better study would try to ensure that the volunteers have similar characteristics such as age, gender, weight, etc. to eliminate alternative hypotheses that could explain the results.
8. **d.** The prediction is that the experimental group that received the supplement would have increased mental activity compared to the control group that received a placebo; this result would lead a scientist to reject the hypothesis that the nutritional supplement increases a person's mental activity level.
9. **c.** If the hypothesis is true and the difference between control and experimental groups using a small sample size is large, then the results are likely to be statistically significant.
10. **True.** The statement is both testable and falsifiable, so it is a valid scientific hypothesis.
11. **a.** Statistical tests help scientists extend their results from their experimental sample to the entire population.
12. **c.** Correct. In a double-blind experiment, both the research subjects and the scientists performing the measurements are unaware of who is in which group.
13. **False.** A hypothesis test can only falsify or support a hypothesis; it cannot prove a hypothesis. Furthermore, initial observations are not controlled experiments, so alternative explanations could account for the observations.

14. **False.** The control group should take a placebo pill that does not contain Ginkgo biloba to eliminate the possibility of subject expectation; in this way it will vary from the experimental group by only one factor.

15. **True.** The random assignment of volunteers to control and experimental groups eliminates alter-native hypotheses. As a note, using the last names of the volunteers might not work if there are related individuals in the group.

16. **True.** If the subjects are similar in all other characteristics, then the results will be less likely to be influenced by alternative hypotheses.

17. **True.** Statistical tests can examine how likely sampling error, uncontrolled variables, or the effects of random chance may affect experimental results.

18. **False.** Large sample sizes reduce sampling error, making it more likely that the differences between control and experimental will be significant.

19. **False.** The statistical significance is not a measure of the accuracy of the experiment; it only evaluates sampling error. One experiment is usually not enough to demonstrate the accuracy of the hypothesis, but if each additional experimental investigation shows that there are no statistically significant side effects, then the confidence increases that there are not effects.

20. **a.** Jeanne is basing her decision on an anecdote, which is not equivalent to studies that might be conducted by a doctor on the effectiveness of the herbal tea.

21. **c.** A peer-reviewed scientific journal is a primary source of scientific information.

22. **False.** Not all written publications are considered primary sources; magazines and newsletters would be secondary sources because they are not peer-reviewed scientific journals, or they report on other peoples' work.

23. **a.** Correct. Anecdotal evidence is based on personal experience and is not equivalent to a scientific test.

24. **d.** Correct. This story involves a scientist who may not be entirely unbiased, since he works for the company whose drug he is promoting.

Answers to the questions of 1.4 Section: Science as a Way of Knowing: Chemistry and Biology

25. **b.** Science.

26. **a.** James McClintock.

27. **True**

28. **False**

29. **a.** Seek another—the amphipods were actively abducting the sea butterflies!

30. **True**

31. **True**

32. **b.** Only one variable.

33. **True**

34. **True**

35. **True**

36. **False**

Chapter 2

Key Terms

Answers	**1.** d	**2.** a	**3.** b	**4.** c	**5.** e

2.1 Energy

◆ Learning Exercise 2.1A

Answers	**1.** c	**2.** a	**3.** d	**4.** b

◆ Learning Exercise 2.1B

Answers	**1.** P	**2.** P	**3.** P	**4.** P	**5.** K
	6. P	**7.** K	**8.** P	**9.** K	**10.** K

◆ Learning Exercise 2.1C

Answers	**1.** b	**2.** c	**3.** a

2.2 Energy and Nutrition

◆ Learning Exercise 2.2A

Answers	**a.** 4 kcal/g	**b.** 4 kcal/g	**c.** 4 kcal/g	**d.** 4 kcal/g	**e.** 9 kcal/g
	f. 9 kcal/g	**g.** 4 kcal/g	**h.** 9 kcal/g	**i.** 4 kcal/g	**j.** 9 kcal/g

◆ Learning Exercise 2.2B

Answers	**a.** 120 kcal	**b.** 120 kcal	**c.** 870 kcal	**d.** 180 kcal
	e. 110 kcal	**f.** 170 kcal	**g.** 110 kcal	

◆ Learning Exercise 2.2C

Answers

1. protein 16 kcal + carbohydrate 124 kcal + fat 45 kcal = 190 kcal
2. fat 18 kcal; 200 kcal − 18 = protein 182 kcal; 46 g protein
3. protein 32 kcal + fat 54 kcal = 86 kcal protein and fat; 220 kcal − 86 kcal = 134 kcal due to carbohydrate; 134 kcal/4 kcal/g = 34 g carbohydrate
4. bread, 136 kcal; peanut butter, 13 g fat; jelly, 10 g carbohydrate; margarine, 45 kcal; total = 400 kcal (4.0×10^2 kcal)

2.3 Temperature Conversions

◆ Learning Exercise 2.3

Answers	**a.** 154°F	**b.** 10.°F	**c.** 103.1°F	**d.** 35°C
	e. 218°C	**f.** 228 K		

2.4 Specific Heat

◆ Learning Exercise 2.4

Answers **1.** 1100 cal **2.** 850 cal
3. 180 000 cal **4.** 3380 cal

2.5 States of Matter

◆ Learning Exercise 2.5

Answers **1.** G **2.** S **3.** L **4.** G **5.** G
6. G **7.** L **8.** G **9.** S **10.** S

2.6 Gases

◆ Learning Exercise 2.6

Answers **a.** T **b.** F **c.** F **d.** T **e.** T

2.7 Changes of State

◆ Learning Exercise 2.7A

Answers **a.** 2 **b.** 2 **c.** 3 **d.** 1

◆ Learning Exercise 2.7B

Answers **a.** 1200 cal **b.** 26 kcal **c.** 50 g

◆ Learning Exercise 2.7C

Answers **a.** 5400 cal **b.** 278 kcal **c.** 504 g

◆ Learning Exercise 2.7D

Answers

1.

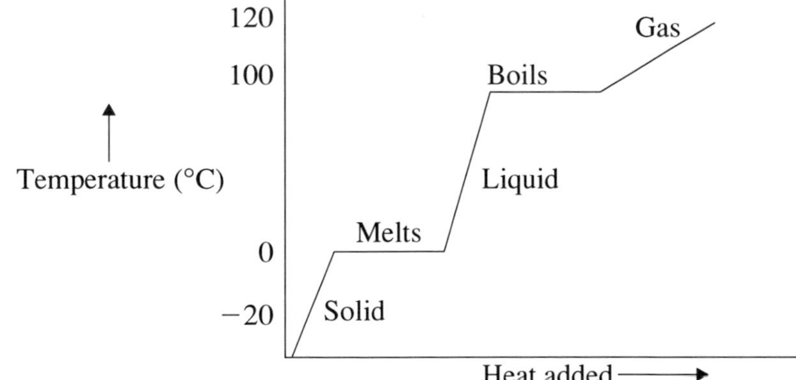

2.

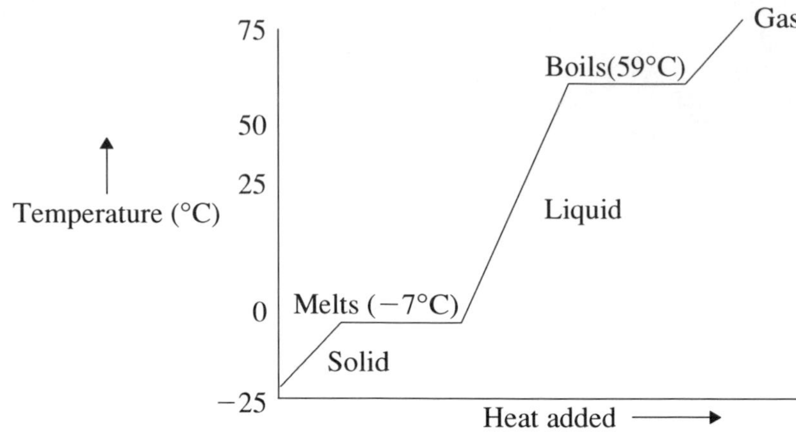

3.

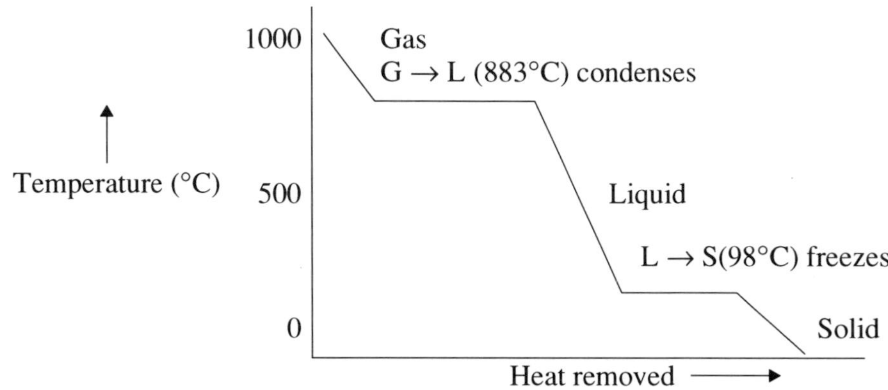

Answers to the Practice Test

1. C	**2.** E	**3.** E	**4.** C	**5.** D
6. E	**7.** C	**8.** E	**9.** B	**10.** C
11. A	**12.** D	**13.** D	**14.** E	**15.** B
16. C	**17.** D	**18.** E	**19.** B	**20.** E
21. D				

Answers and Solutions to Selected Text Problems

2.1 At the top of the hill, all of the energy of the car is in the form of potential energy. As it descends the hill, potential energy is being converted into kinetic energy. When the car reaches the bottom, all of its energy is in the form of motion (kinetic energy).

2.3 **a.** potential **b.** kinetic **c.** potential **d.** potential

2.5 **a.** $3500 \cancel{\text{cal}} \times \dfrac{1 \text{ kcal}}{1000 \cancel{\text{cal}}} = 3.5 \text{ kcal}$

b. $415 \cancel{\text{J}} \times \dfrac{1 \text{ cal}}{4.184 \cancel{\text{J}}} = 99.2 \text{ cal}$

c. $28 \cancel{\text{cal}} \times \dfrac{4.184 \text{ J}}{1 \cancel{\text{cal}}} = 120 \text{ J}$

d. $4.5 \cancel{\text{J}} \times \dfrac{1 \cancel{\text{cal}}}{4.184 \cancel{\text{J}}} \times \dfrac{1 \text{ kcal}}{1000 \cancel{\text{cal}}} = 1100 \text{ cal}$

2.7 **a.** Because the orange juice contains both carbohydrate and protein, two calculations will be needed.

$$26\ \cancel{\text{g carbohydrate}} \times \frac{4\ \cancel{\text{kcal}}}{\cancel{\text{g carbohydrate}}} \times \frac{1\ \text{Cal}}{1\ \cancel{\text{kcal}}} = 100\ \text{Cal}$$

$$2\ \cancel{\text{g protein}} \times \frac{4\ \cancel{\text{kcal}}}{\cancel{\text{g protein}}} \times \frac{1\ \text{Cal}}{1\ \cancel{\text{kcal}}} = 8\ \text{Cal}$$

Total: 100 Cal + 8 Cal = 110 Cal

b. With only carbohydrate present, a single calculation is all that is required.

$$72\ \cancel{\text{kcal}} \times \frac{1\ \text{g carbohydrate}}{4\ \cancel{\text{kcal}}} = 18\ \text{g carbohydrate}$$

c. With only fat present, a single calculation is all that is required.

$$14\ \cancel{\text{g fat}} \times \frac{9\ \cancel{\text{kcal}}}{\cancel{\text{g fat}}} \times \frac{1\ \text{Cal}}{1\ \cancel{\text{kcal}}} = 130\ \text{Cal}$$

d. Three calculations are needed:

$$30.\ \cancel{\text{g carbohydrate}} \times \frac{4\ \cancel{\text{kcal}}}{\text{g}\ \cancel{\text{carbohydrate}}} \times \frac{1\ \text{Cal}}{1\ \cancel{\text{kcal}}} = 120\ \text{Cal}$$

$$15\ \cancel{\text{g fat}} \times \frac{9\ \cancel{\text{kcal}}}{1\ \cancel{\text{g fat}}} \times \frac{1\ \text{Cal}}{1\ \cancel{\text{kcal}}} = 140\ \text{Cal}$$

$$5\ \cancel{\text{g protein}} \times \frac{4\ \cancel{\text{kcal}}}{\cancel{\text{g protein}}} \times \frac{1\ \text{Cal}}{1\ \cancel{\text{kcal}}} = 20\ \text{Cal}$$

Total: 120 Cal + 140 Cal + 20 Cal = 280 Cal

2.9 Three calculations are needed:

$$9\ \cancel{\text{g protein}} \times \frac{4\ \text{kcal}}{\cancel{\text{g protein}}} = 40\ \text{kcal}$$

$$12\ \cancel{\text{g fat}} \times \frac{9\ \text{kcal}}{\cancel{\text{g fat}}} = 110\ \text{kcal}$$

$$16\ \cancel{\text{g carbohydrate}} \times \frac{4\ \text{kcal}}{\cancel{\text{g carbohydrate}}} = 64\ \text{kcal}$$

Total: 40 kcal + 110 kcal + 64 kcal = 210 kcal

2.11 The Fahrenheit temperature scale is still used in the United States. A normal body temperature is 98.6°F on this scale. To convert her temperature to the equivalent reading on the Celsius scale, the following calculation must be performed:

$$\frac{(99.8°\text{F} - 32)}{1.8} = 37.7°\text{C (32 is exact)}$$

Because a normal body temperature is 37.0 on the Celsius scale, her temperature of 37.7°C would be a mild fever.

2.13 **a.** 1.8 (37.0°C) + 32 = 66.6 + 32 = 98.6°F

b. $$\frac{(65.3°\text{F} - 32)}{1.8} = \frac{33.3}{1.8} = 18.5°\text{C (1.8 is exact)}$$

c. −27°C + 273 = 246 K

d. $62°C + 273 = 335\ K$

e. $\frac{(114°F - 32)}{1.8} = \frac{82}{1.8} = 46°C$

f. $\frac{(72°F - 32)}{1.8} = \frac{40.}{1.8} = 22°C;\ 22°C + 273 = 295\ K$

2.15 **a.** $\frac{(106°F - 32)}{1.8} = \frac{74}{1.8} = 41°C$

b. $\frac{(103°F - 32)}{1.8} = \frac{71}{1.8} = 39°C$

No, there is no need to phone the doctor. The child's temperature is less than 40.0°C.

2.17 Copper has the lowest specific heat of the samples and will reach the highest temperature.

2.19 **a.** $\Delta T = 25°C - 15°C = 10°C$ $\qquad 25\ g\ fat \times \frac{1.00\ cal}{\cancel{g°C}} \times 10\cancel{°C} = 250\ cal$

b. $150\ g \times \frac{4.18\ J}{\cancel{g°C}} \times 75\cancel{°C} = 47\ 000\ J$

c. $150\ g \times \frac{1.00\ cal}{\cancel{g°C}} \times 62\cancel{°C} = 9.3\ kcal$

2.21 The heat required is given by the relationship: Heat $= m \times \Delta T \times SH$.

a. Heat $= m \times \Delta T \times SH = 25.0\ g \times (25.7°C - 12.5°C) \times 4.184\ J/g°C =$

$25.0\ g \times 13.2\cancel{°C} \times 4.184\ J/\cancel{g°C} = 1380\ J \qquad 1380\ \cancel{J} \times \frac{1\ cal}{4.184\ \cancel{J}} = 330.\ cal$

b. Heat $= m \times \Delta T \times SH = 38.0\ g \times (246°C - 122°C) \times 0.385\ J/g°C =$

$38.0\ \cancel{g} \times 124\cancel{°C} \times 0.385\ J/\cancel{g°C} = 1810\ J \qquad 1810\ \cancel{J} \times \frac{1\ cal}{4.184\ \cancel{J}} = 434\ cal$

c. Heat $= m \times \Delta T \times SH = 15.0\ g \times (65.0°C + 42.0°C) \times 2.46\ J/g°C =$

$15.0\ \cancel{g} \times 107\cancel{°C} \times 2.46\ J/\cancel{g°C} = 3780\ J \qquad 3780\ \cancel{J} \times \frac{1\ cal}{4.184\ \cancel{J}} = 904\ cal$

d. Heat $= m \times \Delta T \times SH = 125\ g \times (118°C - 55°C) \times 0.450\ J/g°C =$

$125\ \cancel{g} \times 63\cancel{°C} \times 0.450\ J/\cancel{g°C} = 3500\ J \qquad 3500\ \cancel{J} \times \frac{1\ cal}{4.184\ \cancel{J}} = 850\ cal$

2.23 **a.** $505\ \cancel{g} \times \frac{1.00\ \cancel{cal}}{\cancel{g°C}} \times 10.5\cancel{°C} \times \frac{1\ kcal}{1000\ \cancel{cal}} = 5.30\ kcal$

b. $4980\ \cancel{g} \times \frac{1.00\ \cancel{cal}}{\cancel{g°C}} \times 42\cancel{°C} \times \frac{1\ kcal}{1000\ \cancel{cal}} = 208\ kcal$

2.25 **a.** gas **b.** gas **c.** solid

2.27 **a.** melting **b.** sublimation **c.** freezing

2.29 **a.** $65\ \cancel{\text{g ice}} \times \dfrac{80.\ \text{cal}}{1\ \cancel{\text{g ice}}} = 5200\ \text{cal absorbed}$

b. $17.0\ \cancel{\text{g ice}} \times \dfrac{80.\ \text{cal}}{1\ \cancel{\text{g ice}}} = 1400\ \text{cal absorbed}$

c. $225\ \cancel{\text{g water}} \times \dfrac{80.\ \cancel{\text{cal}}}{1\ \cancel{\text{g water}}} \times \dfrac{1\ \text{kcal}}{1000\ \cancel{\text{cal}}} = 18\ \text{kcal released}$

2.31 **a.** condensation **b.** evaporation **c.** boiling **d.** condensation

2.33 **a.** The liquid water in perspiration absorbs heat and changes to vapor. The heat needed for the change is removed from the skin.

b. On a hot day, there are more liquid water molecules in the damp clothing that have sufficient energy to become water vapor. Thus, water evaporates from the clothes more readily on a hot day.

2.35 **a.** $10.0\ \cancel{\text{g water}} \times \dfrac{540\ \text{cal}}{1\ \cancel{\text{g water}}} = 540\ \text{cal absorbed}$

b. $50.0\ \cancel{\text{g water}} \times \dfrac{540\ \cancel{\text{cal}}}{1\ \cancel{\text{g water}}} \times \dfrac{1\ \text{kcal}}{1000\ \cancel{\text{cal}}} = 27\ \text{kcal absorbed}$

c. $8.0\ \cancel{\text{kg steam}} \times \dfrac{1000\ \cancel{\text{g}}}{1\ \cancel{\text{kg}}} \times \dfrac{540\ \cancel{\text{cal}}}{1\ \cancel{\text{g steam}}} \times \dfrac{1\ \text{kcal}}{1000\ \cancel{\text{cal}}} = 4300\ \text{kcal released}$

2.37

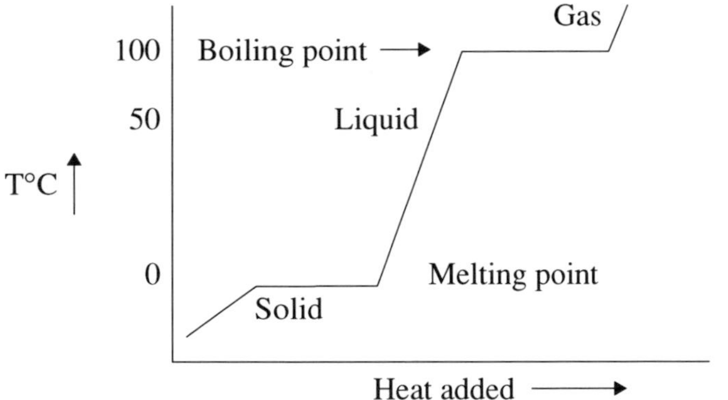

Answers to Additional Problems in your Textbook

2.39 From Table 2.6, we see that liquid water has a high specific heat (1.00 cal/g °C), which means that a large amount of energy is required to cause a significant temperature change. Sand, on the other hand, has a low specific heat (0.19 cal/g °C), so even a small amount of energy will cause a significant temperature change in the sand.

2.41 Both water condensation (formation of rain) and deposition (formation of snow) from the gaseous moisture in the air are exothermic processes (heat is released). The heat released in either of these processes warms the surrounding air, and so the air temperature is in fact raised.

2.43 **a.** For 15% of one's total Calories (kcal) to be supplied by protein, a conversion factor of 15 kcal from protein/100 kcal total in the daily diet will be used in the calculation. Similar factors will be used for the carbohydrate (carbs) and fat calculations.

$$1200\ \cancel{\text{kcal (total)}} \times \frac{15\ \cancel{\text{kcal (protein)}}}{100\ \cancel{\text{kcal (total)}}} \times \frac{1\ \text{g protein}}{4\ \cancel{\text{kcal (protein)}}} = 45\ \text{g protein}$$

$$1200\,\cancel{\text{kcal (total)}} \times \frac{45\text{ kcal (carbs)}}{100\,\cancel{\text{kcal (total)}}} \times \frac{1\text{ g carbs}}{4\,\cancel{\text{kcal (carbs)}}} = 140\text{ g carbohydrate}$$

$$1200\,\cancel{\text{kcal (total)}} \times \frac{40\,\cancel{\text{kcal (fat)}}}{100\,\cancel{\text{kcal (total)}}} \times \frac{1\text{ g fat}}{4\,\cancel{\text{kcal (fat)}}} = 53\text{ g fat}$$

b. The calculations for part b differ from part a only in the total kcal per day.

$$1900\,\cancel{\text{kcal (total)}} \times \frac{15\,\cancel{\text{kcal (protein)}}}{100\,\cancel{\text{kcal (total)}}} \times \frac{1\text{ g protein}}{4\,\cancel{\text{kcal (protein)}}} = 71\text{ g protein}$$

$$1900\,\cancel{\text{kcal (total)}} \times \frac{45\,\cancel{\text{kcal (carbs)}}}{100\,\cancel{\text{kcal (total)}}} \times \frac{1\text{ g carbs}}{4\,\cancel{\text{kcal (carbs)}}} = 210\text{ g carbohydrate}$$

$$1900\,\cancel{\text{kcal (total)}} \times \frac{40\,\cancel{\text{kcal (fat)}}}{100\,\cancel{\text{kcal (total)}}} \times \frac{1\text{ g fat}}{9\,\cancel{\text{kcal (fat)}}} = 84\text{ g fat}$$

c. The calculations for part c again differ only in the total kcal per day.

$$2600\,\cancel{\text{kcal (total)}} \times \frac{15\,\cancel{\text{kcal (protein)}}}{100\,\cancel{\text{kcal (total)}}} \times \frac{1\text{ g protein}}{4\,\cancel{\text{kcal (protein)}}} = 98\text{ g protein}$$

$$2600\,\cancel{\text{kcal (total)}} \times \frac{45\,\cancel{\text{kcal (carbs)}}}{100\,\cancel{\text{kcal (total)}}} \times \frac{1\text{ g carbs}}{4\,\cancel{\text{kcal (carbs)}}} = 290\text{ g carbohydrate}$$

$$2600\,\cancel{\text{kcal (total)}} \times \frac{40\,\cancel{\text{kcal (fat)}}}{100\,\cancel{\text{kcal (total)}}} \times \frac{1\text{ g fat}}{9\,\cancel{\text{kcal (fat)}}} = 120\text{ g fat}$$

2.45 Because each gram of body fat contains 15% water, a person actually loses 85 grams of fat per hundred grams of body fat. (We considered 1 lb of fat as exactly 1 lb.)

$$1\,\cancel{\text{lb body fat}} \times \frac{454\,\cancel{\text{g}}}{1\,\cancel{\text{lb}}} \times \frac{85\,\cancel{\text{g fat}}}{100\,\cancel{\text{g body fat}}} \times \frac{9\text{ kcal}}{1\,\cancel{\text{g fat}}} = 3500\text{ kcal}$$

2.47 $725\,\cancel{\text{g}} \times \frac{1\,\cancel{\text{cal}}}{\cancel{\text{g°C}}} \times 28\,\cancel{\text{°C}} \times \frac{1\text{ kcal}}{1000\,\cancel{\text{cal}}} = 20.\text{ kcal}$

2.49 **a.** 61.4°C **b.** 53.80°C **c.** 4.8°C

2.51 gold 250 J or 59 cal; aluminum 240 J or 58 cal; silver 250 J or 59 cal
The heat needed for 10.0 cm^3-samples of the metals are almost the same.

2.53 **a.** −60°C **b.** 60°C

c. A represents the solid state. B represents the change from solid to liquid or melting of the substance. C represents the liquid state as temperature increases. D represents the change from liquid to gas or boiling of the liquid.

d. At −80°C, solid; at −40°C, liquid; at 25°C, liquid; at 80°C, gas

Chapter 3

Key Terms

Answers	**1.** d	**2.** b	**3.** a	**4.** e	**5.** c

3.1 Classification of Matter

Learning Exercise 3.1A

Answers	**1.** E	**2.** C	**3.** C	**4.** E	**5.** E	**6.** C

Learning Exercise 3.1B

Answers	**1.** M	**2.** P	**3.** P	**4.** M	**5.** P	**6.** M

Learning Exercise 3.1C

Answers	**1.** HO	**2.** HE	**3.** HO	**4.** HE	**5.** HO	**6.** HO

3.2 Elements and Symbols

Learning Exercise 3.2A

Answers	**1.** C	**2.** Fe	**3.** Na	**4.** P	**5.** O
	6. N	**7.** I	**8.** S	**9.** K	**10.** Pb
	11. Ca	**12.** Au	**13.** Cu	**14.** Ne	**15.** Cl

Learning Exercise 3.2B

Answers	**1.** magnesium	**2.** potassium	**3.** gold
	4. fluorine	**5.** copper	**6.** beryllium
	7. silver	**8.** bromine	**9.** zinc
	10. aluminum	**11.** barium	**12.** lithium

Learning Exercise 3.2C

Answers	density 19.3 g/mL	melting point 1064°C
	boiling point 2857°C	metal
	yellow color	soft
	highly malleable	good conductor of heat and electricity

3.3 The Periodic Table

Learning Exercise 3.3A

Answers	**a.** P	**b.** G	**c.** P	**d.** P
	e. G	**f.** N	**g.** G	**h.** P

◆ Learning Exercise 3.3B

Answers

Element and Symbol	Group Number	Period Number
Magnesium, Mg	2A (2)	3
Silicon, Si	4A (14)	3
Nitrogen, N	5A (15)	2
Aluminum, Al	3A (13)	3
Tin, Sn	4A (14)	5
Cesium, Cs	1A (1)	6

◆ Learning Exercise 3.3C

Answers **1.** NM **2.** NM **3.** M **4.** M **5.** M
6. NM **7.** M **8.** M **9.** M **10.** M

◆ Learning Exercise 3.3D

Answers **1.** Cl, Br **2.** He, Ne **3.** K, Li **4.** Mg **5.** Fe, Cu

3.4 The Atom

◆ Learning Exercise 3.4A

Answers **1.** true **2.** false **3.** true **4.** true

◆ Learning Exercise 3.4B

Answers **1.** a and b **2.** c **3.** c **4.** a and b **5.** d **6.** b

3.5 Atomic Number and Mass Number

◆ Learning Exercise 3.5A

Answers **a.** 6 **b.** 15 **c.** 19 **d.** 10 **e.** 18

◆ Learning Exercise 3.5B

Answers **a.** 22 **b.** 5 **c.** 16 **d.** 5 **e.** 12 **f.** 36

◆ Learning Exercise 3.5C

Answers

Symbol	Atomic Number	Mass Number	Number of Protons	Number of Neutrons	Number of Electrons
$^{24}_{12}Mg$	12	24	12	12	12
$^{42}_{20}Ca$	20	42	20	22	20
$^{55}_{26}Fe$	26	55	26	29	26
$^{80}_{35}Br$	35	80	35	45	35
$^{35}_{17}Cl$	17	35	17	18	17
$^{120}_{50}Sn$	50	120	50	70	50

3.6 Isotopes and Atomic Mass

◆ Learning Exercise 3.6A

Answer Atoms A and D are isotopes (At. No. 10); atoms B and C are isotopes (At. No. 11).

◆ Learning Exercise 3.6B

Answer Copper in nature consists of two isotopes with different atomic masses. The atomic mass is the average of the individual masses of the two isotopes and their percent abundance in the sample. The atomic mass does not represent the mass of any individual atom.

3.7 Electron Energy Levels

◆ Learning Exercise 3.7A

Answers

a. 2, 2 **b.** 2, 4 **c.** 2, 8, 8, 1 **d.** 2, 8, 1 **e.** 2, 8, 5
f. 2, 5 **g.** 2, 8, 7 **h.** 2, 8, 4

◆ Learning Exercise 3.7B

Answers

a. 2 **b.** 2 **c.** 8 **d.** 6 **e.** 10 **f.** 18

3.8 Periodic Trends

◆ Learning Exercise 3.8A

Answers

a.	sulfur	$6e^-$	Group 6A (16)	·S: (6 dots)
b.	oxygen	$6e^-$	Group 6A (16)	·O: (6 dots)
c.	magnesium	$2e^-$	Group 2A (2)	Mg· (2 dots)
d.	hydrogen	$1e^-$	Group 1A (1)	
e.	fluorine	$7e^-$	Group 7A (17)	·F: (7 dots)
f.	aluminum	$3e^-$	Group 3A (13)	·Al· (3 dots)

◆ Learning Exercise 3.8B

Answers

a. Ca **b.** Si **c.** Rb **d.** Br
e. Cs **f.** Li **g.** P **h.** Ca

◆ Learning Exercise 3.8C

Answers

a. Na **b.** P **c.** Rb **d.** Br
e. Li **f.** Sb **g.** K **h.** Na

Investigating Matter

Melting Points of the Elements

There is a remarkable degree of organization in the periodic table. As discussed in your textbook, elements within the same atomic group (vertical column) share similar properties. Also, the chemical reactivity of an element can be deduced from its position in the periodic table. Two additional examples of the periodic table's organization are the melting points and densities of the elements.

The periodic table below shows the melting points of nearly all the elements. Note the melting points are not randomly oriented, but, with only a few exceptions, either gradually increase or decrease as you move in any particular direction. This can be clearly illustrated by color coding each element according to its melting point.

Use colored pencils to color in each element according to its melting point. Use the suggested color legend. Color lightly so that symbols and numbers are still visible.

Color	Temperature Range, °C	Color	Temperature Range, °C
Violet	-273 — -50	Yellow	1400 — 1900
Blue	-50 — 300	Orange	1900 — 2900
Cyan	300 — 700	Red	2900 — 3500
Green	700 — 1400		

Melting Points of the Elements

(°C)

1	2	3	4	5	6	7	8	9	10	11	12	13	14	15	16	17	18
H -259																	He -272
Li 180	Be 1278											B 2079	C 3550	N -210	O -218	F -219	Ne -248
Na 97	Mg 648											Al 660	Si 1410	P 44	S 113	Cl -100	Ar -189
K 63	Ca 839	Sc 1541	Ti 1660	V 1890	Cr 1857	Mn 1244	Fe 1535	Co 1495	Ni 1453	Cu 1083	Zn 419	Ga 30	Ge 937	As 817	Se 217	Br -7	Kr -156
Rb 39	Sr 769	Y 1522	Zr 1852	Nb 2468	Mo 2617	Tc 2172	Ru 2310	Rh 1966	Pd 1554	Ag 961	Cd 320	In 156	Sn 231	Sb 630	Te 449	I 113	Xe -111
Cs 28	Ba 725	La 921	Hf 2227	Ta 2996	W 3410	Re 3180	Os 3045	Ir 2410	Pt 1772	Au 1064	Hg -38	Tl 303	Pb 327.	Bi 271	Po 254	At 302	Rn -71
Fr 27	Ra 700	Ac 1050	--	--	--	--	--	--									

TUNGSTEN

Lanthanides:	Ce 799	Pr 931	Nd 1021	Pm 1168	Sm 1077	Eu 822	Gd 1313	Tb 1356	Dy 1412	Ho 1474	Er 1159	Tm 1545	Yb 819	Lu 1663
Actinides:	Th 1750	Pa 1600	U 1132	Np 640	Pu 641	Am 994	Cm 1340	Bk --	Cf --	Es --	Fm --	Md --	No --	Lr --

1. Which elements have the highest melting points?

   THE ONES CLOSER TO TUNGSTEN

2. Which elements have the lowest melting points?

   ELEMENTS TOWARD UPPER RIGHT

3. Which atomic groups tend to go from higher to lower melting points reading from top to bottom? (Identify each group by its group number.)

   1, 2, 3, 12, 13, 14

4. Which atomic groups tend to go from lower to higher melting points reading from top to bottom?

   4 THROUGH 10 AND 15 THROUGH 18

Investigating Matter

Densities of the Elements

The periodic table below shows the densities of nearly all the elements. As with the melting points, the densities of the elements either gradually increase or decrease as you move in any particular direction. Use colored pencils to color in each element according to its density. Shown below is a suggested color legend. Color lightly so that symbols and numbers are still visible. (Note: All gaseous elements are marked with an asterisk and should be the same color. Their densities, which are given in units of g/L, are much less than the densities nongaseous elements, which are given in units of g/mL.)

Color	Density (g/mL)	Color	Density (g/mL)
Violet	gaseous elements	Yellow	16 — 12
Blue	5 — 0	Orange	20 — 16
Cyan	8 — 5	Red.	23 — 20
Green	12 — 8		

Densities of the Elements

(g/mL)

1	2	3	4	5	6	7	8	9	10	11	12	13	14	15	16	17	18
H * 0.09																	He * 0.18
Li 0.5	Be 1.8											B 2.3	C 2.0	N * 1.25	O * 1.43	F * 1.70	Ne * 0.90
Na 1.0	Mg 1.7											Al 2.7	Si 2.3	P 1.8	S 2.1	Cl * 3.21	Ar * 1.78
K 0.9	Ca 1.6	Sc 3.0	Ti 4.5	V 6.1	Cr 7.2	Mn 7.3	Fe 7.8	Co 8.9	Ni 8.9	Cu 9.0	Zn 7.1	Ga 6.1	Ge 5.3	As 5.7	Se 4.8	Br * 7.59	Kr * 3.73
Rb 1.5	Sr 2.5	Y 4.5	Zr 6.5	Nb 8.5	Mo 6.8	Tc 11.5	Ru 12.4	Rh 12.4	Pd 12.0	Ag 10.5	Cd 8.7	In 7.3	Sn 5.7	Sb 6.7	Te 6.2	I 4.9	Xe * 5.89
Cs 1.9	Ba 3.5	La 6.2	Hf 13.3	Ta 16.6	W 19.3	Re 21.0	Os 22.6	Ir 22.4	Pt 21.5	Au 18.9	Hg 13.5	Tl 11.9	Pb 11.4	Bi 9.7	Po 9.3	At --	Rn * 9.73
Fr --	Ra 5.0	Ac 10.1	Unq --	Unp --	Unh --	Uns --	Uno --	Une --									

OSMIUM

* density of gaseous phase in g/L

Lanthanides:	Ce 6.7	Pr 6.7	Nd 6.8	Pm 7.2	Sm 7.5	Eu 5.2	Gd 7.9	Tb 8.2	Dy 8.6	Ho 8.8	Er 9.1	Tm 9.3	Yb 6.9	Lu 9.8
Actinides:	Th 11.7	Pa 15.4	U 19.0	Np 20.1	Pu 19.8	Am 13.7	Cm 13.5	Bk 14	Cf --	Es --	Fm --	Md --	No --	Lr --

1. Which elements are the most dense?

THE ONES CLOSER TO OSMIUM, OS

2. How variable are the densities of the lanthanides compared to the densities of the actinides?

THE ACTINIDES ARE MUCH MORE VARIABLE

3. Which atomic groups tend to go from higher to lower densities reading from top to bottom? (Identify each group by its group number).

NONE

4. Which atomic groups tend to go from lower to higher densities reading from top to bottom?

ALL

Investigating Matter

The Submicroscopic

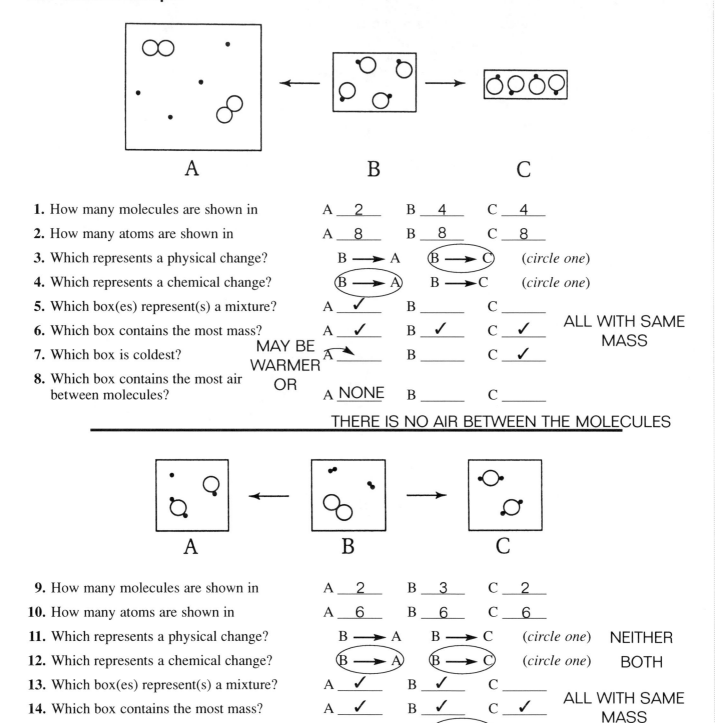

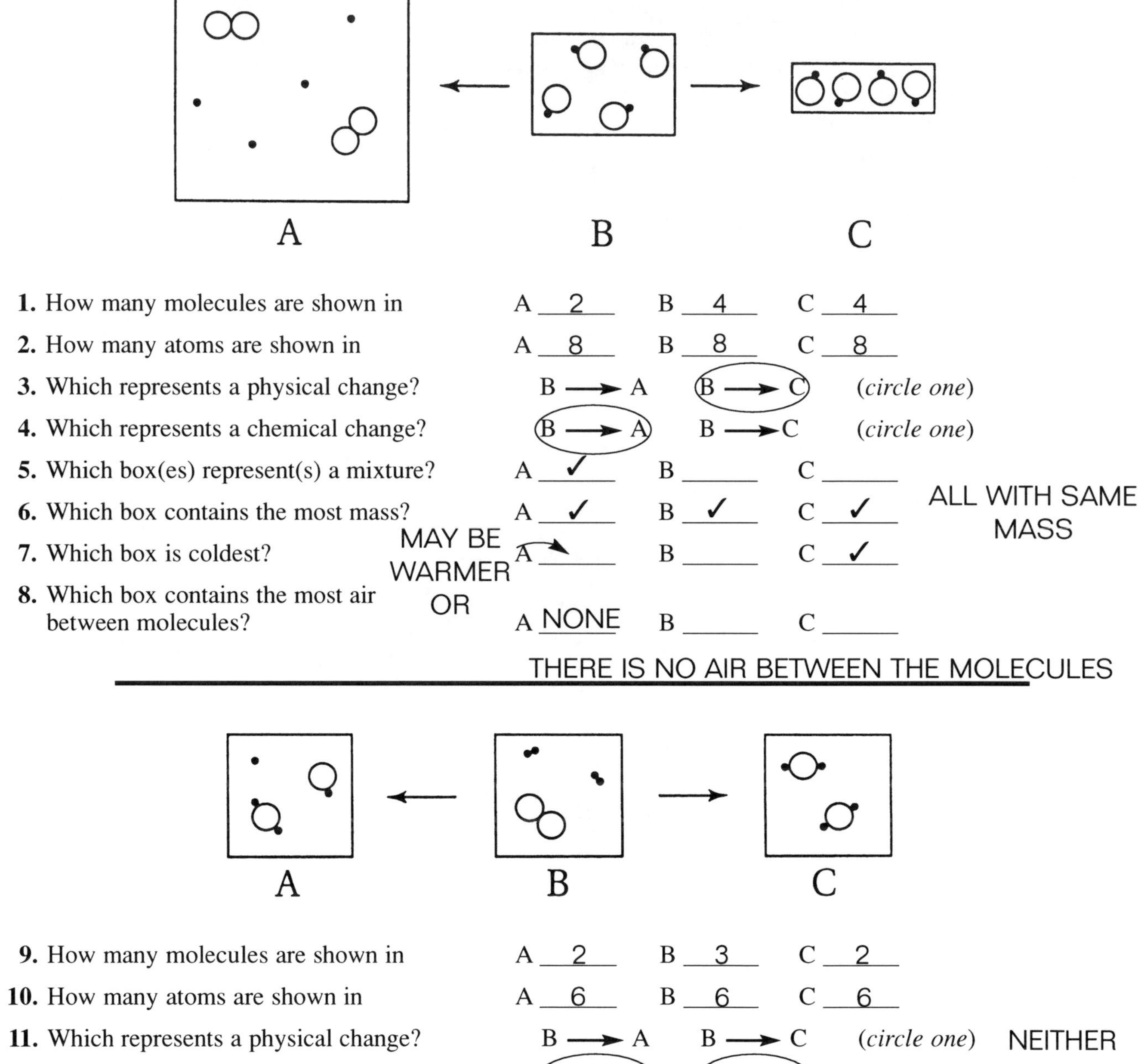

1. How many molecules are shown in — A 2 B 4 C 4
2. How many atoms are shown in — A 8 B 8 C 8
3. Which represents a physical change? — B ⟶ A **(B ⟶ C)** *(circle one)*
4. Which represents a chemical change? — **(B ⟶ A)** B ⟶ C *(circle one)*
5. Which box(es) represent(s) a mixture? — A ✓ B ___ C ___
6. Which box contains the most mass? — A ✓ B ✓ C ✓ ALL WITH SAME MASS
7. Which box is coldest? — A ___ B ___ C ✓ (MAY BE WARMER OR)
8. Which box contains the most air between molecules? — A NONE B ___ C ___

THERE IS NO AIR BETWEEN THE MOLECULES

---

9. How many molecules are shown in — A 2 B 3 C 2
10. How many atoms are shown in — A 6 B 6 C 6
11. Which represents a physical change? — B ⟶ A B ⟶ C *(circle one)* NEITHER
12. Which represents a chemical change? — **(B ⟶ A)** **(B ⟶ C)** *(circle one)* BOTH
13. Which box(es) represent(s) a mixture? — A ✓ B ✓ C ___
14. Which box contains the most mass? — A ✓ B ✓ C ✓ ALL WITH SAME MASS
15. Which should take longer? — B ⟶ A **(B ⟶ C)** *(circle one)*
    ONE LESS STEP IS REQUIRED TO GO FROM B ⟶ A
16. Which box most likely contains ions? — A ✓ B ___ C ___

Investigating Matter

Physical and Chemical Changes

1. What distinguishes a chemical change from a physical change?

DURING A CHEMICAL CHANGE ATOM CHANGE PARTNERS

2. Based upon observations alone, why is distinguishing a chemical change from a physical change not always so straight-forward?

BOTH INVOLVE A CHANGE IN PHYSICAL APPEARANCE

Try your hand at categorizing the following processes as either chemical or physical changes. Some of these examples are debatable! Be sure to discuss your reasoning with fellow classmates or your instructor.

		(circle one)	
3.	A cloud grows dark.	chemical	**physical**
4.	Leaves produce oxygen.	**chemical**	physical
5.	Food coloring is added to water.	chemical	**physical**
6.	Tropical coral reef dies.	**chemical**	physical
7.	Dead coral reef is pounded by waves into beach sand.	chemical	**physical**
8.	Oil and vinegar separate.	chemical	**physical**
9.	Soda drink goes flat.	chemical	**physical**
10.	Sick person develops a fever.	**chemical**	physical
11.	Compost pit turns into mulch.	**chemical**	physical
12.	A computer is turned on. AT THE ELECTRIC POWER PLANT ⟶	**chemical**	**physical**
13.	An electrical short melts a computer's integrated circuits.	chemical	**physical**
14.	A car battery runs down.	**chemical**	physical
15.	A pencil is sharpened.	chemical	**physical**
16.	Mascara is applied to eyelashes.	chemical	**physical**
17.	Sunbather gets tan lying in the sun.	**chemical**	physical
18.	Invisible ink turns visible upon heating.	**chemical**	physical
19.	A light bulb burns out.	**chemical**	physical
20.	Car engine consumes a tank of gasoline.	**chemical**	physical
21.	B vitamins turn urine yellow.	chemical	**physical**

ASSUMING "XS" VITAMIN PASSES THROUGH BODY UNCHANGED

Answers for the Practice Test

1. K	**2.** P	**3.** Ca	**4.** C	**5.** Na
6. iron	**7.** copper	**8.** chlorine	**9.** lead	**10.** silver
11. A	**12.** B	**13.** B	**14.** A	**15.** A
16. E	**17.** C	**18.** A	**19.** A	**20.** A
21. B	**22.** A	**23.** D	**24.** B	**25.** C
26. E	**27.** E	**28.** D	**29.** C	**30.** C

Answers and Solutions to Selected Text Problems

3.1 A *pure substance* has a definite composition. A *mixture* has a variable composition.

a. pure substance **b.** mixture
c. pure substance **d.** pure substance

3.3 *Elements* are the simplest type of pure substance.
Compounds contain two or more elements in the same ratio.

a. element **b.** compound
c. element **d.** compound

3.5 A *homogeneous mixture* has a uniform composition; a *heterogeneous mixture* does not have a uniform composition throughout the mixture.

a. heterogeneous **b.** homogeneous
c. homogeneous **d.** heterogeneous

3.71 **a.** Br, which is above I in Group 7A (17), has a higher ionization energy than I.
b. Ionization energy decreases from Group 2A (2) to Group 3A (13), which gives Mg a higher ionization energy than Al.
c. Ionization energy increases from Group 4A (14) to Group 5A (15), which gives P a higher ionization energy than S.

3.73 **a.** element **b.** compound **c.** mixture **d.** element **e.** mixture

3.75 **a.** Mg, magnesium **b.** Br, bromine **c.** Al, aluminum **d.** O, oxygen

3.77 Any two of the following in each part are correct responses:

a. fluorine, chlorine, bromine, iodine, and astatine
b. helium, neon, argon, krypton, xenon, and radon
c. lithium, sodium, potassium, rubidium, cesium, and francium
d. beryllium, magnesium, calcium, strontium, barium, and radium

3.79 **a.** False. A proton has a positive charge.
b. False. The neutron has about the same mass as a proton.
c. True.
d. False. The nucleus is the tiny, dense central core of an atom.
e. True.

3.81 **a.** protons **b.** protons **c.** alkali metals

3.83 **a.** lithium, Li **b.** fluorine, F **c.** calcium, Ca **d.** arsenic, As
e. tin, Sn **f.** cesium, Cs **g.** gold, Au **h.** oxygen, O

3.85 **a.** 13 protons, 14 neutrons, 13 electrons
b. 24 protons, 28 neutrons, 24 electrons
c. 16 protons, 18 neutrons, 16 electrons
d. 26 protons, 30 neutrons, 26 electrons
e. 54 protons, 82 neutrons, 54 electrons

3.87

Name	Nuclear Symbol	Number of Protons	Number of Neutrons	Number of Electrons
sulfur	$^{34}_{16}S$	16	18	16
zinc	$^{70}_{30}Zn$	30	40	30
magnesium	$^{26}_{12}Mg$	12	14	12
radon	$^{220}_{86}Rn$	86	134	86

3.89 **a.** ^{9}Be **b.** ^{26}Mg **c.** ^{46}Ca **d.** ^{70}Zn **e.** ^{63}Cu

3.91 **a.** 82 protons, 126 neutrons, 82 electrons **b.** ^{214}Pb **c.** ^{214}Bi, bismuth

3.93 **a.** N 2,5 Group 5A (15) **b.** Na 2,8,1 Group 1A (1)
c. S 2,8,6 Group 6A (16) **d.** B 2,3 Group 3A (13)

3.95 Calcium has a greater net nuclear charge than K. The least tightly bound electron in Ca is further from the nucleus than in Mg and needs less energy to remove.

3.97 **a.** Na is on the far left of the heavy zigzag line. Na is a metal.
b. Na at the beginning of Period 3 has the largest atomic radius.
c. F at the top of Group 7A (17) and to the far right in Period 2 has the highest ionization energy.
d. Na has the lowest ionization energy and loses an electron most easily.
e. Cl is found in Period 3 in Group 7A (17).

3.99 **a.** has two different types of atoms combined in the same ration. A is a compound.
b. consists of two different types of atoms; it is a mixture.
c. has only one type of atom; c is an element.

3.101 b and c are not the same throughout the mixture, and b and c are heterogeneous.

3.103 **a.** $^{16}_{8}X$ $^{17}_{8}X$ $^{18}_{8}X$ All have 8 protons.
b. $^{16}_{8}X$ $^{17}_{8}X$ $^{18}_{8}X$ All are isotopes of oxygen.
c. $^{16}_{8}X$ $^{16}_{9}X$ Mass number of 16
$^{18}_{10}X$ $^{18}_{8}X$ Mass number of 18
d. $^{16}_{8}X$ $^{18}_{10}X$ Both have 8 neutrons.

Chapter 4

Key Terms

Answers **1.** d **2.** e **3.** c **4.** a **5.** b

4.1 Octet Rule and Ions

◆ Learning Exercise 4.1A

Answers

Element	Group Number	Electrons Lost	Ion Formed
Magnesium	2A (2)	2	Mg^{2+}
Sodium	1A (1)	1	Na^{+}
Calcium	2A (2)	2	Ca^{2+}
Potassium	1A (1)	1	K^{+}
Aluminum	3A (13)	3	Al^{3+}

◆ Learning Exercise 4.1B

Answers

Element	Group Number	Electrons Gained	Ion Formed
Chlorine	7A (17)	1	Cl^{-}
Oxygen	6A (16)	2	O^{2-}
Nitrogen	5A (15)	3	N^{3-}
Fluorine	7A (17)	1	F^{-}
Sulfur	6A (16)	2	S^{2-}

4.2 Ionic Compounds

◆ Learning Exercise 4.2A

Answers **1.** C **2.** B **3.** A **4.** F
5. E **6.** D **7.** F **8.** C

◆ Learning Exercise 4.2B

Answers **1.** NaCl **2.** K_2S **3.** Al_2O_3 **4.** $MgCl_2$
5. CaS **6.** $AlCl_3$ **7.** Li_3N **8.** Ba_3P_2

4.3 Naming and Writing Ionic Compounds

◆ Learning Exercise 4.3A

Answers

1. Fe^{3+} **2.** copper(II) **3.** Zn^{2+}
4. iron(II) **5.** Cu^{+} **6.** Silver

◆ Learning Exercise 4.3B

Answers

Compound	Positive ion	Negative ion	Formula of compound
Aluminum sulfide	Al^{3+}	S^{2-}	Al_2S_3
Copper(II) chloride	Cu^{2+}	Cl^{-}	$CuCl_2$
Magnesium oxide	Mg^{2+}	O^{2-}	MgO
Iron(II) bromide	Fe^{2+}	Br^{-}	$FeBr_2$
Silver oxide	Ag^{+}	O^{2-}	Ag_2O

◆ Learning Exercise 4.3C

Answers

1. chloride **2.** iron(II) **3.** copper(I) **4.** silver **5.** oxide **6.** calcium
7. sulfide **8.** aluminum **9.** iron(III) **10.** barium **11.** copper(II) **12.** nitride

◆ Learning Exercise 4.3D

Answers

1. Ba^{2+}, Cl^{-}, barium chloride
2. Fe^{3+}, Br^{-}, iron(III) bromide
3. Na^{+}, P^{3-}, sodium phosphide
4. Al^{3+}, O^{2-}, aluminum oxide
5. Cu^{2+}, O^{2-}, copper(II) oxide
6. Mg^{2+}, N^{3-}, magnesium nitride

4.4 Polyatomic Ions

◆ Learning Exercise 4.4A

Answers

1. SO_4^{2-} **2.** OH^{-} **3.** CO_3^{2-} **4.** SO_3^{2-}
5. NH_4^{+} **6.** PO_4^{3-} **7.** NO_3^{-} **8.** NO_2^{-}

◆ Learning Exercise 4.4B

Answers

Compound	Positive ion	Negative ion	Formula
Sodium phosphate	Na^{+}	PO_4^{3-}	Na_3PO_4
Iron(II) hydroxide	Fe^{2+}	OH^{-}	$Fe(OH)_2$
Ammonium carbonate	NH_{4+}	CO_3^{2-}	$(NH_4)_2CO_3$
Silver bicarbonate	Ag^{+}	HCO_3^{-}	$AgHCO_3$
Iron(III) sulfate	Fe^{3+}	SO_4^{2-}	$Fe_2(SO_4)_3$
Iron(II) nitrate	Fe^{2+}	NO_3^{-}	$Fe(NO_3)_2$
Potassium sulfite	K^{+}	SO_3^{2-}	K_2SO_3
Barium phosphate	Ba^{2+}	PO_4^{3-}	$Ba_{3-}(PO_4)_2$

4.5 Covalent Compounds

◆ Learning Exercise 4.5A

Answers

```
                ..  ..  ..                                                ..   ..
                :Cl:N:Cl:                                         ..      :Cl:
                ..  ..  ..                                       H:S:  ..  ..  ..
H:H              :Cl:            H:Cl:        :Cl:Cl:             ..  :Cl:C:Cl:
                  ..               ..          ..  ..              H   ..  ..  ..
                                                                          :Cl:
                                                                           ..
```

◆ Learning Exercise 4.5B

Answers **1.** carbon disulfide **2.** carbon tetrachloride **3.** carbon monoxide
4. sulfur dioxide **5.** dinitrogen tetroxide **6.** phosphorus trichloride

◆ Learning Exercise 4.5C

Answers **1.** N_2O **2.** $SiBr_4$ **3.** NCl_3 **4.** CO_2 **5.** SF_6 **6.** OF_2

◆ Learning Exercise 4.5D

Answers

Mg and Cl	Ionic	Mg^{2+}, Cl^-	$MgCl_2$	Magnesium chloride
N and Cl	Covalent	Cl—N—Cl | Cl	NCl_3	Nitrogen trichloride
K and SO_4	Ionic	K^+, SO_4^{2-}	K_2SO_4	Potassium sulfate
Li and O	Ionic	Li^+, O^{2-}	Li_2O	Lithium oxide
C and Cl	Covalent	Cl | Cl—C—Cl | Cl	CCl_4	Carbon tetrachloride
Na and PO_4	ionic	Na^+, PO_4^{3-}	Na_3PO_4	Sodium phosphate
H and S	covalent	H —S — H	H_2S	Dihydrogen sulfide
Ca and HCO_3	ionic	Ca^{2+}, HCO_3^-	$Ca(HCO_3)_2$	Calcium hydrogen Carbonate (bicarbonate)

◆ Learning Exercise 4.5E

Answers

Compound	**Positive ion**	**Negative ion**	**Formula**
Sodium phosphate	Na^+	PO_4^{3-}	Na_3PO_4
Iron(II) hydroxide	Fe^{2+}	OH^-	$Fe(OH)_2$
Ammonium carbonate	NH_4^+	CO_3^{2-}	$(NH_4)_2CO_3$
Silver bicarbonate	Ag^+	HCO_3^-	$AgHCO_3$
Iron(III) sulfate	Fe^{3+}	SO_4^{2-}	$Fe_2(SO_4)_3$
Copper(II) nitrate	Cu^{2+}	NO_3^-	$Cu(NO_3)_2$
Potassium sulfite	K^+	SO_3^{2-}	K_2SO_3
Barium phosphate	Ba^{2+}	PO_4^{3-}	$Ba_3(PO_4)_2$

4.6 Electronegativity and Bond Polarity

◆ Learning Exercise 4.6

Answers

a. 1.4, PC **b.** 0.5, PC **c.** 2.0, I **d.** 3.0, I
e. 0.9, PC **f.** 0.0, NP **g.** 1.5, PC **h.** 0.4, NP

4.7 Shapes and Polarity of Molecules

◆ Learning Exercise 4.7A

Answers **1.** b **2.** a **3.** c

◆ Learning Exercise 4.7B

Answers

Molecule or ion	Electron-dot formula	Number of electron groups	Number of bonded atoms	Shape and angle
CH_4	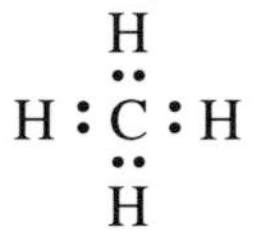 H : C : H with H above and below (8 bonding electrons)	4	4	Tetrahedral, 109°
PCl_3	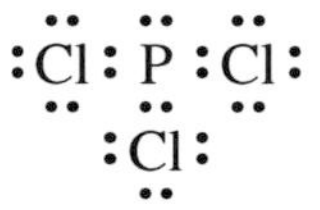 :Cl: P :Cl: with :Cl: below (each Cl with three lone pairs, P with one lone pair)	4	3	Pyramidal, 109°
H_2S	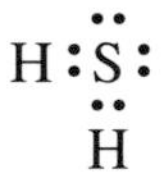 H:S: with H below (S with two lone pairs)	4	2	Bent, 109°

◆ Learning Exercise 4.7C

Answers

1. $\overset{\delta^+}{H}—\overset{\delta^-}{O}$ **2.** $\overset{\delta^-}{N}—\overset{\delta^+}{N}$ **3.** $\overset{\delta^+}{C}—\overset{\delta^-}{Cl}$
4. $\overset{\delta^+}{O}—\overset{\delta^-}{F}$ **5.** $\overset{\delta^+}{N}—\overset{\delta^-}{F}$ **6.** $\overset{\delta^+}{P}—\overset{\delta^-}{Cl}$

◆ Learning Exercise 4.7D

Answers

1. CF_4 F←C→F (with F↑ above and F↓ below) dipoles cancel, nonpolar

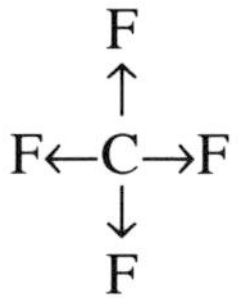

2. HCl $\overset{\delta^+}{H}\,\overset{\delta^-}{Cl}$ ⟶ dipole does not cancel, polar

3. NH_3 H→N̈←H (with ↑H below) dipoles do not cancel, polar

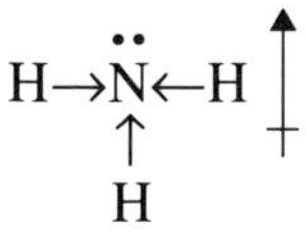

4. OF_2 :Ö→F (with ↓F below) ↘ dipoles do not cancel, polar

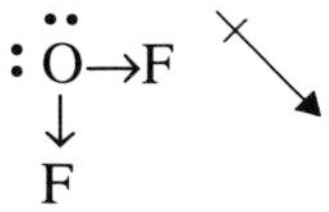

The Nature of Chemical Bonds

Losing Valence Electrons

The shell model can be used to explain a wide variety of properties of atoms. Using the shell model, for example, we can explain how atoms within the same group tend to lose (or gain) the same number of electrons. Let's consider the case of three group 1 elements: lithium, sodium, and potassium. Look to a periodic table and find the nuclear charge of each of these atoms:

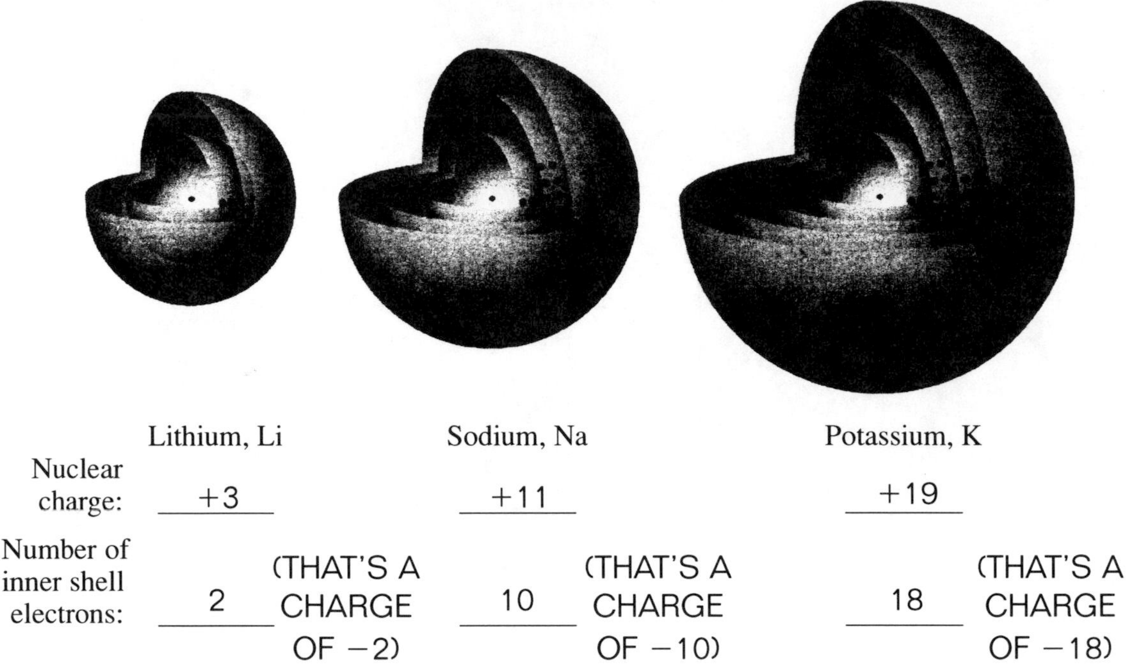

	Lithium, Li	Sodium, Na	Potassium, K
Nuclear charge:	+3	+11	+19
Number of inner shell electrons:	2 (THAT'S A CHARGE OF −2)	10 (THAT'S A CHARGE OF −10)	18 (THAT'S A CHARGE OF −18)

How strongly the valence electron is held to the nucleus depends on the strength of the nuclear charge—the stronger the charge, the stronger the valence electron is held. There's more to it, however, because inner-shell electrons weaken the attraction outer-shell electrons have for the nucleus. The valence shell in lithium, for example, doesn't experience the full effect of three protons. Instead, it experiences a diminished nuclear charge of about +1. We get this by subtracting the number of inner-shell electrons from the actual nuclear charge. What do the valence electrons for sodium and potassium experience?

Diminished nuclear charge:	(+3 − 2 = +1) ABOUT +1	(+11 − 10 = +1) ABOUT +1	(+19 − 18 = +1) ABOUT +1

Question: Potassium has a nuclear charge many times greater than that of lithium. Why is it actually *easier* for a potassium atom to lose its valence electron than it is for a lithium atom to lose its valence electron?

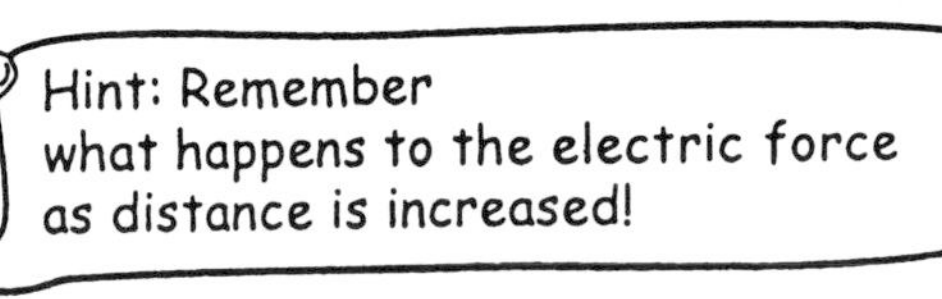

Hint: Remember
what happens to the electric force
as distance is increased!

POTASSIUM'S VALENCE ELECTRON IS MUCH FARTHER FROM THE NUCLEUS. BECAUSE THE ELECTRIC FORCE DECREASES WITH DISTANCE, THE +1 CHARGE FOR POTASSIUM'S VALENCE ELECTRON IS NOT SO EFFECTIVE AT HOLDING TO THE ATOM. HENCE, IT IS EASILY LOST.

The Nature of Chemical Bonds

Drawing Shells

Atomic shells can be represented by a series of concentric circles as shown in your textbook. With a little effort, however, it's possible to show these shells in three dimensions. Grab a pencil and blank sheet of paper and follow the steps shown below. Practice makes perfect.

1. Lightly draw a diagonal guideline. Then, draw a series of seven semicircles. Note how the ends of the semicircles are not perpendicular to the guideline. Instead, they are parallel to the length of the page, as shown in Figure 1.

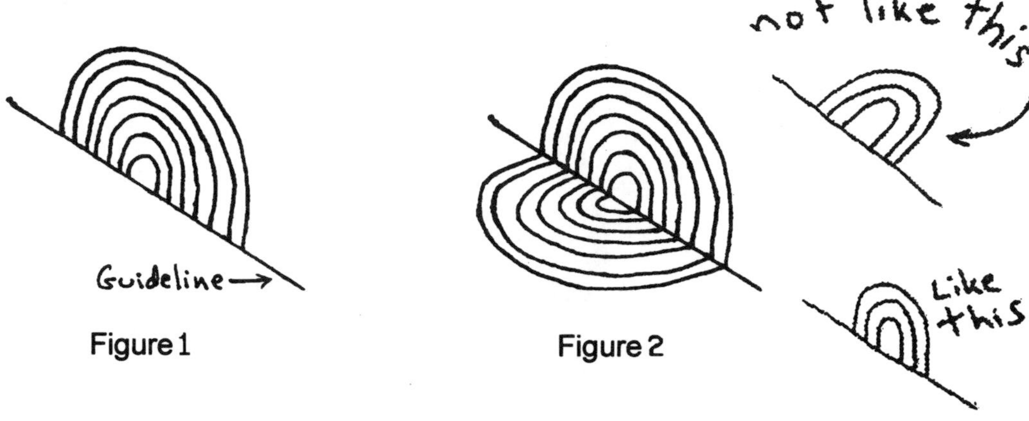

Figure 1 Figure 2

2. Connect the ends of each semicircle with another semicircle such that a series of concentric hearts is drawn. The ends of these new semicircles should be drawn perpendicular to the ends of the previously drawn semicircles, as shown in Figure 2.

3. Now the hard part. Draw a portion of a circle that connects the apex of the largest vertical and horizontal semicircles, as in Figure 3.

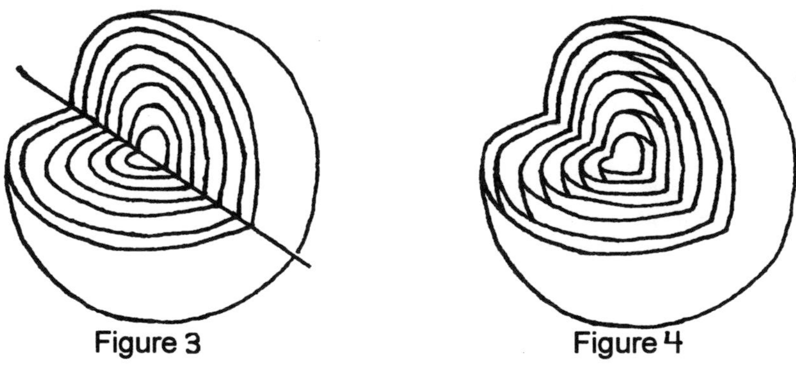

Figure 3 Figure 4

4. Now the fun part. Erase the pencil guideline drawn in Step 1, then add the internal lines, as shown in Figure 4, that create a series of concentric shells.

You need not draw all the shells for each atom. Oxygen, for example, is nicely represented drawing only the first two inner shells, which are the only ones that contain electrons. Remember that these shells are not to be taken literally. Rather, they are a highly simplified view of how electrons tend to organize themselves with an atom. You should know that each shell represents a set of atomic orbitals of similar energy levels as shown in your textbook.

The Nature of Chemical Bonds

Atomic Size

1. Complete the shells for the following atoms using arrows to represent electrons.

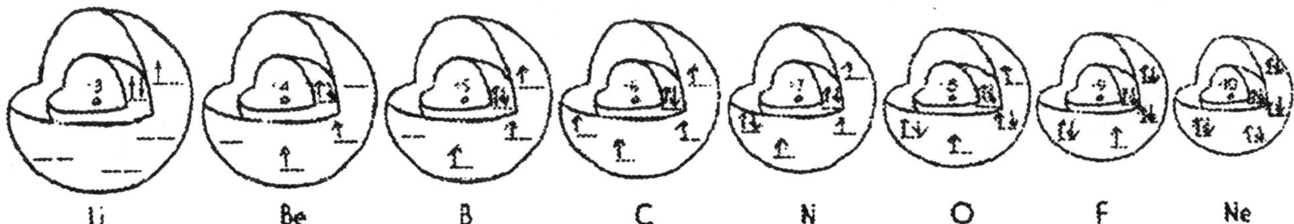

2. Neon, Ne, has many more electrons than lithium, Li, yet it is a much smaller atom. Why?

NEON HAS A STRONGER NUCLEAR CHARGE (+10) THAT PULLS THE ELECTRON IN CLOSER TO IT.

3. Draw the shell model for a sodium atom, Na (atomic number 11), adjacent to the neon atom in the box shown below. Use a pencil because you may need to erase.

a. Which should be larger: neon's first shell or sodium's first shell. Why? Did you represent this accurately within your drawing?

NEON'S FIRST SHELL IS LARGER BECAUSE OF THE WEAKER NUCLEAR CHARGE.

b. Which has a greater nuclear charge, Ne or Na?

SODIUM, Na

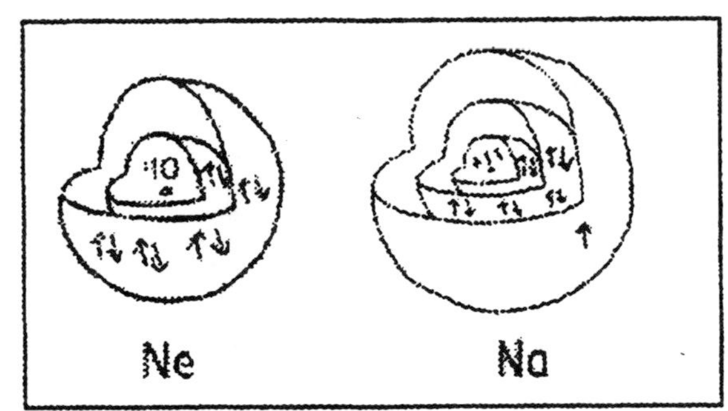

c. Which is a larger atom, Ne or Na?

SODIUM, BUT NOT BECAUSE OF A GREATER NUCLEAR CHARGE, BUT BECAUSE OF THE EXTRA SHELL OF ELECTRONS.

4. Moving from left to right across the periodic table, what happens to the nuclear charge within atoms? What happens to atomic size?

THE NUCLEAR CHARGE INCREASES FROM LEFT TO RIGHT ACROSS THE PERIODIC TABLE, WHICH IS WHY THE ATOMIC SIZE DECREASES.

5. Moving from top to bottom down the periodic table, what happens to the number of occupied shells? What happens to atomic size?

MOVING DOWN A GROUP, THE NUMBER OF OCCUPIED SHELLS INCREASES, WHICH IS WHY THE ATOMIC SIZE ALSO INCREASES.

6. Where in the periodic table are the smallest atoms found? Where are the largest atoms found?

THE SMALLEST ATOMS ARE FOUND TO THE UPPER RIGHT WHILE THE LARGEST ATOMS ARE FOUND TO THE LOWER LEFT.

The Nature of Chemical Bonds

Effective Nuclear Charge

The magnitude of the nuclear charge sensed by an orbiting electron depends upon several factors, including the number of positively–charged protons in the nucleus, the number of inner shell electrons shielding it from the nucleus, and its distance from the nucleus.

1. Place the proper number of electrons in each shell for carbon and silicon (use arrows to represent electrons).

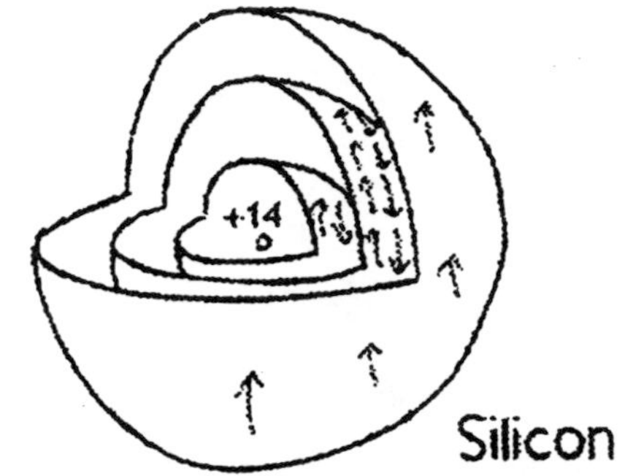

2. According to the shell model, which should experience the greater effective nuclear charge: an electron in

a. carbon's 1st shell or (silicon's 1st shell?) (circle one)

b. carbon's 2nd shell or (silicon's 2nd shell?) (circle one)

c. (carbon's 2nd shell) or silicon's 3rd shell? (circle one)

3. List the shells of carbon and silicon in order of decreasing effective nuclear charge.

SILICON'S 1ST > SILICON'S 2ND > CARBON'S 1ST > CARBON'S 2ND > SILICON'S 3RD

$\sim+14$ | $\sim+12$ | $\sim+6$ | $\sim+4$ | $\leq+4$

4. Which should have the greater ionization energy, the carbon atom or the silicon atom?

Defend your answer. THE CARBON ATOM BECAUSE ITS OUTERMOST ELECTRON IS EXPERIENCING A GREATER EFFECTIVE NUCLEAR CHARGE.

5. How many additional electrons are able to fit in the outermost shell of carbon? 4 silicon? 4

6. Which should be stronger, a (C-H bond) or an Si-H bond? Defend your answer. C-H IS STRONGER. THEIR VALENCE ELECTRONS EXPERIENCE A GREATER EFFECTIVE NUCLEAR CHARGE, HENCE, THEY ARE HELD TIGHTER.

7. Which should be larger in size, the (ion C^{41}) or the ion Si^{41}? Why?

THE ARRANGEMENTS OF ELECTRONS ARE THE SAME. SILICON, HOWEVER, HAS A GREATER NUCLEAR CHARGE, WHICH PULLS ELECTRONS INWARD MAKING S^{4+} SMALLER.

The Nature of Chemical Bonds

Solutions

1. Use these terms to complete the following sentences. Some terms may be used more than once.

solution	**solvent**	**solute**
dissolve	**concentrated**	**dilute**
saturated	**concentration**	**mole**
molarity	**solubility**	**soluble**
insoluble	**precipitate**	

Sugar is __SOLUBLE__ in water for the two can be mixed homogeneously to form a __SOLUTION__. The __SOLUBILITY__ of sugar in water is so great that __CONCENTRATED__ homogeneous mixtures are easily prepared. Sugar, however, is not infinitely __SOLUBLE__ in water for when too much of this __SOLUTE__ is added to water, which behaves as the __SOLVENT__, the solution becomes __SATURATED__. At this point any additional sugar is __INSOLUBLE__ for it will not __DISSOLVE__. If the temperature of a saturated sugar solution is lowered, the __SOLUBILITY__ of the sugar in water is also lowered. If some of the sugar comes out of solution, it is said to form a __PRECIPITATE__. If, however, the sugar remains in solution despite the decrease in solubility, then the solution is said to be supersaturated. Adding only a small amount of sugar to water results in a __DILUTE__ solution. The __CONCENTRATION__ of this solution or any solution can be measured in terms of __MOLARITY__, which tells us the number of solute molecules per liter of solution. If there are 6.022×10^{23} molecules in 1 liter of solution, then the __CONCENTRATION__ of the solution is 1 __MOLE__ per liter.

2. Temperature has a variety of effects on the solubilities of various solutes. With some solutes, such as sugar, solubility increases with increasing temperature. With other solutes, such as sodium chloride (table salt), changing temperature has no significant effect. With some solutes, such as lithium sulfate, Li_2SO_4, the solubility actually decreases with increasing temperature.

a. Describe how you would prepare a supersaturated solution of lithium sulfate.

FORM A SATURATED SOLUTION AND THEN SLOWLY RAISE THE TEMPERATURE

b. How might you cause a saturated solution of lithium sulfate to form a precipitate?

INCREASE ITS TEMERATURE

The Nature of Chemical Bonds

Pure Mathematics

Using a scientist's definition of *pure*, identity whether each of the following is 100% pure:

	100% pure?
Freshly squeezed orange juice. . .	Yes (No)
Country air.	Yes (No)
Ocean water.	Yes (No)
Fresh drinking water	Yes (No)
Skim milk	Yes (No)
Stainless steel	Yes (No)
A single water molecule	(Yes) No

A glass of water contains on the order of a trillion trillion (1×10^{24}) molecules. If the water in this were 99.9999% pure, you could calculate the percent of impurities by subtracting from 100.0000%.

$$\begin{array}{r} 100.0000\% \text{ water} + \text{impurity molecules} \\ -\ 99.9999\% \text{ water molecules} \\ \hline 0.0001\% \text{ impurity molecules} \end{array}$$

Pull out your calculator and calculate the number of impurity molecules in the glass of water. Do this by finding 0.0001% of 1×10^{24}, which is the same as multiplying 1×10^{24} by 0.000001.

$$(1 \times 10^{24})(0.000001) = \underline{\quad 1 \times 10^{18} \quad}$$

1. How many impurity molecules are there in a glass of water that's 99.9999% pure?
   a. 1000 (one thousand: 10^3)
   b. 1,000,000 (one million: 10^6)
   c. 1,000,000,000 (one billion: 10^9)
   (d.) 1,000,000,000,000,000,000 (one million trillion: 10^{18}).
2. How does your answer make you feel about drinking water that is 99.9999 percent free of some poison, such as pesticide?
   THAT THERE ARE A MILLION TRILLION POISON MOLECULES IN A GLASS OF WATER MIGHT MAKE ONE HESITATE . . . BUT READ ON!
3. For every one impurity molecule, how many water molecules are there? (Divide the number of water molecules by the number of impurity molecules.)
   $10^{24}/10^{18} = 10^6 = 1{,}000{,}000 =$ one million
4. Would you describe these impurity molecules within water that's 99.9999% pure as "rare" or "common"?
   FOR EVERY ONE IMPURITY MOLECULE THERE ARE ONE MILLION WATER MOLECULES. ONE IN A MILLION IS RARE!
5. A friend argues that he or she doesn't drink tap water because it contains thousands of molecules of some impurity in each glass. How would you respond in defense of the water's purity, if it indeed does contain thousands of molecules of some impurity per glass?
   ONLY 1,000 IMPURITY MOLECULES IN THIS GLASS OF WATER WOULD MAKE THIS WATER INCREDIBLY PURE . . . ABOUT 99.9999999999999999999% PURE!

The Nature of Chemical Bonds

Chemical Bonds

1. Based upon their positions in the periodic table, predict whether each pair of elements will form an ionic bond, covalent bond, or neither (atomic number in parenthesis).

a. Gold (79) and platinum (78) __N__

b. Rubidium (37) and iodine (53) __C__

c. Sulfur (16) and chlorine (17) __I__

d. Sulfur (16) and magnesium (12) __N__

e. Calcium (20) and chlorine (17) __C__

f. Germanium (32) and arsenic (33) __I__

g. Iron (26) and chromium (24) __I__

h. Chlorine (17) and iodine (53) __C__

i. Carbon (6) and bromine (35) __C__

j. Barium (56) and astatine (85) __I__

2. The most common ions of lithium, magnesium, aluminum, chlorine, oxygen, and nitrogen and their respective charges are as follows:

Positively Charged Ions	Negatively Charged Ions
Lithium ion: Li^{1+}	Chloride ion: Cl^{1-}
Barium ion: Ba^{2+}	Oxide ion: O^{2-}
Aluminum ion: Al^{3+}	Nitride ion: N^{3-}

Use this information to predict the chemical formulas for the following ionic compounds:

a. Lithium chloride: $LiCl$

b. Barium chloride: Li_2O

c. Aluminum chloride: Li_3O

d. Lithium oxide: $BaCl_2$

e. Barium oxide: BaO

f. Aluminum oxide: Ba_3N_2

g. Lithium nitride: $AlCl_2$

h. Barium nitride: Al_2O_3

i. Aluminum nitride: AlN

j. How are elements that form positive ions grouped in the periodic table relative to elements that form negative ions? POSITIVE ION ELEMENTS TOWARD THE LEFT AND NEGATIVE IONS TOWARD THE RIGHT.

3. Specify whether the following chemical structures are polar or nonpolar:

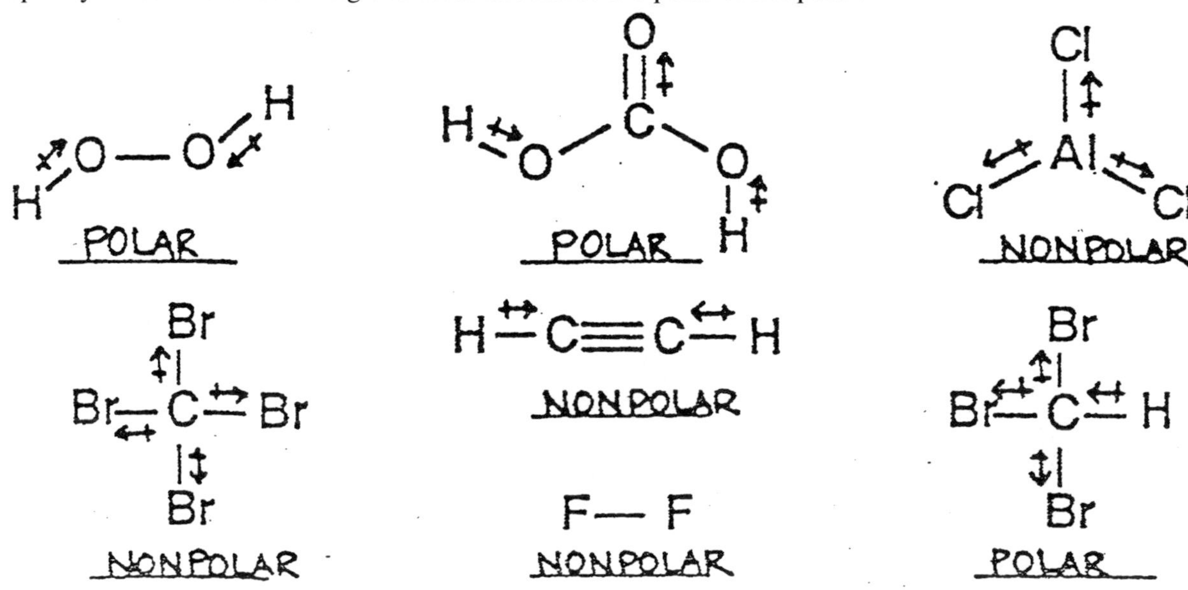

The Nature of Chemical Bonds

Shells and the Covalent Bond

When atoms bond covalently, their atomic shells overlap so that shared electrons can occupy both shells at the same time.

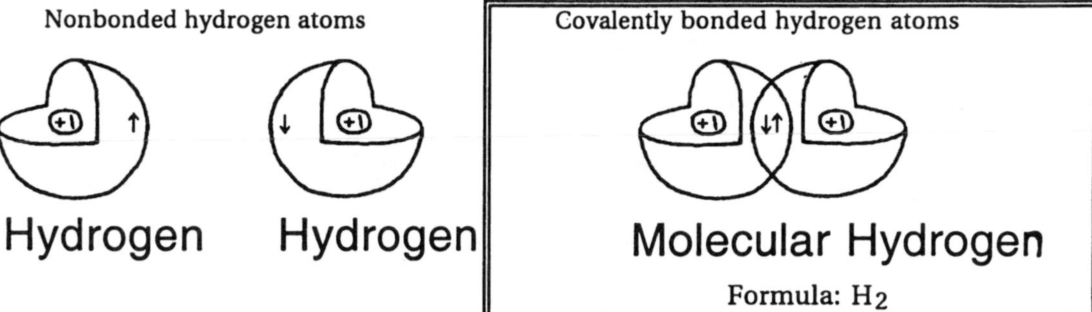

Fill each shell model shown below with enough electrons to make each atom electrically neutral. Use arrows to represent electrons. Within the box draw a sketch showing how the two atoms bond covalently. Draw hydrogen shells more than once when necessary so that no electrons remain unpaired. Write the name and chemical formula for each compound.

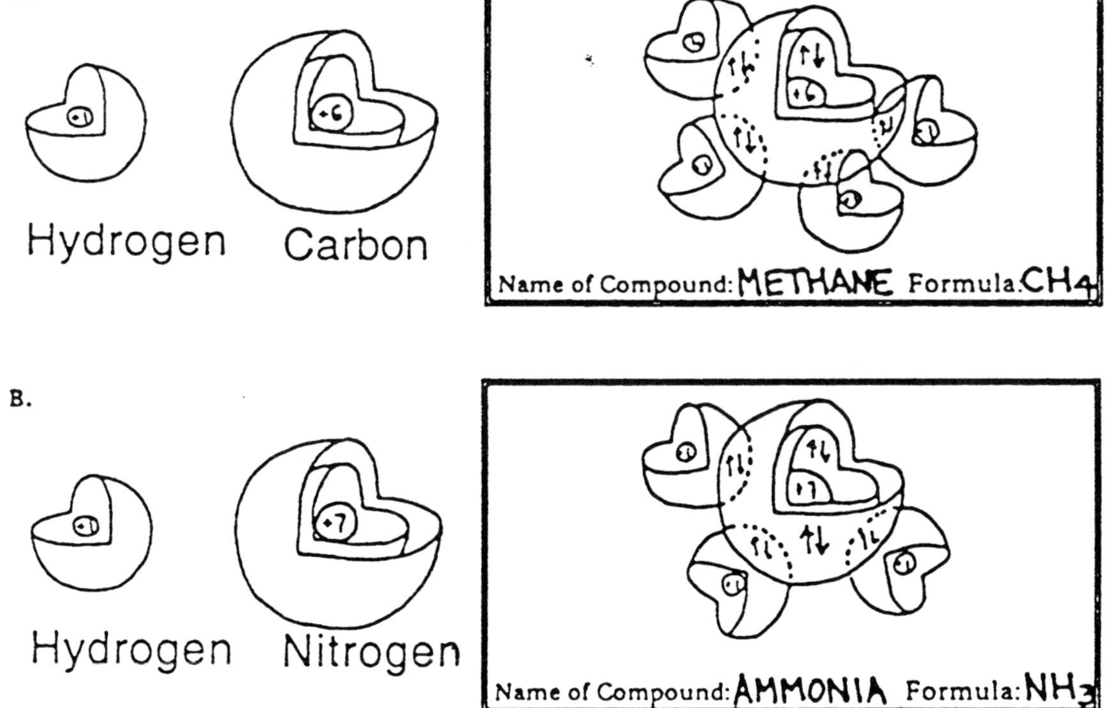

Shells and the Covalent Bond—continued

C.

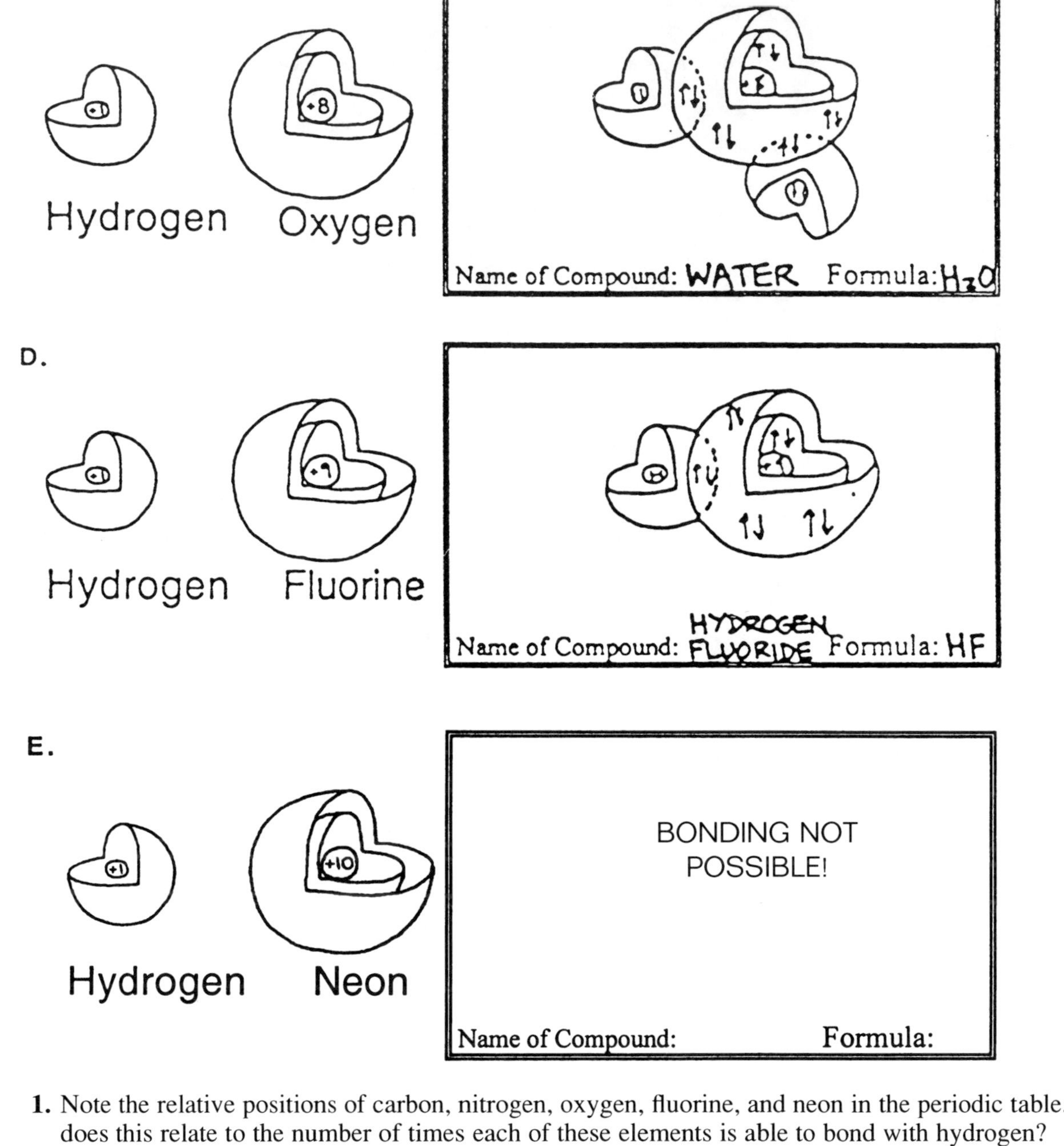

1. Note the relative positions of carbon, nitrogen, oxygen, fluorine, and neon in the periodic table. How does this relate to the number of times each of these elements is able to bond with hydrogen?

   IT'S IN A DESCENDING ORDER FROM LEFT TO RIGHT.

2. How many times is the element boron (atomic number 5) able to bond with hydrogen? Use the shell model to help you with your answer.

   ONLY 3 VALENCE ELECTRONS, THEREFORE, ONLY 3 BONDS

The Nature of Chemical Bonds

Bond Polarity

Pretend you are one of two electrons being shared by a hydrogen atom and a fluorine atom. Say, for the moment, you are centrally located between the two nuclei. You find that both nuclei are attracted to you. Hence, because of your presence, the two nuclei are held together.

You are here.

H : F

1. Why are the nuclei of these atoms attracted to you? BECAUSE OF YOUR NEGATIVE CHARGE
2. What type of chemical bonding is this? COVALENT

You are held within hydrogen's 1st shell and at the same time within fluorine's 2nd shell. Draw a sketch using the shell models below to show how this is possible. Represent yourself and all other electrons using arrows. Note your particular location with a circle.

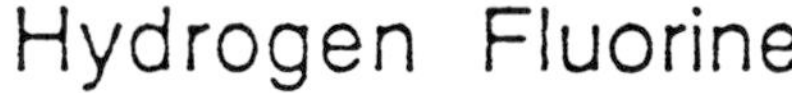

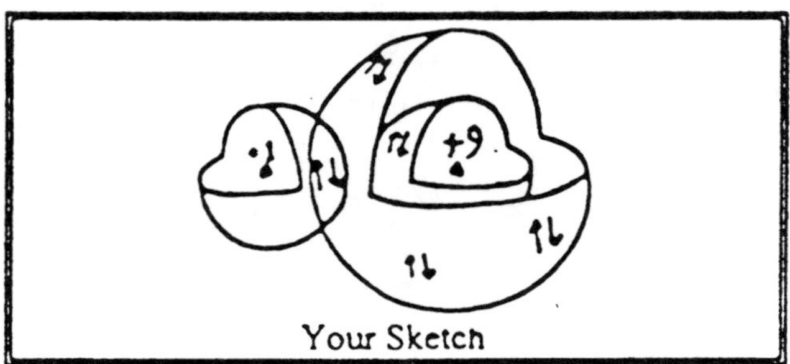

According to the laws of physics, if the nuclei are both attracted to you, then you are attracted to both of the nuclei.

3. You are pulled toward the hydrogen nucleus, which has a positive charge. How strong is this charge from your point of view—what is its *electronegativity?* ~+1
4. You are also attracted to the fluorine nucleus. What is its electronegativity? ~+7

You are being shared by the hydrogen and fluorine nuclei. But as a moving electron you have some choice as to your location.

5. Consider the electronegativities you experience from both nuclei. Which nucleus would you tend to be closest to? FLUORINE

Bond Polarity—continued

Stop pretending you are an electron and observe the hydrogen-fluorine bond from outside the hydrogen fluoride molecule. Bonding electrons tend to congregate to one side because of the differences in effective nuclear charges. This makes one side slightly negative in character and the opposite side slightly positive. Indicate this on the following structure for hydrogen fluoride using the symbols δ- and δ+

H : F

By convention, bonding electrons are not shown. Instead, a line is simply drawn connecting the two bonded atoms. Indicate the slightly negative and positive ends.

6. Would you describe hydrogen fluoride as a polar or nonpolar molecule? POLAR
7. If two hydrogen fluoride molecules were thrown together, would they stick or repel? (Hint: What happens when you throw two small magnets together?) STICK
8. Place bonds between the hydrogen and fluorine atoms to show many hydrogen fluoride molecules grouped together. Each element should be bonded only once. Circle each molecule and indicate the slightly negative and slightly positive ends.

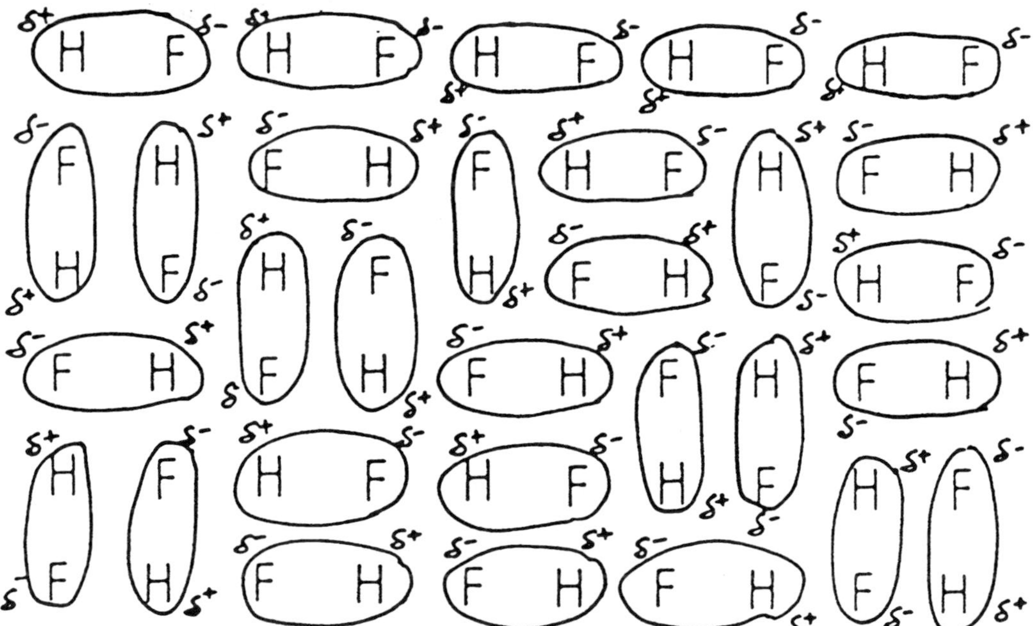

The Nature of Chemical Bonds

Atoms to Molecules

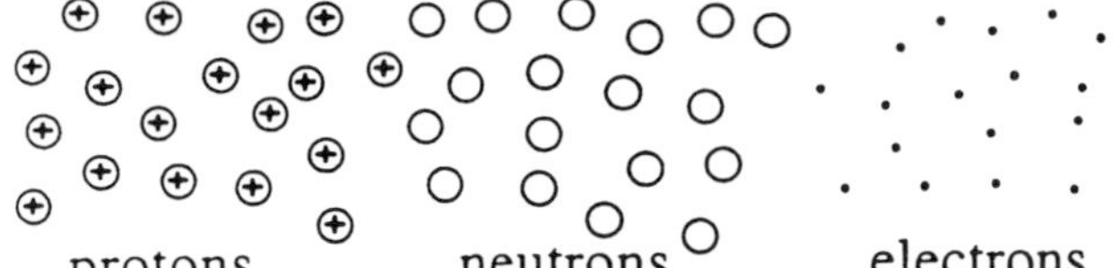

SUBATOMIC PARTICLES

Subatomic particles are the fundamental building blocks of all ATOMS.

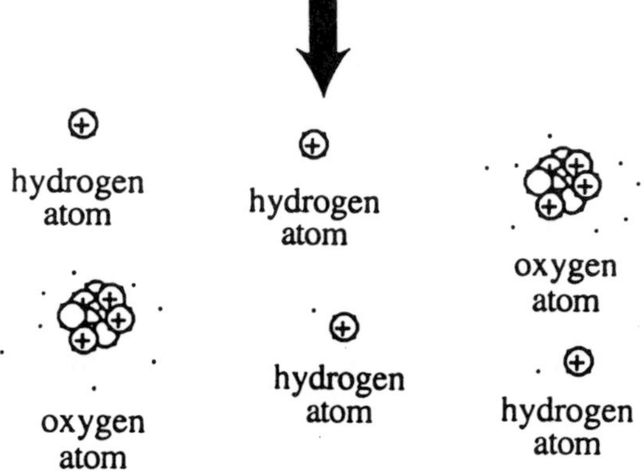

ATOMS

An atom is a group of SUBATOMIC PARTICLES held tightly together. An oxygen atom is a group of 8 PROTONS, 8 NEUTRONS, and 8 ELECTRONS. A hydrogen atom is a group of only 1 PROTON and 1 ELECTRON.

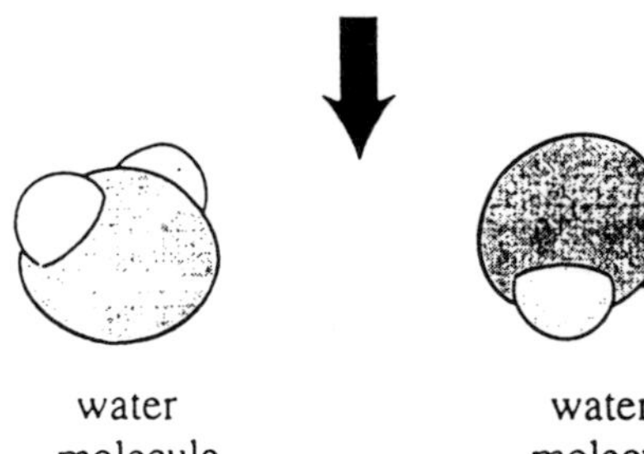

MOLECULES

A MOLECULE is a group of atoms held tightly together. A water MOLECULE consists of 2 OXYGEN atoms and 1 HYDROGEN atom.

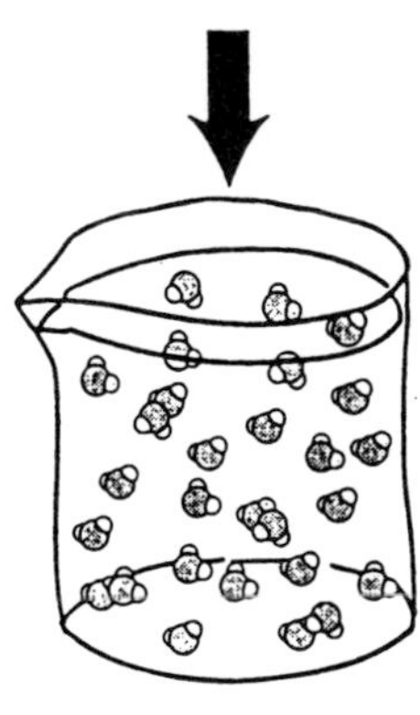

WATER

Water is a material made up of billions upon billions of water MOLECULES. The physical properties of water are based upon how these water MOLECULES interact with one another. The electronic attractions between MOLECULES is one of the major topics.

Answers to the Practice Test

1. C	2. C	3. E	4. E	5. B
6. D	7. B	8. B	9. A	10. E
11. C	12. D	13. A	14. E	15. B
16. A	17. D	18. C	19. D	20. A
21. E	22. E	23. D	24. C	25. B
26. A	27. E	28. C	29. E	30. C
31. E	32. A	33. B	34. A	35. C
36. A	37. A	38. B	39. C	40. D
41. B	42. A	43. C		

Answers and Solutions to Selected Text Problems

4.1 **a.** If a sodium atom loses its valence electron in the third energy level, its second energy level has a complete octet.

b. A neon atom has the same electronic arrangement as a sodium ion.

c. Group 1A (1) and Group 2A (2) elements do not have a stable octet until each has lost one or two electrons, respectively. Electrically charged ions are formed when electrons are lost, and these positively-charged ions are attracted to negatively-charged ions resulting in the formation of compounds. Group 8A (18) elements have stable octets while remaining electrically neutral, and thus have no tendency to form compounds.

4.3 Atoms with 1, 2, or 3 valence electrons lose those electrons to form ions.

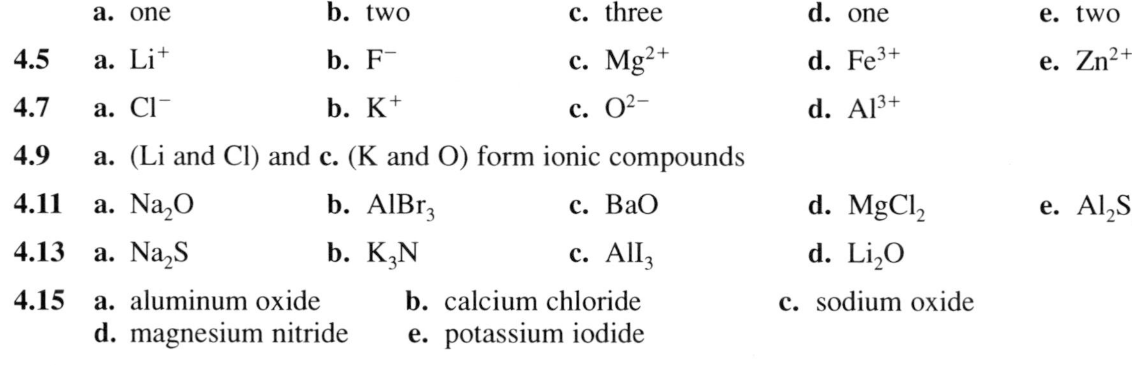

a. one **b.** two **c.** three **d.** one **e.** two

4.5 **a.** Li^+ **b.** F^- **c.** Mg^{2+} **d.** Fe^{3+} **e.** Zn^{2+}

4.7 **a.** Cl^- **b.** K^+ **c.** O^{2-} **d.** Al^{3+}

4.9 **a.** (Li and Cl) and **c.** (K and O) form ionic compounds

4.11 **a.** Na_2O **b.** $AlBr_3$ **c.** BaO **d.** $MgCl_2$ **e.** Al_2S_3

4.13 **a.** Na_2S **b.** K_3N **c.** AlI_3 **d.** Li_2O

4.15 **a.** aluminum oxide **b.** calcium chloride **c.** sodium oxide
d. magnesium nitride **e.** potassium iodide

4.17 The Roman numeral is used to specify the positive charge on the transition metal in the compound. It is necessary for most transition metal compounds because many transition metals can exist as more than one cation; transition metals have variable ionic charges.

4.19 **a.** iron(II) **b.** copper(II) **c.** zinc **d.** lead(IV) **e.** chromium(III)

4.21 **a.** tin(II) chloride **b.** iron(II) oxide **c.** copper(I) sulfide
d. copper(II) sulfide **e.** chromium(III) bromide

4.23 **a.** Au^{3+} **b.** Fe^{3+} **c.** Pb^{4+} **d.** Sn^{2+}

4.25 **a.** $MgCl_2$ **b.** Na_2S **c.** Cu_2O
d. Zn_3P_2 **e.** AuN **f.** $CrCl_2$

4.27 **a.** HCO_3^- **b.** NH_4^+ **c.** PO_4^{3-} **d.** HSO_4^-

4.29 **a.** sulfate **b.** carbonate **c.** phosphate **d.** nitrate

4.31	OH^-	NO_2^-	CO_3^{2-}	HSO_4^-	PO_4^{3-}
Li^+	$LiOH$	$LiNO_2$	Li_2CO_3	$LiHSO_4$	Li_3PO_4
Cu^{2+}	$Cu(OH)_2$	$Cu(NO_2)_2$	$CuCO_3$	$Cu(HSO_4)_2$	$Cu_3(PO_4)_2$
Ba^{2+}	$Ba(OH)_2$	$Ba(NO_2)_2$	$BaCO_3$	$Ba(HSO_4)_2$	$Ba_3(PO_4)_2$

4.33 **a.** CO_3^{2-}, sodium carbonate **b.** NH_4^+, ammonium chloride
c. PO_4^{3-}, lithium phosphate **d.** NO_2^-, copper(II) nitrite
e. SO_3^{2-}, iron(II) sulfite

4.35 **a.** $Ba(OH)_2$ **b.** Na_2SO_4 **c.** $Fe(NO_3)_2$ **d.** $Zn_3(PO_4)_2$ **e.** $Fe_2(CO_3)_3$

4.37 **a.** $:\underset{..}{\ddot{Br}}:\underset{..}{\ddot{Br}}:$ **b.** $H:H$ **c.** $H:\underset{..}{\ddot{F}}:$ **d.** $\begin{array}{c} :\underset{..}{\ddot{F}}:\ddot{O}: \\ \quad :\underset{..}{F}: \end{array}$

4.39 **a.** phosphorus tribromide **b.** carbon tetrabromide **c.** silicon dioxide
d. hydrogen fluoride

4.41 **a.** dinitrogen trioxide **b.** nitrogen trichloride **c.** silicon tetrabromide
d. phosphorus pentachloride

4.43 **a.** CCl_4 **b.** CO **c.** PCl_3 **d.** N_2O_4

4.45 **a.** OF_2 **b.** BF_3 **c.** N_2O_3 **d.** SF_6

4.47 **a.** This is an ionic compound with Al^{3+} ion and the sulfate SO_4^{2-} polyatomic ion. The correct name is aluminum sulfate.

b. This is an ionic compound with Ca^{2+} ion and the carbonate CO_3^{2-} polyatomic ion. The correct name is calcium carbonate.

c. This is a covalent compound because it contains two nonmetals. Using prefixes, it is named dinitrogen oxide.

d. This is an ionic compound with sodium ion Na^+ and the PO_4^{3-} polyatomic ion. The correct name is sodium phosphate.

e. This ionic compound contains two polyatomic ions ammonium NH_4^+ and sulfate SO_4^{2-}. It is named ammonium sulfate.

f. This is an ionic compound containing the variable metal ion Fe^{3+} and oxide ion O^{2-}. It is named using the Roman numeral as iron(III) oxide.

4.49 The electronegativity increases going across a period.

4.51 A nonpolar covalent bond would have an electronegativity difference of 0.0 to 0.4.

4.53 **a.** Si—Br electronegativity difference 1.0, polar covalent

b. Li—F electronegativity difference 3.0, ionic

c. Br—F electronegativity difference 1.2, polar covalent

d. Br—Br electronegativity difference 0, nonpolar covalent

e. N—P electronegativity difference 0.9, polar covalent

f. C—P electronegativity difference 0.4, nonpolar covalent

4.55 **a.** $\overset{\delta+}{N}-\overset{\delta-}{F}$ $\overset{+}{\longrightarrow}$ **b.** $\overset{\delta+}{Si}-\overset{\delta-}{Br}$ $\overset{+}{\longrightarrow}$ **c.** $\overset{\delta+}{C}-\overset{\delta-}{O}$ $\overset{+}{\longrightarrow}$

d. $\overset{\delta+}{P}-\overset{\delta-}{Br}$ $\overset{+}{\longrightarrow}$ **e.** $\overset{\delta+}{B}-\overset{\delta-}{Cl}$ $\overset{+}{\longrightarrow}$

4.57 Tetrahedral. Four atoms bonded to the central atom form a tetrahedron.

4.59 The four electron groups in PCl_3 have a tetrahedral arrangement, but three bonded atoms around a central atom give a pyramidal shape.

4.61 In the electron-dot formula of PH_3, the central atom P has three bonded atoms and one lone pair, which give PH_3 a pyramidal shape. In the molecule NH_3, the central atom N is bonded to three atoms and one lone pair. The structure of the electron groups is tetrahedral, which gives NH_3 a pyramidal shape.

4.63 **a.** The central oxygen atom has four electron pairs with two bonded to fluorine atoms. Its shape is bent with 109° angles.

b. The central atom C is bonded to four chlorine atoms; CCl_4 has a tetrahedral shape.

4.65 Cl_2 is a nonpolar molecule because there is a nonpolar covalent bond between Cl atoms, which have identical electronegativity values. In HCl, the bond is a polar covalent bond, which is a dipole and makes HCl a polar molecule.

4.67 **a.** polar **b.** dipoles do not cancel; polar

c. four dipoles cancel; nonpolar

4.69 **a.** 2, 8 **b.** 2, 8 **c.** 2, 8 **d.** 2, 8 **e.** 2

4.71 **a.** Chlorine in Group 7A (17) gains one electron to form chloride ion Cl^-.

b. Potassium in Group 1A (1) loses one electron to form potassium ion K^+.

c. Oxygen in Group 6A (16) gains two electrons to form oxide ion O^{2-}.

d. Aluminum in Group 3A (13) loses three electrons to form aluminum ion Al^{3+}.

4.73 **a.** potassium ion **b.** sulfide ion **c.** calcium ion **d.** nitride ion

4.75 **a.** Ions: Co^{3+} and Cl^- $\rightarrow$ $CoCl_3$

b. Ions: Pb^{4+} and O^{2-} $\rightarrow$ PbO_2

c. Ions: Ag^+ and Cl^- $\rightarrow$ AgCl

d. Ions: Ca^{2+} and N^{3-} $\rightarrow$ Ca_3N_2

e. Ions: Cu^+ and P^{3-} $\rightarrow$ Cu_3P

f. Ions: Cr^{2+} and Cl^- $\rightarrow$ $CrCl_2$

4.77 **a.** 1 N and 3 Cl $\rightarrow$ nitrogen trichloride

b. 1 S and 2 Cl $\rightarrow$ sulfur dichloride

c. 2 N and 1 O $\rightarrow$ dinitrogen monoxide

d. 2 F $\rightarrow$ fluorine (named as the element)

e. 1 P and 5 Cl $\rightarrow$ phosphorus pentachloride

f. 2 P and 5 O $\rightarrow$ diphosphorus pentoxide

4.79 **a.** 1 C and 1 O $\rightarrow$ CO

b. di(2) and penta (5) $\rightarrow$ P_2O_5

c. di(2) and 1 S $\rightarrow$ H_2S

d. 1 S and di(2) Cl $\rightarrow$ SCl_2

4.81 **a.** ionic, iron(III) chloride

b. ionic, sodium sulfate

c. covalent, 2 N and 1 O $\rightarrow$ dinitrogen oxide

d. covalent, fluorine (named as the element)

e. covalent, 1 P and 5 Cl $\rightarrow$ phosphorus pentachloride

f. covalent, 1 C and 4 F $\rightarrow$ carbon tetrafluoride

4.83 **a.** Tin(II) is Sn^{2+}; carbonate is CO_3^{2-}. With charges balanced the formula is $SnCO_3$.

b. Lithium is Li^+; phosphide is P^{3-}. Using three Li^+ for charge balance, the formula is Li_3P.

c. Silicon has 4 valence electrons to share with four chlorine atoms to give $SiCl_4$.

d. Iron(III) is Fe^{3+}; sulfide is S^{2-}. Charge is balanced with two Fe^{3+} and three S^{2-} to write the formula Fe_2S_3.

e. Carbon has 4 valence electrons to form two double bonds with two oxygen atoms to give the formula CO_2.

f. Calcium is Ca^{2+}; bromide is Br^-. With charges balanced the formula is $CaBr_2$.

4.85 Determine the difference in electronegativity values:

a. C—O (1.0) C—N is less (0.5)

b. N—F (1.0) N—Br is less (0.2)

c. S—Cl (0.5) Br—Cl is less (0.2)

d. Br—I (0.3) Br—Cl is less (0.2)

e. C—O (1.0) C—S is less (0)

4.87 A dipole arrow points from the atom with the lower electronegativity value (more positive) to the atom in the bond that has the higher electronegativity value (more negative).

a. Si has the lower electronegativity value of 1.8 making Si the positive end of the dipole. The Cl atom has a higher electronegativity value of 3.0.

Si—Cl
$\longmapsto$

b. C has the lower electronegativity value of 2.5 making C the positive end of the dipole. The N atom has a higher electronegativity value of 3.0.

C—N
$\longmapsto$

c. Cl has the lower electronegativity value of 3.0 making Cl the positive end of the dipole. The F atom has a higher electronegativity value of 4.0.

F—Cl
$\longmapsto$

d. C has the lower electronegativity value of 2.5 making C the positive end of the dipole. The F atom has a higher electronegativity value of 4.0.

C—F
$\longmapsto$

e. N has the lower electronegativity value of 3.0 making N the positive end of the dipole. The O atom has a higher electronegativity value of 3.5.

N—O
$\longmapsto$

4.89 **a.** polar covalent (Cl 3.0 − Si 1.8 = 1.2)

b. nonpolar covalent (C 2.5 − C 2.5 = 0.0)

c. ionic (Cl 3.0 − Na 0.9 = 2.1)

d. nonpolar covalent (C 2.5 − H 2.1 = 0.4)

e. nonpolar covalent (F 4.0 − F 4.0 = 0.0)

4.91 **a.** Polar. A molecule with three bonded atoms with a lone pair is polar.

b. Polar.

c. Nonpolar. There are four equal Si-F bonds (four dipoles) in opposing directions in a tetrahedron. Thus, dipoles cancel and the molecule is nonpolar.

4.93 **a.** pyramidal, dipoles do not cancel, polar

b. bent, dipoles do not cancel, polar

4.95 **a.** bent, dipoles do not cancel, polar

b. pyramidal, dipoles do not cancel, polar

Answers to Understanding the Concepts

4.97 **a.** P^{3-} ion **b.** O atom **c.** Zn^{2+} ion **d.** Fe^{3+} ion

4.99 **a.** 2–pyramidal, polar **b.** 1–bent, polar **c.** 3–tetradral, nonpolar

4.101 **1.** H (E) **2.** Li (C) **3.** Li^{+} (A)
4. H^{+} (B) **5.** N^{3-} (D)

Chapter 5

Key Terms

Answers **1.** d **2.** a **3.** e **4.** c **5.** b

5.1 Chemical Changes

◆ Learning Exercise 5.1

Answers **1.** P **2.** C **3.** C **4.** C **5.** P **6.** P **7.** P **8.** C

5.2 Chemical Equations

◆ Learning Exercise 5.2A

Answers

a. $CaCO_3\ (s) \rightarrow CaO\ (g) + CO_2\ (g)$

Element	Atoms on reactant side	Atoms on product side
Ca	1	1
C	1	1
O	3	3

b. $2Na\ (s) + H_2O\ (l) \rightarrow Na_2O\ (s) + H_2(g)$

Element	Atoms on reactant side	Atoms on product side
Na	2	2
H	2	2
O	1	1

c. $C_5H_{12}\ (g) + 8O_2\ (g) \rightarrow 5CO_2\ (g) + 6H_2O\ (g)$

Element	Atoms on reactant side	Atoms on product side
C	5	5
H	12	12
O	16	16

d. $2AgNO_3\ (aq) + K_2S\ (aq) \rightarrow 2KNO_3\ (aq) + Ag_2S\ (s)$

Element	Atoms on reactant side	Atoms on product side
Ag	2	2
N	2	2
O	6	6
K	2	2
S	1	1

e. $2Al(OH)_3\ (aq) + 3H_2SO_4\ (aq) \rightarrow Al_2(SO_4)_3\ (s) + 6H_2O\ (l)$

Element	Atoms on reactant side	Atoms on product side
Al	2	2
O	18	18
H	12	12
S	3	3

◆ Learning Exercise 5.2B

Answers

a. $2MgO(s) \rightarrow 2Mg(s) + O_2(g)$

b. $Zn(s) + 2HCl(aq) \rightarrow ZnCl_2(aq) + H_2(g)$

c. $2Al(s) + 3CuSO_4(aq) \rightarrow 3Cu(s) + Al_2(SO_4)_3(aq)$

d. $Al_2S_3(s) + 6H_2O(l) \rightarrow 2Al(OH)_3 + 3H_2S(g)$

e. $BaCl_2(aq) + Na_2SO_4 \rightarrow BaSO_4(s) + 2NaCl(aq)$

f. $3CO(g) + Fe_2O_3(s) \rightarrow 2Fe(s) + 3CO_2(g)$

g. $2K(s) + H_2O(l) \rightarrow K_2O(s) + H_2(g)$

h. $2Fe(OH)_3\ (a) \rightarrow Fe_2O_3(s) + 3H_2O(l)$

5.3 Types of Reactions

◆ Learning Exercise 5.3A

Answers **1.** a **2.** d **3.** b **4.** c **5.** a **6.** b **7.** b **8.** c

◆ Learning Exercise 5.3B

Answers **a.** $2Al(s) + 3Ag_2S(s) \rightarrow 6Ag(s) + Al_2S_3(s)$ **b.** single replacement

5.4 Oxidation–Reduction Reactions

◆ Learning Exercise 5.4

Answers

a. Al is oxidized to Al^{3+}; loss of electrons (addition of O)
b. Fe^{3+} is reduced to Fe^{2+}; gain of electrons
c. Cu^{2+} is reduced to Cu; gain of electrons (loss of O)

d. $2Cl^-$ is oxidized to Cl_2; loss of electrons
e. 2 Br^- is oxidized to Br_2; loss of electrons
f. Na is oxidized to Na^+; loss of electrons
g. Cu^{2+} is reduced to Cu; gain of electrons

5.5 The Mole

Learning Exercise 5.5A

Answers **a.** 9.03×10^{23} P atom **b.** 4.52×10^{22} H_2S molecules
c. 0.90 mole Ag **d.** 13.7 moles C_3H_8

Learning Exercise 5.5B

Answers **a.** 12 moles of carbon (C) **b.** 40. moles of hydrogen (H)
c. 9.0 moles of oxygen (O)

Learning Exercise 5.5C

Answers **a.** 28.6 moles of C **b.** 9 moles of H
c. 1.5 moles of O **d.** 2.0 moles of ibuprofen

5.6 Molar Mass

Learning Exercise 5.6A

Answers **a.** 94.2 g **b.** 133.5 g **c.** 206.0 g **d.** 58.0 g
e. 164.1 g **f.** 100.9 g **g.** 115.9 g **h.** 149.0 g

Learning Exercise 5.6B

Answers **a.** 6.41 g **b.** 9.81 g **c.** 42.5 g **d.** 40.0 g
e. 12.2 g **f.** 10.0 g **g.** 1380 g **h.** 12.8 g

Learning Exercise 5.6C

Answers **a.** 2.00 moles **b.** 10.0 moles **c.** 0.182 mole
d. 0.352 mole **e.** 0.00500 mole **f.** 0.0490 mole
g. 45.3 moles **h.** 0.032 mole

5.7 Mole Relationships in Chemical Equations

Learning Exercise 5.7A

Answers

$$\frac{1 \text{ mole } N_2}{1 \text{ mole } O_2} \text{ and } \frac{1 \text{ mole } O_2}{1 \text{ mole } N_2}; \frac{1 \text{ mole } N_2}{2 \text{ moles NO}} \text{ and } \frac{2 \text{ moles NO}}{1 \text{ mole } N_2}$$

$$\frac{1 \text{ mole } O_2}{2 \text{ moles NO}} \text{ and } \frac{2 \text{ moles NO}}{1 \text{ mole } O_2}$$

Learning Exercise 5.7B

Answers **a.** 10.0 moles O_2 **b.** 2.4 moles CO_2
c. 0.600 mole C_3H_8 **d.** 2.0 moles of H_2O

5.8 Energy in Chemical Reactions

◆ Learning Exercise 5.8

Answers: **1.** exothermic **2.** endothermic **3.** exothermic
4. exothermic **5.** exothermic

Chemical Reactions

Balancing Chemical Equations

In a balanced chemical equation the number of times each element appears as a reactant is equal to the number of times it appears as a product. For example,

$$2\ H_2 \quad + \quad O_2 \quad \text{--->} \quad 2\ H_2O$$

Recall that *coefficients* (the integer appearing before the chemical formula) indicate the number of times each chemical formula is to be counted and *subscripts* indicate when a particular element occurs more than once within the formula.

Check whether or not the following chemical equations are balanced.

$3\ NO$ ---> $N_2O + NO_2$ ☐ balanced ☐ unbalanced

$SiO_2 + 4\ HF$ ---> $SiF_4 + 2\ H_2O$ ☐ balanced ☐ unbalanced

$4\ NH_3 + 5\ O_2$ ---> $4\ NO + 6\ H_2O$ ☐ balanced ☐ unbalanced

Unbalanced equations are balanced by changing the coefficients. Subscripts, however, should never be changed because this changes the chemical's identity—H_2O is water, but H_2O_2 is hydrogen peroxide! The following steps may help guide you:

1. Focus on balancing only one element at a time. Start with the left-most element and modify the coefficients such that this element appears on both sides of the arrow the same number of times.
2. Move to the next element and modify the coefficients so as to balance this element. Do not worry if you incidentally unbalance the previous element. You will come back to it in subsequent steps.
3. Continue from left to right balancing each element individually.
4. Repeat steps 1–3 until all elements are balanced.

Use the above methodology to balance the following chemical equations.

1 N_2O + 6 N_2 ---> 4 O_2

2 $NaClO_3$ ---> 2 $NaCl$ + 3 O_2

3 $MnCl_2$ + 2 Al ---> 0 Mn + 2 $AlCl_3$

2 K + 2 H_2O ---> 1 H_2 + 2 KOH

2 Al_2O_3 + 3 C ---> 4 Al + 3 CO_2

4 NH_3 + 3 F_2 ---> 3 NH_4F + 1 NF_3

This is just one of the many methods that chemists have developed to balance chemical equations.

Knowing how to balance a chemical equation is a useful technique, but understanding why a chemical equation needs to be balanced in the first place is far more important.

Chemical Reactions

Exothermic and Endothermic Reactions

During a chemical reaction atoms are neither created nor destroyed. Instead, atoms rearrange—they change partners. This rearrangement of atoms necessarily involves the input and output of energy. First, energy must be supplied to break chemical bonds that hold atoms together. Separated atoms then form new chemical bonds, which involves the release of energy. In an **exothermic** reaction more energy is released than is consumed. Conversely, in an **endothermic** reaction more energy is consumed than is released.

Table 1 Bond Energies

Bond	Bond Energy*	Bond	Bond Energy*
H—H	436	Cl—Cl	243
H—C	414	N—N	159
H—N	389	O=O	498
H—O	464	O=C	803
H—Cl	431	N≡N	946

*In kJ/mol

Table 1 shows bond energies—the amount of energy required to break a chemical bond, and also the amount of energy released when a bond is formed. Use these bond energies to determine whether the following chemical reactions are exothermic or endothermic.

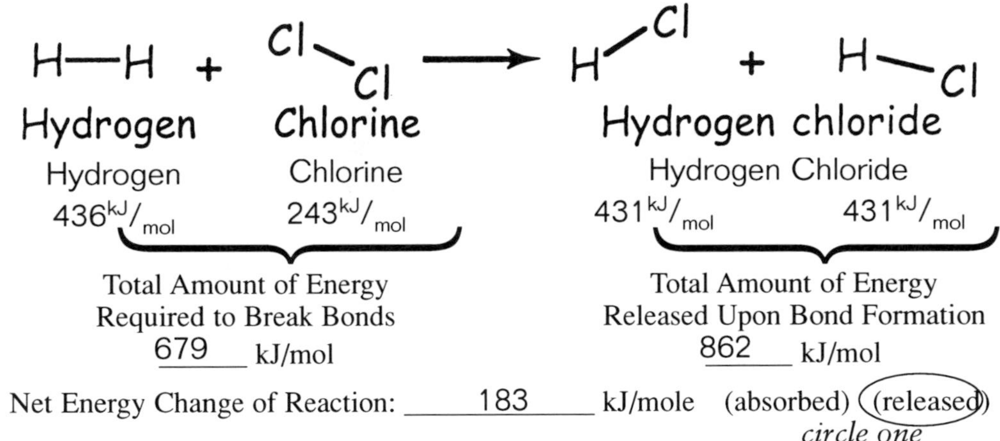

1. Is this reaction exothermic or endothermic? EXOTHERMIC
2. Write the balanced equation for this reaction using chemical formulas and coefficients. If it is exothermic, write "Energy" as a product. If it is endothermic, write "Energy" as a reactant.

$$H_2 + Cl_2 \longrightarrow 2\,HCl + \text{ENERGY}$$

Exothermic and Endothermic Reactions—continued

Methane + Oxygen → Carbon Dioxide + Water

Methane	Oxygen	Carbon Dioxide	Water
414 kJ/mol	498 kJ/mol	803 kJ/mol	464 kJ/mol
× 4	× 2	× 2	× 4
1656 kJ/mol	996 kJ/mol	1606 kJ/mol	1856 kJ/mol

Total Amount of Energy Required to Break Bonds 2652 kJ/mol

Total Amount of Energy Released Upon Bond Formation 3462 kJ/mol

Net Energy Change of Reaction: 810 kJ/mole (absorbed/released) *circle one*

3. Is this reaction exothermic or endothermic? EXOTHERMIC
4. Write the balanced equation for this reaction using chemical formulas and coefficients. If it is exothermic write "Energy" as a product. If it is endothermic write "Energy" as a reactant.

$$CH_4 + 2\ O_2 \longrightarrow CO_2 + 2\ H_2O + \text{ENERGY}$$

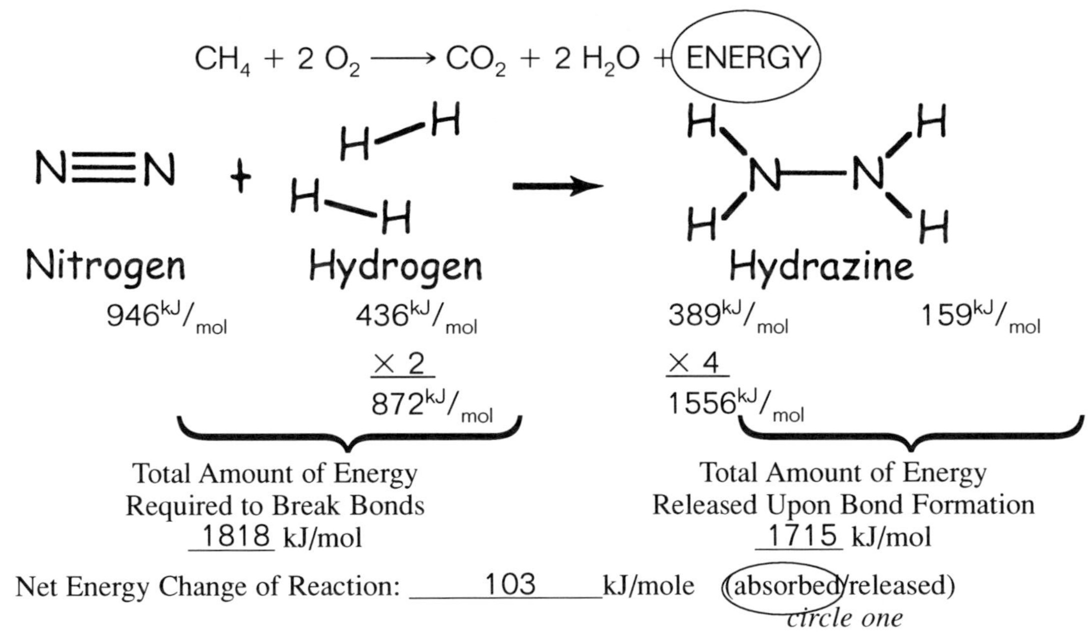

5. Is this reaction exothermic or endothermic? ENDOTHERMIC
6. Write the balanced equation for this reaction using chemical formulas and coefficients. If it is exothermic write "Energy" as a product. If it is endothermic write "Energy" as a reactant.

$$\text{ENERGY} + N_2 + 2\ H_2 \longrightarrow N_2H_4$$

Chemical Reactions

Donating and Accepting Hydrogen Ions

A chemical reaction that involves the transfer of a hydrogen ion from one molecule to another is classified as an acid-base reaction. The molecule that donates the hydrogen ion behaves as an acid. The molecule that accepts the hydrogen ion behaves as a base.

On paper, the acid-base process can be depicted through a series of frames:

Frame 1

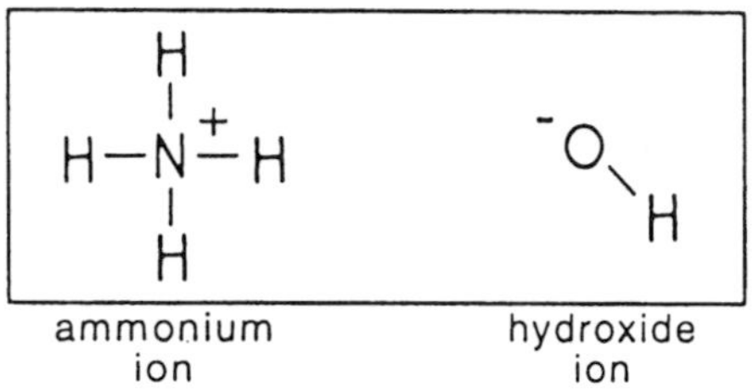

ammonium ion

hydroxide ion

Ammonium and hydroxide ions in close proximity.

Frame 2

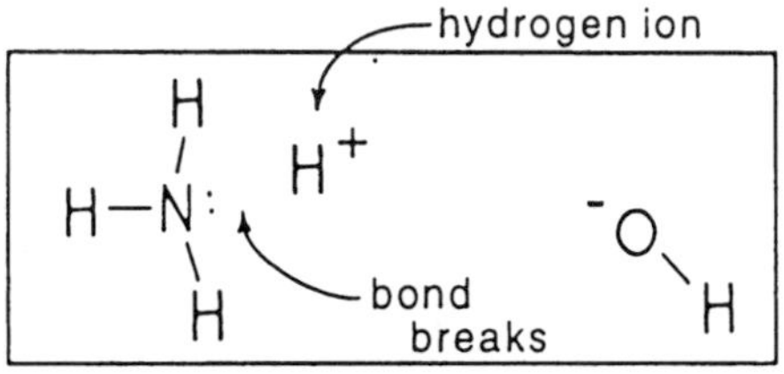

hydrogen ion

bond breaks

Bond is broken between the nitrogen and a hydrogen of the ammonium ion. The two electrons of the broken bond stay with the nitrogen leaving the hydrogen with a positive charge.

Frame 3

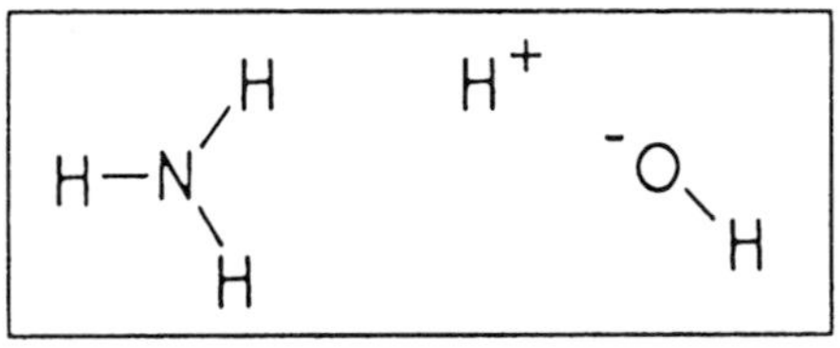

The hydrogen ion migrates to the hydroxide ion.

Frame 4

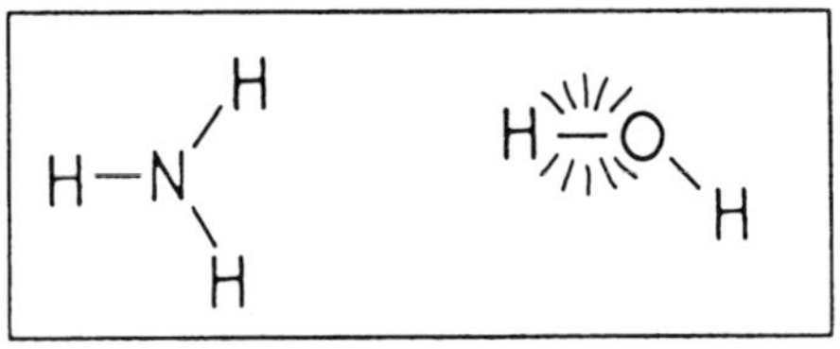

The hydrogen ion bonds with the hydroxide ion to form a water molecule.

In equation form we abbreviate this process by only showing the before and after:

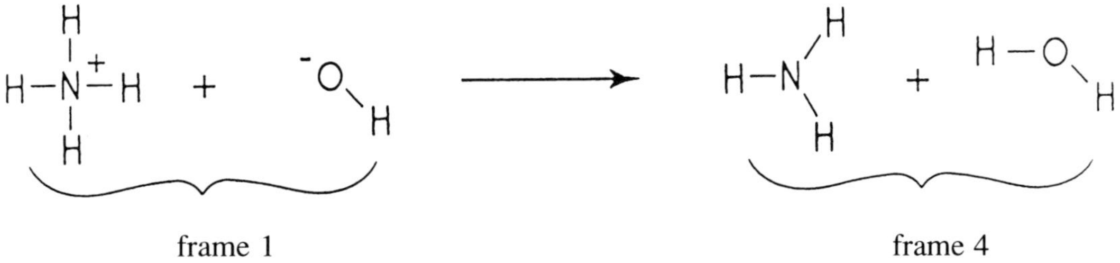

$$NH_4^+ + {}^-OH \longrightarrow NH_3 + H-O-H$$

frame 1

frame 4

Donating and Accepting Hydrogen Ions—continued

We see from the previous reaction that because the ammonium ion donated a hydrogen ion, it behaved as an acid. Conversely, the hydroxide ion by accepting a hydrogen ion behaved as a base. How do the ammonia and water molecules behave during the reverse process?

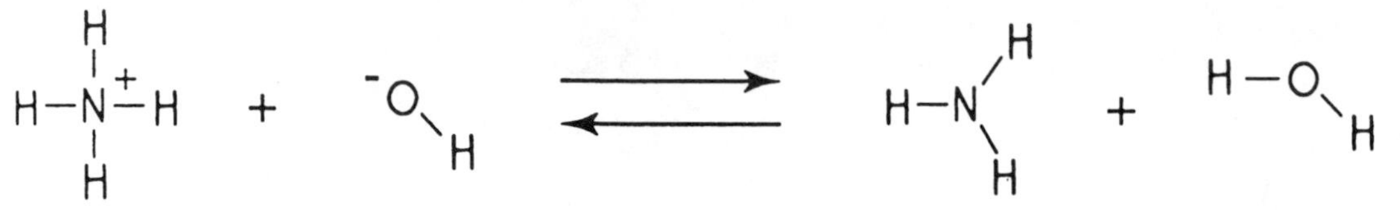

$$NH_4^+ + {}^-OH \rightleftharpoons NH_3 + H_2O$$

acid | base | BASE (ammonia) | ACID (water)

Identify the following molecules as behaving as an acid or a base:

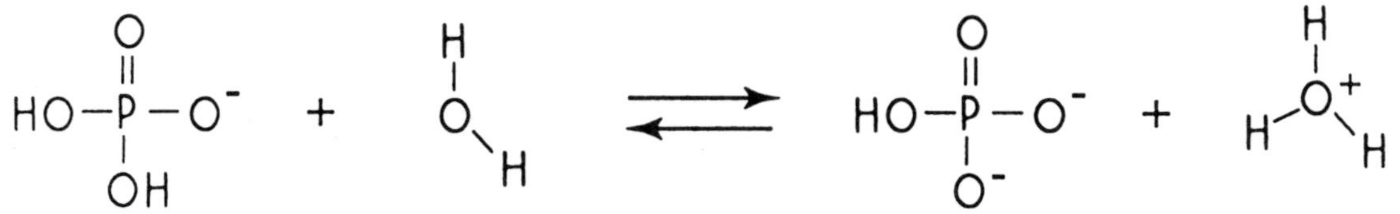

$$H_2PO_4^- + H_2O \rightleftharpoons HPO_4^{2-} + H_3O^+$$

ACID | BASE | BASE | ACID

$$NH_3 + NaH \rightleftharpoons Na^+\,{}^-NH_2 + H\text{-}H$$

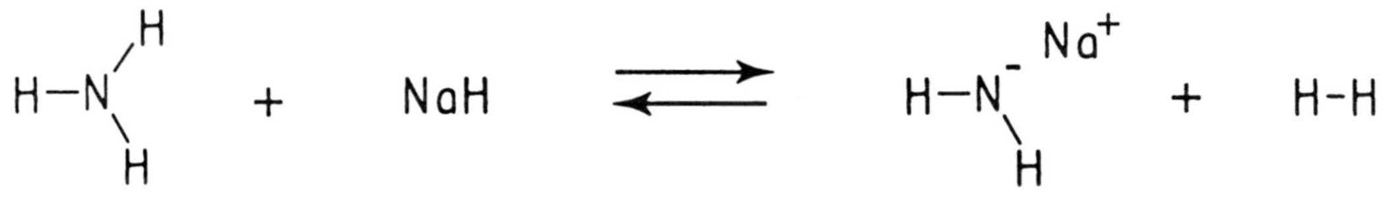

ACID | BASE | BASE | ACID

$$H\text{-}H + {}^-H \rightleftharpoons H^- + H\text{-}H$$

ACID | BASE | BASE | ACID

$$HNO_3 + NH_3 \rightleftharpoons {}^-NO_3 + {}^+NH_4$$

ACID | BASE | BASE | ACID

Chemical Reactions

Loss and Gain of Electrons

A chemical reaction that involves the transfer of an electron is classified as an oxidation–reduction reaction. Oxidation is the process of losing electrons, while reduction is the process of gaining them. Any chemical that causes another chemical to lose electrons (become oxidized) is called an *oxidizing agent*. Conversely, any chemical that causes another chemical to gain electrons is called a *reducing agent*.

1. What is the relationship between an atom's ability to behave as an oxidizing agent and its electron affinity?

   THE GREATER THE ELECTRON AFFINITY, THE GREATER ITS ABILITY TO BEHAVE AS AN OXIDIZING AGENT.

2. Relative to the periodic table, which elements tend to behave as strong oxidizing agents?

   THOSE TO THE UPPER RIGHT WITH THE EXCEPTION OF THE NOBLE GASES

3. Why don't the noble gases behave as oxidizing agents?

   THEY HAVE NO SPACE IN THEIR SHELLS TO ACCOMODATE ADDITIONAL ELECTRONS.

4. How is it that an oxidizing agent is itself reduced?

   REDUCTION IS THE GAINING OF ELECTRONS. IN PULLING AN ELECTRON AWAY FROM ANOTHER ATOM AN OXIDIZING AGENT NECESSARILY GAINS AN ELECTRON.

5. Specify whether each reactant is about to be oxidized or reduced.

   $2\ K$ (OX) + H_2O (RED) ⟶ $2\ K^+$ + ^-OH

   $2\ Mg$ (OX) + O_2 (RED) ⟶ $2\ Mg^{2+}O^{2-}$

   $2\ Na$ (OX) + Cl_2 (RED) ⟶ $2\ Na^+Cl^-$

   CH_4 (OX) + $2\ O_2$ (RED) ⟶ O=C=O + H–O–H

6. Which oxygen atom enjoys a greater negative charge?

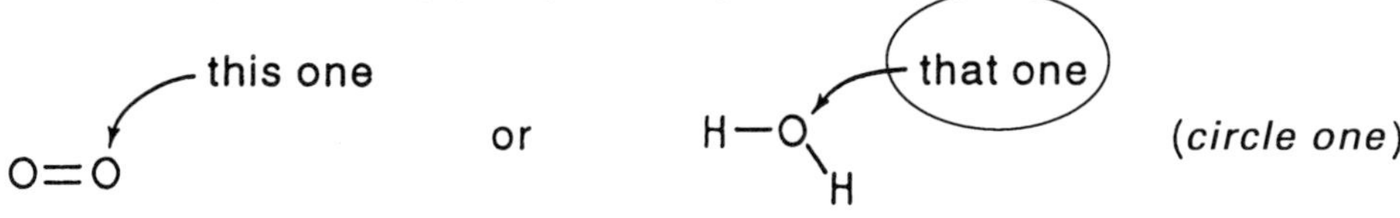

7. Relate your answer to Question 6 to how it is that O_2 is reduced upon reacting with CH_4 to form carbon dioxide and water.

   IN TRANSFORMING FROM O_2 TO H_2O, AN OXYGEN ATOM IS GAINING ELECTRONS AS BEST AS IT CAN. WITH ITS GREATER NEGATIVE CHARGE IT CAN BE THOUGHT OF AS "REDUCED."

Answers to the Practice Test

1. A	**2.** A	**3.** B	**4.** B	**5.** B
6. B	**7.** C	**8.** E	**9.** D	**10.** A
11. A	**12.** C	**13.** B	**14.** C	**15.** D
16. A	**17.** B	**18.** B	**19.** B	**20.** A
21. E	**22.** D	**23.** E	**24.** C	**25.** D
26. B	**27.** C	**28.** C	**29.** D	**30.** A
31. E	**32.** D	**33.** E	**34.** C	**35.** B
36. 1	**37.** 2	**38.** 1		

Answers and Solutions to Selected Text Problems

5.1 A chemical change occurs when the atoms of the initial substances rearrange to form new substances. Chemical change is indicated by a change in properties of the reactants. For example, a rusting nail, souring milk, and a burning match are all chemical changes.

a. physical: the shape changes, but not the substance
b. chemical: new substances form
c. physical: water evaporates forming gaseous water
d. chemical: the composition of the substances change to give new substances
e. physical: water freezes
f. chemical: new substances form

5.3 An equation is balanced when there are equal numbers of atoms of each element on the reactant as on the product side.

a. not balanced **b.** balanced **c.** not balanced **d.** balanced

5.5 Place coefficients in front of formulas until you make the atoms of each element equal on each side of the equation. Try starting with the formula that has subscripts.

a. $N_2(g) + O_2(g) \rightarrow 2NO(g)$ **b.** $2HgO(s) \rightarrow 2Hg(l) + O_2(g)$
c. $4Fe(s) + 3O_2(g) \rightarrow 2Fe_2O_3(s)$ **d.** $2Na(s) + Cl_2(g) \rightarrow 2NaCl(s)$
e. $2Cu_2O(s) + O_2(g) \rightarrow 4CuO(s)$

5.7 **a.** There are two NO_3 in the product. Balance by placing a 2 before $AgNO_3$.
$Mg(s) + 2AgNO_3(aq) \rightarrow Mg(NO_3)_2(aq) + 2Ag(s)$

b. Start with the formula $Al_2(SO_4)_3$. Balance the Al by writing 2 Al and balance the SO_4 by writing 3 $CuSO_4$.
$Al(s) + 3CuSO_4(aq) \rightarrow 3Cu(s) + Al_2(SO_4)_3(aq)$

c. $Pb(NO_3)_2(aq) + 2NaCl(aq) \rightarrow PbCl_2(s) + 2NaNO_3(aq)$

d. $2Al(s) + 6HCl(aq) \rightarrow 2AlCl_3(aq) + 3\ H_2(g)$

5.9 **a.** This is a decomposition reaction because a single reactant splits into two simpler substances.
b. This is a single replacement reaction because I_2 in BaI_2 is replaced by Br_2.

5.11 **a.** combination **b.** single replacement
c. decomposition **d.** double replacement
e. decomposition **f.** double replacement
g. combination

5.13 **a.** oxidation **b.** reduction **c.** oxidation **d.** reduction

5.15 **a.** Zinc(Zn) is oxidized because it loses electrons to form Zn^{2+}; chlorine (Cl_2) is reduced
b. Bromide ion ($2Br^-$) is oxidized to Br_2^0; chlorine (Cl_2) is reduced to $2Cl^-$ (gains electrons)
c. Oxide ion (O^{2-}) is oxidized to O_2^0 (loses electrons); lead(II) ion Pb^{2+} is reduced
d. Sn^{2+} ion is oxidized to Sn^{4+} (loses electrons); Fe^{3+} ion is reduced to Fe^{2+}(gains electrons)

5.17 **a.** $Fe^{3+} + e^- \rightarrow Fe^{2+}$ is a reduction. **b.** $Fe^{2+} \rightarrow Fe^{3+} + e^-$ is an oxidation.

5.19 Because the linoleic acid adds hydrogen, the acid has been reduced.

5.21 A mole is the amount of a substance that contains 6.02×10^{23} items. For example, one mole of water contains 6.02×10^{23} molecules of water.

5.23 The subscripts indicate the moles of each element in one mole of that compound.

a. $1.0\,\cancel{\text{mole quinine}} \times \dfrac{24\text{ moles H}}{1\,\cancel{\text{mole quinine}}} = 24\text{ moles H}$

b. $5.0\,\cancel{\text{moles quinine}} \times \dfrac{20\text{ moles C}}{1\,\cancel{\text{mole quinine}}} = 100\text{ moles C}$

c. $0.020\,\cancel{\text{mole quinine}} \times \dfrac{2\text{ moles N atoms}}{1\,\cancel{\text{mole quinine}}} = 0.040\text{ mole N atoms}$

5.25 **a.** $0.500\,\cancel{\text{mole C}} \times \dfrac{6.02 \times 10^{23}\text{ atoms C}}{1\,\cancel{\text{mole C}}} = 3.01 \times 10^{23}\text{ C atoms}$

b. $1.28\,\cancel{\text{moles }SO_2} \times \dfrac{6.02 \times 10^{23}\text{ molecules }SO_2}{1\,\cancel{\text{mole }SO_2}} = 7.71 \times 10^{23}\ SO_2\text{ molecules}$

c. $5.22 \times 10^{22}\,\cancel{\text{atoms Fe}} \times \dfrac{1\text{ mole Fe}}{6.02 \times 10^{23}\,\cancel{\text{atoms Fe}}} = 0.0867\text{ mole of Fe}$

d. $8.50 \times 10^{24}\,\cancel{\text{atoms }C_2H_5OH} \times \dfrac{1\text{ mole }C_2H_5OH}{6.02 \times 10^{23}\,\cancel{\text{atoms }C_2H_5OH}} = 14.1\text{ mole of }C_2H_5OH$

5.27 1 mol H_3PO_4 molecules contains 3 moles H atoms, 1 mole P atoms, and 4 moles O atoms.

a. $2.00\,\cancel{\text{moles }H_3PO_4} \times \dfrac{3\text{ moles H}}{1\,\cancel{\text{mole }H_3PO_4}} = 6.00\text{ moles of H}$

b. $2.00\,\cancel{\text{moles }H_3PO_4} \times \dfrac{4\text{ moles O}}{1\,\cancel{\text{mole }H_3PO_4}} = 8.00\text{ moles of O}$

c. $2.00\,\cancel{\text{moles }H_3PO_4} \times \dfrac{1\,\cancel{\text{mole P}}}{1\,\cancel{\text{mole }H_3PO_4}} \times \dfrac{6.02 \times 10^{23}\text{ atoms P}}{1\,\cancel{\text{mole P}}} = 1.20 \times 10^{24}\text{ P atoms}$

d. $2.00\,\cancel{\text{moles }H_3PO_4} \times \dfrac{4\,\cancel{\text{moles O}}}{1\,\cancel{\text{mole }H_3PO_4}} \times \dfrac{6.02 \times 10^{23}\text{ atoms O}}{1\,\cancel{\text{mole O}}} = 4.82 \times 10^{24}\text{ O atoms}$

5.29 **a.** 1 mole of Na and 1 mole of Cl:
23.0 g + 35.5 g = 58.5 g/mole NaCl

b. 2 moles of Fe and 3 moles of O:
111.8 g + 48.0 g = 159.8 g/mole Fe_2O_3

c. 2 moles of Li and 1 mole of C and 3 moles of O:
13.8 g + 12.0 g + 48.0 g = 73.8 g/mole Li_2CO_3

d. 2 moles of Al and 3 moles of S and 12 moles of O:
54.0 g + 96.3 g + 192.0 g = 342.3 g/mole $Al_2(SO_4)_3$

e. 1 mole of Mg and 2 moles of O and 2 moles of H:
24.3 g + 32.0 g + 2.0 g = 58.3 g/mole $Mg(OH)_2$

f. 16 moles of C and 19 moles of H and 3 moles of N and 5 moles of O and 1 mole of S:
192.0 g + 19.0 g + 42.0 g + 80.0 g + 32.1 g = 365.1 g/mole $C_{16}H_{19}N_3O_5S$

5.31 **a.** $2.00\ \cancel{\text{moles Na}} \times \dfrac{23.0\text{ g Na}}{1\ \cancel{\text{mole Na}}} = 46.0\text{ g Na}$

b. $2.80\ \cancel{\text{moles Ca}} \times \dfrac{40.1\text{ g Ca}}{1\ \cancel{\text{mole Ca}}} = 112\text{ g Ca}$

c. $0.125\ \cancel{\text{mole Sn}} \times \dfrac{118.7\text{ g Sn}}{1\ \cancel{\text{mole Sn}}} = 14.8\text{ g Sn}$

5.33 **a.** $0.500\ \cancel{\text{mole NaCl}} \times \dfrac{58.5\text{ g NaCl}}{1\ \cancel{\text{mole NaCl}}} = 29.3\text{ g NaCl}$

b. $1.75\ \cancel{\text{moles Na}_2\text{O}} \times \dfrac{62.0\text{ g Na}_2\text{O}}{1\ \cancel{\text{mole Na}_2\text{O}}} = 109\text{ g Na}_2\text{O}$

c. $0.225\ \cancel{\text{mole H}_2\text{O}} \times \dfrac{18.0\text{ g H}_2\text{O}}{1\ \cancel{\text{mole H}_2\text{O}}} = 4.05\text{ g H}_2\text{O}$

5.35 **a.** $5.00\ \cancel{\text{moles MgSO}_4} \times \dfrac{120.4\text{ g MgSO}_4}{1\ \cancel{\text{mole MgSO}_4}} = 602\text{ g MgSO}_4$

b. $0.25\ \cancel{\text{mole CO}_2} \times \dfrac{44.0\text{ g CO}_2}{1\ \cancel{\text{mole CO}_2}} = 11\text{ g CO}_2$

5.37 **a.** $50.0\ \cancel{\text{g Ag}} \times \dfrac{1\text{ mole Ag}}{107.9\ \cancel{\text{g Ag}}} = 0.463\text{ mole Ag}$

b. $0.200\ \cancel{\text{g C}} \times \dfrac{1\text{ mole C}}{12.0\ \cancel{\text{g C}}} = 0.0167\text{ mole C}$

c. $15.0\ \cancel{\text{g NH}_3} \times \dfrac{1\text{ mole NH}_3}{17.0\ \cancel{\text{g NH}_3}} = 0.882\text{ mole NH}_3$

d. $75.0\ \cancel{\text{g SO}_2} \times \dfrac{1\text{ mole SO}_2}{64.1\ \cancel{\text{g SO}_2}} = 1.17\text{ moles SO}_2$

5.39 $480\ \cancel{\text{g NaOH}} \times \dfrac{1\text{ mole NaOH}}{40.0\ \cancel{\text{g NaOH}}} = 12\text{ mole NaOH}$

5.41 **a.** $25\ \cancel{\text{g S}} \times \dfrac{1\text{ mole S}}{32.1\ \cancel{\text{g S}}} = 0.78\text{ mole of S}$

b. $125\ \cancel{\text{g SO}_2} \times \dfrac{1\ \cancel{\text{mole SO}_2}}{64.1\ \cancel{\text{g SO}_2}} \times \dfrac{1\text{ mole S}}{1\ \cancel{\text{mole SO}_2}} = 1.95\text{ moles of S}$

c. $2.0\ \cancel{\text{moles Al}_2\text{S}_3} \times \dfrac{3\text{ moles S}}{1\ \cancel{\text{mole Al}_2\text{S}_3}} = 6.0\text{ moles of S}$

5.43 **a.** Two SO_2 molecules react with one O_2 molecule to produce two SO_3 molecules. Two moles of SO_2 react with one mole of O_2 to produce two moles of SO_3.

b. Four P atoms react with five O_2 molecules to produce two P_2O_5 molecules. Four moles of P react with five moles of O_2 to produce two moles of P_2O_5.

5.45 **a.** $\dfrac{2\text{ moles SO}_2}{1\text{ mole O}_2}$ and $\dfrac{1\text{ mole O}_2}{2\text{ moles SO}_2}$ $\quad$ $\dfrac{2\text{ moles SO}_2}{2\text{ moles O}_3}$ and $\dfrac{2\text{ moles O}_3}{2\text{ moles SO}_3}$

$\dfrac{1\text{ mole O}_2}{2\text{ moles SO}_3}$ and $\dfrac{2\text{ moles SO}_3}{1\text{ mole O}_2}$

b. $\frac{4 \text{ moles P}}{5 \text{ moles } O_2}$ and $\frac{5 \text{ moles } O_2}{4 \text{ moles P}}$ $\quad$ $\frac{4 \text{ moles P}}{2 \text{ moles } P_2O_5}$ and $\frac{2 \text{ moles } P_2O_5}{4 \text{ moles P}}$

$\frac{5 \text{ moles } O_2}{2 \text{ moles } P_2O_5}$ and $\frac{2 \text{ moles } P_2O_5}{5 \text{ moles } O_2}$

5.47 **a.** $2.0 \cancel{\text{moles } H_2} \times \frac{1 \text{ mole } O_2}{2 \cancel{\text{moles } H_2}} = 1.0 \text{ mole } O_2$

b. $5.0 \cancel{\text{moles } O_2} \times \frac{2 \text{ moles } H_2}{1 \cancel{\text{mole } O_2}} = 10. \text{ moles } H_2$

c. $2.5 \cancel{\text{moles } O_2} \times \frac{2 \text{ moles } H_2O}{1 \cancel{\text{mole } O_2}} = 5.0 \text{ moles } H_2O$

5.49 **a.** $0.500 \cancel{\text{mole } SO_2} \times \frac{5 \text{ moles C}}{2 \cancel{\text{moles } SO_2}} = 1.25 \text{ moles C}$

b. $1.2 \cancel{\text{moles C}} \times \frac{4 \text{ moles CO}}{5 \cancel{\text{moles C}}} = 0.96 \text{ mole CO}$

c. $0.50 \cancel{\text{mole } CS_2} \times \frac{2 \text{ moles } SO_2}{1 \cancel{\text{mole } CS_2}} = 1.0 \text{ mole } SO_2$

d. $2.5 \cancel{\text{moles C}} \times \frac{1 \text{ mole } CS_2}{5 \cancel{\text{moles C}}} = 0.50 \text{ mole } CS_2$

5.51 **a.** $2.50 \cancel{\text{moles Na}} \times \frac{2 \cancel{\text{moles } Na_2O}}{4 \cancel{\text{moles Na}}} \times \frac{62.0 \text{ g } Na_2O}{1 \cancel{\text{mole } Na_2O}} = 77.5 \text{ g } Na_2O$

b. $18.0 \cancel{\text{g Na}} \times \frac{1 \cancel{\text{mole Na}}}{23.0 \cancel{\text{g Na}}} \times \frac{1 \cancel{\text{mole } O_2}}{4 \cancel{\text{moles Na}}} \times \frac{32.0 \text{ g } O_2}{1 \cancel{\text{mole } O_2}} = 6.26 \text{ g } O_2$

c. $75.0 \cancel{\text{g } Na_2O} \times \frac{1 \cancel{\text{mole } Na_2O}}{62.0 \cancel{\text{g } Na_2O}} \times \frac{1 \cancel{\text{mole } O_2}}{2 \cancel{\text{moles } Na_2O}} \times \frac{32.0 \text{ g } O_2}{1 \cancel{\text{mole } O_2}} = 19.4 \text{ g } O_2$

5.53 **a.** $8.00 \cancel{\text{moles } NH_3} \times \frac{3 \cancel{\text{moles } O_2}}{4 \cancel{\text{moles } NH_3}} \times \frac{32.0 \text{ g } O_2}{1 \cancel{\text{mole } O_2}} = 192 \text{ g } O_2$

b. $6.50 \cancel{\text{g } O_2} \times \frac{1 \cancel{\text{mole } O_2}}{32.0 \cancel{\text{g } O_2}} \times \frac{2 \cancel{\text{moles } N_2}}{3 \cancel{\text{moles } O_2}} \times \frac{28.0 \text{ g } N_2}{1 \cancel{\text{mole } N_2}} = 3.79 \text{ g } N_2$

c. $34.0 \cancel{\text{g } NH_3} \times \frac{1 \cancel{\text{mole } NH_3}}{17.0 \cancel{\text{g } NH_3}} \times \frac{6 \cancel{\text{moles } H_2O}}{4 \cancel{\text{moles } NH_3}} \times \frac{18.0 \text{ g } H_2O}{1 \cancel{\text{mole } H_2O}} = 54.0 \text{ g } H_2O$

5.55 **a.** $28.0 \cancel{\text{g } NO_2} \times \frac{1 \cancel{\text{mole } NO_2}}{46.0 \cancel{\text{g } NO_2}} \times \frac{1 \cancel{\text{mole } H_2O}}{3 \cancel{\text{moles } NO_2}} \times \frac{18.0 \text{ g } H_2O}{1 \cancel{\text{mole } H_2O}} = 3.65 \text{ g } H_2O$

b. $15.8 \cancel{\text{g } NO_2} \times \frac{1 \cancel{\text{mole } NO_2}}{46.0 \cancel{\text{g } NO_2}} \times \frac{1 \cancel{\text{mole NO}}}{3 \cancel{\text{moles } NO_2}} \times \frac{30.0 \text{ g NO}}{1 \cancel{\text{mole NO}}} = 3.44 \text{ g NO}$

c. $8.25 \cancel{\text{g } NO_2} \times \frac{1 \cancel{\text{mole } NO_2}}{46.0 \cancel{\text{g } NO_2}} \times \frac{2 \cancel{\text{moles } HNO_3}}{3 \cancel{\text{moles } NO_2}} \times \frac{63.0 \text{ g } HNO_3}{1 \cancel{\text{mole } HNO_3}} = 7.53 \text{ g NO}$

5.57 **a.** $2PbS(s) + 3O_2(g) \rightarrow 2PbO(s) + 2SO_2(g)$

b. $0.125 \cancel{\text{mole PbS}} \times \frac{3 \cancel{\text{moles } O_2}}{2 \cancel{\text{moles PbS}}} \times \frac{32.0 \text{ g } O_2}{1 \cancel{\text{mole } O_2}} = 6.00 \text{ g } O_2$

c. $65.0\text{ g PbS} \times \frac{1\text{ mole PbS}}{239.3\text{ g PbS}} \times \frac{2\text{ moles SO}_2}{2\text{ moles PbS}} \times \frac{64.1\text{ g SO}_2}{1\text{ mole SO}_2} = 17.4\text{ g SO}_2$

d. $128\text{ g PbO} \times \frac{1\text{ mole PbO}}{223.2\text{ g PbO}} \times \frac{2\text{ moles PbS}}{2\text{ moles PbO}} \times \frac{239.3\text{ g PbS}}{1\text{ mole PbS}} = 137\text{ g PbS}$

5.59 **a.** The energy of activation is the energy required to break the bonds in the reactants.

b. A catalyst lowers the activation energy by providing an alternate path, which increases the rate of a reaction.

c. In exothermic reactions, the energy of the products is lower than the reactants.

d.

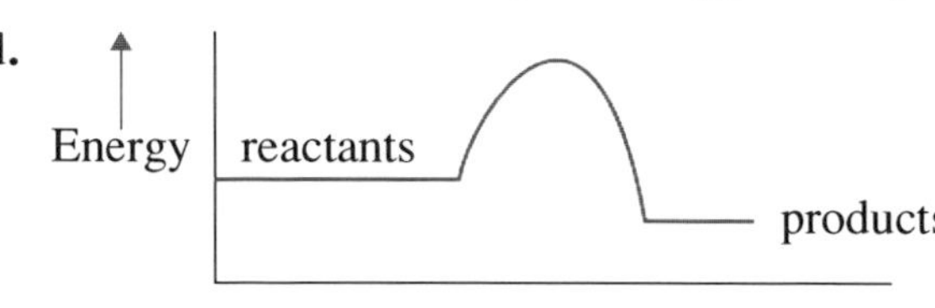

5.61 **a.** exothermic; heat loss **b.** endothermic; heat gain **c.** exothermic; heat loss

5.63 **a.** exothermic **b.** endothermic **c.** exothermic

5.65 **a.** The rate of a reaction relates the speed at which reactants are transformed into products.

b. Because more reactants will have the energy necessary to proceed to products (the activation energy) at room temperature than at refrigerator temperature, the rate of formation of mold will be higher at room temperature.

5.67 **a.** Addition of a reactant increases the reaction rate.

b. Increasing the temperature increases the number of collisions with the energy of activation. The rate of reaction will be increased.

c. Addition of a catalyst increases the reaction rate.

d. Removal of reactant decreases the reaction rate.

5.69 **a.** $NH_3(g) + HCl\,(g) \rightarrow NH_4Cl(s)$ combination

b. $Fe_3O_4(s) + 4H_2(g) \rightarrow 3\,Fe(s) + 4H_2O\,(g)$ single replacement

c. $2Sb(s) + 3Cl_2(g) \rightarrow 2SbCl_3(s)$ combination

d. $2\,NI_3(s) \rightarrow N_2(g) + 3I_2(g)$ decomposition

e. $2\,KBr(aq) + Cl_2(aq) \rightarrow 2KCl(aq) + Br_2(l)$ single replacement

f. $2Fe(s) + 3H_2SO_4(aq) \rightarrow Fe_2(SO_4)_3(s) + 3H_2(g)$ single replacement

g. $Al_2(SO_4)_3(aq) + 6\,NaOH(aq) \rightarrow 3\,Na_2SO_4(aq) + 2\,Al(OH)_3(s)$ double replacement

5.71 **a.** $Zn^{2+} + 2e^- \rightarrow Zn$ reduction **b.** $Al \rightarrow Al^{3+} + 3\,e^-$ oxidation

c. $Pb \rightarrow Pb^{2+} + 2e^-$ oxidation **d.** $Cl_2 + 2e^- \rightarrow 2Cl^-$ reduction

5.73 **a.** $0.500\text{ mole C}_3\text{H}_6\text{O}_3 \times \frac{6.02 \times 10^{23}\text{ molecules}}{1\text{ mole C}_3\text{H}_6\text{O}_3} = 3.01 \times 10^{23}\text{ molecules}$

b. $1.50\text{ moles C}_3\text{H}_6\text{O}_3 \times \frac{3\text{ moles C}}{1\text{ mole C}_3\text{H}_6\text{O}_3} \times \frac{6.02 \times 10^{23}\text{ atoms}}{1\text{ mole C}} = 2.71 \times 10^{24}\text{ C atoms}$

c. $4.5 \times 10^{24}\text{ O atoms} \times \frac{1\text{ mole O}}{6.02 \times 10^{23}\text{ O atoms}} \times \frac{1\text{ mole C}_3\text{H}_6\text{O}_3}{3\text{ moles O}} = 2.5\text{ moles C}_3\text{H}_6\text{O}_3$

d. $3 \times C\,(12.0) + 6 \times H\,(1.01) + 3 \times O\,(16.0) = 90.1\text{ g/mole}$

5.75 **a.** $1\,\cancel{\text{Fe atom}} \times \dfrac{55.9\text{ amu}}{1\,\cancel{\text{Fe atom}}} = 55.9\text{ amu}$

$1\,\cancel{\text{S atom}} \times \dfrac{32.1\text{ amu}}{1\,\cancel{\text{S atom}}} = 32.1\text{ amu}$

$4\,\cancel{\text{O atoms}} \times \dfrac{16.0\text{ amu}}{1\,\cancel{\text{O atom}}} = \begin{array}{c}\underline{64.0\text{ amu}}\\ 152.0\text{ amu}\end{array}$

b. $1\,\cancel{\text{Ca atom}} \times \dfrac{40.1\text{ amu}}{1\,\cancel{\text{Ca atom}}} = 40.1\text{ amu}$

$2\,\cancel{\text{I atoms}} \times \dfrac{126.9\text{ amu}}{1\,\cancel{\text{I atom}}} = 253.8\text{ amu}$

$6\,\cancel{\text{O atoms}} \times \dfrac{16.0\text{ amu}}{1\,\cancel{\text{O atom}}} = \begin{array}{c}\underline{96.0\text{ amu}}\\ 389.9\text{ amu}\end{array}$

c. $5\,\cancel{\text{C atoms}} \times \dfrac{12.0\text{ amu}}{1\,\cancel{\text{C atom}}} = 60.0\text{ amu}$

$8\,\cancel{\text{H atom}} \times \dfrac{1.01\text{ amu}}{1\,\cancel{\text{H atom}}} = 8.08\text{ amu}$

$1\,\cancel{\text{N atom}} \times \dfrac{14.0\text{ amu}}{1\,\cancel{\text{N atom}}} = 14.0\text{ amu}$

$1\,\cancel{\text{Na atom}} \times \dfrac{23.0\text{ amu}}{1\,\cancel{\text{Na atom}}} = 23.0\text{ amu}$

$4\,\cancel{\text{O atom}} \times \dfrac{16.0\text{ amu}}{1\,\cancel{\text{O atom}}} = \begin{array}{c}\underline{64.0\text{ amu}}\\ 169.1\text{ amu}\end{array}$

d. $6\,\cancel{\text{C atoms}} \times \dfrac{12.0\text{ amu}}{1\,\cancel{\text{C atom}}} = 72.0\text{ amu}$

$12\,\cancel{\text{H atom}} \times \dfrac{1.01\text{ amu}}{1\,\cancel{\text{H atom}}} = 12.1\text{ amu}$

$2\,\cancel{\text{O atom}} \times \dfrac{16.0\text{ amu}}{1\,\cancel{\text{O atom}}} = \begin{array}{c}\underline{32.0\text{ amu}}\\ 116.1\text{ amu}\end{array}$

5.77 **a.** $0.150\,\cancel{\text{mole K}} \times \dfrac{39.1\text{ g K}}{1\,\cancel{\text{mole K}}} = 5.87\text{ g K}$

b. $0.150\,\cancel{\text{mole Cl}_2} \times \dfrac{71.0\text{ g Cl}_2}{1\,\cancel{\text{mole Cl}_2}} = 10.7\text{ g Cl}_2$

c. $0.150\,\cancel{\text{mole Na}_2\text{CO}_3} \times \dfrac{106.0\text{ g Na}_2\text{CO}_3}{1\,\cancel{\text{mole Na}_2\text{CO}_3}} = 15.9\text{ g Na}_2\text{CO}_3$

5.79 **a.** $25.0\,\cancel{\text{g CO}_2} \times \dfrac{1\text{ mole CO}_2}{44.0\,\cancel{\text{g CO}_2}} = 0.568\text{ mole CO}_2$

b. $25.0\,\cancel{\text{g Al(OH)}_3} \times \dfrac{1\text{ mole Al(OH)}_3}{78.0\,\cancel{\text{g Al(OH)}_3}} = 0.321\text{ mole Al(OH)}_3$

c. $25.0\,\cancel{\text{g Mg(Cl)}_2} \times \dfrac{1\text{ mole Mg(Cl)}_2}{95.3\,\cancel{\text{g Mg(Cl)}_2}} = 0.262\text{ mole Mg(Cl)}_2$

5.81 **a.** $124\ \text{g } C_2H_6O \times \dfrac{1\ \text{mole } C_2H_6O}{46.0\ \text{g } C_2H_6O} \times \dfrac{1\ \text{mole } C_6H_{12}O_6}{2\ \text{moles } C_2H_6O} = 1.35\ \text{moles } C_6H_{12}O_6$

b. $0.240\ \text{kg } C_6H_{12}O_6 \times \dfrac{1000\ \text{g}}{1\ \text{kg}} \times \dfrac{1\ \text{mole } C_6H_{12}O_6}{180.0\ \text{g } C_6H_{12}O_6} \times \dfrac{2\ \text{moles } C_2H_6O}{1\ \text{mole } C_6H_{12}O_6} \times \dfrac{46.0\ \text{g } C_2H_6O}{1\ \text{mole } C_2H_6O}$
$= 123\ \text{g } C_2H_6O$

5.83 $2NH_3(g) + 5F_2(g) \rightarrow N_2F_4(g) + 6HF(g)$

a. $4.00\ \text{moles HF} \times \dfrac{2\ \text{moles } NH_3}{6\ \text{moles HF}} = 1.33\ \text{moles } NH_3$

$4.00\ \text{moles HF} \times \dfrac{5\ \text{moles } F_2}{6\ \text{moles HF}} = 3.33\ \text{moles } F_2$

b. $1.50\ \text{moles } NH_3 \times \dfrac{5\ \text{moles } F_2}{2\ \text{moles } NH_3} \times \dfrac{38.0\ \text{g } F_2}{1\ \text{mole } F_2} = 1.43\ \text{g } F_2$

c. $3.40\ \text{g } NH_3 \times \dfrac{1\ \text{mole } NH_3}{17.0\ \text{g } NH_3} \times \dfrac{1\ \text{mole } N_2F_4}{2\ \text{moles } NH_3} \times \dfrac{104.0\ \text{g } N_2F_4}{1\ \text{mole } N_2F_4} = 10.4\ \text{g } N_2F_4$

5.85 **a.** $4.0\ \text{moles } H_2O \times \dfrac{1\ \text{mole } C_5H_{12}}{6\ \text{moles } H_2O} \times \dfrac{72.2\ \text{g } C_5H_{12}}{1\ \text{mole } C_5H_{12}} = 48\ \text{g } C_5H_{12}$

b. $32.0\ \text{g } O_2 \times \dfrac{1\ \text{mole } O_2}{32.0\ \text{g } O_2} \times \dfrac{5\ \text{moles } CO_2}{8\ \text{moles } O_2} \times \dfrac{44.0\ \text{g } CO_2}{1\ \text{mole } CO_2} = 27.5\ \text{g } CO_2$

5.87 **a.** Heat is a product; exothermic

b. Heat is given off; the energy of the products is lower than the energy of the reactants.

Answers to Understanding the Concepts

5.89 Physical: solid candle wax melts (changes state), candle height is shorter, melted wax turns solid (changes state), shape of the wax changes, the wick becomes shorter.
Chemical: wax burns in oxygen, heat and light are emitted, wick burns in the presence of oxygen.

5.91 **a.** 1, 4, 2 combination reaction
b. 1, 1, 2 combination reaction
c. 2, 2, 1 decomposition reaction
d. 1, 1, 1, 1 double replacement reaction

5.93 **a.** $3\ Pb(NO_3)_2\ (aq) + 2Na_3PO_4(aq) \rightarrow Pb_3(PO_4)_2(s) + 6\ NaNO_3(aq)$ double replacement
b. $4Ga(s) + 3O_2(g) \rightarrow 2Ga_2O_3(s)$ combination
c. $2\ NaNO_3(s) \rightarrow 2\ NaNO_2\ (s) + O_2(g)$ decomposition
d. $Bi_2O_3(s) + 3\ C(s) \rightarrow 2\ Bi(s) + 3CO(g)$ single replacement

5.95 **a.** $4Al(s) + 3O_2(g) \rightarrow 2Al_2O_3(s)$
b. This is a combination reaction.
c. 5.63 moles of oxygen
d. 94.9 g of aluminum oxide
e. 17.0 g of aluminum oxide
f. 59.6 g of aluminum oxide

5.97 **a.** 5.00 g of gold
b. 1.52×10^{22} Au atoms
c. 0.61 g of oxygen
d. Au_2O_3

Chapter 6

Key Terms

Answers **1.** e **2.** d **3.** b **4.** c **5.** a

6.1 Solutions

◆ Learning Exercise 6.1A

Answers
a. KCl; water **b.** CO_2; water **c.** Cu; Zn
d. oxygen; helium **e.** Br_2; CCl_4

◆ Learning Exercise 6.1B

Answer The O—H bonds in water molecules are polar because the hydrogen atoms are partially positive and the oxygen atoms are partially negative. Hydrogen bonding occurs because the partially positive hydrogen atoms in one water molecule are attracted to partially negative oxygen atoms of other water molecules.

◆ Learning Exercise 6.1C

Answers **a.** hexane **b.** water **c.** hexane **d.** hexane **e.** water

6.2 Electrolytes and Nonelectrolytes

◆ Learning Exercise 6.2A

Answers

a. $LiCl(s) \xrightarrow{H_2O} Li^+\,(aq) + Cl^-(aq)$

b. $Mg(NO_3)_2(s) \xrightarrow{H_2O} Mg^{2+}\,(aq) + 2NO_3^-\,(aq)$

c. $Na_3PO_4(s) \xrightarrow{H_2O} 3Na^+\,aq + PO_4^{3-}\,(aq)$

d. $K_3SO_4(s) \xrightarrow{H_2O} 2K^+\,aq + SO_4^{2-}\,(aq)$

e. $MgCl_2(s) \xrightarrow{H_2O} Mg^{2+}\,(aq) + 2Cl^{-2}\,(aq)$

◆ Learning Exercise 6.2B

Answers

a. $C_6H_{12}O_6(s) \rightarrow C_6H_{12}O_6\,(aq)$ molecules only
b. $NaOH(s) \rightarrow Na^+(aq) + OH^-\,(aq)$ mostly ions
c. $K_2SO_4(s) \rightarrow 2K^+(aq) + SO_4^{2-}\,(aq)$ mostly ions
d. $HF(g) + H_2O(l) \rightleftarrows H_3O^+(aq) + F^-\,(aq)$ mostly molecules and a few ions

◆ Learning Exercise 6.2C

Answers **a.** 2 Eq **b.** 2.5 Eq **c.** 4.0 Eq

6.3 Solubility

◇ Learning Exercise 6.3A

Answers **1.** U **2.** S **3.** S **4.** S **5.** U

◇ Learning Exercise 6.3B

Answers
a. 65 g **b.** 330 g
c. Yes, 10 g of KNO_3 will not dissolve.
d. Yes, all 200 g of KNO_3 will dissolve.

6.4 Percent Concentration

◇ Learning Exercise 6.4A

Answers **a.** 20.0% **b.** 0.25% **c.** 8.0% **d.** 5.0%

◇ Learning Exercise 6.4B

Answers **a.** 40.0 g **b.** 1.0 g **c.** 1.2 g **d.** 2.5 g

◇ Learning Exercise 6.4C

Answers **a.** 200. mL **b.** 500 mL **c.** 300 mL **d.** 300. mL

6.5 Molarity and Dilution

◇ Learning Exercise 6.5A

Answers **a.** 2.0 M HCl **b.** 5.0 M glucose **c.** 0.50 M NaOH

6.6 Properties of Solutions

◆ Learning Exercise 6.6A

Answers **1.** solution **2.** suspension **3.** suspension **4.** colloid **5.** colloid **6.** suspension

◇ Learning Exercise 6.6B

Answers (1) higher (2) lower (3) 10 (4) 5 (5) 10 (6) 10

◇ Learning Exercise 6.6C

Answers **a.** A, B **b.** B, A **c.** 6%

◇ Learning Exercise 6.6D

Answers
(1) 0.9 (2) 5 (3) iso (4) hemolysis
(5) hypo (6) crenation (7) hyper

◇ Learning Exercise 6.6E

Answers **a.** 3 **b.** 2 **c.** 1 **d.** 1 **e.** 3 **f.** 2

◆ Learning Exercise 6.6F

Answers **a.** 1 **b.** 2 **c.** 3 **d.** 2 **e.** 1 **f.** 2

◆ Learning Exercise 6.6G

Answers

a. Glucose, NaCl, urea; they are solution particles.
b. Starch, protein; colloids are retained by semipermeable membranes.

Answers to the Practice Test

1. B	**2.** A	**3.** A	**4.** B	**5.** C
6. E	**7.** C	**8.** E	**9.** C	**10.** D
11. E	**12.** E	**13.** A	**14.** A	**15.** C
16. C	**17.** B	**18.** A	**19.** C	**20.** C
21. C	**22.** C	**23.** B	**24.** B	**25.** E
26. C	**27.** B	**28.** B	**29.** C	**30.** E
31. D	**32.** A	**33.** D	**34.** C	**35.** A
36. C	**37.** A	**38.** D	**39.** A	**40.** E

Answers and Solutions to Selected Problems

6.1 The component present in the smaller amount is the solute; the larger amount is the solvent.

a. Sodium chloride, solute; water, solvent
b. Water, solute; ethanol, solvent
c. Oxygen, solute; nitrogen, solvent

6.3 The K^+ and I^- ions at the surface of the solid are pulled into solution by the polar water molecules where the hydration process surrounds separate ions with water molecules.

6.5 **a.** Potassium chloride, an ionic solute, would be soluble in water (a polar solvent).
b. Iodine, a nonpolar solute would be soluble in carbon tetrachloride (a nonpolar solvent).
c. Sugar, a polar solute, would be soluble in water, which is a polar solvent.
d. Gasoline, a nonpolar solute, would be soluble in carbon tetrachloride, which is a nonpolar solvent.

6.7 The salt KF dissociates into ions when it dissolves in water. The weak acid HF exists as mostly molecules along with some ions when it dissolves in water.

6.9 Strong electrolytes dissociate into ions.

a. $KCl\ (s) \xrightarrow{H_20} K^+\ (aq) + Cl^-\ (aq)$

b. $CaCl_2\ (s) \xrightarrow{H_20} Ca^{2+}\ (aq) + 2Cl^-\ (aq)$

c. $K_3PO_4\ (s) \xrightarrow{H_20} 3\ K^+\ (aq) + PO_4^{-3}\ (aq)$

d. $Fe(NO_3)_3\ (s) \xrightarrow{H_20} Fe^{3+}\ (aq) + 3NO_3^-\ (aq)$

6.11 **a.** In solution, a weak electrolyte exists mostly as molecules with a few ions.
b. Sodium bromide is a strong electrolyte and forms ions in solution.
c. A nonelectrolyte does not dissociate and forms only molecules in solution.

6.13 **a.** Strong electrolyte because only ions are present in the K_2SO_4 solution.
b. Weak electrolyte because both ions and molecules are present in the NH_4OH solution.
c. Nonelectrolyte because only molecules are present in the $C_6H_{12}O_6$ solution.

6.15 **a.** $1 \cancel{\text{mole K}^+} \times \frac{1 \text{ Eq K}^+}{1 \cancel{\text{mole K}^+}} = 1 \text{ Eq K}^+$

b. $2 \cancel{\text{moles OH}^+} \times \frac{1 \text{ Eq OH}^-}{1 \cancel{\text{mole OH}^-}} = 2 \text{ Eq OH}^-$

c. $1 \cancel{\text{mole Ca}^{2+}} \times \frac{2 \text{ Eq Ca}^+}{1 \cancel{\text{mole Ca}^{2+}}} = 2 \text{ Eq Ca}^{2+}$

d. $3 \cancel{\text{moles CO}_3^{2-}} \times \frac{2 \text{ Eq CO}_3^{2-}}{1 \cancel{\text{mole CO}_3^{2-}}} = 6 \text{ Eq CO}_3^{2-}$

6.17 $1.0 \cancel{\text{L}} \times \frac{154 \cancel{\text{mEq}}}{1 \cancel{\text{L}}} \times \frac{1 \cancel{\text{Eq}}}{1000 \cancel{\text{mEq}}} \times \frac{1 \text{ mole Na}^+}{1 \cancel{\text{Eq}}} = 0.154 \text{ mole Na}^+$

$1.0 \cancel{\text{L}} \times \frac{154 \cancel{\text{mEq}}}{1 \cancel{\text{L}}} \times \frac{1 \cancel{\text{Eq}}}{1000 \cancel{\text{mEq}}} \times \frac{1 \text{ mole Cl}^-}{1 \cancel{\text{Eq}}} = 0.154 \text{ mole Cl}^-$

6.19 The total equivalents of anions must be equal to the equivalents of cations in any solution.

mEq of anions = 40 mEq Cl^-/L + 15 mEq HPO_4^{2-} /L = 55 mEq/L
mEq Na^+ = mEq anions = 55 mEq Na^+ /L

6.21 **a.** The solution must be saturated because no additional solute dissolves.
b. The solution was unsaturated because the sugar cube dissolves.

6.23 **a.** It is unsaturated because 34.0 g KCl is the maximum that dissolves in 100 g H_2O at 20°C.
b. 11.0 g $NaNO_3$ in 25 g H_2O is 94.0 g in 100 g H_2O. At 20°C, 88.0 g $NaNO_3$ can dissolve so the solution is unsaturated.
c. Adding 400.0 g sugar to 125 g H_2O is 320 g in 100 g H_2O at 20°C, only 203.9 g sugar can dissolve, which is less than 320 g. The sugar solution is saturated and excess undissolved sugar is present.

6.25 **a.** $\frac{34.0 \text{ g KCl}}{100 \cancel{\text{g H}_2\text{O}}} \times 200 \cancel{\text{g H}_2\text{O}} = 68.0 \text{ g KCl}$ (This will dissolve at 20°C)

At 20°C 68.0 g KCl can dissolve in 200 g H_2O.

b. Since 80.0 g of KCl dissolves at 50°C and 68.0 g is in solution at 20°C, the mass of solid is 80.0g − 68.0g = 12.0 g KCl.

6.27 **a.** In general, the solubility of solid ionic solutes increases as temperature is increased.
b. The solubility of a gaseous solute (CO_2) decreases as the temperature is increased.
c. The solubility of a gaseous solute is lowered as temperature increases. When the can of warm soda is opened, more CO_2 is released producing more spray.

6.29 A 5% (m/m) glucose solution contains 5 g glucose in 100 g of solution (5 g glucose + 95 g water), while a 5% (m/v) glucose solution contains 5 g glucose in 100 mL solution.

6.31 **a.** $\frac{25 \text{ g of KCl}}{150 \text{ g solution}} \times 100 = 17\% \text{ (m/m)}$

b. $\frac{12 \text{ g sugar}}{225 \text{ g solution}} \times 100 = 5.3\% \text{ (m/m)}$

6.33 **a.** $\frac{75 \text{ g Na}_2\text{SO}_4}{250 \text{ mL solution}} \times 100 = 30.\% \text{ (m/v)}$

b. $\frac{39 \text{ g sucrose}}{355 \text{ mL solution}} \times 100 = 11\% \text{ (m/v)}$

6.35 **a.** $50.0\ \cancel{\text{mL solution}} \times \dfrac{5.0\text{ g KCl}}{100\ \cancel{\text{mL solution}}} = 2.5\text{ g KCl}$

b. $1250\ \cancel{\text{mL solution}} \times \dfrac{4.0\text{ g KCl}}{100\ \cancel{\text{mL solution}}} = 50.\text{ g } NH_4Cl$

6.37 $355\ \cancel{\text{mL solution}} \times \dfrac{22.5\text{ mL alcohol}}{100\ \cancel{\text{mL solution}}} = 79.9\text{ mL alcohol}$

6.39 **a.** $1\ \cancel{\text{hr}} \times \dfrac{100\ \cancel{\text{mL solution}}}{1\ \cancel{\text{hr}}} \times \dfrac{20\text{ g mannitol}}{100\ \cancel{\text{mL solution}}} = 20\text{ g mannitol}$

b. $15\ \cancel{\text{hr}} \times \dfrac{100\ \cancel{\text{mL solution}}}{1\ \cancel{\text{hr}}} \times \dfrac{20\text{ g mannitol}}{100\ \cancel{\text{mL solution}}} = 300\text{ g mannitol}$

6.41 $100\ \cancel{\text{g glucose}} \times \dfrac{100\ \cancel{\text{mL}}\text{ solution}}{5\ \cancel{\text{g glucose}}} \times \dfrac{1\text{ L}}{1000\ \cancel{\text{mL}}} = 2\text{ L solution}$

6.43 Molarity = moles of solute/L of solution

a. $\dfrac{2.0\text{ moles glucose}}{4.0\text{ L solution}} = 0.50\text{ M glucose}$

b. $\dfrac{4.0\ \cancel{\text{g KOH}}}{2.0\text{ L solution}} \times \dfrac{1\text{ mole KOH}}{56.1\ \cancel{\text{g KOH}}} = 0.036\text{ M KOH}$

6.45 **a.** $1.0\text{ L solution} \times \dfrac{3.0\text{ moles NaCl}}{1\text{ L solution}} = 3.0\text{ moles NaCl}$

b. $0.40\ \cancel{\text{L solution}} \times \dfrac{1.0\text{ mole KBr}}{1\ \cancel{\text{L solution}}} = 0.40\text{ mole KBr}$

6.47 **a.** $2.0\ \cancel{\text{L}} \times \dfrac{1.5\ \cancel{\text{moles NaOH}}}{1\ \cancel{\text{L}}} \times \dfrac{40.0\text{ g NaOH}}{1\ \cancel{\text{mole NaOH}}} = 120\text{ g NaOH}$

b. $4.0\ \cancel{\text{L}} \times \dfrac{0.20\ \cancel{\text{mole KCl}}}{1\ \cancel{\text{L}}} \times \dfrac{74.6\text{ g KCl}}{1\ \cancel{\text{mole KCl}}} = 60.\text{ g KCl}$

6.49 **a.** $3.0\ \cancel{\text{moles NaOH}} \times \dfrac{1\text{ L}}{2\ \cancel{\text{moles NaOH}}} = 1.5\text{ L NaOH}$

b. $15\ \cancel{\text{moles NaCl}} \times \dfrac{1\text{ L}}{1.5\ \cancel{\text{moles NaCl}}} = 10\text{ L NaCl}$

6.51 Adding water (solvent) to the soup increases the volume and dilutes the tomato concentration.

6.53 The concentration of a diluted solution can be calculated using the relationship:

$$\%\text{ (m/v) of dilute solution} = \frac{\text{grams of solute}}{\text{volume dilute solution}} \times 100$$

$$\text{or Molarity of dilute solution} = \frac{\text{moles of solute}}{\text{volume dilute solution in L}}$$

a. From the initial solution: moles solute is $2.0\ \cancel{\text{L}} \times 6.0\text{ moles HCl}/\cancel{\text{L}} = 12\text{ moles of HCl}$

$$\text{Molarity of the dilute solution} = \frac{12\text{ moles HCl}}{6.0\text{ L}} = 2.0\text{ M HCl}$$

b. The moles of solute is 12 moles NaOH /~~L~~ × 0.50 ~~L~~ = 6.0 moles NaOH

Final molarity is $\frac{6.0 \text{ moles NaOH}}{3.0 \text{ L}} = 2.0 \text{ M NaOH}$

c. Initial grams of solute is $10.0 \cancel{\text{mL solution}} \times \frac{25 \text{ g KOH}}{100 \cancel{\text{mL solution}}} = 2.5 \text{ g KOH}$

d. Initial grams of solute is $50.0 \cancel{\text{mL}} \times \frac{15 \text{ g } H_2SO_4}{100 \cancel{\text{mL}}} = 7.5 \text{ g } H_2SO_4$

Final % (m/v) is $\frac{7.5 \text{ g } H_2SO_4}{50.0 \text{ mL}} \times 100 = 3.0\ \%\ \text{(m/v) } H_2SO_4$

6.55 The final volume of a diluted solution can be found by using the relationship: $C_1V_1 = C_2V_2$ where C_1 is the concentration (M or %) of the initial (concentrated) and C_2 is the concentration (M or %) of the final (dilute) solution and V_1 is the volume of the initial solution. Solving for V_2 gives the volume of the dilute solution.

a. $V_2 = \frac{M_1V_1}{M_2} = \frac{6.0 \cancel{\text{moles/L}}}{0.20 \cancel{\text{mole/L}}} \times 0.0200 \text{ L} = 0.60 \text{ L}$

b. $V_2 = \frac{\%_1 V_1}{\%_2} = \frac{10.0 \cancel{\%}}{2.0 \cancel{\%}} \times 50.0 \cancel{\text{mL}} \times \frac{1 \text{ L}}{1000 \cancel{\text{mL}}} = 0.25 \text{ mL}$

c. $V_2 = \frac{M_1V_1}{M_2} = \frac{6.0 \cancel{\text{moles/L}}}{0.50 \cancel{\text{mole/L}}} \times 0.500 \text{ L} = 6.0 \text{ L}$

6.57 **a.** $50.0 \cancel{\text{mL}} \times \frac{1 \text{ L}}{1000 \cancel{\text{mL}}} = 0.0500 \cancel{\text{L}} \times \frac{1.50 \text{ moles KCl}}{1 \cancel{\text{L}}} = 0.0750 \text{ mole KCl}$

$0.0750 \cancel{\text{mole KCl}} \times \frac{1 \cancel{\text{mole } PbCl_2}}{2 \cancel{\text{moles KCl}}} \times \frac{278.1 \text{ g}}{1 \cancel{\text{mole } PbCl_2}} = 10.4 \text{ g } PbCl_2$

b. $50.0 \cancel{\text{mL}} \times \frac{1 \text{ L}}{1000 \cancel{\text{mL}}} = 0.0500 \cancel{\text{L}} \times \frac{1.50 \cancel{\text{moles KCl}}}{1 \cancel{\text{L}}} = 0.0750 \text{ mole KCl}$

$0.0750 \cancel{\text{mole KCl}} \times \frac{1 \cancel{\text{mole } Pb(NO_3)_2}}{2 \cancel{\text{moles KCl}}} \times \frac{1 \text{ L solution}}{2.00 \cancel{\text{moles } Pb(NO_3)_2}} = 0.0188 \text{ L solution}$

$0.0188 \cancel{\text{L}} \times \frac{1000 \text{ mL}}{1 \cancel{\text{L}}} = 18.8 \text{ mL solution}$

6.59 **a.** $15.0 \cancel{\text{g Mg}} \times \frac{1 \text{ mole Mg}}{24.3 \cancel{\text{g Mg}}} = 0.617 \text{ mole Mg}$

$0.617 \cancel{\text{mole Mg}} \times \frac{2 \text{ moles HCl}}{1 \cancel{\text{mole Mg}}} = 1.23 \cancel{\text{moles HCl}} \times \frac{1\text{L}}{6.00 \cancel{\text{mole HCl}}} = 0.206 \text{ L}$

$0.206 \cancel{\text{L}} \times \frac{1000 \text{ mL}}{1 \cancel{\text{L}}} = 206 \text{ mL}$

b. $\frac{2.00 \text{ moles HCl}}{1 \cancel{\text{L solution}}} \times 0.500 \cancel{\text{L}} = 1.00 \cancel{\text{mole HCl}} \times \frac{1 \text{ mole } H_2}{2 \cancel{\text{moles HCl}}} = 0.500 \text{ mole } H_2 \text{ gas}$

6.61 **a.** A solution cannot be separated by a semipermeable membrane.
b. A suspension settles as time passes.

6.63 **a.** Water in the soil diffuses through the plant's root membranes to dilute the solutions in these cells. Because the plant's cells above these root cells contain more concentrated solutions than the root cells, water moves up from the roots to dilute the more concentrated cell solutions.
b. The pickling (brine) solution contains more solutes and less solvent than the cucumber's cells. Thus, solvent flows out of the cells of the cucumber and into the brine solution, and the cucumber shrivels and becomes a pickle.

6.65 **a.** The 10% (m/v) starch solution has a higher osmotic pressure than pure water.
b. The water will initially flow into the starch solution to dilute solute concentration.
c. The volume of the starch solution will increase due to inflow of water.

6.67 Water flows out of the solution with the higher solvent concentration (which corresponds to a lower solute concentration) to the solution with a lower solvent concentration (which corresponds to a higher solute concentration).

a. Water flows into compartment B, which contains the 10% (m/v) glucose solution.
b. Water flows into compartment B, which contains the 8% (m/v) albumin solution.
c. Water flows into compartment B, which contains the 10% (m/v) NaCl solution.

6.69 A red blood cell has osmotic pressure of a 5% (m/v) glucose solution or a 0.90% (m/v) NaCl solution. In a hypotonic solution (lower osmotic pressure), solvent flows from the hypotonic solution into the red blood cell. When a red blood cell is placed in a hypertonic solution (higher osmotic pressure), solvent (water) flows from the red blood cell to the hypertonic solution. Isotonic solutions have the same osmotic pressure, and a red blood cell in an isotonic solution will not change volume because the flow of solvent into and out of the cell is equal.

a. Distilled water is a hypotonic solution when compared to a red blood cell's contents.
b. A 1% (m/v) glucose solution is a hypotonic solution.
c. A 0.90% (m/v) NaCl solution is isotonic with a red blood cell's contents.
d. A 5% (m/v) glucose solution is an isotonic solution.

6.71 Colloids cannot pass through the semipermeable dialysis membrane; water and solutions freely pass through semipermeable membranes.

a. Sodium and chloride ions will both pass through the membrane into the distilled water.
b. The amino acid alanine can pass through a dialysis membrane; the colloid starch will not.
c. Sodium and chloride ions will both be present in the water surrounding the dialysis bag; the colloid starch will not.
d. Urea will diffuse through the dialysis bag into the water.

6.73 Iodine is a nonpolar molecule and needs a nonpolar solvent such as hexane. Iodine does not dissolve in water because water is a polar solvent.

6.75
$$\frac{15.5 \text{ g } Na_2SO_4}{15.5 \text{ g } Na_2SO_4 + 75.5 \text{ g water}} \times 100 = 17.0\% \text{ m/m}$$

6.77 **a.**
$$24 \cancel{\text{hr}} \times \frac{750 \cancel{\text{mL solution}}}{12 \cancel{\text{hr}}} \times \frac{4 \text{ g amino acids}}{100 \cancel{\text{mL solution}}} = 60 \text{ g amino acids}$$

$$24 \cancel{\text{hr}} \times \frac{750 \cancel{\text{mL solution}}}{12 \cancel{\text{hr}}} \times \frac{25 \text{ g glucose}}{100 \cancel{\text{mL solution}}} = 380 \text{ g glucose}$$

$$24 \cancel{\text{hr}} \times \frac{500 \cancel{\text{mL solution}}}{12 \cancel{\text{hr}}} \times \frac{10 \text{ g lipid}}{100 \cancel{\text{mL solution}}} = 100 \text{ g lipid}$$

b. $60 \cancel{\text{g amino acids (protein)}} \times \frac{4 \text{ kcal}}{1 \cancel{\text{g protein}}} = 240 \text{ kcal}$

$380 \cancel{\text{g glucose (carb)}} \times \frac{4 \text{ kcal}}{1 \cancel{\text{g carb}}} = 1520 \text{ kcal}$

$100 \cancel{\text{g lipid (fat)}} \times \frac{9 \text{ kcal}}{1 \cancel{\text{g fat}}} = 900 \text{ kcal}$

Sum: 240 kcal + 1520 kcal + 900 kcal = (2660) = 2700 kcal/day

6.79 $4.5 \cancel{\text{mL propyl alcohol}} \times \frac{100 \text{ mL solution}}{12 \cancel{\text{mL propyl alcohol}}} = 38 \text{ mL of solution}$

6.81 $250 \cancel{\text{mL}} \times \frac{1 \cancel{\text{L}}}{1000 \cancel{\text{mL}}} \times \frac{2 \cancel{\text{moles KCl}}}{1 \cancel{\text{L}}} \times \frac{74.6 \text{ g KCl}}{1 \cancel{\text{mole KCl}}} = 37.3 \text{ g KCl}$

To make a 2.00 M KCl solution, weigh out 37.3 g KCl (0.500 mole) and place in a volumetric flask. Add enough water to dissolve the KCl and give a final volume of 0.250 L.

6.83 Mass of solution: 70.0 g solute + 130.0 g solvent = 200.0 g

a. $250 \cancel{\text{mL}} \times \frac{1 \cancel{\text{L}}}{1000 \cancel{\text{mL}}} \times \frac{2 \cancel{\text{moles KCl}}}{1 \cancel{\text{L}}} \times \frac{74.6 \text{ g KCl}}{1 \cancel{\text{mole KCl}}} = 37.3 \text{ g KCl}$

b. $200.0 \cancel{\text{g solution}} \times \frac{100 \text{ mL solution}}{1.21 \cancel{\text{g solution}}} = 165 \text{ mL of solution}$

c. $\frac{70.0 \text{ g } HNO_3}{165 \text{ mL solution}} \times 100 = 42.4\% \text{ (m/v) } HNO_3$

d. $\frac{70.0 \cancel{\text{g } HNO_3}}{0.165 \text{ L solution}} \times \frac{1 \text{ mole } HNO_3}{63.0 \cancel{\text{g } HNO_3}} = 6.73\% \text{ M } HNO_3$

6.85 **a.** $2.5 \cancel{\text{L}} \times \frac{3.0 \cancel{\text{moles } Al(NO_3)_3}}{1 \cancel{\text{L}}} \times \frac{213 \text{ g } Al(NO_3)_3}{1 \cancel{\text{mole } Al(NO_3)_3}} = 1600 \text{ g } Al(NO_3)_3$

b. $75 \cancel{\text{mL}} \times \frac{1 \cancel{\text{L}}}{1000 \cancel{\text{mL}}} \times \frac{0.50 \cancel{\text{mole } C_6H_{12}O_6}}{1 \cancel{\text{L}}} \times \frac{180 \text{ g } C_6H_{12}O_6}{1 \text{ mole } \cancel{C_6H_{12}O_6}} = 6.8 \text{ g of } C_6H_{12}O_6$

6.87 $60.0 \cancel{\text{mL } Al(OH)_3} \times \frac{1 \cancel{\text{L}}}{1000 \cancel{\text{mL } Al(OH)_3}} \times \frac{1.00 \cancel{\text{mole } Al(OH)_3}}{1 \cancel{\text{L}}} \times \frac{3 \cancel{\text{moles HCl}}}{1 \cancel{\text{mole } Al(OH)_3}} \times$

$\frac{1000 \text{ mL HCl}}{6.00 \cancel{\text{moles HCl}}} = 30.0 \text{ mL HCl solution}$

6.89 A solution with a high salt (solute) concentration will dry flowers because water (solvent) flows out of the flowers' cells and into the salt solution to dilute the salt concentration.

6.91 Drinking seawater, which is hypertonic, will cause water to flow out of the body cells and dehydrate the body's cells.

Answers to Understanding the Concepts

6.93 **a.** 3 (no dissociation) **b.** 1 (some dissociation, a few ions)
c. 2 (all ionized)

6.95 A "brine" salt-water solution has a high concentration of Na^+ Cl^-, which is hypertonic to the pickle. Therefore, water flows from the cucumber into the hypertonic salt solution that surrounds it. The loss of water causes the cucumber to become a wrinkled pickle.

6.97 **a.** 2 To halve the % concentration, the volume would double.
b. 3 To go to one-fourth the % concentration, the final volume would be four times the initial volume.

6.99 **a.** 2 Water will flow into the B (8%) side.
b. 1 Water will continue to flow equally in both directions; no change in volumes.
c. 3 Water will flow into the A (5%) side.
d. 2 Water will flow into the B (1%) side.

Chapter 7

Key Terms

Answers **1.** b **2.** d **3.** a **4.** e **5.** c

7.1 Acids and Bases

◆ Learning Exercise 7.1A

Answers **1.** A **2.** A **3.** B **4.** A **5.** B **6.** B **7.** A **8.** B

◆ Learning Exercise 7.1B

Answers
1. hydrochloric acid **2.** NaOH **3.** H_2SO_3
4. HNO_3 **5.** calcium hydroxide **6.** carbonic acid
7. aluminum hydroxide **8.** KOH

7.2 Brønsted–Lowry Acids and Bases

◆ Learning Exercise 7.2A

Answers
1. OH^- **2.** SO_4^{2-} **3.** HF **4.** HCO_3^-
5. NO_3^- **6.** NH_3 **7.** H_2S **8.** H_3PO_4

◆ Learning Exercise 7.2B

Answers
1. HF/F^- and H_2O/H_3O^+ **2.** NH_4^+/NH_3 and SO_4^{2-}/HSO_4^-
3. NH_3/NH_4^+ and H_2O/OH^- **4.** HNO_3/NO_3^- and OH^-/H_2O

7.3 Strengths of Acids and Bases

◆ Learning Exercise 7.3A

Answers
1. strong acid **2.** weak acid **3.** weak acid **4.** weak base
5. strong base **6.** weak acid **7.** strong base **8.** strong acid

◆ Learning Exercise 7.3B

Answers **1.** HCl **2.** HNO_2 **3.** HBr **4.** H_2SO_4 **5.** H_3PO_4

7.4 Ionization of Water

◆ Learning Exercise 7.4

Answers
a. 1.0×10^{-4} M **b.** 5.0×10^{-10} M **c.** 2.2×10^{-8} M
d. 1.3×10^{-11} M **e.** 1.8×10^{-7} M

7.5 The pH Scale

Learning Exercise 7.5A

Answers **1.** basic **2.** acidic **3.** acidic **4.** acidic **5.** acidic
6. acidic **7.** neutral **8.** basic **9.** basic **10.** acidic

◆ Learning Exercise 7.5B

Answers **a.** 8.0 **b.** 2.0 **c.** 3.0 **d.** 4.0

Learning Exercise 7.5C

Answers **a.** 3.0 **b.** 8.0 **c.** 8.0 **d.** 4.0

Learning Exercise 7.5D

Answers

	$[H_3O^+]$	$[OH^-]$	pH
a.	1×10^{-2} M	1×10^{-12} M	2.0
b.	1×10^{-8} M	1×10^{-6} M	8.0
c.	1×10^{-10} M	1×10^{-4} M	10.0
d.	1×10^{-7} M	1×10^{-7} M	7.0
e.	1×10^{-1} M	1×10^{-13} M	1.0

7.6 Reactions of Acids and Bases

Learning Exercise 7.6A

Answers

1. $1\ Zn(s) + 2\ HCl(aq) \rightarrow 1\ ZnCl_2(aq) + H_2(g)$
2. $2\ HCl(aq) + 1\ Li_2CO_3(s) \rightarrow 1\ CO_2(g) + 1\ H_2O(l) + 2\ LiCl(aq)$
3. $1\ HCl(aq) + 1\ NaHCO_3(s) \rightarrow 1\ CO_2(g) + 1\ H_2O(l) + 1\ NaCl(aq)$
4. $2\ Al(s) + 3\ H_2SO_4(aq) \rightarrow 1\ Al_2(SO_4)_3(aq) + 3\ H_2(g)$

Learning Exercise 7.6B

Answers

1. $2\ NaOH(aq) + 1\ H_2SO_4(aq) \rightarrow 1\ Na_2SO_4(aq) + 2\ H_2O(l)$
2. $1\ Mg(OH)_2(aq) + 2HCl(aq) \rightarrow 1MgCl_2(aq) + 2\ H_2O(l)$
3. $1\ Al(OH)_3(aq) + 3HNO_3(aq) \rightarrow 1\ Al(NO_3)_3(aq) + 3\ H_2O(l)$
4. $3\ Ca(OH)_2(aq) + 2H_3PO_4(aq) \rightarrow 1Ca_3(PO_4)_2(s) + 6\ H_2O(l)$

Learning Exercise 7.6C

Answers

a. $3\ KOH(aq) + 1\ H_3PO_4(aq) \rightarrow 1\ K_3PO_4(aq) + 3\ H_2O(l)$
b. $2\ NaOH(aq) + 1\ H_2SO_4(aq) \rightarrow 1\ Na_2SO_4(aq) + 2H_2O(l)$
c. $Al(OH)_3(aq) + 3\ HCl(aq) \rightarrow 1\ AlCl_3(aq) + 3H_2O(l)$
d. $2\ Fe(OH)_3(aq) + 3H_2SO_4(aq) \rightarrow 1\ Fe_2(SO_4)_3(s) + 6H_2O(l)$

Learning Exercise 7.6D

Answers **1.** 0.298 M HCl **2.** 0.165 M H_2SO_4

7.7 Buffers

Learning Exercise 7.7

Answers

a. No. A strong acid is not a buffer.
b. No. A salt alone cannot act as a buffer.
c. No. A weak acid alone cannot act as a buffer.
d. Yes. A weak acid and its salt act as a buffer system.

Answers to the Practice Test

1. A	**2.** C	**3.** B	**4.** A	**5.** C
6. D	**7.** D	**8.** B	**9.** B	**10.** C
11. C	**12.** B	**13.** C	**14.** A	**15.** C
16. B	**17.** E	**18.** E	**19.** B	**20.** A
21. E	**22.** C			

Answers and Solutions to Selected Text Problems

7.1 According to the Arrhenius theory,

a. acids taste sour.
b. acids neutralize bases.
c. acids produce H_3O^+ ions in water.
d. potassium hydroxide is the name of a base.

7.3 The names of nonoxy acids begin with *hydro-*, followed by the name of the anion. The names of oxyacids use the element root with *-ic acid*. Acids with one oxygen less than the common *-ic acid* name are named as *-ous acids*.

a. hydrochloric acid **b.** calcium hydroxide **c.** carbonic acid
d. nitric acid **e.** sulfurous acid

7.5 **a.** $Mg(OH)_2$ **b.** HF **c.** H_3PO_4
d. LiOH **e.** $Cu(OH)_2$

7.7 The acid donates a proton (H^+), while the base accepts a proton.

a. Acid (proton donor) HI proton acceptor (base) H_2O
b. Acid (proton donor) H_2O proton acceptor (base) F^-

7.9 To form the conjugate base, remove a proton (H^+) from the acid.

a. F^-, fluoride ion **b.** OH^-, hydroxide ion
c. HCO_3^-, bicarbonate ion or hydrogen carbonate **d.** SO_4^{2-}, sulfate ion

7.11 To form the conjugate acid, add a proton (H^+) to the base.

a. HCO_3^-, bicarbonate ion or hydrogen carbonate **b.** H_3O^+, hydronium ion
c. H_3PO_4, phosphoric acid **d.** HBr, hydrobromic acid

7.13 The conjugate acid is a proton donor and the conjugate base is a proton acceptor.

a. acid H_2CO_3; conjugate base HCO_3^-; base H_2O; conjugate acid H_3O^+
b. acid NH_4^+; conjugate base NH_3; base H_2O; conjugate acid H_3O^+
c. acid HCN; conjugate base CN^-; base NO_2^- conjugate acid HNO_2

7.15 Use Table 7.3 to answer.

a. HBr **b.** HSO_4^- **c.** H_2CO_3

7.17 Use Table 7.3 to answer.

a. HSO_4^- **b.** HF **c.** HCO_3^-

7.19 In pure water, a small fraction of the water molecules breaks apart to form H^+ and OH^-. The H^+ combines with H_2O to form H_3O^+. Every time a H^+ is formed a OH^- is also formed. Therefore, the concentration of the two must be equal in pure water.

7.21 In an acidic solution, $[H_3O^+]$ is greater than $[OH^-]$, which means that the $[H_3O^+]$ is greater than 1×10^{-7} M and the $[OH^-]$ is less than 1×10^{-7} M.

7.23 A neutral solution has $[OH^-] = [H_3O^+] = 1.0 \times 10^{-7}$ M. If $[OH^-]$ is greater than 1×10^{-7}, the solution is basic; if $[H_3O^+]$ is greater than 1×10^{-7} M, the solution is acidic.

a. Acidic; $[H_3O^+]$ is greater than 1×10^{-7} M.
b. Basic; $[H_3O^+]$ is less than 1×10^{-7} M.
c. Basic; $[OH^-]$ is greater than 1×10^{-7} M.
d. Acidic; $[OH^-]$ is less than 1×10^{-7} M.

7.25 The $[H_3O^+]$ multiplied by the $[OH^-]$ is equal to K_w, which is 1.0×10^{-14}. When $[H_3O^+]$ is known, the $[OH^-]$ can be calculated.

Rearranging the K_w gives $[OH^-] = K_w/[H_3O^+]$.

a. 1.0×10^{-9} M
b. 1.0×10^{-6} M
c. 2.0×10^{-5} M
d. 4.0×10^{-13} M

7.27 The value of the $[H_3O^+]$ multiplied by the value of the $[OH^-]$ is always equal to K_w, which is 1×10^{-14}. When $[H_3O^+]$ is known, the $[OH^-]$ can be calculated.

Rearranging the K_w gives $[OH^-] = K_w /[H_3O^+]$.

a. 1.0×10^{-11} M
b. 2.0×10^{-9} M
c. 5.6×10^{-3} M
d. 2.5×10^{-2} M

7.29 In neutral solutions, the $[H_3O^+]$ is equal to 1.0×10^{-7} M. The pH is the $-\log [H_3O^+]$ and the $-\log [1.0 \times 10^{-7}] = 7.00$. Note that the pH has two *decimal places* because the coefficient 1.0 has two significant figures.

7.31 An acidic solution has a pH less than 7. A neutral solution has a pH equal to 7. A basic solution has a pH greater than 7.

a. basic **b.** acidic **c.** basic **d.** acidic

7.33 The value of $[H_3O^+][OH^-]$ is equal to K_w, which is 1.0×10^{-14}. Rearranging the K_w gives $[H_3O^+] = K_w / [OH^-]$.

a. 4.0 **b.** 8.5 **c.** 9.0 **d.** 3.40

7.35 On a calculator, pH is calculated by entering -log, followed by the coefficient EE (EXP) key and the power of 10 followed by the change sign (+/−) key. On some calculators the concentration is entered first (coefficient EXP − power) followed by log and +/− key.

$[H_3O^+]$	$[OH^-]$	pH	Acidic, Basic, or Neutral?
1×10^{-8} M	1×10^{-6} M	8.0	Basic
1×10^{-3} M	1×10^{-11} M	3.0	Acidic
2×10^{-5} M	5×10^{-10} M	4.7	Acidic
1×10^{-12} M	1×10^{-2} M	12.0	Basic

7.37 Acids react with active metals to form H_2 and a salt of the metal. The reaction of acids with carbonates yields CO_2, H_2O, and a salt of the metal. In a neutralization reaction, an acid and a base form a salt and H_2O.

a. $ZnCO_3(s) + 2HBr(aq) \rightarrow ZnBr_2(aq) + CO_2(g) + H_2O(l)$
b. $Zn(s) + 2HCl(aq) \rightarrow ZnCl_2(aq) + H_2(g)$
c. $HCl(aq) + NaHCO_3(s) \rightarrow NaCl(aq) + H_2O(l) + CO_2(g)$
d. $H_2SO_4(aq) + Mg(OH)_2(s) \rightarrow MgSO_4(aq) + 2\,H_2O(l)$

7.39 In balancing a neutralization equation, the number of H^+ and OH^- must be equalized by placing coefficients in front of the formulas for the acid and base.

a. $2HCl(aq) + Mg(OH)_2(s) \rightarrow MgCl_2(aq) + 2H_2O(l)$
b. $H_3PO_4(aq) + 3LiOH(aq) \rightarrow Li_3PO_4(aq) + 3H_2O(l)$

7.41 In balancing a neutralization equation, the number of H^+ and OH^- must be equalized by placing coefficients in front of the formulas for the acid and base.

a. $H_2SO_4(aq) + 2NaOH(aq) \rightarrow Na_2SO_4(aq) + 2H_2O(l)$
b. $3HCl(aq) + Fe(OH)_3(aq) \rightarrow FeCl_3(aq) + 3H_2O(l)$
c. $H_2CO_3(aq) + Mg(OH)_2(s) \rightarrow MgCO_3(aq) + 2H_2O(l)$

7.43 In the equation, one mole HCl reacts with one mole NaOH.

$$\text{Moles of NaOH: } 28.6\,\cancel{\text{mL}} \times \frac{1\text{ L}}{1000\,\cancel{\text{mL}}} = 0.0286\,\cancel{\text{L}} \times \frac{0.145\text{ mole NaOH}}{1\,\cancel{\text{L}}}$$

$= 0.00415$ mole NaOH

$$0.00415\,\cancel{\text{mole NaOH}} \times \frac{1\text{ mole HCl}}{1\text{ mole }\cancel{\text{NaOH}}} = 0.00415\text{ mole HCl}$$

$$\text{Molarity of HCl: } 5.00\,\cancel{\text{mL}} \times \frac{1\text{ L}}{1000\,\cancel{\text{mL}}} = 0.00500\,\cancel{\text{L}} \qquad \frac{0.00415\text{ mole HCl}}{0.00500\text{ L}} = 0.829\text{ M}$$

7.45 In the equation, one mole H_2SO_4 reacts with two moles KOH.

$$\text{Moles of KOH: } 38.2\,\cancel{\text{mL}} \times \frac{1\text{ L}}{1000\,\cancel{\text{mL}}} = 0.0382\,\cancel{\text{L}} \times \frac{0.163\text{ mole KOH}}{1\,\cancel{\text{L}}} = 0.00623\text{ mole KOH}$$

$$\text{Moles of } H_2SO_4: 0.00623\,\cancel{\text{mole KOH}} \times \frac{1\text{ mole } H_2SO_4}{2\,\cancel{\text{moles KOH}}} = 0.00312\text{ mole } H_2SO_4$$

$$\text{Molarity of } H_2SO_4: 25.0\,\cancel{\text{mL}} \times \frac{1\text{ L}}{1000\,\cancel{\text{mL}}} = 0.0250\,\cancel{\text{L}} \qquad \frac{0.00312\text{ mole } H_2SO_4}{0.0250\text{ L}} = 0.125\text{ M}$$

7.47 A buffer system contains a weak acid and its salt, or a weak base and its salt.

a. This is not a buffer system, because it only contains a strong acid.
b. This is a buffer system; it contains the weak acid H_2CO_3 and its salt $NaHCO_3$.
c. This is a buffer system; it contains HF, a weak acid, and its salt KF.
d. This is not a buffer system because it contains the salts KCl and NaCl.

7.49 **a.** A buffer system keeps the pH of a solution constant.
b. The salt of the acid in a buffer is needed to neutralize any acid added.
c. When H^+ is added to the buffer, the F^-, which is the salt of the weak acid, reacts with the acid to neutralize it.
d. When OH^- is added to the buffer solution, HF (weak acid) reacts to neutralize the OH^-.

7.51 The name of an acid from a simple nonmetallic anion is formed by adding the prefix *hydro-* to the name of the anion and changing the anion ending to *-ic acid.* If the acid has polyatomic anion, the name of the acid uses the name of the polyatomic anion and ends in *-ic acid* or *-ous acid.* There is no prefix *hydro.* Bases are named as ionic compounds containing hydroxide anions.

a. sulfuric acid **b.** potassium hydroxide
c. calcium hydroxide **d.** hydrochloric acid **e.** nitrous acid

7.53 Both strong and weak acids dissolve in water to give H_3O^+. They both neutralize bases, turn litmus red and phenolphthalein clear. Both taste sour and are electrolytes in solution. However, weak acids are only slightly dissociated in solution and are weak electrolytes. Strong acids, which are nearly completely dissociated in solution, are strong electrolytes.

7.55 **a.** $Mg(OH)_2$ is a strong base because all the base that dissolves is dissociated in aqueous solution.
b. $Mg(OH)_2(aq) + 2\,HCl(aq) \rightarrow 2\,H_2O(l) + MgCl_2(aq)$

7.57 If the $[OH^-]$ is given, the $[H_3O^+]$ can be found from $[H_3O^+][OH^-] = 1 \times 10^{-14}$.

a. pH 7.70
b. pH 1.30
c. $[H_3O^+] = 2.9 \times 10^{-11}$, pH 10.54
d. $[H_3O^+] = 2. \times 10^{-12}$, pH 11.7

7.59 If the pH is given, the $[H_3O^+]$ can be found by using the relationship $[H_3O^+] = 1.0 \times 10^{-pH}$. The $[OH^-]$ can be found from $[H_3O^+][OH^-] = 1 \times 10^{-14}$.

a. $[H_3O^+] = 1 \times 10^{-3}$ M $\quad [OH^-] = 1 \times 10^{-11}$ M
b. $[H_3O^+] = 1 \times 10^{-6}$ M $\quad [OH^-] = 1 \times 10^{-8}$ M
c. $[H_3O^+] = 1 \times 10^{-8}$ M $\quad [OH^-] = 1 \times 10^{-6}$ M
d. $[H_3O^+] = 1 \times 10^{-11}$ M $\quad [OH^-] = 1 \times 10^{-3}$ M

7.61 In a buffer, the anion accepts H^+ and the cation provides H^+.

a. $H_2PO_4^-(aq) + H_3O^+(aq) \rightarrow H_3PO_4(aq) + H_2O(l)$
b. $H_3PO_4(aq) + OH^-(aq) \rightarrow H_2PO_4^-(aq) + H_2O(l)$

7.63 **a.** One mole HCl reacts with one mole NaOH.

$$\text{Moles of HCl: } 25.0\,\cancel{\text{mL}} \times \frac{1\text{ L}}{1000\,\cancel{\text{mL}}} = 0.0250\,\cancel{\text{L}} \times \frac{0.288\text{ mole HCl}}{1\,\cancel{\text{L}}} = 0.00720\text{ mole HCl}$$

$$0.00720\,\cancel{\text{mole HCl}} \times \frac{1\text{ mole NaOH}}{1\,\cancel{\text{mole HCl}}} = 0.00720\text{ mole NaOH}$$

$$\text{Volume of NaOH: } 0.00720\,\cancel{\text{mole}} \times \frac{1\,\cancel{\text{L}}}{0.150\,\cancel{\text{mole}}} \times \frac{1000\text{ mL}}{1\,\cancel{\text{L}}} = 48.0\text{ mL}$$

b. One mole H_2SO_4 reacts with two moles NaOH.

$$\text{Moles of } H_2SO_4: 10.0\,\cancel{\text{mL}} \times \frac{1\text{ L}}{1000\,\cancel{\text{mL}}} = 0.0100\,\cancel{\text{L}} \times \frac{0.560\text{ mole}}{1\,\cancel{\text{L}}} = 0.00560\text{ mole } H_2SO_4$$

$$0.00560\,\cancel{\text{mole } H_2SO_4} \times \frac{2\text{ mole NaOH}}{1\,\cancel{\text{mole } H_2SO_4}} = 0.0112\text{ mole NaOH}$$

$$\text{Volume of NaOH: } 0.0112\,\cancel{\text{mole}} \times \frac{1\,\cancel{\text{L}}}{0.150\,\cancel{\text{mole}}} \times \frac{1000\text{ mL}}{1\,\cancel{\text{L}}} = 74.7\text{ mL}$$

7.65 One mole H_2SO_4 reacts with two moles NaOH.

$$\text{Moles of NaOH: } 45.6\,\cancel{\text{mL}} \times \frac{1\text{ L}}{1000\,\cancel{\text{mL}}} = 0.0456\,\cancel{\text{L}} \times \frac{0.205\text{ mole}}{1\,\cancel{\text{L}}} = 0.00935\text{ mole NaOH}$$

$$\text{Moles of } H_2SO_4: 0.00935\,\cancel{\text{mole NaOH}} \times \frac{1\text{ mole } H_2SO_4}{2\,\cancel{\text{moles NaOH}}} = 0.00468\text{ mole } H_2SO_4$$

$$\text{Molarity of } H_2SO_4: 20.0\,\cancel{\text{mL}} \times \frac{1\text{ L}}{1000\,\cancel{\text{mL}}} = 0.0200\,\cancel{\text{L}} \qquad \frac{0.00468\text{ mole } H_2SO_4}{0.0200\text{ L}} = 0.234\text{ M}$$

7.67 **A.** This diagram represents a weak acid; only a few HX molecules are broken up into H_3O^+ and X^- ions.
B. This diagram represents a strong acid; all the HX molecules are broken up into H_3O^+ and X^- ions.
C. This diagram represents a weak acid; only a few HX molecules are broken up into H_3O^+ and X^- ions.

7.69 **a.** During hyperventilation, a person will lose CO_2 and the blood pH will rise.
b. Breathing into a paper bag will increase the CO_2 concentration and lower the blood pH.

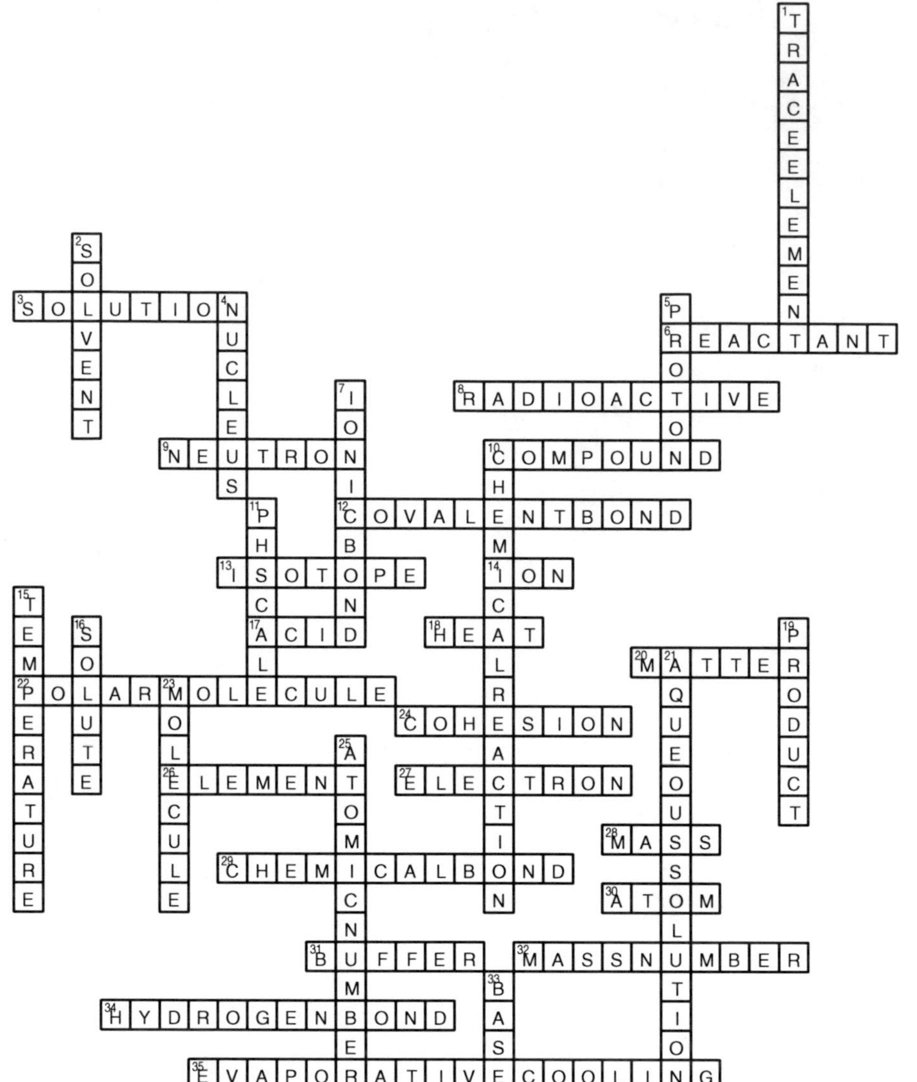

1 TRACEELEMENT
2 SOLVENT
3 SOLUTION
4 NUCLEUS
5 PROTON
6 REACTANT
7 IONICBOND
8 RADIOACTIVE
9 NEUTRON
10 CHEMICALREACTION
COMPOUND
11 PHYSICAL
12 COVALENTBOND
13 ISOTOPE
14 ION
15 TEMPERATURE
16 SOLUTE
17 ACID
18 HEAT
19 PRODUCT
20 MATTER
21 AQUEOUSSOLUTION
22 POLARMOLECULE
23 MOLECULE
24 COHESION
25 ATOMICNUMBER
26 ELEMENT
27 ELECTRON
28 MASS
29 CHEMICALBOND
30 ATOM
31 BUFFER
32 MASSNUMBER
33 BASS
34 HYDROGENBOND
35 EVAPORATIVECOOLING

Chapter 8

Organic Chemistry

Structures of Organic Compounds

1. What are the chemical formulas for the following structures?

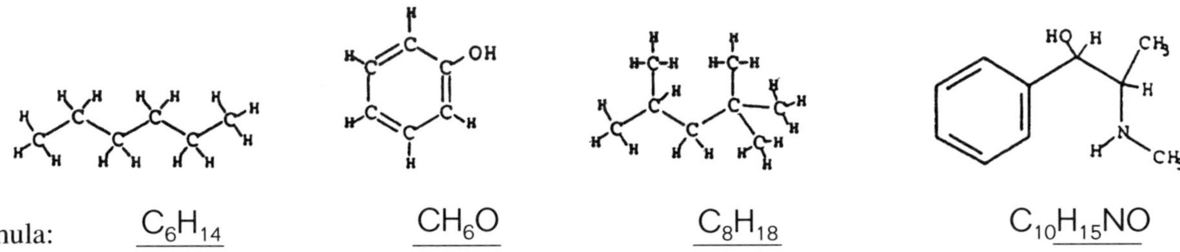

Formula: C_6H_{14} CH_6O C_8H_{18} $C_{10}H_{15}NO$

2. How many covalent bonds is carbon able to form? 4

3. What is wrong with the structure shown in the box at right?

THE CARBON OF THE CARBONYL IS BONDED 5 TIMES

4. a. Draw a hydrocarbon that contains 4 carbon atoms.

b. Redraw your structure and transform it into an amine.

c. Transform your amine into an amide. You may need to relocate the nitrogen.

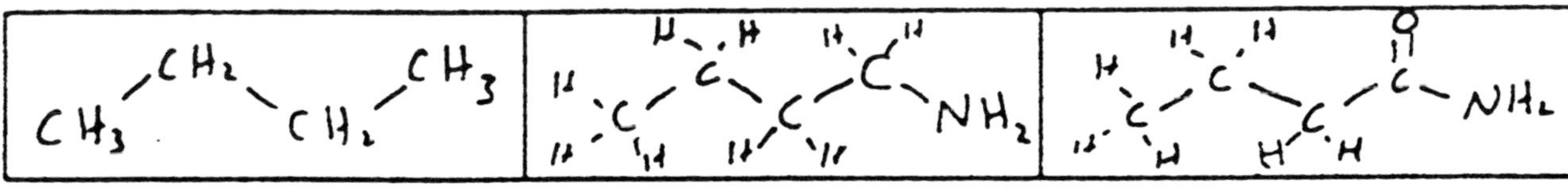

d. Redraw your amide, transforming it into a carboxylic acid.

e. Redraw your carboxylic acid, transforming it into an alcohol.

f. Rearrange the carbons of your alcohol to make an ether.

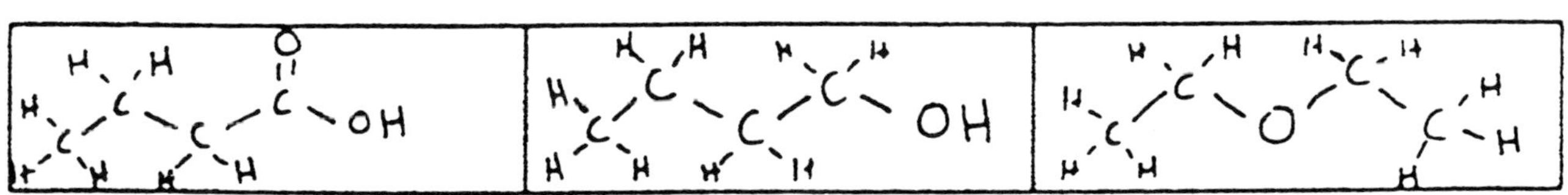

Organic Chemistry

Polymers

1. Circle the monomers that may be useful for forming an addition polymer and draw a box around the ones that may be useful for forming a condensation polymer.

$H_2C{=}CH_2$ (circled)

$HO{-}C({=}O){-}CH_2CH_2CH_2CH_3$

$H_2N{-}C_6H_{10}{-}NH_2$ (cyclohexane ring, boxed)

$H_2N{-}CH(CH_3){-}C({=}O){-}OH$ (boxed)

$HO{-}C({=}O){-}CH_2{-}CH{=}CH_3$ (circled)

$HO{-}C({=}O){-}CH_2CH_2CH_2CH_2{-}C({=}O){-}OH$ (boxed)

2. Which type of polymer always weighs less than the sum of its parts? Why?

THE CONDENSATION POLYMERS LOSE SMALL MOLECULES SUCH AS WATER WHEN THEY FORM AND THUS THE POLYMER THAT FORMS WEIGHS LESS THAN THE SUM OF ITS MONOMERS.

3. Would a material with the following arrangement of polymer molecules have a relatively high or low melting point? Why?

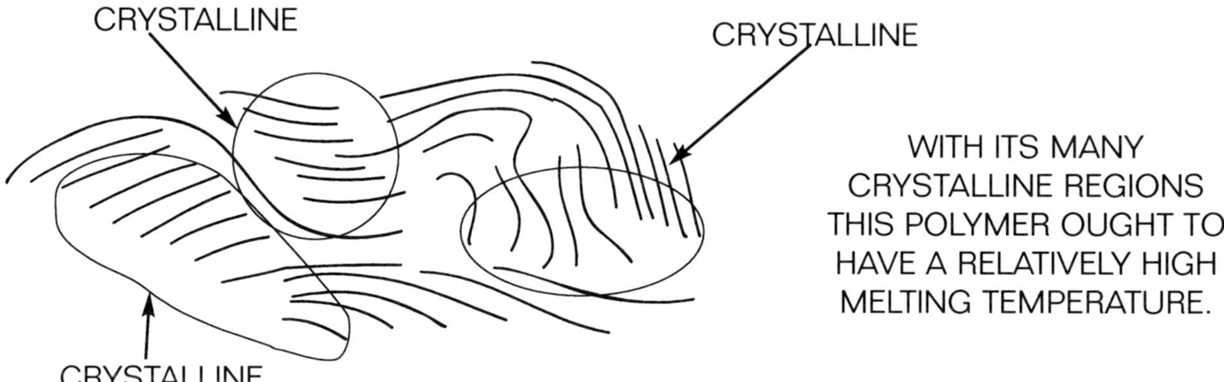

WITH ITS MANY CRYSTALLINE REGIONS THIS POLYMER OUGHT TO HAVE A RELATIVELY HIGH MELTING TEMPERATURE.

Answers to the Practice Test

Multiple Choice

1. D
2. A
3. C
4. C
5. C
6. D
7. B
8. A
9. A
10. B
11. B
12. C

Fill in the Blanks

1. protons
2. atoms, molecule
3. O═O, O::O
4. Reaction a: decomposition reaction; Reaction b: exchange or transfer reaction; Reaction c: synthesis reaction
5. hydrogen (H^+), hydroxyl (OH^-)
6. buffers, protein
7. hydrophilic, hydrophobic
8. peptide, hydrogen
9. deoxyribose, ribose
10. DNA sequence: 3' — TAACGATGGCTA — 5';

    RNA sequence: 3' — UAACGAUGGCUA — 5'

Short Answer

1. An element (gold is an example) is matter composed of only one type of atom. A molecule (molecular oxygen, O_2, is an example) is matter composed of two or more atoms held together by chemical bonds. A compound (water, H_2O, is an example) is matter composed of two or more different elements.
2. See pictures of the electron shells of both calcium and chlorine. The valence of calcium is +2 and the valence of chlorine is –1 (thus 2 chlorine atoms are needed to balance the +2 of calcium). Chlorine has 7 electrons in its valence shell and calcium has 2; each chlorine will pull one of calcium's electrons to it to complete the shell.
3. Polyunsaturated fats would contribute least to atherosclerosis because they will not pack as well and should not produce the solid deposits in the arteries that cause heart disease (they should remain more liquid at body temperature).
4. The five primary functions of proteins are: 1) structure, 2) catalysis, 3) regulation, 4) transportation, and 5) defense and offense. Without proteins to give the cell structure, the cells could not physically form or maintain stable shape in the environment. Without proteins to perform catalysis, metabolism would not occur and the cell would die. Without proteins to regulate the function of the cell, it could not know when to take in nutrients, grow, or divide, and thus would not be able to respond to its environment. Without proteins for transportation, the cells could not move molecules across their membranes and thus could not acquire food. Without proteins for defense and offense, the cell would be unable to protect itself from pathogens.

Critical Thinking

1. Metabolism is the sum total of all chemical reactions inside an organism. Anabolism is the reaction that builds and catabolism is the reaction that takes apart (synthesis and decomposition, respectively). The bacterium in the human intestinal tract would be expected to have higher metabolic function because it has more nutrients available to fuel catabolism which in turn drives anabolism of new components or microbes. Fewer nutrients will be available to the bacterium living in the flowerpot.

2. Microbes that can drastically alter the environment to suit their own needs can outcompete other microbes essentially by eliminating them. Organisms that cannot adapt to acid conditions, for example, will die, leaving the acid producer in charge of the field. Specialization of environment is one way microbes survive, and is one of the things that makes them so prevalent in the biosphere.

3. Neutral mutations predominate in nature because they run the least risk of doing something harmful. If a protein is destroyed by a single substitution, then chances are some function of the cell no longer works. That cell is less able to survive and thus dies before propagating. It is, essentially, deselected by evolutionary processes. Mutations that have no particular effect on survival do not get deselected, and thus remain in the population.

Concept Building Questions

1. In the fermentation of wine, sugar molecules are broken down into smaller alcohol molecules as well as carbon dioxide. The chemical reaction represented is a decomposition reaction. Decomposition reactions are important because they allow microbes to take large, complex molecules and break them down into smaller, more versatile molecules that can be used in a variety of subsequent chemical reactions.

2. Understanding how chemical bonds form helps us to understand how relationships form between molecules and organisms in that it gives us a sense of permanence (covalent vs. ionic associations), specificity (more bonds/better bonding usually implies a closer "match" between objects), and coexistence possibilities (the longer microbes live together the more probable it is for them to engage in shared associations). In the environment, these ideas can tell us about which microbes live together in a certain place, how long they have lived together, what types of animals a pathogenic organism can infect, etc.

Answers to Integrated Science Concepts

Drug Action and Discovery

1. The drug is viewed as the key.

3. Whether a drug is isolated from nature or synthesized in the laboratory makes no difference as to "how good it may be for you." There are a multitude of natural products that are downright harmful, just as there are many synthetic drugs that are also harmful. The effectiveness of a drug depends on its chemical structure, not the source of this chemical structure.

Exercises

1. To make it to the top of the fractionating column, a substance must remain in the gaseous phase. Only substances with very low boiling points, such as methane (−160°C) are able to make it to the top. According to Figure 14.3, gasoline travels higher than kerosene and so it must have a lower boiling point. Kerosene, therefore, has the higher boiling point.

3. The percent carbon increases as the hydrocarbon gets bigger. Methane's percent carbon is 20%; ethane, 25%; propane, 27%; butane, 29%.

5. C_4H_8O

7. In order of least to most oxidized $b < a < d < c$, whereas c is the most oxidized. Note how this was the order of their presentation within the chapter. The most reduced hydrocarbons were introduced first, followed by the alcohols, followed by the aldehydes, followed by the carboxylic acids.

9. The second and the fourth structures are the same. In all, there are three different structures shown.

11. The long, nonpolar hydrocarbon tail embeds itself in a person's oily skin, where the molecule initiates an allergic response. Scratching the itch spreads tetrahydrourushiol molecules over a greater surface area, causing the zone of irritation to grow.

13. Aspirin's chemical name is acetyl salicylic acid. It is the acidic nature of aspirin that gives rise to its sour taste.

15. The transformation of benzaldehyde to benzoic acid is an oxidation.

17. Ultimately, this is the energy that was captured from the sun by photosynthetic plants that turned into fossil fuels after decaying under anaerobic conditions.

19. Note the similarities between the structure of SBR and polyethylene and polystyrene, all of which possess no heteroatoms. SBR is an addition polymer made from the monomers 1,3-butadiene and styrene mixed together in a 3:1 ratio. Notably, SBR is the key ingredient that allows the formation of bubbles within bubble gum.

21. Today we take polymers and their remarkable properties for granted. Not so back during the time of World War II when their remarkable properties had a significant impact on how the war was won—Nylon for parachutes, synthetic rubber for tires, polyethylene for RADAR, Plexiglas for airplane gunner turets, and Teflon to help in the development of the nuclear bomb.

Problems

1.

3.

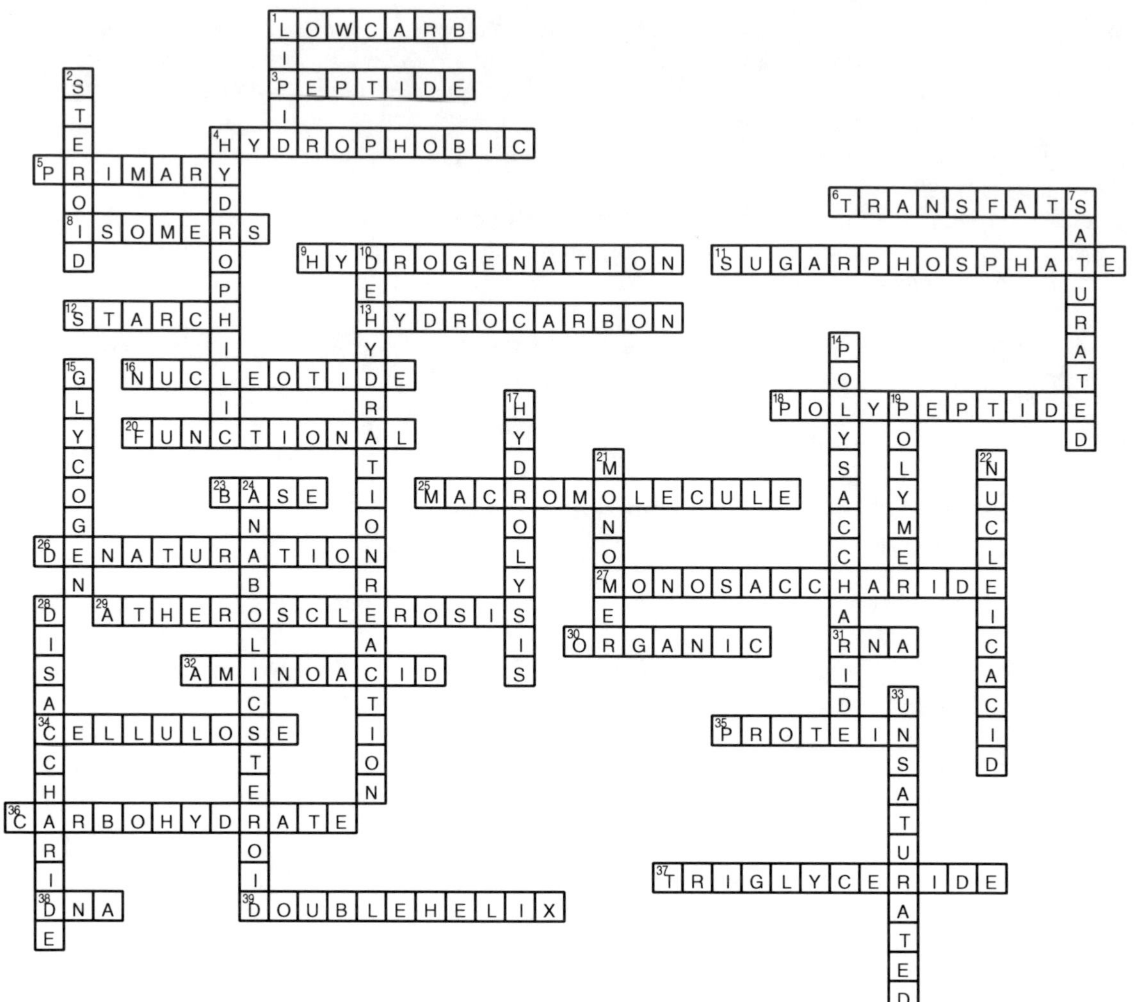

1 LOWCARB
1 LIPID
2 STEROID
3 PEPTIDE
4 HYDROPHOBIC
4 HYDROPHILIC
5 PRIMARY
6 TRANSFATS
7 SATURATED
8 ISOMERS
9 HYDROGENATION
10 DEHYDRATIONREACTION
11 SUGARPHOSPHATE
12 STARCH
13 HYDROCARBON
14 POLYSACCHARIDE
15 GLYCOGEN
16 NUCLEOTIDE
17 HYDROLYSIS
18 POLYPEPTIDE
19 POLYMER
20 FUNCTIONAL
21 MONOMER
22 NUCLEICACID
23 BASE
24 ANABOLICSTEROID
25 MACROMOLECULE
26 DENATURATION
27 MONOSACCHARIDE
28 DISACCHARIDE
29 ATHEROSCLEROSIS
30 ORGANIC
31 RNA
32 AMINOACID
33 UNSATURATED
34 CELLULOSE
35 PROTEIN
36 CARBOHYDRATE
37 TRIGLYCERIDE
38 DNA
39 DOUBLEHELIX

Chapter 9

Answers to the Practice Test

1. A
2. True
3. False, do not regenerate
4. oxygen
5. A
6. C
7. C
8. B
9. True
10. False, nucleus
11. organelles
12. 1000
13. scanning
14. transmission
15. eukaryotic, prokaryotic
16. cell
17. pili
18. cytoplasm
19. cytosol
20. E
21. B
22. D
23. proteins
24. mosaic
25. junctions
26. D
27. A
28. True
29. messenger RNA
30. ribosomes
31. C
32. A
33. A
34. False, Golgi apparatus
35. lysosomes
36. rough
37. E
38. E
39. True
40. ATP
41. cristae
42. E
43. D
44. False, microtubules
45. microtubules
46. B
47. A
48. True
49. phospholipids

The Basic Unit of Life—The Cell

Features of Prokaryotic and Eukaryotic Cells

1. Are the following associated with prokaryotic cells, eukaryotic cells, or both?

a. nucleic acids —BOTH
b. cell membrane —BOTH
c. nucleus —EUKARYOTIC
d. organelles —EUKARYOTIC
e. mitochondria —EUKARYOTIC
f. chloroplasts —EUKARYOTIC
g. bacteria —PROKARYOTIC
h. circular chromosome —PROKARYOTIC
i. cytoplasm —BOTH
j. human cells —EUKARYOTIC

2. Match the following organelles with their functions:

ribosome —G
rough endoplasmic reticulum —A
smooth endoplasmic reticulum —F
golgi apparatus —D
lysosome —H
mitochondrion —B
chloroplast —C
cytoskeleton —E

a. assembles proteins destined to go either to the cell membrane or to leave the cell
b. obtains energy for the cell to use
c. in plant cells, captures energy from sunlight to build organic molecules
d. receives products from the endoplasmic reticulum and packages them for transport
e. helps cell hold its shape
f. assembles membranes and performs other specialized functions in certain cells
g. assembles proteins for the cell
h. breaks down organic materials

Features of Prokaryotic and Eukaryotic Cells—continued

3. What are the three components of a cell membrane? Draw a portion of a cell membrane showing each of these components.

THE THREE PRIMARY COMPONENTS OF THE CELL MEMBRANE ARE PHOSPHOLIPIDS, PROTEINS, AND SHORT CARBOHYDRATES

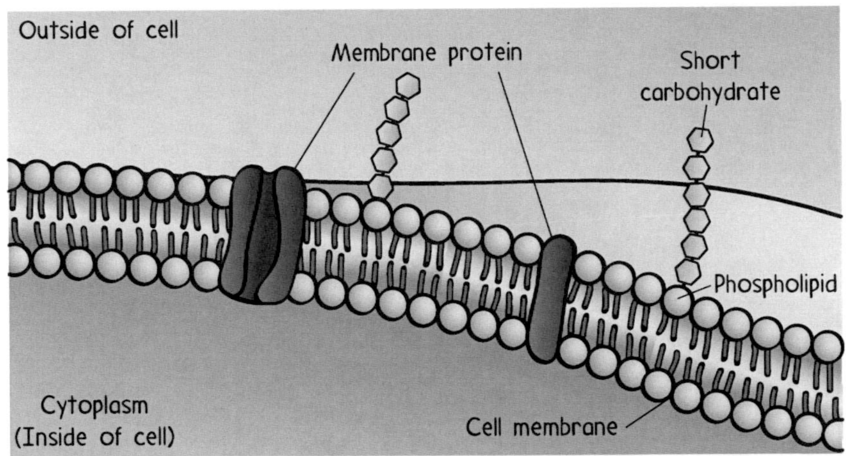

4. What are some functions carried out by membrane proteins?

MEMBRANE PROTEINS SERVE A VARIETY OF FUNCTIONS—THEY HELP CELLS COMMUNICATE WITH OTHER CELLS, CONTROL TRANSPORT INTO AND OUT OF CELLS CONTROL THE CHEMICAL REACTIONS THAT OCCUR IN CELLS, AND JOIN CELLS TO ONE ANOTHER.

5. What are the functions of short carbohydrates?

THE SHORT CARBOHYDRATES PLAY AN IMPORTANT ROLE IN CELL RECOGNITION—THE ABILITY TO DISTINGUISH ONE TYPE OF CELL FROM ANOTHER. FOR EXAMPLE, IMMUNE SYSTEM CELLS USE THESE CARBOHYDRATES TO IDENTIFY FOREIGN MATERIALS SUCH AS DISEASE CAUSING BACTERIA AND VIRUSES.

Transport In and Out of Cells

1. Assume that the square-shaped molecules shown below can pass freely across the cell membrane. What is the name of the process by which they move across the cell membrane?

Transport In and Out of Cells—continued

Diffusion

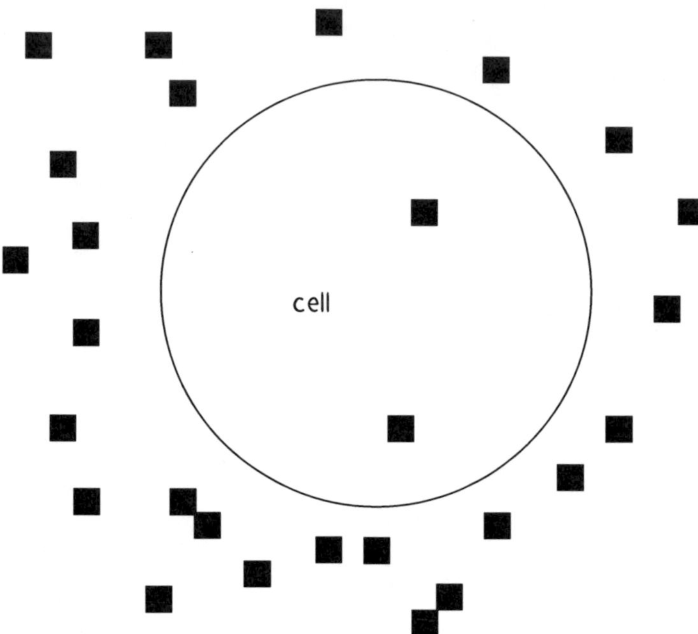

Will the square-shaped molecules tend to move out of the cell or into the cell? Why?

THE SQUARES SHAPED MOLECULES WILL TEND TO MOVE INTO THE CELL BECAUSE MOLECULES TEND TO DIFFUSE FROM AN AREA OF HIGHER CONCENTRATION TO AN AREA OF LOWER CONCENTRATION. THERE IS HIGHER CONCENTRATION OUTSIDE THE CELL AND LOWER CONCENTRATION INSIDE THE CELL. CONSEQUENTLY THE MOLECULES TEND TO DIFFUSE INTO THE CELL

2. The diffusion of water has a special name. It is called OSMOSIS.
In the figure below, a membrane allows water to move freely between two compartments. The dark circles represent solute molecules, which are not free to move between the two compartments. Which way will water tend to flow? Why?

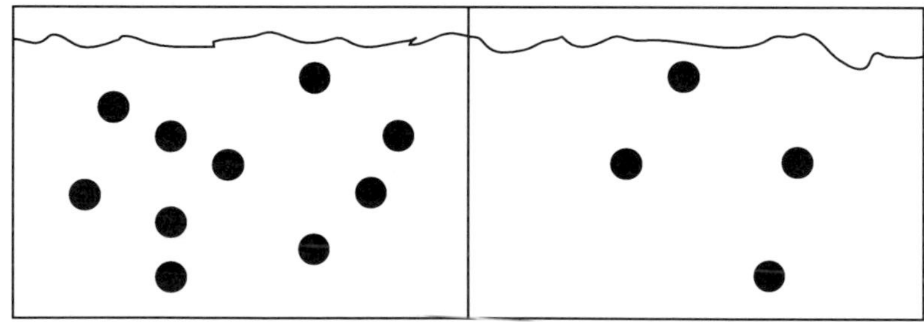

WATER WILL TEND TO MOVE TO THE LEFT, WHERE THERE IS A GREATER CONCENTRATION OF SOLUTE MOLECULES. THIS IS BECAUSE WATER, LIKE OTHER MOLECULES, MOVES FROM AN AREA OF HIGHER WATER CONCENTRATION AND WHERE THERE IS HIGHER SOLUTE CONCENTRATION. THERE IS LOWER CONCENTRATION OF WATER MOLECULES.

Transport In and Out of Cells—continued

3. a. If a molecule needs a carrier protein, but no energy input in order to cross a cell membrane, it provides an example of FACILITATED DIFFUSION.

b. If a molecule requires energy input in order to cross a cell membrane, it provides an example of ACTIVE TRANSPORT.

c. Which process is illustrated in (a)? Which is illustrated in (b)?

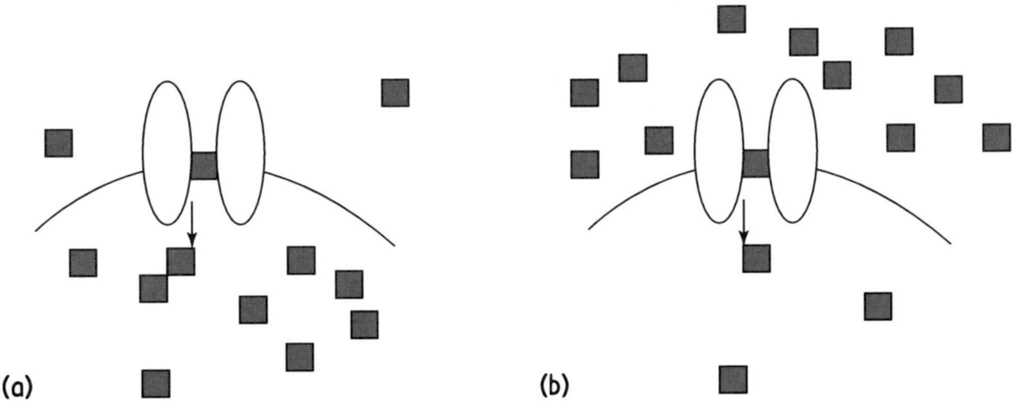

ACTIVE TRANSPORT IS ON THE LEFT. FACILITATED DIFFUSION IS ON THE RIGHT
ENERGY IS REQUIRED (ACTIVE TRANSPORT) WHEN MOLECULES ARE MOVED FROM AN AREA OF LOW CONCENTRATION TO AN AREA OF HIGH CONCENTRATION
ENERGY IS NOT REQUIRED (FACILITATED DIFFUSION) IN THE OPPOSITE SITUATION.

4. The cell below is going to take in the triangular molecule below via endocytosis. Draw what happens.

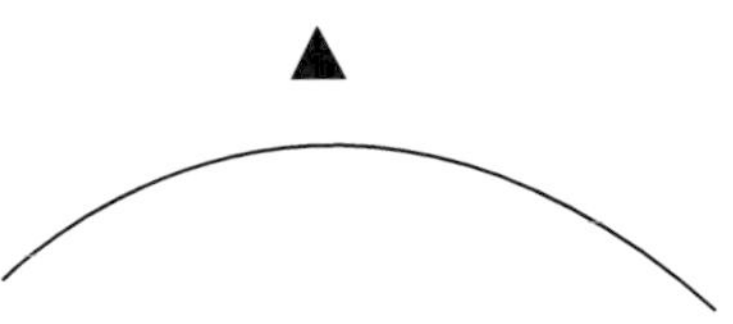

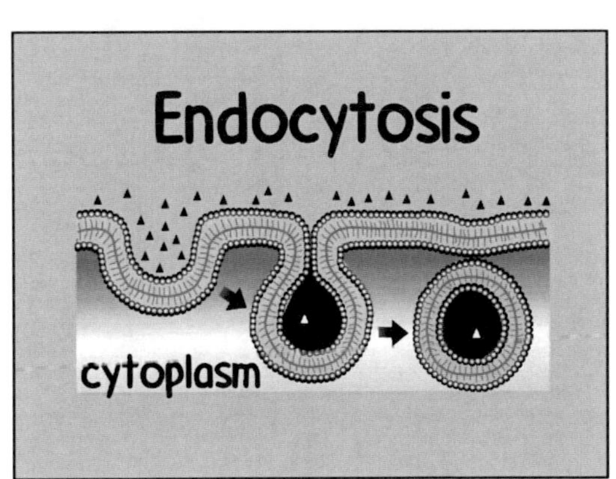

Photosynthesis and Cellular Respiration

1. The chemical reaction for photosynthesis is (use words or chemical formulae):

______ + ______ + ______ → ______ + ______

CARBON DIOXIDE + WATER + SUNLIGHT ⟶ GLUCOSE + OXYGEN

$$6CO_2 + 6H_2O + \text{SUNLIGHT} \longrightarrow C_6H_{12}O_6 + 6O_2.$$

2. a. Where in plant cells does photosynthesis take place?
b. Where do plants get carbon dioxide from?
c. Where do plants get water from?
d. What parts of plants capture sunlight?

A. CHLOROPLASTS

B. THE ATMOSPHERE

C. THE ENVIRONMENT—TYPICALLY, THEIR ROOTS ABSORB WATER FROM SOIL

D. THE STEMS AND LEAVES

3. For each of the following events that occur during photosynthesis, indicate whether it occurs during the light-dependent or light-independent reactions:

a. sunlight strikes a chlorophyll molecule — LIGHT DEPENDENT

b. Calvin cycle — LIGHT INDEPENDENT

c. energy is generated in the form of molecules of ATP and NADPH — LIGHT DEPENDENT

d. free oxygen is produced — LIGHT DEPENDENT

e. carbon is fixed — LIGHT INDEPENDENT

f. glucose is produced — LIGHT INDEPENDENT

4. The chemical reaction for cellular respiration is

______ + ______ + ______ → ______ + ______ + ______

GLUCOSE + OXYGEN + ADP ⟶ CARBON DIOXIDE + WATER + ATP

$$C_6H_{12}O_6 + 6O_2 + \text{ABOUT 38 MOLECULES OF ADP} \longrightarrow 6CO_2 + 6H_2O + \text{ABOUT 38 MOLECULES OF ATP}$$

5. Cellular respiration allows cells to produce ATP. How do cells later obtain energy from ATP?

ENERGY IS OBTAINED FROM ATP WHEN ONE OF ITS THREE PHOSPHATE GROUPS IS REMOVED, LEAVING ADP. (CELLS EVENTUALLY TURN ADP BACK INTO ATP BY ADDING A PHOSPHATE GROUP DURING CELLULAR RESPIRATION.)

Photosynthesis and Cellular Respiration—continued

6. Which of the following processes requires oxygen?
   glycolysis

   Krebs cycle and electron transport

   alcoholic fermentation

   lactic acid fermentation

   KREBS CYCLE AND ELECTRON TRANSPORT

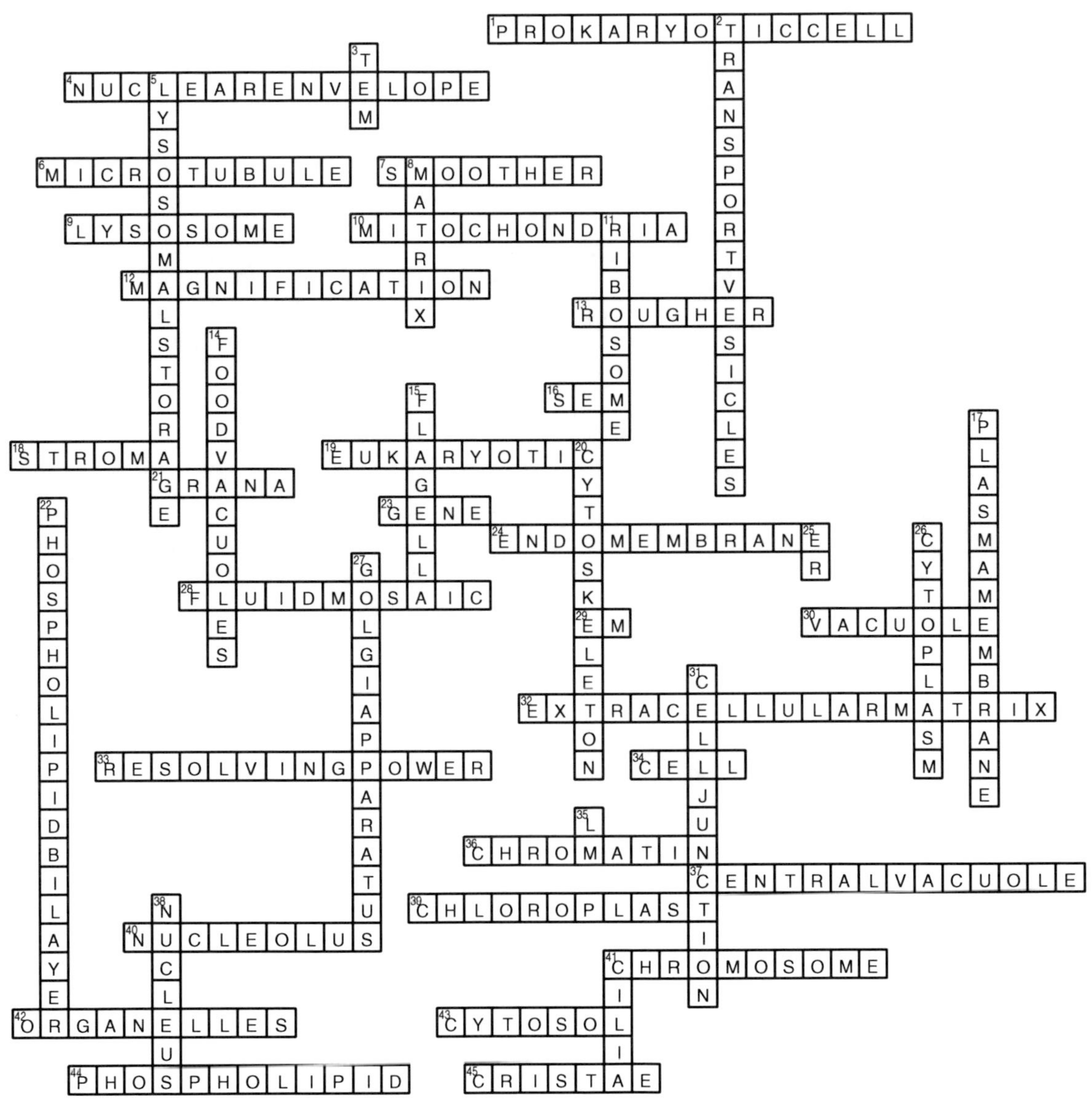

Chapter 10

Answers to the Practice Test

1. B
2. False, less
3. cellulose
4. B
5. True
6. conservation of energy
7. C
8. True
9. entropy
10. A
11. C
12. False, potential
13. chemical
14. B
15. True
16. calorie, kilocalorie / food Calorie
17. B
18. False, more
19. triphosphate tail
20. D
21. A
22. ADP
23. E
24. False, lower
25. metabolism
26. D
27. False, substrates
28. substrate, active site
29. C
30. True
31. inhibitors
32. A
33. C
34. True
35. energy
36. facilitated diffusion
37. B
38. C
39. C
40. False, isotonic
41. osmoregulation
42. C
43. False, active
44. active
45. D
46. False, exocytosis
47. pinocytosis
48. E
49. True
50. proteins
51. C
52. True
53. molecular

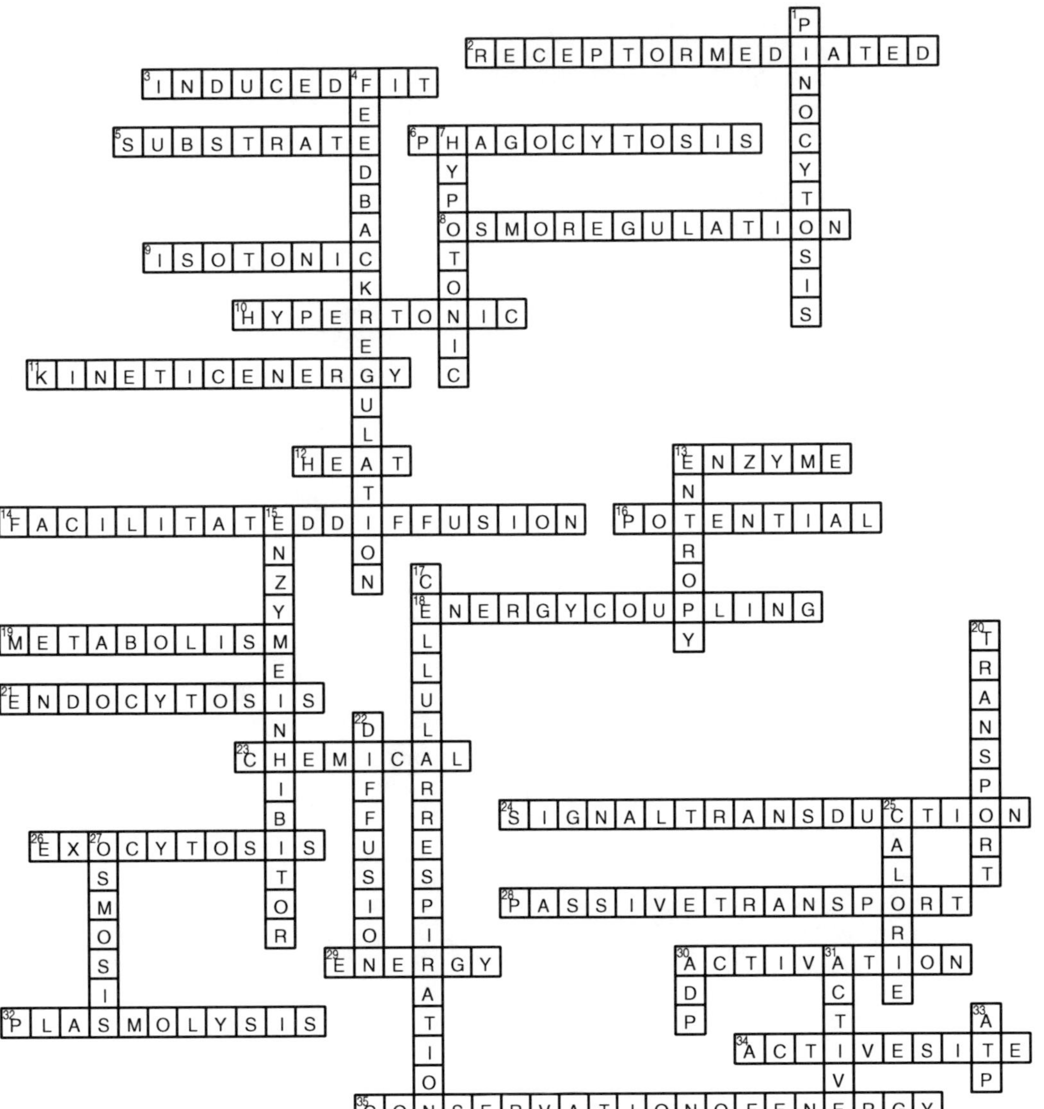
PINOCYTOSIS
RECEPTORMEDIATED
INDUCEDFIT
FEEDBACKREGULATION
SUBSTRATE
PHAGOCYTOSIS
HYPOTONIC
OSMOREGULATION
ISOTONIC
HYPERTONIC
KINETICENERGY
HEAT
ENZYME
ENTROPY
FACILITATEDDIFFUSION
POTENTIAL
ENZYMEINHIBITOR
CELLULARRESPIRATION
ENERGYCOUPLING
METABOLISM
TRANSPORT
ENDOCYTOSIS
DIFFUSION
CHEMICAL
SIGNALTRANSDUCTION
CALORIE
EXOCYTOSIS
OSMOSIS
PASSIVETRANSPORT
ENERGY
ACTIVATION
ADP
ACTIVE
ATP
PLASMOLYSIS
ACTIVESITE
CONSERVATIONOFENERGY

Chapter 11

Answers to the Practice Test

1. D
2. False, anaerobic
3. lactic acid
4. A
5. True
6. False, producers
7. heterotrophs
8. A
9. D
10. D
11. False, mitochondria
12. ATP
13. water, carbon dioxide
14. D
15. False, oxygen
16. cellular respiration
17. C
18. True
19. hydrogen
20. B
21. A
22. B
23. False, oxygen
24. oxidation
25. C
26. D
27. C
28. C
29. H^+ ions
30. metabolism
31. B
32. True
33. lactic acid
34. C
35. True
36. obligate
37. A
38. A
39. C
40. B
41. C
42. True
43. oxygen

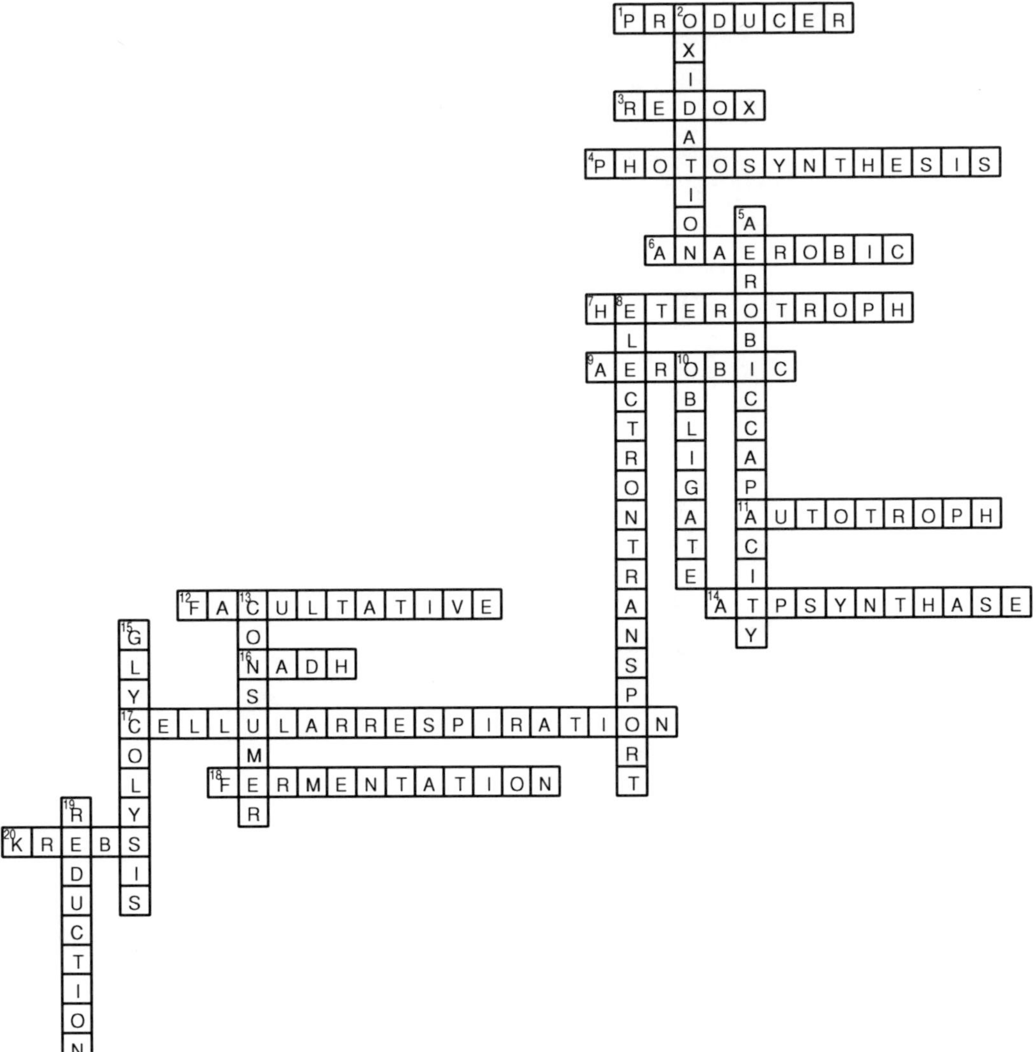
1 PRODUCER
2 OXIDATION
3 REDOX
4 PHOTOSYNTHESIS
5 AEROBIC CAPACITY
6 ANAEROBIC
7 HETEROTROPH
8 ELECTRON TRANSPORT
9 AEROBIC
10 OBLIGATE
11 AUTOTROPH
12 FACULTATIVE
13 CONSUMER
14 ATP SYNTHASE
15 GLYCOLYSIS
16 NADH
17 CELLULAR RESPIRATION
18 FERMENTATION
19 REDUCTION
20 KREBS

Chapter 12

Answers to the Practice Test

1. A
2. D
3. False, plants
4. fossil fuels
5. D
6. D
7. False, stroma
8. stomata
9. B
10. False, water
11. glucose
12. A
13. C
14. True
15. ATP and NADPH
16. C
17. True
18. more
19. A
20. False, some
21. green
22. D
23. False, thylakoid
24. Chlorophyll a
25. E
26. D
27. True
28. photon
29. C
30. D
31. A
32. True
33. ATP
34. A
35. A
36. True
37. stomata
38. water
39. A
40. False, decrease
41. greenhouse effect
42. C
43. False, aerobic
44. oxygen

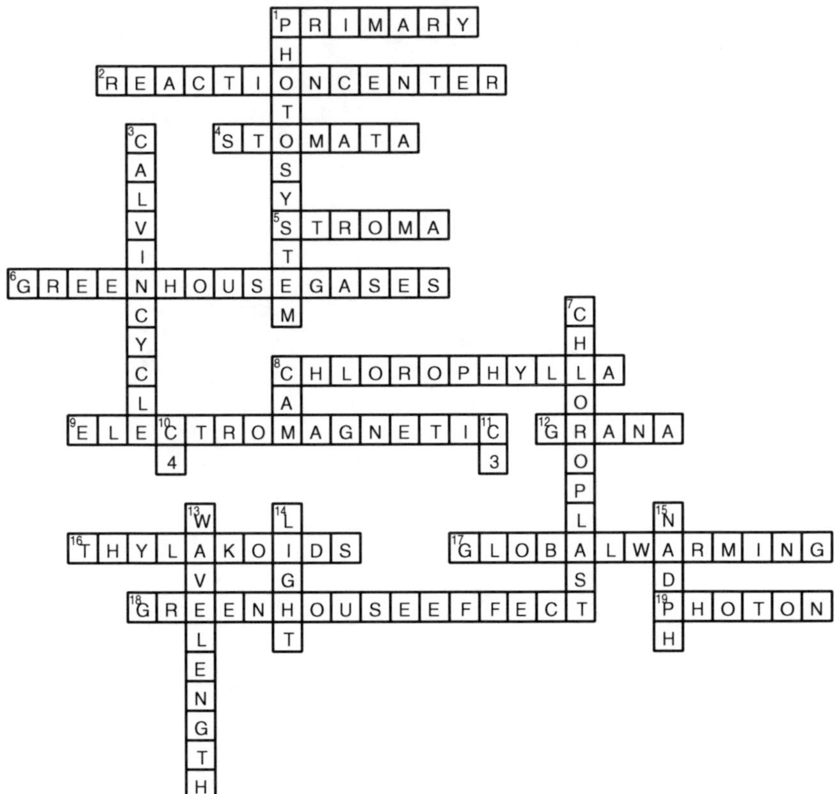
PRIMARY
REACTIONCENTER
STOMATA
STROMA
GREENHOUSEGASES
CHLOROPHYLLA
ELECTROMAGNETIC
GRANA
THYLAKOIDS
GLOBALWARMING
GREENHOUSEEFFECT
PHOTON
PHOTOSYSTEM
CALVINCYCLE
CHLOROPLASTS
CAM
C4
C3
WAVELENGTH
LIGHT
NADPH

Chapter 13

Answers to the Practice Test

1. A
2. False, ten
3. infertility
4. A
5. True
6. chromosomes
7. D
8. False, half
9. asexual
10. C
11. False, proteins
12. centromere
13. D
14. True
15. True
16. mitosis, cytokinesis
17. S
18. B
19. B
20. D
21. B
22. centrosomes
23. B
24. C
25. True
26. benign
27. chemotherapy
28. D
29. False, autosomes
30. homologous
31. B
32. True
33. 25
34. E
35. B
36. True
37. haploid
38. A
39. False, do
40. meiosis II
41. C
42. False, meiosis
43. chiasma
44. E
45. E
46. False, sex chromosomes
47. Down syndrome
48. C
49. True
50. tetraploid

Exercises in Genetics

Meiosis

Consider the following diploid cell. The long, dot-filled chromosomes are homologous, but are shaded differently to distinguish them from each other. This is true for the shorter checkerboard chromosomes as well.

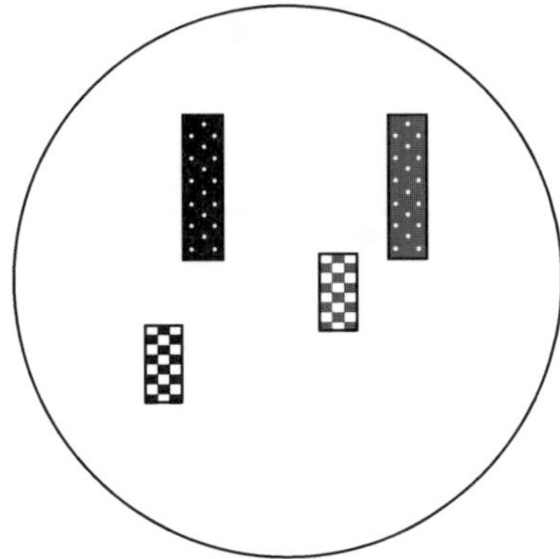

1. **a.** How many chromosomes are there in this diploid cell? 4
   b. If this cell were to undergo meiosis, how many chromosomes would there be in the resulting haploid cells? 2
2. Draw the cell during the following phases of meiosis:
   a. What does the cell look like when it has duplicated its genetic material in preparation for meiosis?

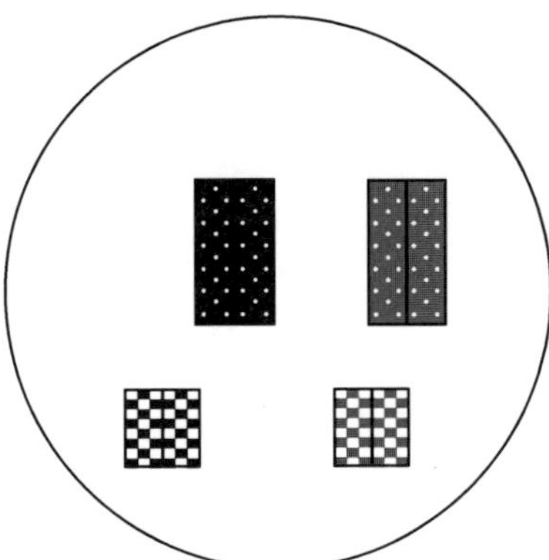

   b. What does the cell look like during metaphase I, before crossing over and recombination have occurred?

HOMOLOGOUS CHROMOSOMES ARE LINED UP AT THE EQUATORIAL PLANE OF THE CELL.

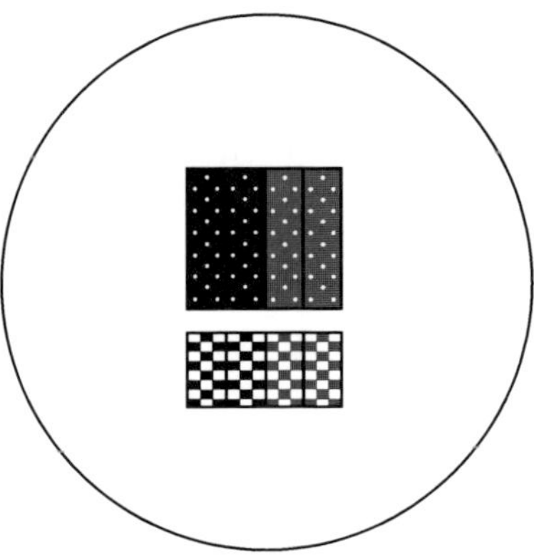

c. Suppose each chromosome experiences a single crossing over event with its homologue. Draw the cell during metaphase I, after crossing over has occurred.

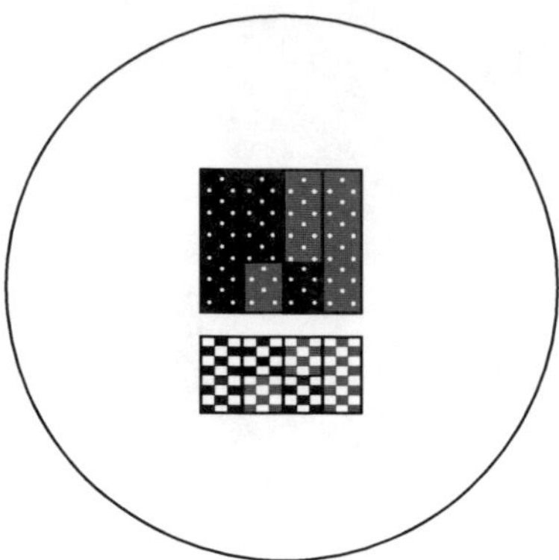

d. Draw the two daughter cells at the end of meiosis I.

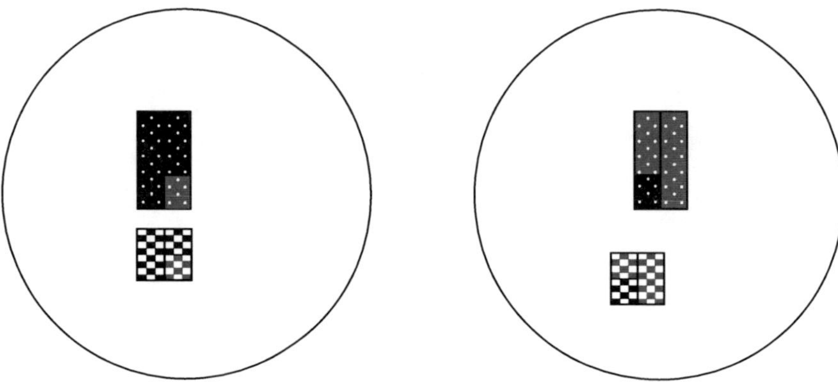

e. Draw the four daughter cells at the end of meiosis II.

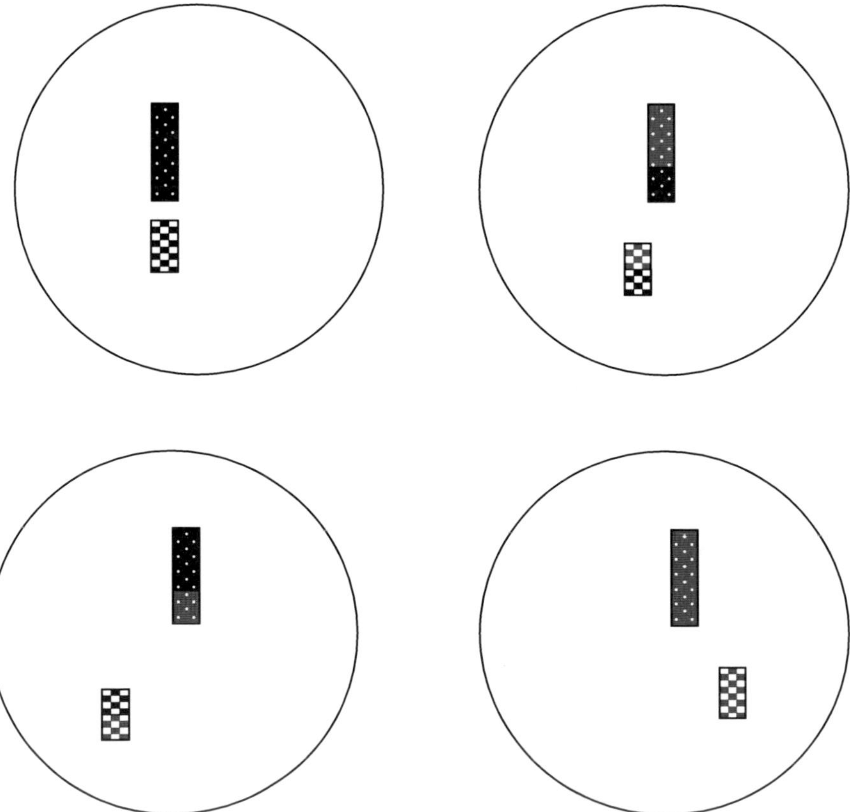

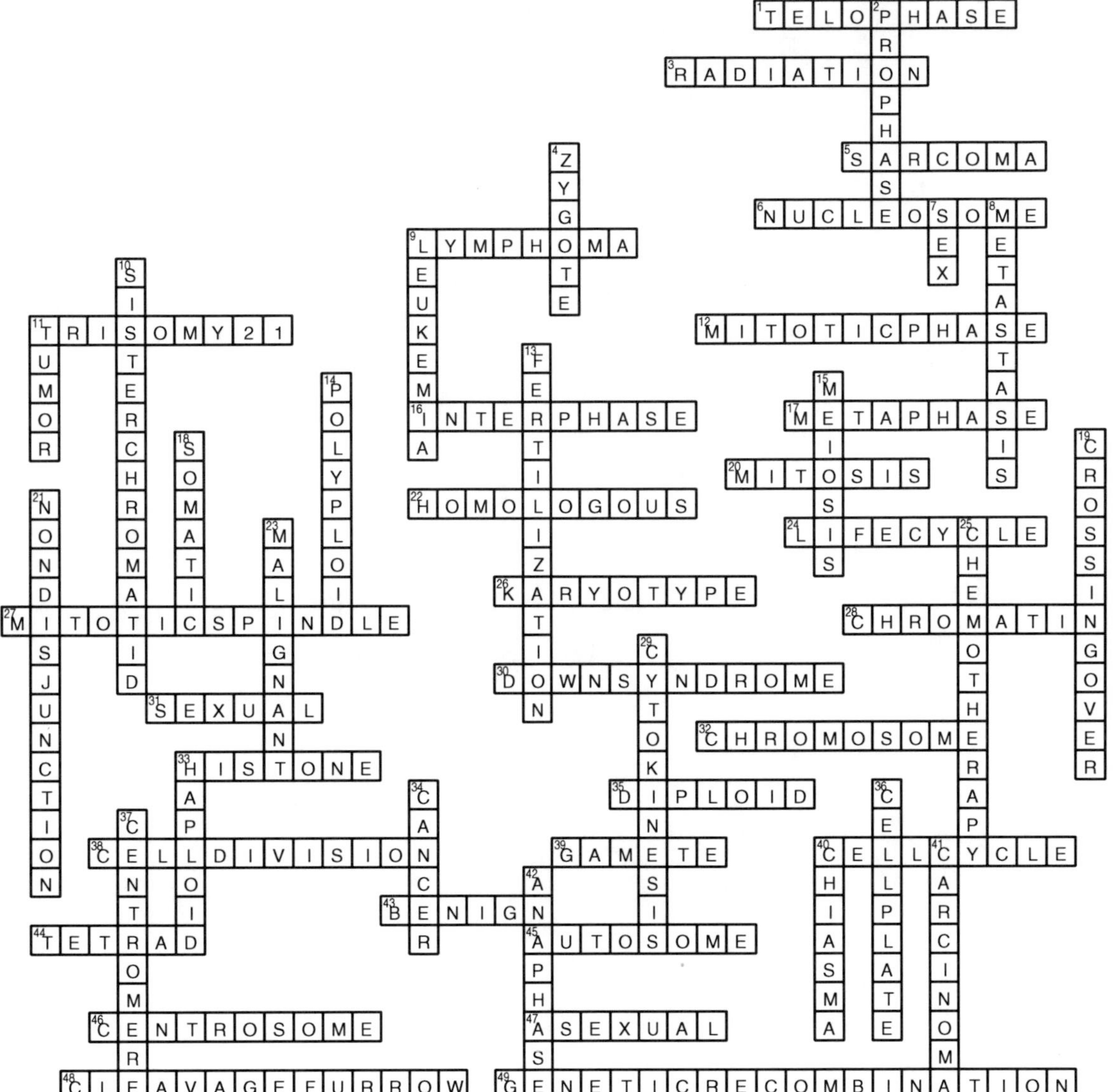

Chapter 14

Answers to the Practice Test

1. D
2. True
3. fetal cells
4. A
5. False, self-fertilize
6. F_2
7. A
8. A
9. D
10. False, heterozygous
11. locus
12. D
13. False, all
14. monohybrid
15. C
16. True
17. genotype
18. C
19. False, genotypes
20. D
21. C
22. False, are not
23. True
24. carriers
25. E
26. False, more
27. heterozygotes
28. Huntington's disease
29. cystic fibrosis
30. B
31. False, did not show
32. hypercholesterolemia
33. A
34. C
35. False, dominant
36. AB
37. B
38. True
39. pleiotropy
40. E
41. True
42. polygenic inheritance
43. A
44. True
45. genetic
46. D
47. B
48. C
49. True
50. True
51. chromosome theory of inheritance
52. fruit flies

53. D

54. True

55. sex

56. A

57. False, occur

58. False, several

59. hemophilia

60. Duchenne muscular dystrophy

61. D

62. True

63. Y

Exercises in Genetics

Inheritance

1. Suppose there exists a species of small woodland creature in which fur is either spotted or striped. It turns out that fur pattern is determined by a single gene, and that the striped phenotype is dominant to the spotted phenotype. Which of the following must be a homozygote?

THE SPOTTED ONE MUST BE A HOMOZYGOTE, SINCE YOU HAVE TO HAVE TWO RECESSIVE ALLELES TO HAVE SPOTS. THE STRIPED ONE COULD BE EITHER A HOMOZYGOTE OR HETEROZYGOTE.

2. Suppose, in fact, both the woodland creatures above are homozygotes. Their genotypes are aa and AA. Fill in the blanks below:

Genotype	aa	AA
Phenotype	SPOTTED	STRIPED

3. What phenotype would an Aa heterozygote have? Draw it below:

Aa HETEROZYGOTE WOULD HAVE STRIPES

4. Now, you breed together an aa individual with an AA individual. Draw the cross below:

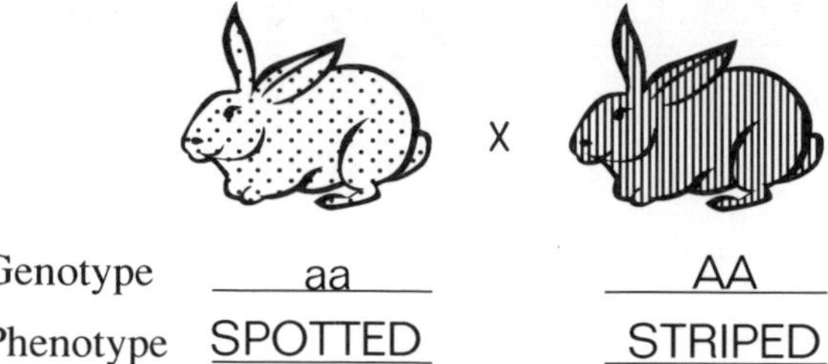

Genotype	aa	AA
Phenotype	SPOTTED	STRIPED

What are the progeny like?

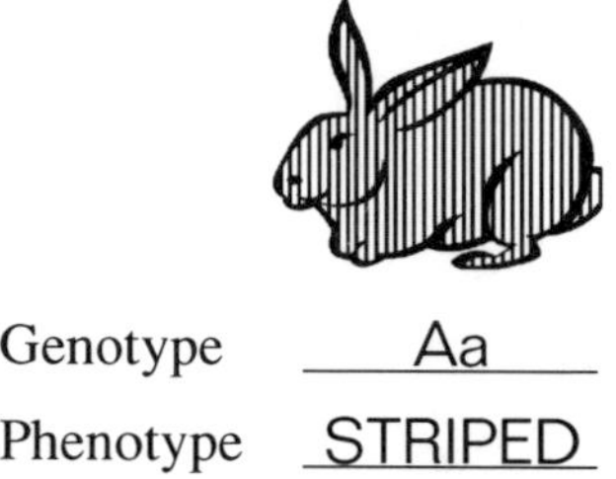

Genotype Aa

Phenotype STRIPED

5. Cross together two of the progeny from Problem 4 above. Fill in the boxes below.

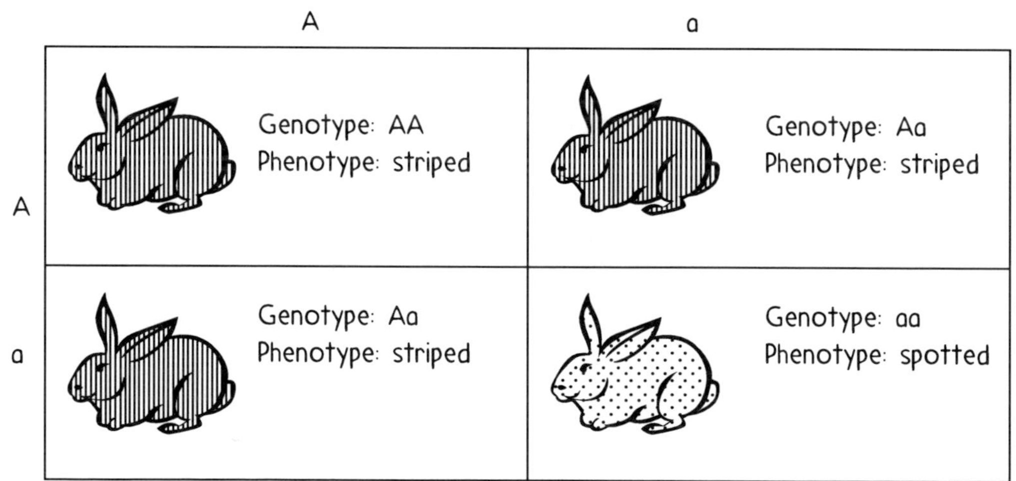

So, the progeny are spotted/striped/both; And found in a ratio ______:_______

BOTH

3 STRIPED: 1 SPOTTED

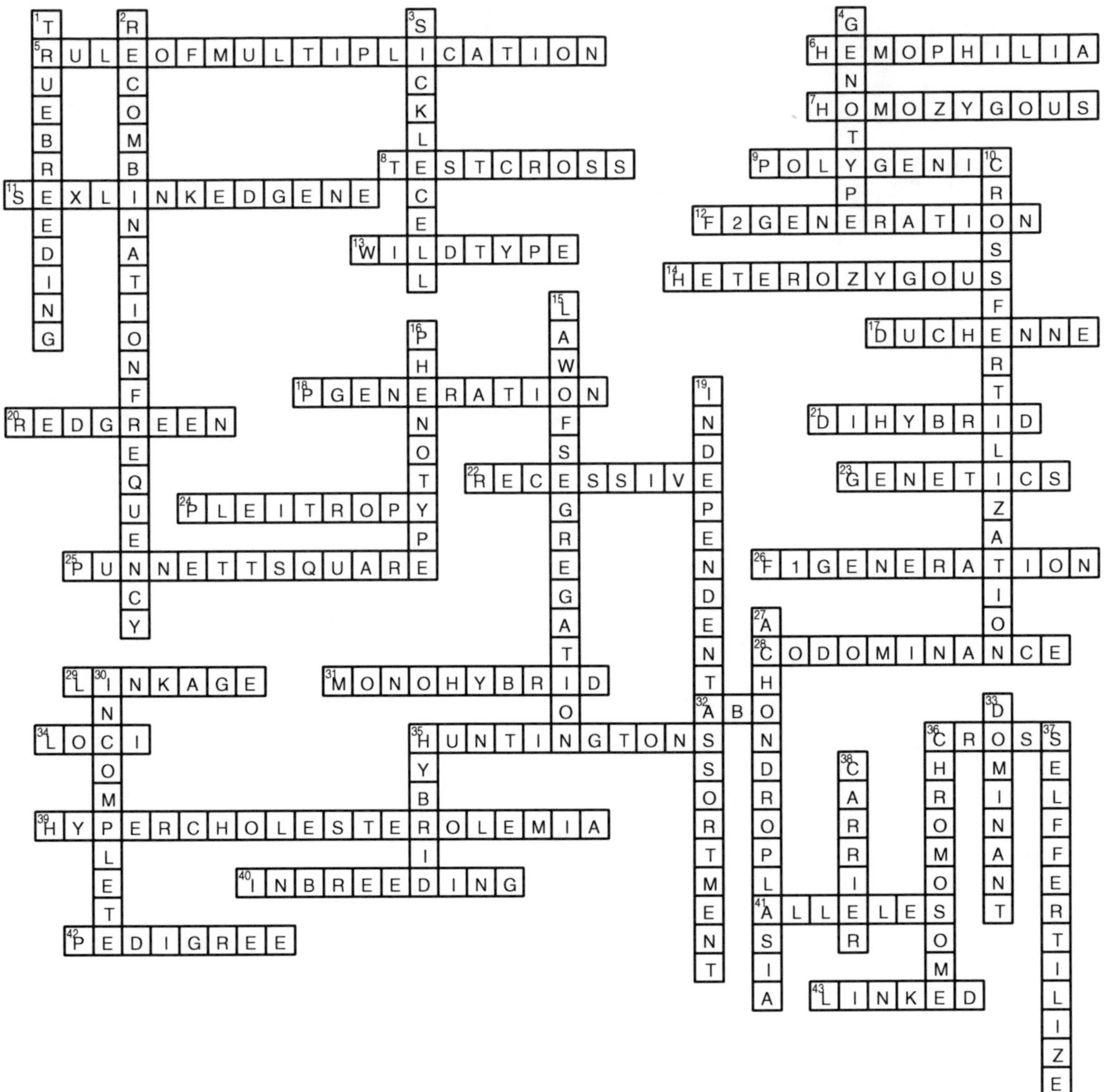
1 TRUEBREEDING
2 RECOMBINATIONFREQUENCY
3 SICKLECELL
4 GENOTYPE
5 RULEOFMULTIPLICATION
6 HEMOPHILIA
7 HOMOZYGOUS
8 TESTCROSS
9 POLYGENIC
10 CROSSFERTILIZATION
11 SEXLINKEDGENE
12 F2GENERATION
13 WILDTYPE
14 HETEROZYGOUS
15 LAWOFSEGREGATION
16 PHENOTYPE
17 DUCHENNE
18 PGENERATION
19 INDEPENDENTASSORTMENT
20 REDGREEN
21 DIHYBRID
22 RECESSIVE
23 GENETICS
24 PLEITROPY
25 PUNNETTSQUARE
26 F1GENERATION
27 ACHONDROPLASIA
28 CODOMINANCE
29 LINKAGE
30 INCOMPLETE
31 MONOHYBRID
32 ABO
33 DOMINANT
34 LOCI
35 HUNTINGTONS
35 HYBRID
36 CROSS
36 CHROMOSOME
37 SELFFERTILIZE
38 CARRIER
39 HYPERCHOLESTEROLEMIA
40 INBREEDING
41 ALLELES
42 PEDIGREE
43 LINKED

Chapter 15

Answers to the Practice Test

1. E

2. B

3. False, DNA

4. B

5. True

6. structure

7. C

8. False, is missing an

9. deoxyribose, ribose

10. uracil

11. thymine / cytosine, adenine / guanine

12. polynucleotides, nucleotides

13. A

14. B

15. A

16. False, outside

17. GCTA

18. C

19. B

20. False, many replication origins

21. DNA polymerase

22. DNA polymerase

23. D

24. B

25. False, proteins

26. genotype, phenotype

27. transcription, translation

28. C

29. True

30. True

31. three

32. amino acids

33. A

34. C

35. False, no gaps

36. True

37. genetic code

38. C

39. True

40. promoter

41. RNA polymerase

42. A

43. True

44. introns, exons

45. B

46. E

47. D

48. False, anticodon

49. mRNA, tRNA

50. A

51. A

52. True

53. amino acid

54. A, P, translocation

55. stop codon

56. C

57. A

58. True

59. False, does not shift

60. False, not beneficial

61. mutation

62. mutagens

63. D

64. A

65. False, lytic

66. False, can

67. True

68. prophage

69. E

70. E

71. False, are not

72. True

73. mini-chromosomes

74. plasma membrane, nuclear membrane

75. B

76. plasma membrane

77. retrovirus

78. reverse transcriptase

79. D

80. True

81. True

82. emerging

Exercises in Genetics

DNA Replication, Transcription, and Translation

1. Let's start with the following strand of DNA:

AT
GC
CG
TA
TA
AT
CG
CG
GC
TA
AT
CG
GC

The strand is unwound, so that the DNA can be replicated. Fill in the nucleotides on the new strands.

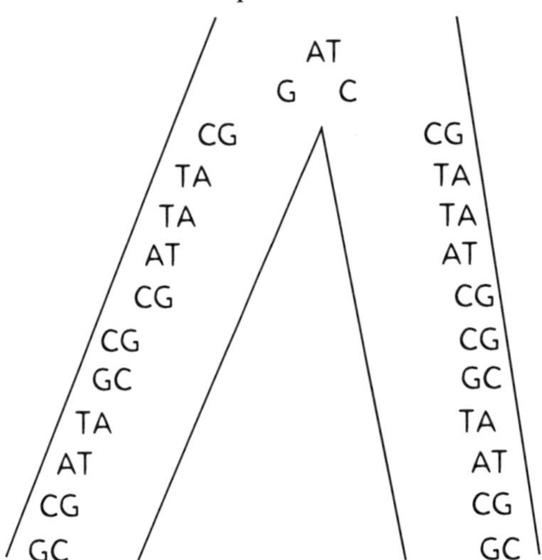

2. Transcription takes place in the ______NUCLEUS______.
During transcription, DNA is used to make a molecule of MESSENGER RNA OR mRNA______.
If the following length of DNA is being transcribed, what are the bases found on the transcript?

____________________ ATGGTCATACGTACAATG (DNA TEMPLATE)
ATGGTCATACGTACAATG UACCAGUAUGCAUGUUAC (mRNA TRANSCRIPT)

DNA Replication, Transcription, and Translation—continued

3. Translation takes place in the ______ of cells in organelles called _______. CYTOPLASM, RIBOSOMES
During translation, _____ is used to build a _____. mRNA, PROTEIN

Divide the transcript from Problem 2 into codons and indicate the sequence of amino acids that is assembled in the ribosome. How many amino acids are coded for by this sequence?

For reference, the genetic code table is shown below:

Second base

First base	U	C	A	G	Third base
U	UUU, UUC: Phenylalanine (Phe)	UCU, UCC, UCA, UCG: Serine (Ser)	UAU, UAC: Tyrosine (Tyr)	UGU, UGC: Cysteine (Cys)	U, C
U	UUA, UUG: Leucine (Leu)		UAA Stop; UAG Stop	UGA Stop; UGG Tryptophan (Trp)	A, G
C	CUU, CUC, CUA, CUG: Leucine (Leu)	CCU, CCC, CCA, CCG: Proline (Pro)	CAU, CAC: Histidine (His)	CGU, CGC, CGA, CGG: Arginine (Arg)	U, C
C			CAA, CAG: Glutamine (Gln)		A, G
A	AUU, AUC, AUA: Isoleucine (Ile)	ACU, ACC, ACA, ACG: Threonine (Thr)	AAU, AAC: Asparagine (Asn)	AGU, AGC: Serine (Ser)	U, C
A	AUG Met or start		AAA, AAG: Lysine (Lys)	AGA, AGG: Arginine (Arg)	A, G
G	GUU, GUC, GUA, GUG: Valine (Val)	GCU, GCC, GCA, GCG: Alanine (Ala)	GAU, GAC: Aspartic acid(Asp)	GGU, GGC, GGA, GGG: Glycine (Gly)	U, C
G			GAA, GAG: Glutamic acid (Glu)		A, G

UAC-CAG-UAU-GCA-UGU-UAC (mRNA TRANSCRIPT)

TYR-GLN-TYR-ALA-CYS-TYR

THERE ARE SIX AMINO ACIDS

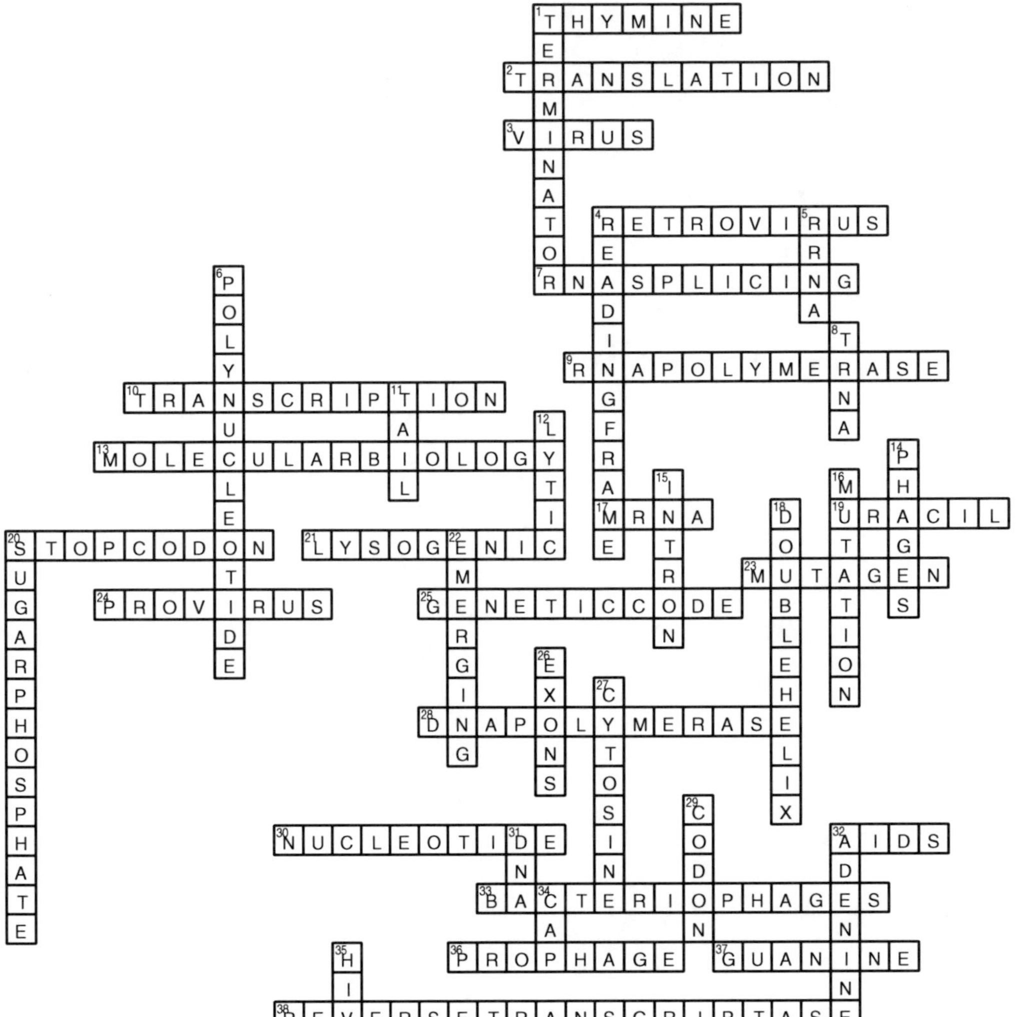
THYMINE
TERMINATOR
TRANSLATION
VIRUS
RETROVIRUS
RNA
READINGFRAME
RNASPLICING
TRNA
RNAPOLYMERASE
POLYNUCLEOTIDE
TRANSCRIPTION
TAIL
LYTIC
MOLECULARBIOLOGY
PHAGES
INTRON
MUTATION
MRNA
DOUBLEHELIX
URACIL
STOPCODON
LYSOGENIC
EMERGING
MUTAGEN
SUGARPHOSPHATE
PROVIRUS
GENETICCODE
EXONS
CYTOSINE
DNAPOLYMERASE
CODON
NUCLEOTIDE
DNA
AIDS
ADENINE
BACTERIOPHAGES
CAPSID
HIV
PROPHAGE
GUANINE
REVERSETRANSCRIPTASE

Chapter 16

Answers to the Practice Test

1. A
2. False, have not
3. genome
4. E
5. B
6. False, some
7. cellular differentiation
8. D
9. D
10. A
11. B
12. False, promoter
13. operon
14. C
15. B
16. D
17. D
18. B
19. False, prevent
20. True
21. False, DNA
22. enhancers
23. silencers
24. A
25. False, cDNA
26. True
27. signal transduction
28. genes
29. A
30. D
31. True
32. True
33. False, nucleus
34. regeneration
35. False, 1950s
36. E
37. False, Adult
38. therapeutic
39. A
40. C
41. D
42. True
43. False, DNA
44. True
45. False, not caused
46. growth factors
47. E
48. B
49. False, fiber
50. carcinogens
51. E
52. False, similar
53. nucleotides

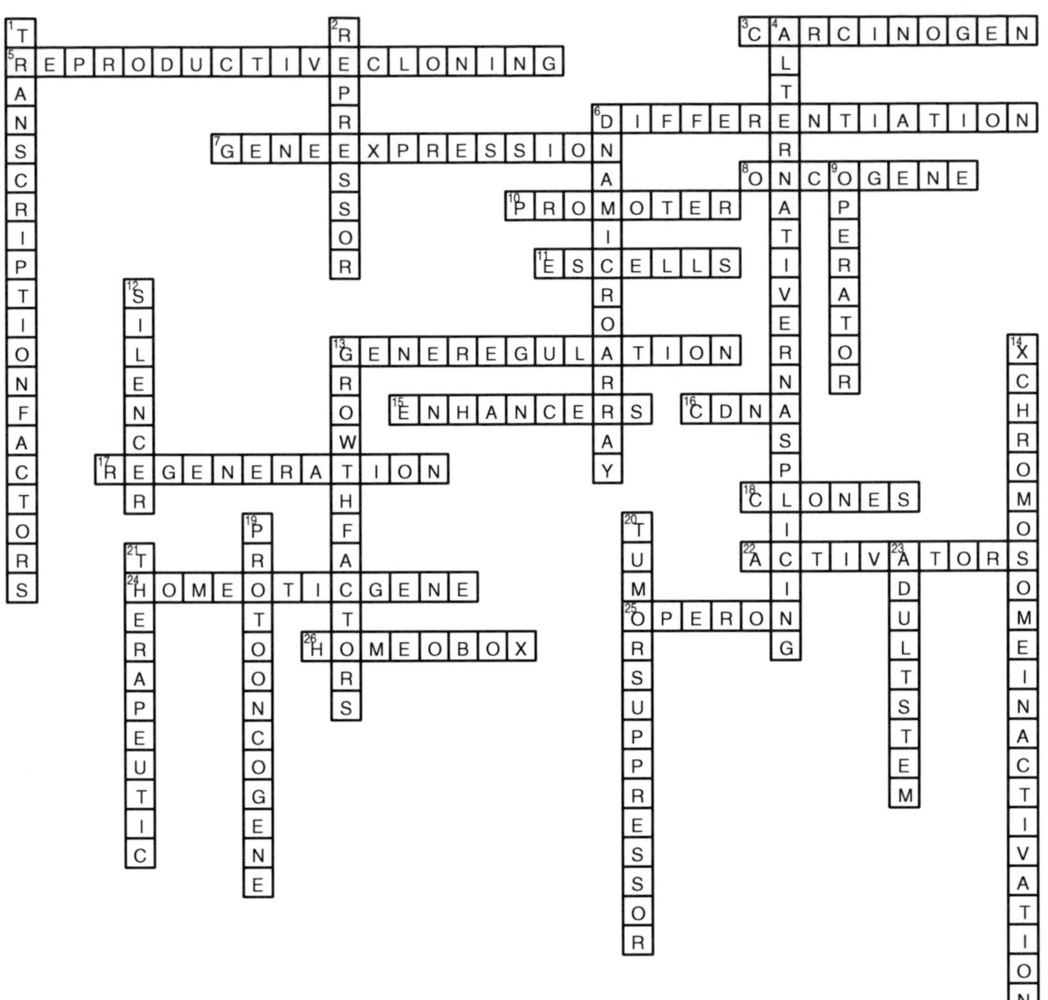
TRANSCRIPTIONFACTORS
REPRESSOR
CARCINOGEN
REPRODUCTIVECLONING
ALTERNATIVERNASPLICING
DIFFERENTIATION
GENEEXPRESSION
DNAMICROARRAY
ONCOGENE
OPERATOR
PROMOTER
ESCELLS
SILENCER
GENEREGULATION
GROWTHFACTORS
XCHROMOSOMEINACTIVATION
ENHANCERS
CDNA
REGENERATION
CLONES
PROTOONCOGENE
TUMORSUPPRESSOR
THERAPEUTIC
ACTIVATORS
ADULTSTEM
HOMEOTICGENE
OPERON
HOMEOBOX

Chapter 17

Answers to the Practice Test

1. A
2. False, genetic
3. forensics
4. A
5. True
6. False, thousands
7. recombinant DNA technology
8. biotechnology
9. E
10. True
11. vitamin A
12. bacteria
13. cholera
14. vaccination
15. 4
16. 2
17. 7
18. 1
19. 6
20. 3
21. 5
22. D
23. False, separate from
24. True
25. False, the same
26. True
27. nucleic acid probe
28. restriction enzymes
29. genomic library
30. vectors
31. bacteria
32. DNA ligase
33. C
34. True
35. DNA fingerprinting
36. A
37. polymerase chain reaction
38. STR
39. DNA polymerase
40. repetitive
41. D
42. A
43. False, chromosomes
44. genomics
45. repetitive DNA
46. D
47. False, 96%
48. C
49. D
50. False, have not
51. False, many humans
52. genetic makeup
53. A
54. True
55. proteomics
56. C
57. False, artificial
58. marrow
59. E
60. True
61. C
62. True
63. C
64. False, do
65. True

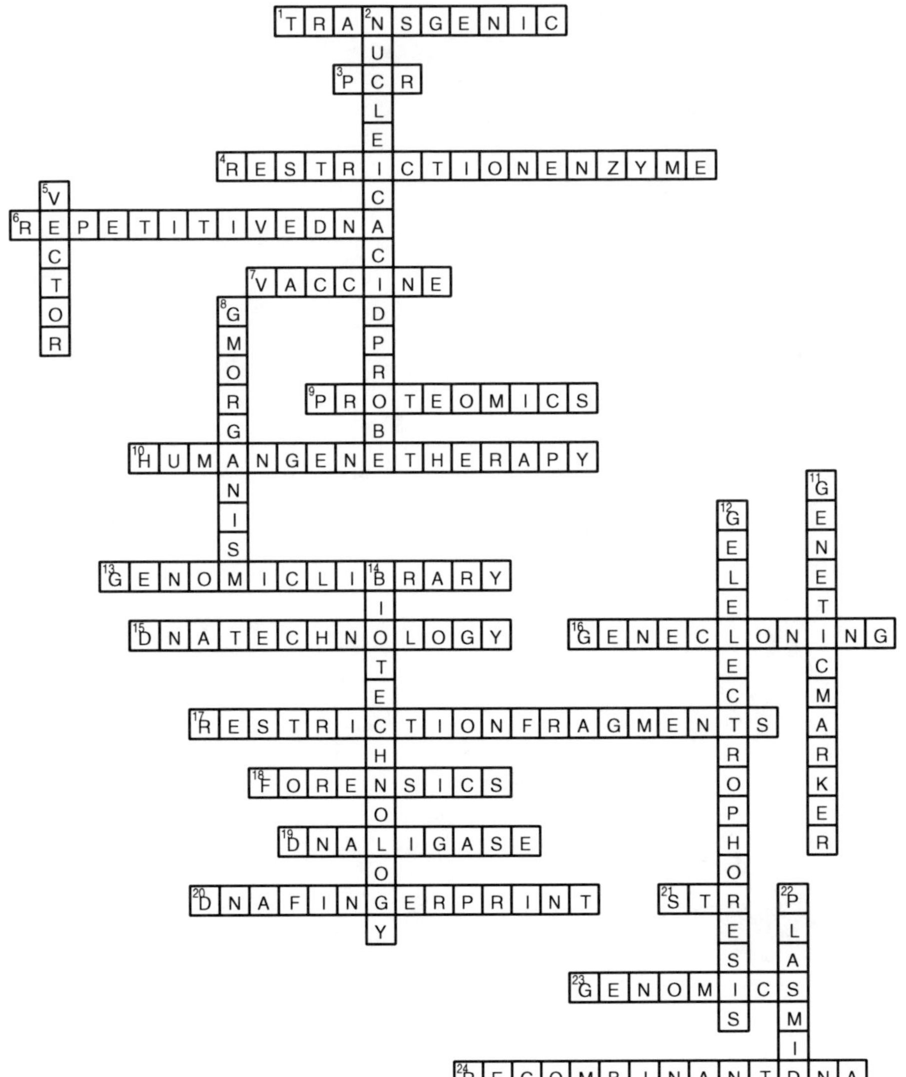
1 TRANSGENIC
2 NUCLEICACIDPROBE
3 PCR
4 RESTRICTIONENZYME
5 VECTOR
6 REPETITIVEDNA
7 VACCINE
8 GMORGANIS
9 PROTEOMICS
10 HUMANGENETHERAPY
11 GENETICMARKER
12 GELELECTROPHORESIS
13 GENOMICLIBRARY
14 BIOTECHNOLOGY
15 DNATECHNOLOGY
16 GENECLONING
17 RESTRICTIONFRAGMENTS
18 FORENSICS
19 DNALIGASE
20 DNAFINGERPRINT
21 STR
22 PLASMID
23 GENOMICS
24 RECOMBINANTDNA

Chapter 18

The Evolution of Life

Natural Selection

1. A. One of the best-documented instances of natural selection in the wild is the evolution of bird beak sizes during a severe drought on the Galápagos Islands in 1977. Before the drought, there was natural variation in beak size in a species of finch found on the islands. Draw a series of finches, showing this variation in beak size.

Natural Selection—continued

B. What happened was this: The drought made seeds scarce. Small seeds were quickly eaten up, leaving only larger, tougher seeds. Birds with larger, stronger beaks were better at cracking these larger seeds. Many birds died during the drought. Which were most likely to survive? Mark X's through some of the individuals in your drawing likely to have died, and circle individuals likely to have survived.

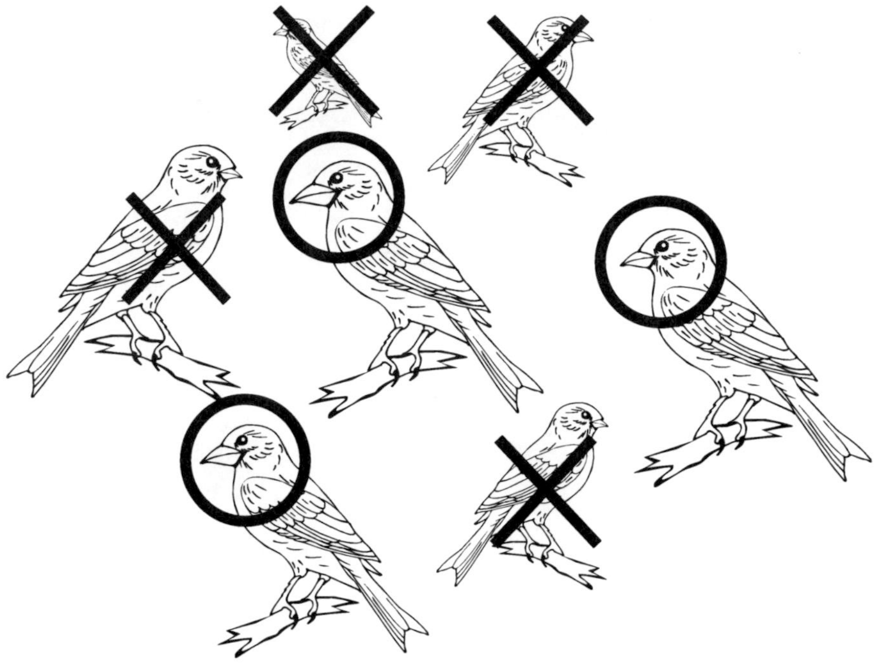

C. Beak size is a trait that is partly genetically determined, so parents with larger, stronger beaks tend to have offspring with larger, stronger beaks. Draw the offspring of the individuals you circled as surviving the drought.

Natural Selection—continued

D. How does the population you drew in part (c) compare with the population you drew in part (a)?

THEY HAVE, IN GENERAL, LARGER, STRONGER BILLS.

2. Of the human traits listed below, put a V by traits that are variable and put an H by traits that are heritable. Which traits have the potential of evolving via natural selection?

A. age	V
B. eye color	V AND H
C. number of toes	H
D. curliness or straightness of hair	V AND H
E. presence or absence of dimples	V AND H
F. upright posture	H
G. owning versus not owning a dog	V
H. height	V AND H

TRAITS THAT ARE BOTH VARIABLE AND HERITABLE HAVE THE POTENTIAL OF EVOLVING BY NATURAL SELECTION—SO, OF THE TRAITS LISTED, EYE COLOR, CURLINESS OR STRAIGHTNESS OF HAIR, PRESENCE OR ABSENCE OF DIMPLES, AND HEIGHT.

Adaptation

1. The imaginary mammal below occupies temperate forests in the Eastern United States.

If a population of these mammals moved to and successfully colonized an Arctic habitat, how might you predict that it would evolve? Draw the Arctic form below.

If a population of these mammals moved to and successfully colonized a desert habitat, how might you predict that it would evolve? Draw the desert form below.

Explain your drawings.

THE HEAT AN ANIMAL GENERATES IS PROPORTIONAL TO ITS VOLUME. THE HEAT AN ANIMAL DISSIPATES IS PROPORTIONAL TO ITS SURFACE AREA, SINCE HEAT IS LOST TO THE ENVIRONMENT THROUGH ITS BODY SURFACE. CONSEQUENTLY, ANIMALS ARE BETTER ABLE TO LOSE HEAT IF THEY HAVE A HIGH SURFACE AREA-TO-VOLUME RATIO, AND BETTER ABLE TO RETAIN HEAT IF THEY ARE HAVE A LOW SURFACE AREA-TO-VOLUME RATIO. THIS INFLUENCES BOTH THE SIZE AND SHAPE OF ANIMALS THAT OCCUPY EXTREME HABITATS. LARGER ORGANISMS, WHETHER THEY ARE CELLS OR ANIMALS, TEND TO HAVE *SMALLER* SURFACE AREA-TO-VOLUME RATIOS. THIS IS BECAUSE VOLUME INCREASES MORE QUICKLY THAN SURFACE AREA AS ORGANISMS GET BIGGER. FOR THIS REASON, ANIMALS FOUND IN COLD HABITATS ARE OFTEN LARGER THAN RELATED FORMS IN WARM HABITATS. ANIMALS ADAPTED TO HOT VERSUS COLD CLIMATES ALSO VARY IN SHAPE. DESERT SPECIES TYPICALLY HAVE LONG LEGS AND LARGE EARS THAT INCREASE THE SURFACE AREA AVAILABLE FOR HEAT DISSIPATION. THESE PARTS OF THE BODY ARE ALSO COVERED WITH EXTENSIVE BLOOD VESSELS THAT CARRY HEAT FROM THE CORE OF THE BODY TO THE SKIN, WHERE CONVECTION, THE TRANSFER OF HEAT BY MOVING AIR, COOLS THE ANIMAL. ARCTIC SPECIES TYPICALLY HAVE SHORT APPENDAGES AND SMALL EARS THAT HELP CONSERVE HEAT.

2. You are studying peppered moth populations in various locales. In order to determine whether light moths or dark moths survive better in different habitats, you mark 500 light moths and 500 dark moths and release them in different places.

If light moths survive better, you expect to recapture more LIGHT MOTHS.

Similarly, if dark moths survive better, you expect to recapture more DARK MOTHS.

Do you expect light moths or dark moths to survive better in the following habitats?

A. polluted areas DARK

B. unpolluted areas LIGHT

C. industrial centers before pollution laws were passed DARK

D. industrial centers some time after pollution laws were passed LIGHT

E. the countryside LIGHT

Speciation

1. What's the difference between a prezygotic reproductive barrier and a postzygotic reproductive barrier?

PREZYGOTIC REPRODUCTIVE BARRIERS PREVENT MEMBERS OF DIFFERENT SPECIES FROM MATING IN THE FIRST PLACE OR KEEP FERTILIZATION FROM OCCURRING IF THEY DO MATE. POSTZYGOTIC REPRODUCTIVE BARRIERS ACT AFTER FERTILIZATION HAS TAKEN PLACE. POSTZYGOTIC BARRIERS OCCUR WHEN MATING PRODUCES HYBRIDS THAT EITHER DON'T SURVIVE OR ARE STERILE—UNABLE TO BREED THEMSELVES.

2. Which of the following are prezygotic reproductive barriers and which are postzygotic reproductive barriers?

A. different courtship rituals in different bird species PRE

B. incompatible anatomical structures that prevent copulation in insects PRE

C. different-sounding calls by males in different frog species PRE

D. sterility in offspring produced when members of two different species mate POST

E. two species that mate at different times of year PRE

F. two species that use different mating sites PRE

G. offspring that are unable to survive when members of two species mate POST

3. What's the difference between allopatric speciation and sympatric speciation?

IN ALLOPATRIC SPECIATION NEW SPECIES ARE FORMED AFTER A GEOGRAPHIC BARRIER DIVIDES A SINGLE POPULATION INTO TWO. IN SYMPATRIC SPECIATION, SPECIATION OCCURS WITHOUT THE INTRODUCTION OF A GEOGRAPHIC BARRIER.

4. Are the following examples of allopatric or sympatric speciation?

A. speciation after developing glaciers divide a population ALLOPATRIC

B. speciation by hybridization SYMPATRIC

C. speciation after a river cuts through a population's habitat ALLOPATRIC

D. speciation after plate tectonics causes a continent to split ALLOPATRIC

E. speciation by polyploidy SYMPATRIC

Answers to the Practice Test

1. B
2. A
3. True
4. True
5. True
6. True
7. RNA, DNA, RNA
8. A
9. True
10. True
11. True
12. True
13. A
14. D
15. A
16. A
17. True
18. True
19. True
20. Ozone
21. A
22. A
23. D
24. D
25. True
26. True
27. C
28. B
29. Lamarck

30. See the table below.

Charles Lyell — G.	**A.** Human populations grow much faster than available food supplies
Darwin — B	**B.** Evolution—heritable changes
Lamarck — C	**C.** *Evolution — inheritance of acquired characteristics.*
Darwin's finches — D.	**D.** Galápagos Islands
Endosymbiotic — F.______	**E.** Released Rabbits in southern Victoria, Australia.
Thomas Austin — E	**F.** to live with"
Thomas Malthus — A	**G.** geological features of the Earth were created by gradual processes that produced their effects over long time periods.

31. Darwin.
32. Lamarck
33. Darwin
34. A
35. Thomas Malthus
36. True
37. True
38. True
39. True
40. A
41. True
42. Variation
43. True
44. True
45. True
46. Natural selection
47. Adaptations
48. True
49. True

50. See the table below

Natural selection — A	D. Produced remarkable adaptations over time
Bergmann's Rule — C	E. Natural selection that is related to acquiring mates.
Sexual selection. — B	F. In animals, volume increases more quickly than surface area as organisms get bigger

51. True

52. volume.

53. surface area

54. high surface area-to-volume ratio

55. low surface area-to-volume ratio

56. True

57. True

58. True

59. Small

60. Large

61. True

62. Directional; directional

63. directional selection

64. Stabilizing; stabilizing

65. Stabilizing selection

66. Diversifying; diversifying

67. diversifying selection

68. allele frequencies

69. D

70. D

71. See the table below

Term	**Discretion**
Directional selection. ___ C	**A.** Selection for organisms that have a trait at the population average. It causes the distribution of traits in the population to become narrower. An example of this type of selection is birth weight in humans.
Natural selection. ___ B	**B.** Produced remarkable adaptations over time. It is sometimes classified into different modes depending on the effect it has on populations.
Stabilizing selection. ____ A	**C.** Selects for organisms that differ from the population average. It causes the average trait in a population to shift. An example of this type of selection is the increase in beak size in a finch population on the Galápagos Islands following a drought.
Diversifying selection. _____ E	**G.** Exists if the alleles responsible for color are more likely to mutate in one direction than the other. For example, a brown allele may be more likely to mutate into a green allele than vice versa. This would cause the lizard population to evolve to a higher frequency of green alleles.
Mutation pressure. _____ D.	**H.** Selection selects for traits at two extremes within a population. It causes the population to diverge in the trait. This type of selection occurs in the coloration of butterflies that mimic the appearance of two different toxic species.

Term	Discretion
Genetic drift. ___________ F	**I.** Occurs when, by chance rather than because it confers greater fitness, more alleles of one color are transmitted to the next generation than alleles of the other color. For example, even if brown and green lizards have equal fitness, green lizards might just happen to leave more offspring (and therefore more green alleles) than brown lizards one year, causing the population to evolve to a greater frequency of green alleles.
Speciation ______ H.	**J.** A group of organisms whose members can interbreed among themselves but not with members of other species.
Species ___ G.	**K.** The formation of new species
Allopatric speciation ___ I	**L.** New species are formed after a geographic barrier divides a single population into two.

72. True

73. A

74. Bernard Kettlewell

75. True

76. D

77. True

78. See the table below

Adaptive radiation _____. B	**A.** Chromosomal change in which two species interbred and produce fertile offspring.
Sympatric speciation ______ C	**B.** The evolution of a large number of new species, each adapted to a distinct way of life, from a single ancestor.
Humans __________ D.	**C.** Speciation occurs without the introduction of a geographic barrier. It is much less common than other type of speciation.
Hybridization. _________ A.	**D.** *Primates* and also *hominids.*
Artificial selection _____ F.	**E.** Punctuated equilibrium
Gould and Eldredge _____ E	**G.** Selective breeding of organisms with desirable traits in order to produce offspring with the same traits.

79. A

80. B

81. prezygotic barriers.

82. Postzygotic barriers.

83. allopatric speciation.

84. A

85. A

86. Adaptive radiations

87. sympatric speciation

88. B

89. sympatric speciation

90. True

91. True

92. True

93. True

94. True

95. D

96. D

97. True

98. True

99. Ture

100. Ture

101. True

102. True

103. True

104. True

105. True

106. E.

107. E

108. A.

Answers for the Critical Thinking Questions

1. Pasteur's experiment relates to conditions on Earth today, whereas life originated on a very different, younger Earth. Miller and Urey modeled conditions that may have been present on this early Earth. Also, of course, it is a long way from organic molecules of the sort that Miller and Urey obtained to the microscopic organisms Pasteur was looking for.

2. A meteorite from Mars contains structures that could be the fossils of very small bacteria-like creatures. That these potential fossils were found very close to complex organic molecules and carbonate minerals associated with living organisms on Earth is particularly intriguing.

3. The primary objection to the argument is the supposed fossils' small size—they are smaller than any bacteria found on Earth and perhaps too small to contain all the molecules necessary for a living organism to function.

4. No—evolution describes heritable changes in organisms over time—that is, genetic changes that can be passed onto offspring. The adjustments the body makes to high attitude do not affect the genes that are passed to a person's offspring.

5. If Lamarck were correct, the body builder's children would inherit the increased muscle mass that the body builder had acquired over a lifetime of weight lifting. However, because Lamarck's theory turned out to be incorrect, the children will have to do their own body building.

6. There is lots of variation in fur color among cats—there are tabby cats, black cats, white cats, gray cats, and so on. There is variation in tail length among cats—not all cat tails are exactly the same length. There is no variation in the number of eyes among cats—all cats have two eyes.

7. Yes, all three traits are heritable because they are all determined genetically. (Note that not all heritable traits are necessarily variable—here, having two eyes is a heritable trait but not a variable one.)

8. Yes, this could lead to natural selection. There is variation in the fighting abilities of males, and this variation is due to heritable traits such as size and strength. And, because the winners of fights have more mates, winning males are likely to leave more offspring than losing males. The effect of natural selection would be to cause elephant seals to become stronger, like their fathers.

9. Because camouflage against the snow has also been selected for—camouflage allows prey to avoid being seen by predators, and predators to hide from the prey they're stalking. A trait's overall contribution to an animal's survival and reproduction is what is relevant for natural selection. After all, polar bears could reduce their surface area-to-volume ratio further by having no legs at all, but that wouldn't be advantageous good for survival and reproduction.

10. Babies have higher surface area-to-volume ratios than adult humans because they are smaller in size. So yes, they are likely to appreciate the extra bundling.

11. Not necessarily. Because genetic drift depends on some individuals leaving more offspring than other individuals by chance, there's no guarantee that chance would produce the same result the next year. It's the same as flipping coins—if you flip a coin 100 times and then repeat the process, you may get more heads the first time and more tails the second time.

12. Migration would cause the population to evolve towards a greater frequency of brown alleles.

13. Yes, the moles on the two sides of the river now represent two different species because they don't interbreed. This is allopatric speciation, because it occurred after a geographic barrier (the river) separated the populations.

14. Probably not, since a river is not much of a geographic barrier for flying organisms.

15. Prezygotic—it prevents mating.

16. It suggests that island species evolved from mainland species, rather than that species were distributed purposefully around the Earth.

17. All the definitions corresponding correctly with their matching terms.

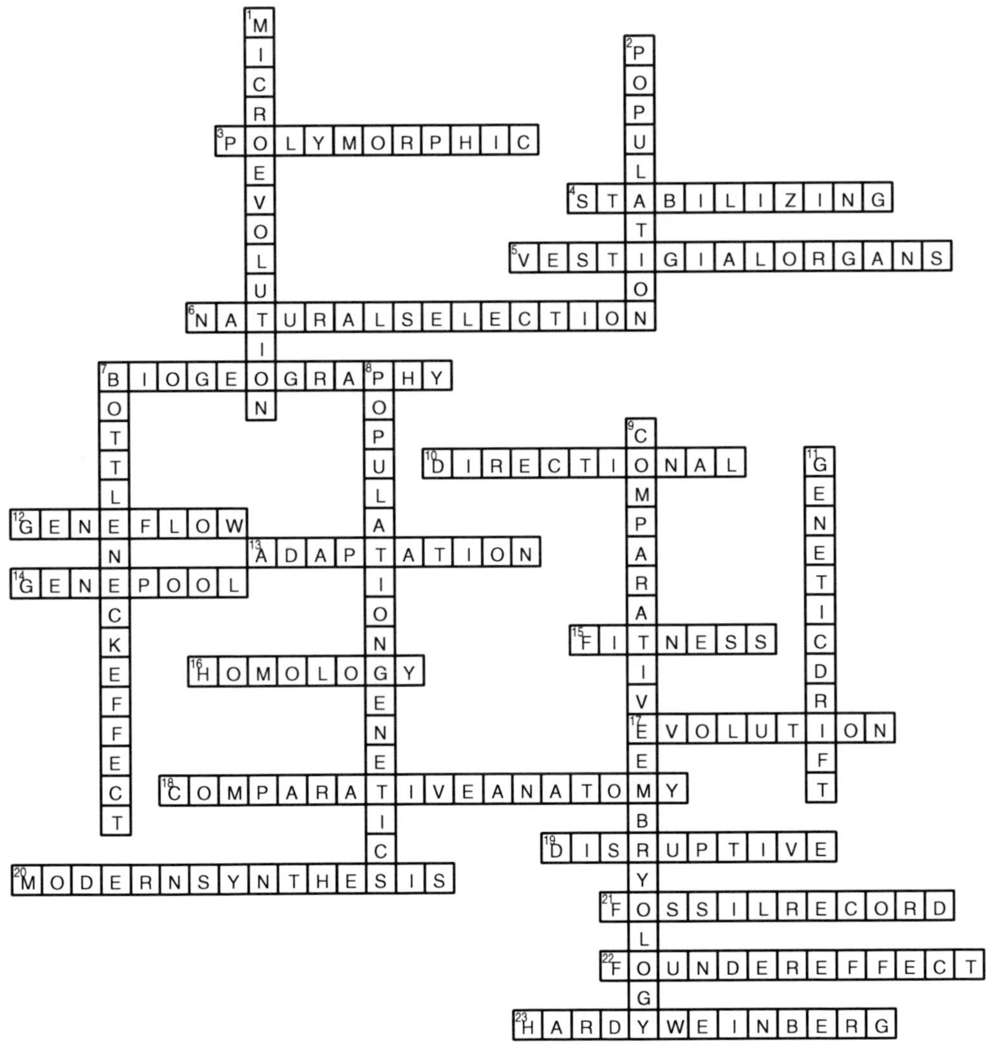

Answers to Science as a way of Knowing in your Textbook pages 590–592

Did Life on Earth Originate on Mars?

1. Because in 1996, NASA scientists found what could be fossils of tiny bacteria in a Martian meteorite. Moreover, the potential fossils were found very close to complex organic molecules and carbonate minerals that, on Earth, are associated with living organisms.
3. Perhaps, scientists proposed, life found its way to Earth in Martian dust set adrift in space when a comet collided with Mars.

Animal Adaptations to Heat and Cold

5. The heat an animal generates is proportional to its volume. The heat an animal dissipates is proportional to its surface area, since heat is lost to the environment through its body surface. Consequently, animals are better able to lose heat if they have a high surface area-to-volume ratio and better able to retain heat if they have a low surface area-to-volume ratio.
7. Allen's Rule says that desert species typically have long legs and large ears that increase the surface area available for heat dissipation, whereas Arctic species typically have short appendages and small ears that help conserve heat. Desert and Arctic rabbit species provide an example of Allen's Rule.

Earth's Tangible Evidence of Evolution

9. Fossils of now-extinct relatives of the horse show that species grew larger in size over time, as well as more specialized for eating grass and running. Some fossil whales exhibit some of the characteristics of the hoofed animals they evolved from-hind limbs, nostrils on their noses rather than blowholes, and different types of teeth. *Archaeopteryx*, the famous 150-million-year-old fossil bird, has many birdlike features-feathers, wings, a wishbone-but also has dinosaur-like features absent in modern birds, including claws on its wings, bones in its tail, and teeth.

Exercises

1. The types of environments where living organisms were thought to spontaneously appear-rotting carcasses or meat broths-had to be isolated from living organisms so that they would not be contaminated by life that already existed. This isolation proved difficult to achieve, and contamination often did occur.
3. Liposomes have double membranes and behave in ways that are eerily cell-like, growing and shrinking, even budding and dividing. Liposomes also control the absorption of materials and run chemical reactions within their membranes, like cells. However, they do not have genetic material like real cells.
5. Lamarck would say that over a lifetime of swimming, the shapes of fish became more streamlined as they fought their way through the water. They then pass this more streamlined shape to their offspring. Darwin would say that fish vary in their body shape, and that more streamlined individuals were more effective swimmers, so survived and reproduced better, leaving more streamlined individuals in the population.
7. Answers will vary. Traits that don't show variation include having a four-chambered heart, five fingers on each hand, two arms, two legs, one nose, etc. Traits that show variation include height, weight, arm length, foot length, eye color, hair color, etc.
9. No, color band color is not a heritable trait.
11. Alternative explanations are genetic drift, migration into or out of the population, and mutation pressure. To determine whether natural selection is responsible for the shift, you could compare the fitness (number of offspring left) of red individuals versus yellow individuals. If this turned out to be difficult, you could also compare their survival or ability to acquire mates in an attempt to identify underlying causes of potential fitness differences.
13. It could be, but it could also be the result of better nutrition.
15. The kit fox is the one with pale brownish fur, large ears, and long limbs. The fur color helps it reflect heat and stay camouflaged in its environment. The large ears and long limbs help it increase surface area available for heat dissipation. The Arctic fox has white fur, which helps it stay camouflaged, and small ears and short limbs that help it decrease the surface area from which heat is lost.

17. No, you cannot conclude they are distinct species merely because they are distinguishable. You can determine whether they are distinct species by figuring out whether they interbreed.

19. Hawaii is extremely isolated from all mainlands, so organisms that arrived there then had plenty of time to evolve in isolation and speciate from mainland species.

21. Both these biogeographical patterns suggest that organisms dispersed where they could, not that they were purposefully distributed across the globe.

Problems

1. Yes, this is natural selection because color is a variable, heritable trait and brown and green individuals have different fitness. What is happening here is that, over time, the population is shifting toward a greater and greater proportion of brown individuals.

Generation	Brown	Green	Proportion Brown
1	2	2	0.50
2	4	2	0.67
3	8	2	0.80
4	16	2	0.89
5	32	2	0.94
6	64	2	0.97
7	128	2	0.98
8	256	2	0.992
9	512	2	0.996
10	1024	2	0.998

3. Since there is a RR organism and a RW organism, the frequency of the R allele in the population is $\frac{3}{4} = 0.75$. The frequency of the W allele is $\frac{1}{4} = 0.25$.

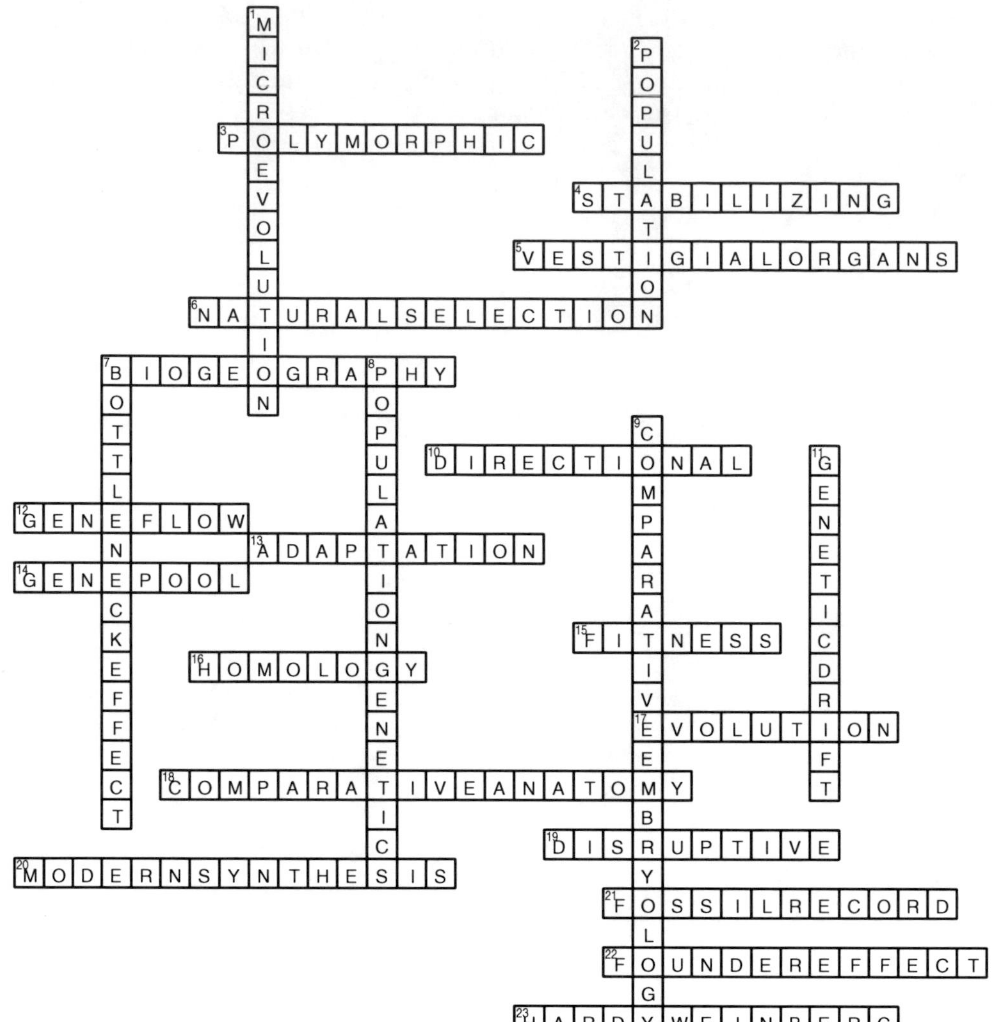
1 MICROEVOLUTION
2 POPULATION
3 POLYMORPHIC
4 STABILIZING
5 VESTIGIALORGANS
6 NATURALSELECTION
7 BOTTLENECKEFFECT
BIOGEOGRAPHY
8 POPULATIONGENETIC
9 COMPARATIVEEMBRYOLOGY
10 DIRECTIONAL
11 GENETICDRIFT
12 GENEFLOW
13 ADAPTATION
14 GENEPOOL
15 FITNESS
16 HOMOLOGY
17 EVOLUTION
18 COMPARATIVEANATOMY
19 DISRUPTIVE
20 MODERNSYNTHESIS
21 FOSSILRECORD
22 FOUNDEREFFECT
23 HARDYWEINBERG

Chapter 19

Exercises in Biological Diversity

Classification

1. Linnaean classification groups species together based on ______.

   SHARED SIMILARITIES

2. Fill in the levels of Linnaean classification from the largest group to the smallest group below.

   Domain

   ____ KINGDOM

   ____ PHYLUM

   ____ CLASS

   ____ ORDER

   ____ FAMILY

   ____ GENUS

   Species

3. A species' scientific name consists of its ______ name and its ______ name.

   GENUS, SPECIES

4. Cladistic classification groups species together based on their ____.

   EVOLUTIONARY HISTORY OR EVOLUTIONARY RELATIONSHIPS

5. The following cladogram shows evolutionary relationships between the rufous hummingbird, the honey mushroom, and the bristlecone pine.

   This cladogram suggests that ______ and ______ should be classified together to the exclusion of ________.

   HONEY MUSHROOM, RUFOUS HUMMINGBIRD, BRISTLECONE PINE

Biological Diversity I: Bacteria, Archaea, Protists

1. What are the three domains of life?

BACTERIA, ARCHAEA, EUKARYA

Of the three domains, ______ and ______ consist of prokaryotes and ______ consists of eukaryotes.

BACTERIA, ARCHAEA, EUKARYA

2. The four kingdoms that make up Eukarya are:

PLANTS, ANIMALS, PROTISTS, FUNGI

3. Are there any bacteria that can photosynthesize? Are there any heterotrophic bacteria?

YES, YES

4. How do bacteria typically reproduce?

BACTERIA TYPICALLY REPRODUCE ASEXUALLY BY DIVIDING.

5. Can bacteria exchange genetic material? If so, how?

YES, MOST SPECIES EXCHANGE GENETIC MATERIAL AT LEAST OCCASIONALLY, WHEN THEY TAKE UP SMALL PIECES OF NAKED DNA FROM THE ENVIRONMENT, WHEN BACTERIAL VIRUSES INADVERTENTLY TRANSFER DNA BETWEEN ORGANISMS, OR WHEN TWO BACTERIA JOIN TOGETHER AND ONE PASSES DNA TO THE OTHER.

6. Do the many bacteria that live in and on our bodies benefit us in any way?

YES, SOME PRODUCE VITAMINS AND OTHERS KEEP MORE DANGEROUS BACTERIA FROM INVADING OUR BODIES.

7. Are archaea more closely related to bacteria or to eukaryotes? What evidence supports this?

ARCHAEA ARE MORE CLOSELY RELATED TO EUKARYOTES THAN TO BACTERIA. MANY FEATURES OF ARCHAEAN GENETICS IN PARTICULAR LINK THEM TO EUKARYOTES—THEIR RIBOSOMES AND tRNA RESEMBLE THOSE OF EUKARYOTES, THEIR GENES CONTAIN INTRONS LIKE THOSE OF EUKARYOTES, AND THEIR DNA IS ASSOCIATED WITH HISTONE PROTEINS, LIKE THAT OF EUKARYOTES.

8. What's an extremophile? Are all archaea extremophiles?

EXTREMOPHILES ARE "LOVERS OF THE EXTREME," ORGANISMS THAT ARE ADAPTED TO EXTREME ENVIRONMENTS SUCH AS VERY SALTY PONDS OR THE SCALDING WATERS OF HOT SPRINGS AND HYDROTHERMAL VENTS. SOME ARCHAEA ARE EXTREMOPHILES—BUT NOT ALL. MANY OCCUR IN MORE FAMILIAR LOCALES, SUCH AS THE OPEN OCEAN OR THE DIGESTIVE TRACTS OF TERMITES AND COWS.

Biological Diversity I: Bacteria, Archaea, Protists—continued

9. What is a chemoautotroph?

CHEMOAUTOTROPHS MAKE FOOD USING CHEMICAL ENERGY RATHER THAN ENERGY FROM SUNLIGHT. ARCHAEA IN HYDROTHERMAL VENT HABITATS, FOR EXAMPLE, OBTAIN ENERGY FROM A CHEMICAL ABUNDANT THERE, HYDROGEN SULFIDE.

10. Are each of the following groups of protists autotrophs or heterotrophs?

A. diatoms — AUTOTROPHS

B. amoebas — HETEROTROPHS

C. kelp — AUTOTROPHS

D. dinoflagellates — AUTOTROPHS OR HETEROTROPHS

E. *PLASMODIUM* (the protist that causes malaria) — HETEROTROPHS

Biological Diversity II: Plants, Fungi, Animals

1. Match the following plant structures with their function:

stomata	B	**A.** move water and nutrients up from the roots
roots	F	**B.** take in carbon dioxide
shoots	C	**C.** conduct photosynthesis
xylem	A	**D.** move sugars produced during photosynthesis
phloem	D	**E.** transport resources to different parts of plant
vascular system	E	**F.** absorb water and nutrients from soil

2. The life history of plants involves a(n) ______ in which plants move between a haploid _______ stage and a diploid ______ stage.

ALTERNATION OF GENERATIONS, GAMETOPHYTE, SPOROPHYTE

3. Mosses are unique among plants in that the ______ is much larger than the ______. When you see a moss in the forest, you are looking at a(n) ______. The sperm are released by the male ______ directly into the environment, where they use their flagella to swim through a film of water to eggs in the female gametophyte. Sperm and egg then fuse and grow into a tiny (haploid/diploid) ______ that is completely dependent on the female gametophyte for nutrients and water. Eventually, cells in the sporophyte undergo meiosis to produce (haploid/diploid) spores that scatter and grow into new ______ (moss plants).

GAMETOPHYTE; SPOROPHYTE; GAMETOPHYTE; GAMETOPHYTE; DIPLOID; SPOROPHYTE; HAPLOID; GAMETOPHYTES

4. Why are ferns less tied to a moist environment than mosses? Why are they more tied to a moist environment than seed plants?

FERNS ARE LESS TIED TO A MOIST ENVIRONMENT THAN MOSSES BECAUSE, UNLIKE MOSSES, THEY HAVE A VASCULAR SYSTEM FOR TRANSPORTING WATER AND NUTRIENTS AROUND THE PLANT. HOWEVER, THEY ARE MORE TIED TO MOIST ENVIRONMENTS THAN SEED PLANTS, BECAUSE UNLIKE SEED PLANTS, THEY HAVE SPERM THAT MUST SWIM THROUGH THE ENVIRONMENT TO FERTILIZE EGGS.

Biological Diversity II: Plants, Fungi, Animals—continued

5. What is pollen? What is a seed? What is a fruit? In what groups of plants are each of these structures found?

POLLEN CONSISTS OF IMMATURE MALE GAMETOPHYTES WRAPPED IN PROTECTIVE COATINGS. POLLEN IS TRANSPORTED TO THE FEMALE GAMETOPHYTE DURING PLANT REPRODUCTION. SEEDS ARE SMALL EMBRYONIC SPOROPHYTES THAT ARE ENCASED IN A TOUGH OUTER COATING ALONG WITH A FOOD SUPPLY. SEEDS ARE ABLE TO SURVIVE IN A DORMANT STATE, DURING WHICH GROWTH AND DEVELOPMENT ARE SUSPENDED, UNTIL CONDITIONS ARE FAVORABLE FOR GROWTH. FRUITS ARE STRUCTURES SURROUNDING THE SEEDS OF FLOWERING PLANTS THAT HELP DISPERSE THE SEEDS. POLLEN AND SEEDS ARE FOUND IN SEED PLANTS. FRUITS ARE FOUND IN FLOWERING PLANTS.

6. Fungi are autotrophs/heterotrophs/both. Fungi are unicellular/multicellular/both. Fungi reproduce sexually/asexually/both.

HETEROTROPHS; BOTH; BOTH

7. Match the following animal groups with the list of features. Some groups may have more than one feature.

sponges	C, K
cnidarians	F, N
flatworms	U, V
roundworms	E
arthropods	I, P
mollusks	A
annelids	H, G
echinoderms	M, R
chordates	Q
catilaginous fishes	
ray-finned fishes	B
amphibians	J, Y
reptiles	L
turtles	W
snakes	D
birds	O, X
mammals	T, V

A. muscular foot responsible for locomotion
B. swim bladder
C. the only animals that lack tissues
D. adaptations for subduing large prey and swallowing them whole
E. muscles all run longitudinally—from head to tail—down the body, resulting in a flailing whiplike motion
F. polyp stage and medusa stage alternate
G. leeches
H. segmented worms
I. segmented bodies and jointed legs
J. terrestrial vertebrates restricted to moist environments because their skins are composed of living cells that are vulnerable to drying out, and lay eggs without shells
K. maintain a constant flow of water in through numerous pores, into the central cavity, and out the top, whose purpose is for food capture
L. birds and crocodiles
M. tube feet
N. tentacles armed with barbed stinging cells
O. hollow bones, air sacs in the body, and a four-chambered heart
P. includes the most diverse group of living things on Earth, the insects
Q. a notochord, gill slits, and a tail that extends beyond the anus
R. starfish
S. have a skeleton made of cartilage
T. have hair and feed their young milk
U. tapeworms
V. platypus
W. squeezes its entire body inside its ribcage
X. flying endotherms
Y. frogs

Answers to the Practice Test

1. A
2. B
3. True
4. True
5. E
6. shared similarities
7. genus, species
8. Latinized, italicized, capitalized
9. D
10. True
11. True
12. molecular clocks
13. True
14. D
15. D
16. True
17. False
18. True
19. True
20. Pongo, abelii
21. True
22. True
23. True
24. False
25. bacteria
26. Bacteria
27. False, Bacteria
28. True
29. True
30. True
31. True
32. True
33. C
34. True
35. chemical, chemical
36. B
37. True
38. True
39. False
40. True
41. E
42. Amoebas
43. Ciliates
44. Flagellates
45. True
46. Malaria
47. False – Malaria
48. True
49. True
50. True
51. False leaves
52. xylem, phloem
53. True
54. mosses, ferns, seed plants
55. True
56. True
57. True
58. B
59. C
60. True
61. False – Seedless
62. B
63. True
64. A
65. True
66. True
67. B
68. True
69. Flowering plants
70. Conifers
71. flowers, fruit
72. stamen, carpel
73. Darwin
74. True

75. True
76. Fruits
77. False
78. A
79. Quinine
80. Aspirin
81. periwinkle
82. Fungi
83. mycorrhizae
84. True
85. True
86. True
87. sexually
88. True
89. True
90. True
91. Sponges
92. D
93. C
94. cnidarians
95. True
96. True
97. True
98. A
99. True
100. True
101. True
102. flatworms
103. False – Flatworms
104. True
105. B
106. True
107. Arthropods
108. A
109. True
110. Uniramians
111. chelicerates
112. Crustaceans
113. True
114. B
115. True
116. B
117. Cephalopods
118. Bivalves
119. Gastropods
120. C
121. False – Earthworms
122. Leeches
123. D
124. E
125. chordates
126. Tunicates, Lancelets, lancelets, Vertebrates
127. True
128. True
129. A
130. A
131. same as
132. True
133. True
134. True
135. Frogs, Salamanders, caecilians.
136. C
137. Most
138. True
139. rue
140. F
141. Reptiles
142. True
143. B
144. C
145. True
146. Mammals
147. Placentals, Marsupials, and Monotremes
148. Monotremes

149. Marsupials

150. Placentals

151. True

152. A

153. True

154. C

155. True

156. True

157. True

158. C

159. Match each term in the right to its best discretion on the left column

Cladogram, ____ C	**A.** Accumulating changes in their DNA sequence at a fairly constant rate over time.
Bacteria _____ D.	**B.** Small, seedless plants that have no vascular systems.
Molecular clocks. ____ A	**C.** *Evolutionary tree*
Mosses _____ B	**D.** Reproduce asexually by dividing, and most exchange genetic material at least occasionally—when they take up small pieces of naked DNA from the environment
Ethnobotany _____ F.	**E.** Focus on plant use in prehistoric times by examining seeds, pollen, wood, and other plant remains found at archaeological sites.
Paleoethnobotanists ____ E.	**F.** The study of how people use plants, generally by interviewing local peoples and studying their traditions and habits.
Exoskeleton ____ G.	**G.** It is incapable of growth and must be shed periodically as animals grow.
Dragonflies ___ J.	**H.** Have *electroreceptive organs* that are able to detect the electric currents given off by the muscles and nerves of nearby prey.
Annelids ____ *M.*	**I.** Animals that regulate their body temperature behaviorally by seeking sunlight when they need to warm up and shade when they need to cool down.
Sharks ____ H.	**J.** Their wings always stick straight out. They still retains the old trait.
Endotherms ____ L	**K.** Circular molecules of RNA, lack a protein coat and infect plants
Viroids ____ *K.*	**L.** Animals that maintain a relatively constant and relatively high body temperature by metabolizing large amounts of food.
Ectotherms ____ I	**M.** Able to contract one part of the body while keeping the rest of the body still.

Answers for Critical Thinking Questions

CHECK YOUR ANSWERS

1. A cladistic classification reveals, rather than obscures, the evolutionary history of species. Knowing that birds are reptiles, for example, allows biologists to ask appropriate questions about the evolution of their traits. For example, birds are "warm-blooded" rather than "cold-blooded" like the other reptiles—how did they evolve warm-bloodedness? Birds have feathers, rather than the scales seen in other reptiles—could scales have been modified to form feathers? Under Linnaean classification, where reptiles and birds are separate classes, there is no clear relationship between the two groups.

2. Humans are animals, button mushrooms are fungi, and celery is a plant. In the cladogram above, we see that animals and fungi are more closely related to each other than either is to plants. So, we are more closely related to button mushrooms.

3. Antibiotics kill both the targeted "bad" bacteria as well as normal "good" bacteria in our bodies. The normal bacteria help keep yeast in check. Without them, yeast proliferates and causes an infection.

4. In mosses, the gametophyte is much larger than the sporophyte, and the sporophyte is completely dependent on the gametophyte for water and nutrients. In ferns, the sporophyte is larger than the gametophyte. The gametophyte is very small but independent. In seed plants, the sporophyte is larger than the gametophyte, and the gametophyte is completely dependent on the sporophyte—in other words, seed plants are sort of the "opposites" of mosses.

5. In both groups, gametophytes release sperm that swim directly to the eggs to fertilize them.

6. Dispersal allows plants to spread their seeds to a variety of environments, some of which may be well suited to their survival and reproduction.

7. Corals are found only in shallow waters, where there is enough sunlight for their dinoflagellates to photosynthesize. Rising sea levels will require them to either shift their ranges to shallower ground, or to grow upward quickly. Whether they are able to find appropriate habitat and keep pace with sea-level changes remains to be seen.

8. Coral species that are currently adapted to warmer water temperatures may spread as global warming continues. In addition, coral reefs are likely to include more species that are better able to resist bleaching. For example, many reefs may come to be dominated by species that have fluorescent pigments, as species that lack these sunscreens die out.

9. Much of the answer has to do with the way insects breathe. Insects rely on *trachea,* series of branched tubules connected to the outside air, for oxygen. Oxygen must diffuse through the trachea to reach the tissues, a strategy that works well only in extremely small bodies. (This is because the time it takes a molecule to diffuse a certain distance is proportional to the square of that distance.) Interestingly, there were much bigger insects during the Carboniferous Period, some 300 million years ago, when atmospheric oxygen levels were much higher than they are today. Those insects included a 5-foot millipede and a dragonfly with a 2 1/2 foot wingspan!

10. Most animals are able to move. The ones that are sedentary (sponges, some bivalves, barnacles, and so forth) typically release their eggs into the water, where water currents disperse them. Some sedentary animals also have a mobile larval stage. Plants, which are sedentary, are able to disperse by forming spores or seeds that are carried by wind, water, or mobile animals. Flowering plants form special structures called fruit that help them disperse their seeds.

11. An eagle produces more lift. Birds must produce enough lift to counter gravity in order to stay in the air. An eagle weighs more than a sparrow, and so produces more lift.

12. Large birds have a more difficult time keeping themselves aloft. This is because lift is generated by air pressure under the wings, and so is proportional to the surface area of the wings. Lift must counter gravity, which is proportional to the volume of the bird. Since the surface area-to-volume ratio is smaller in larger animals, larger birds have more difficulty generating the necessary lift. This explains why the wings of large birds are relatively larger than the wings of small birds. It also explains why small birds are more adept fliers than larger birds. For example, tiny hummingbirds have tremendous maneuverability in the air and can even hover, an ability that is rare among birds and critical to the way they feed. On the other hand, many large birds have trouble getting off the ground and then actually spend much of their time soaring on thermals.

13. All the definitions corresponding correctly with their matching terms.

Endoskeleton vs. Exoskeleton	
Ectotherms vs. Endotherms	
Kingdom vs. Phylum	
Fruit vs. Seed	
Staman vs. carpel	
Gametophyte vs. sporophyte	
Xylem vs. phloem	
Genus vs. Species	
Viruses vs. *Prions*	

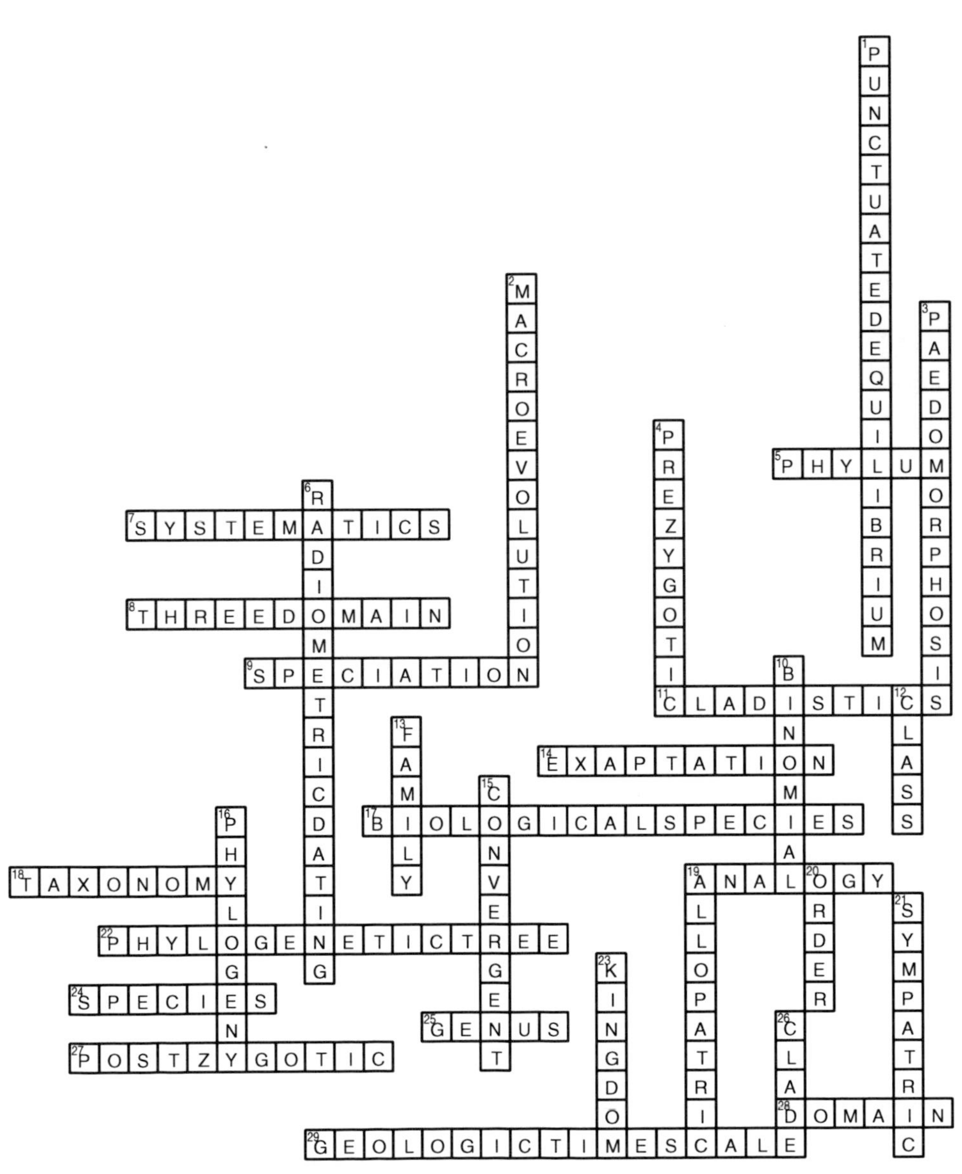

Answers to the Practice Test

1. C
2. True
3. people, birds
4. E
5. False, speciation
6. Galápagos
7. macroevolution
8. D
9. True
10. True
11. fossil
12. D
13. C
14. True
15. hybrid sterility
16. D
17. D
18. False, two
19. sympatric
20. A
21. S
22. A
23. A
24. S
25. A
26. C
27. True
28. False, little
29. B
30. False, could not have
31. exaptation
32. C
33. A
34. D
35. True
36. paedomorphosis
37. C
38. D
39. B
40. D
41. False, relative
42. radiometric dating
43. C
44. A
45. False, allopatric
46. continental drift
47. D
48. D
49. False, many
50. A
51. E
52. A
53. True
54. binomial
55. A
56. D
57. E
58. D
59. False, analogous, homologous
60. the same structure
61. analogous
62. homologous
63. convergent, homology
64. cladistics
65. E
66. False, Protista
67. cladistics
68. B
69. True

Answers to Science as a Way of Knowing from your Textbook page 623–624

Coral Bleaching

1. Increases in seawater temperature that last for an extended period of time.
3. Because of continued global warming due to human greenhouse gas emissions.

How Birds Fly

5. Birds move forward through the air by flapping their wings. During the downstroke, the wings push against the air and the air pushes back. This propels them forward.

Exercises

1. Because archaea are more closely related to eukaryotes than either is to bacteria, classifying archaea and bacteria together to the exclusion of eukaryotes obscures the evolutionary history of the three groups. It is like the example in the text of grouping humans and daisies together to the exclusion of elephants. In terms of a cladistic classification, the fact that archaea and bacteria are both prokaryotes is not relevant–only the evolutionary relationships among the three groups matters in constructing biological groups.
3. Spores are very hardy, able to survive for long periods under tough conditions. This allows bacteria, fungi, and other organisms capable of generating spores to produce descendants that can survive tough periods and then grow into mature individuals when conditions improve.
5. No, life would do just fine without eukaryotes, as it did for billions of years before the first eukaryotes evolved.
7. Mosses are most dependent on living in a moist environment. This is because they have no vascular systems—instead, every part of a moss plant receives water directly from the environment. In addition, mosses have swimming sperm that require moisture in the environment in order to travel to and fertilize moss eggs. Seed plants are least dependent on living in a moist environment because they use pollen rather than swimming sperm during sexual reproduction, and they have vascular systems. (The third group, ferns, have vascular systems, but also use swimming sperm, so are more moisture-dependent than seed plants.)
9. Seed plants produce pollen. Pollen is carried to the female flower/cone by wind or by animals. Most flowering plants use animal pollinators, particularly insects.
11. Wind-pollinated plants are most likely to cause allergies because they make larger quantities of pollen due to the haphazard nature of wind pollination.
13. Many cnidarians, including jellyfish and sea anemones, catch prey using tentacles armed with barbed stinging cells. Corals, however, house dinoflagellates in their bodies and obtain the bulk of their nutrients from these photosynthesizers.
15. The muscles of roundworms all run longitudinally (from head to tail) down the body. As a result, roundworms move like flailing whips as muscles on alternate sides of the body contract. The muscles of annelids are arranged in both circular (around the body) and longitudinal (head-to-tail) orientations, allowing for great flexibility of motion. Unlike roundworms, for example, annelids are able to contract one part of the body while keeping the rest of the body still.
17. Amphibians have a skin made of living cells that is vulnerable to drying out. In addition, their eggs are unshelled and also vulnerable to drying out.
19. Because birds are descended from the last common ancestor of all reptiles. What they do or do not have in common with mammals is not a factor in how they are classified.
21. The advantage of genetic exchange is genetic diversity among the offspring. This way, you don't put all your eggs in one (genetic) basket, and at least some of your offspring are likely to do well under a wide array of potential environmental conditions.

23. Viruses are small pieces of genetic material wrapped in a protein coat. Many viruses have normal, double-stranded DNA genomes, but others use single-stranded DNA, single-stranded RNA, or double-stranded RNA. Viruses reproduce by infecting a host cell and then using the cell's enzymes and ribosomes to copy their genetic material and build viral proteins. These are then assembled to form new viruses. One feature of viruses that makes them hard to deal with from the point of view of disease control is that they mutate very quickly. This is particularly true of viruses with RNA genomes, since there is no error-checking and repair system for copying RNA, as there is with DNA. Bird flu, which has devastated populations of domesticated birds, is caused by a virus that occurs naturally among wild birds. In 1997, the first case of a human infected by bird flu was reported in Hong Kong, and dozens of additional cases have been seen since then. So far, however, the virus cannot be transmitted easily from person to person. The evolution of this capability is the event scientists await with trepidation. This fear turns out to be more than justified. Scientists recently discovered that the infamous "Spanish flu" epidemic of 1918—which killed more people than any other disease over a similar length of time—was a bird flu that became easily transmissible among humans.

Problems

1. The population doubles every 20 minutes, so:

8:00	1
8:20	2
8:40	4
9:00	8
9:20	16
9:40	32
10:00	64
10:20	128
10:40	256
11:00	512
11:20	1024
11:40	2048
12:00	4096

3.

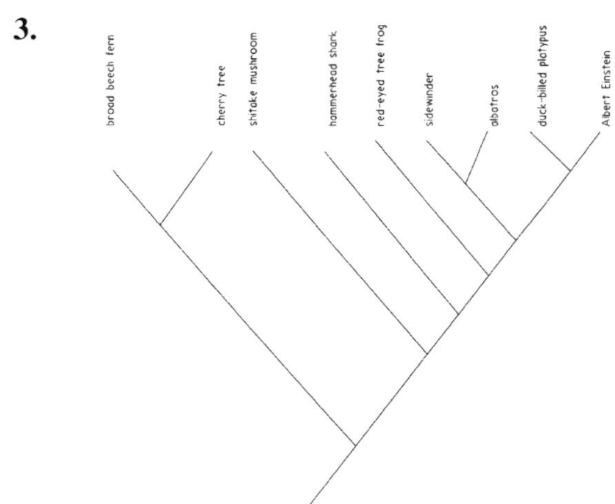

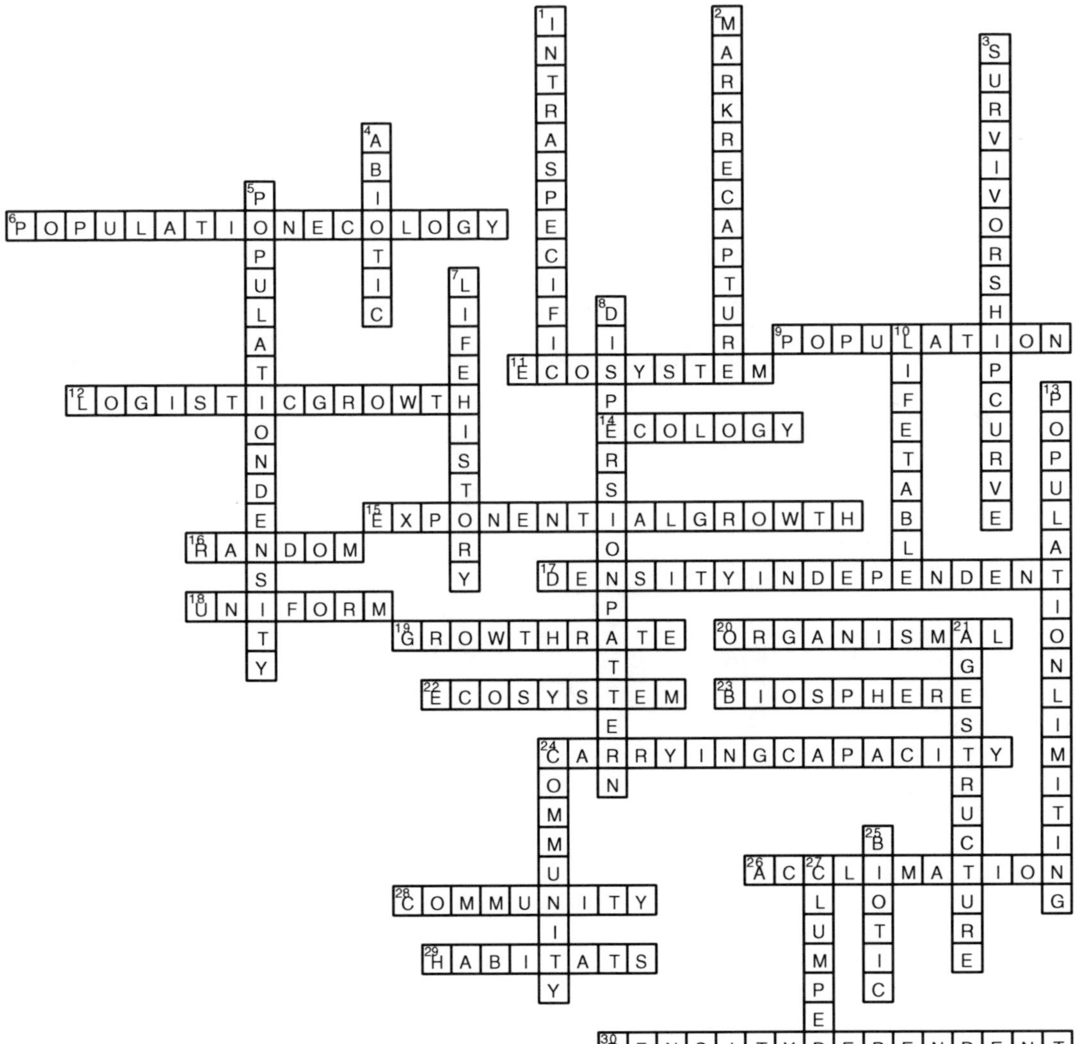
1 INTRASPECIFIC
2 MARKRECAPTURE
3 SURVIVORSHIPCURVE
4 ABIOTIC
5 POPULATIONDENSITY
6 POPULATIONECOLOGY
7 LIFEHISTORY
8 DISPERSIONPATTERN
9 POPULATION
10 LIFETABLE
11 ECOSYSTEM
12 LOGISTICGROWTH
13 POPULATIONLIMITING
14 ECOLOGY
15 EXPONENTIALGROWTH
16 RANDOM
17 DENSITYINDEPENDENT
18 UNIFORM
19 GROWTHRATE
20 ORGANISMAL
21 AGESTRUCTURE
22 ECOSYSTEM
23 BIOSPHERE
24 CARRYINGCAPACITY
24 COMMUNITY
25 BIOTIC
26 ACCLIMATION
27 CLUMPED
28 COMMUNITY
29 HABITATS
30 DENSITYDEPENDENT

Chapter 20

Ecosystems and Environment

Species Interactions

Define the following terms.

1. A population is ______.

A POPULATION IS A GROUP OF INDIVIDUALS OF A SINGLE SPECIES THAT OCCUPIES A GIVEN AREA.

A community is ______.

A COMMUNITY CONSISTS OF ALL THE ORGANISMS THAT LIVE WITHIN A GIVEN AREA.

An ecosystem is ______.

AN ECOSYSTEM CONSISTS OF ALL THE ORGANISMS THAT LIVE WITHIN A GIVEN AREA AND ALL THE ABIOTIC FEATURES OF THEIR ENVIRONMENT.

2. Look at the food chain below

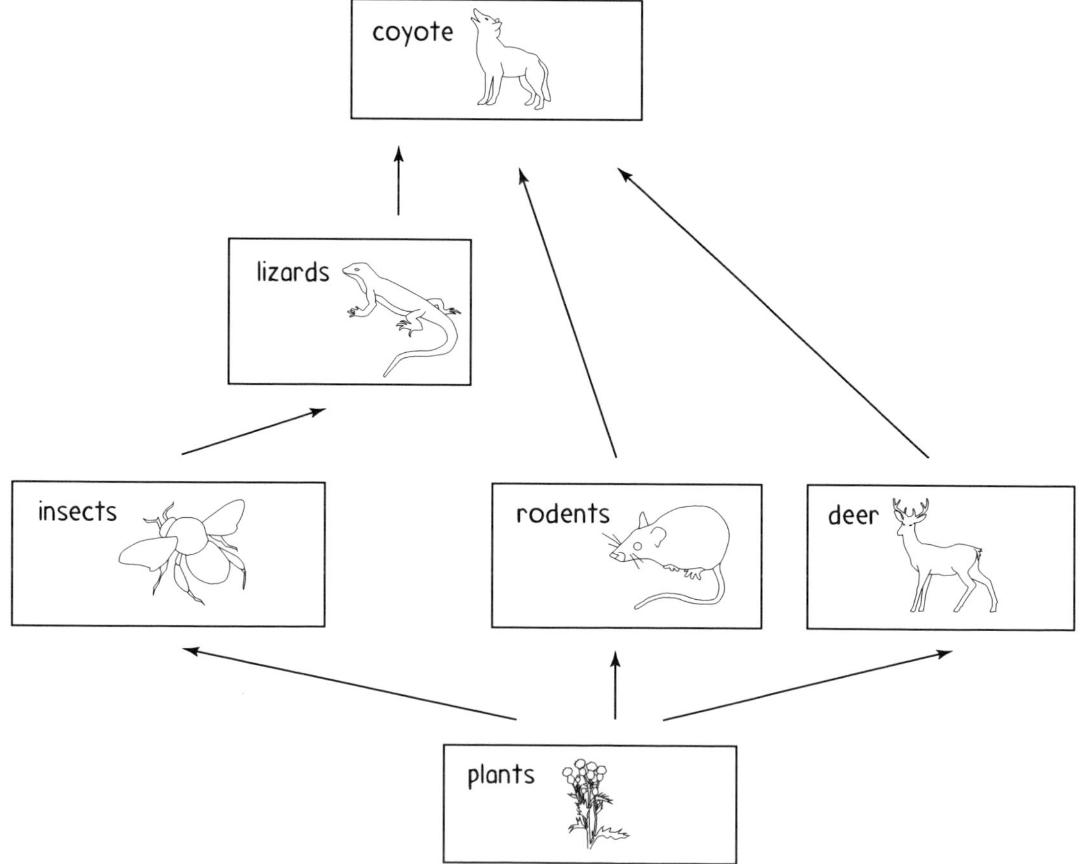

Species Interactions—continued

A. Who are the producers in this community?

PLANTS

B. Who are the primary consumers?

INSECTS, RODENTS, DEER

C. Who are the secondary consumers?

LIZARDS AND COYOTE

D. Who are the tertiary consumers?

COYOTE

E. Who is the top predator?

COYOTE

3. What is a species's niche?

THE TOTAL SET OF BIOTIC AND ABIOTIC RESOURCES IT USES WITHIN A COMMUNITY.

4. What is symbiosis?

A SITUATION IN WHICH INDIVIDUALS OF TWO SPECIES LIVE IN CLOSE ASSOCIATION WITH ONE ANOTHER.

Of the three types of symbiosis, _________ benefits one member of the interaction and harms the other, _________ benefits one species of the interaction while having no effect on the other, and _________ benefits both species.

PARASITISM; COMMENSALISM; MUTUALISM

Ecosystems

1. Match each of the following features with the appropriate biome or aquatic life zone:

tropical forest	I	**A.** tropical grassland
temperate forest	L	**B.** habitats that receive very little precipitation, may be cold or hot
coniferous forest	F	**C.** permafrost
tundra	C	**D.** plants that are adapted to surviving in changing salinity conditions
savanna	A	**E.** in the water column
temperate grassland	J	**F.** evergreen trees with needlelike leaves
desert	B	**G.** inhabitants have adaptations that allow them to deal with exposure, temperature fluctuations, and the action of waves
littoral zone	K	**H.** deep water habitats in ponds and lakes
limnetic zone	M	**I.** more species are found in this biome than in all other biomes combined
profundal zone	H	**J.** grassland with fertile soil, in areas with four distinct seasons
estuary	D	**K.** lake habitat close to the water surface and to shore
pelagic zone	E	**L.** trees drop their leaves in the autumn
benthic zone	N	**M.** lake and pond habitats that are close to the water surface, but far from shore
intertidal zone	G	**N.** on the ocean bottom
neritic zone	P	**O.** marine habitats far from coasts
oceanic zone	O	**P.** underwater marine habitats near the coasts

Ecosystems— continued

2. Carbon is an essential component of all organic molecules. Most of the inorganic carbon on Earth exists as ___________ and is found either in the ___________ or dissolved in ___________. Carbon moves into the biotic world when ____. This carbon becomes available to other organisms as it passes up the food chain. Carbon is returned to the environment by living organisms as ___________ during the process of ___________. An important part of Earth's carbon supply is also found in fossil fuels such as ___________. Human burning of fossil fuels has released so much carbon dioxide that atmospheric carbon dioxide levels are now higher than they have been for 420,000 years. Because atmospheric carbon dioxide traps heat on the planet, this has resulted in ___________.

CARBON DIOXIDE; ATMOSPHERE; OCEAN WATERS;
PLANTS AND OTHER PRODUCERS CONVERT CARBON DIOXIDE TO GLUCOSE DURING PHOTOSYNTHESIS;
CARBON DIOXIDE; CELLULAR RESPIRATION; COAL AND OIL; GLOBAL WARMING

3. How do living things obtain water?

WATER MOVES INTO THE BIOTIC WORLD WHEN IT IS ABSORBED OR SWALLOWED BY ORGANISMS.

How do living things return water to the abiotic world?

WATER IS RETURNED TO THE ABIOTIC ENVIRONMENT IN A VARIETY OF WAYS, INCLUDING THROUGH RESPIRATION, PERSPIRATION, EXCRETION, AND ELIMINATION.

4. The difference between primary succession and secondary succession is that

PRIMARY SUCCESSION DESCRIBES THE COLONIZATION OF BARE LAND DEVOID OF SOIL, WHEREAS SECONDARY SUCCESSION OCCURS WHEN A DISTURBANCE DESTROYS EXISTING LIFE IN A HABITAT, BUT LEAVES SOIL INTACT.

During ecological succession, the total biomass of the ecosystem typically___________, and the number of species present in the habitat typically ___________. INCREASES; INCREASES
Ecological succession ends with the ___________.

CLIMAX COMMUNITY

5. What does the intermediate disturbance hypothesis state?

REGULAR DISTURBANCES, IF NOT TOO EXTREME, ACTUALLY CONTRIBUTE TO BIODIVERSITY BECAUSE DIFFERENT SPECIES MAKE USE OF DIFFERENT HABITATS, AND PERIODIC DISTURBANCES GUARANTEE THAT THERE WILL ALWAYS BE HABITAT AT VARYING STAGES OF RECOVERY.

Populations

1. Which of the following graphs shows exponential growth and which shows logistic growth? Using words, describe the difference between exponential growth and logistic growth.

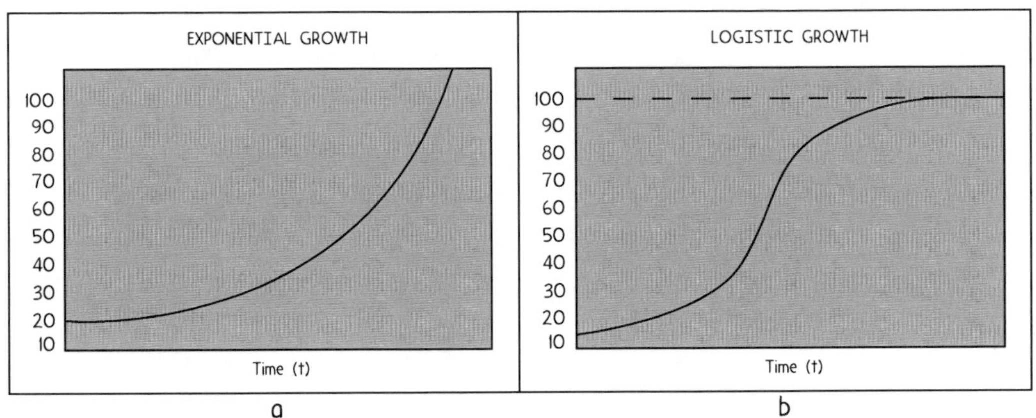

EXPONENTIAL GROWTH OCCURS WHEN A POPULATION GROWS AT A RATE THAT IS PROPORTIONAL TO ITS SIZE. *LOGISTIC GROWTH* OCCURS WHEN POPULATION GROWTH SLOWS AS IT REACHES THE HABITAT'S CARRYING CAPACITY, THAT IS, THE MAXIMUM NUMBER OF INDIVIDUALS OR MAXIMUM POPULATION DENSITY THE HABITAT CAN SUPPORT.

What is the carrying capacity in the graph on the right?

100

2. Label the three survivorship curves shown below. Indicate which organisms at right correspond to which survivorship curve.

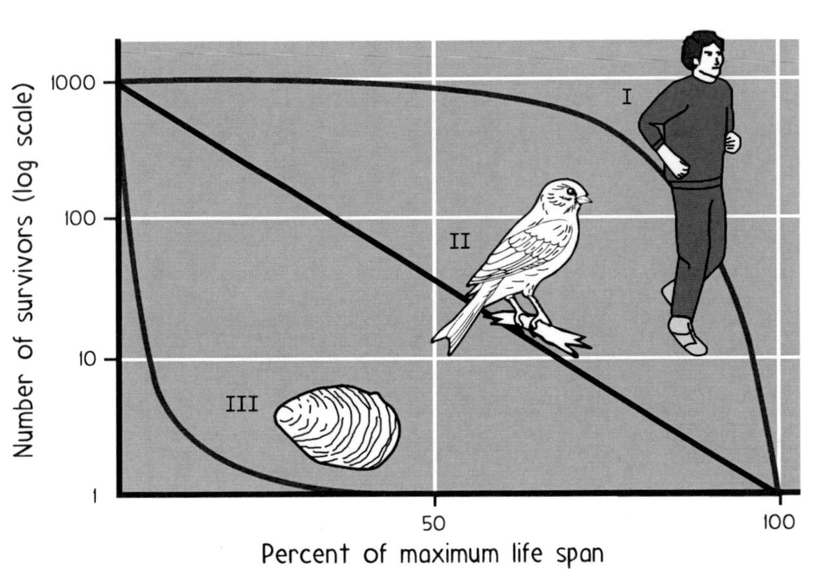

Using words, describe Type I, Type II, and Type III survivorship.

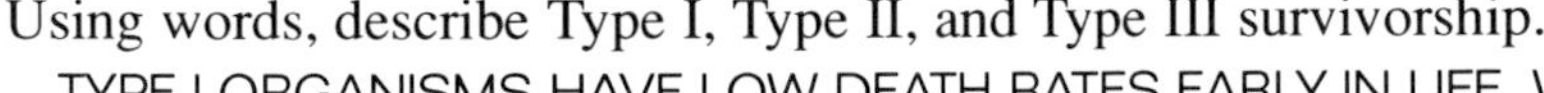

TYPE I ORGANISMS HAVE LOW DEATH RATES EARLY IN LIFE, WITH MOST INDIVIDUALS SURVIVING UNTIL FAIRLY LATE IN LIFE. TYPE II ORGANISMS HAVE A STEADY DEATH RATE THAT DOES NOT DEPEND ON AGE. INDIVIDUALS ARE AS LIKELY TO DIE EARLY IN LIFE AS LATE IN LIFE. TYPE III ORGANISMS HAVE HIGH DEATH RATES EARLY IN LIFE, WITH FEW INDIVIDUALS SURVIVING UNTIL LATE IN LIFE.

Populations—continued

3. Of the following traits, indicate which are associated with K-selected populations and which are associated with r-selected populations.

unstable environment	R-SELECTED POPULATIONS
large body size	K-SELECTED POPULATIONS
few offspring	K-SELECTED POPULATIONS
no parental care	R-SELECTED POPULATIONS
reach sexual maturity slowly	K-SELECTED POPULATIONS
long life expectancy	K-SELECTED POPULATIONS
exponential population growth	R-SELECTED POPULATIONS
Type III survivorship	R-SELECTED POPULATIONS
parental care	K-SELECTED POPULATIONS
stable environment	K-SELECTED POPULATIONS
short life expectancy	R-SELECTED POPULATIONS
small body size	R-SELECTED POPULATIONS
Type I survivorship	K-SELECTED POPULATIONS

Answers to the Practice Test, Part I

Content Quiz

Directions: Identify the one best answer for the multiple-choice questions. For true/false questions, determine if the statement is true or false. If false, change the underlined word(s) to make the statement true. Finally, add the correct word(s) to the fill-in-the-blank questions to make the statements true.

1. F

2. True

3. Human population explosion

4. A

5. True

6. abiotic

7. See the table below

Level of Ecology	Best Description
Organismal Ecology _____ B	**A.** the study of all the interactions between the abiotic factors and the environment of species that exists in a certain area.
Community Ecology _____D	**B.** the study of the evolutionary adaptations species that exists in a certain area that enable individual organisms to meet the abiotic factors and the community of the challenges posed by their abiotic environments.
Ecosystem Ecology _____ A	**C.** the study of the factors that affect population size, growth, and composition.
Population Ecology _____C	**D.** the study of all the organisms that inhabit a particular area.

8. E

9. True

10. Biosphere

11. Ecology

12. B

13. D

14. D

15. True

16. True

17. False (Surface)

18. True

19. winds

20. False (Endotherms)

21. False (Plants and Animals)

22. Matching: Match the term on the left to its best description on the right.

Level of Ecology	**Best Description**
Population Ecology ___ B	**D.** a group of individuals of the same species living in a given area at a given time
Population density ___ C	**E.** the field that examines the factors that influence a population's size, density, and characteristics
Mark recapture method __ D	**B.** a sampling technique used to estimate wildlife populations
Population __ A	**F.** the number of individuals of a species per unit area or volume

23. C

24. True

25. Opportunistic

26. B

27. False (intermediate)

28. True

29. Exponential growth

30. Logistic Growth

31. Population limiting

32. C

33. B

34. D

35. False, increase

36. True

37. True

38. Density-dependent

39. A

40. C

41. False (a decrease)

42. True

43. True

44. True

45. Birth, Death

46. A

47. Survivorship curve

48. C

49. True

Answers to the Practice Test, Part II

1. B
2. False (Shallow)
3. (Predators)
4. Ecosystems.
5. B
6. True
7. Species diversity
8. Environment
9. Community
10. C
11. C
12. D
13. True
14. Interspecific
15. Interspecific competition
16. Niche
17. Resource partitioning
18. C
19. A
20. True
21. warning
22. keystone
23. C
24. D
25. B
26. False (parasitism)
27. True
28. immune
29. C
30. B
31. Ecological succession
32. C
33. True
34. A
35. False (Sunlight)
36. True
37. Ecosystem
38. abiotic
39. air and soil
40. trophic
41.

	Best Description
Detritivore _____ C	**B.** an organism that uses photosynthesis.
Primary consumer _____ D	**B.** an animal that eats herbivores
Producer _____ A	**C.** decomposer
Secondary consumer ____ B	**D.** herbivore

42. B
43. D
44. C
45. False (producer)
46. Trophic levels
47. Food chain
48. prokaryotes, and fungi
49. Webs
50. D
51. True
52. True
53. D
54. True
55. Plants
56. A
57. C

58. False (ammonium or nitrate)

59. True

60. True

61. biogeochemical

62. A

63. B

64. True

65. C

66. C

67. B

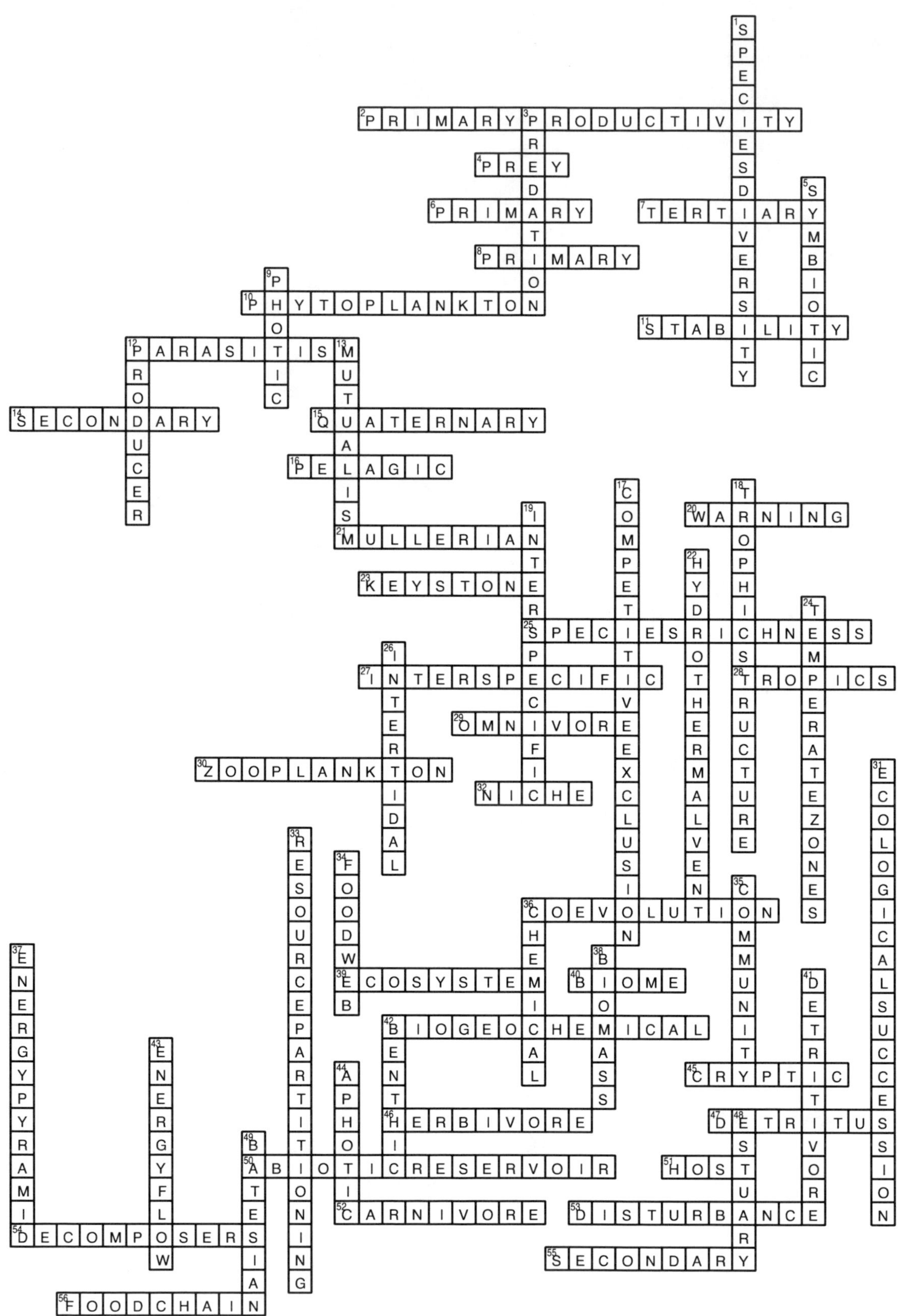
1 SPECIES DIVERSITY
2 PRIMARY PRODUCTIVITY
3 PREDATOR
4 PREY
5 SYMBIOTIC
6 PRIMARY
7 TERTIARY
8 PRIMARY
9 PHOTIC
10 PHYTOPLANKTON
11 STABILITY
12 PRODUCER
PARASITISM
13 MUTUALISM
14 SECONDARY
15 QUATERNARY
16 PELAGIC
17 COMPETITIVE EXCLUSION
18 TROPHIC STRUCTURE
19 INTERSPECIFIC
20 WARNING
21 MULLERIAN
22 HYDROTHERMAL VENT
23 KEYSTONE
24 TEMPERATE ZONES
25 SPECIES RICHNESS
26 INTERTIDAL
27 INTERSPECIFIC
28 TROPICS
29 OMNIVORE
30 ZOOPLANKTON
31 ECOLOGICAL SUCCESSION
32 NICHE
33 RESOURCE PARTITIONING
34 FOOD WEB
35 COMMUNITY
36 COEVOLUTION
CHEMICAL
37 ENERGY PYRAMID
38 BIOMASS
39 ECOSYSTEM
40 BIOME
41 DETRITIVORE
42 BIOGEOCHEMICAL
BENTHIC
43 ENERGY FLOW
44 APHOTIC
45 CRYPTIC
46 HERBIVORE
47 DETRITUS
48 ESTUARY
49 BATESIAN
50 ABIOTIC RESERVOIR
51 HOST
52 CARNIVORE
53 DISTURBANCE
54 DECOMPOSERS
55 SECONDARY
56 FOOD CHAIN

Supplement 1

Key Terms

Answers

1. c	**2.** d	**3.** e
4. b	**5.** a	

◆ Learning Exercise 1.1A

Answers

a. 2	**b.** 1	**c.** 4
d. 3	**e.** 4	**f.** 2

◆ Learning Exercise 1.1B

Answers

a. 2.4×10^5 cm	**b.** 8×10^2 m	**c.** 2.3×10^5 kg	**d.** 5×10^4 years
e. 2×10^{-3} m	**f.** 1.5×10^{26} g	**g.** 8×10^{-2} kg	**h.** 1×10^{-4} sec

◆ Learning Exercise 1.2A

Answers

a. E (counted)	**b.** M (use a watch)	**c.** E (metric definition)
d. M (use a balance)	**e.** E (counted)	**f.** M (use a metric ruler)

◆ Learning Exercise 1.2B

Answers

a. 4	**b.** 2	**c.** 2	**d.** 3
e. 4	**f.** 1	**g.** 4	**h.** 3

◆ Learning Exercise 1.3A

Answers

a. 89 m	**b.** 0.0029 g	**c.** 51 g	**d.** 1.7 m
e. 0.0011 kg	**f.** 82 L		

◆ Learning Exercise 1.3B

Answers

a. 93	**b.** 2.00	**c.** 5.3	**d.** 0.0479
e. 52 000	**f.** 27.1	**g.** 12.4	**h.** 110.00

◆ Learning Exercise 1.4A

Answers

1. h	**2.** d	**3.** b	**4.** g
5. e	**6.** a	**7.** c	**8.** f

◆ Learning Exercise 1.4B

Answers

a. milligram, gram, kilogram
b. millimeter, centimeter, kilometer
c. mL, dL, L
d. μg, mg, kg

◆ Learning Exercise 1.4C

Answers

a. 1000	b. 10	c. 100	d. 100
e. 1000	f. 10	g. 1000	h. 0.1
i. 1000	j. 0.01		

◆ Learning Exercise 1.5

Answers

a. $\frac{1000\text{ mm}}{1\text{ m}}$ and $\frac{1\text{ m}}{1000\text{ mm}}$

b. $\frac{1000\text{ g}}{1\text{ kg}}$ and $\frac{1\text{ kg}}{1000\text{ g}}$

c. $\frac{2.20\text{ lb}}{1\text{ kg}}$ and $\frac{1\text{ kg}}{2.20\text{ lb}}$

d. $\frac{2.54\text{ cm}}{1\text{ in.}}$ and $\frac{1\text{ in.}}{2.54\text{ cm}}$

e. $\frac{100\text{ cm}}{1\text{ m}}$ and $\frac{1\text{ m}}{100\text{ cm}}$

f. $\frac{946\text{ mL}}{1\text{ qt}}$ and $\frac{1\text{ qt}}{946\text{ mL}}$

g. $\frac{10\text{ dL}}{1\text{ L}}$ and $\frac{1\text{ L}}{10\text{ dL}}$

h. $\frac{10\text{ mm}}{1\text{ cm}}$ and $\frac{1\text{ cm}}{10\text{ mm}}$

◆ Learning Exercise 1.6A

Answers

a. 0.189 L	b. 27 mm	c. 2.5 mL	d. 0.076 g
e. 1.75 m	f. 0.285 L	g. 0.2 g	h. 1500 m

◆ Learning Exercise 1.6B

Answers

a. 46 cm	b. 3.8 L	c. 0.291 qt	d. 0.0029 lb
e. 68 kg	f. 1.9 lb	g. 460 cm	h. 241 g

◆ Learning Exercise 1.6C

Answers

a. 4.7 inches	b. 110 kg	c. 1.9 m
d. 1420 mL	e. 3 tablets	

◆ Learning Exercise 1.7

Answers

a. 1.26 g/mL	b. 1.002	c. 8.4 g/mL	d. 300. g
e. 6.1 mL	f. 3.52	g. 489 g	h. 0.0391 L

Answers to the Practice Test

1. C	**2.** E	**3.** B	**4.** E	**5.** D
6. B	**7.** C	**8.** E	**9.** B	**10.** C
11. D	**12.** D	**13.** B	**14.** B	**15.** E
16. D	**17.** A	**18.** B	**19.** D	**20.** A
21. E	**22.** A	**23.** B	**24.** D	**25.** B
26. D	**27.** C	**28.** E	**29.** C	**30.** A
31. E	**32.** D	**33.** E	**34.** B	**35.** A

Answers and Solutions to Selected Text Problems

1.1 A student in the United States would use pounds, feet, gallons, and °F while a student in France would use kilograms, meters, liters, and °C to measure weight (mass), length, volume, and temperature, respectively.

1.3 **a.** meters (used to measure length) **b.** grams (mass) **c.** milliliters (volume)
d. meters (length) **e.** Celsius degrees (temperature)

1.5 **a.** Move the decimal point left four decimal places to give 5.5×10^4 m
b. 4.8×10^2 g
c. Move the decimal point right six decimal places to give 5×10^{-6} cm
d. 1.4×10^{-4} s
e. 7.2×10^{-3} L

1.7 Measured numbers are obtained using some kind of measuring tool. Exact numbers are numbers obtained by counting or from a definition in the metric or the U.S. measuring system.
a. measured **b.** exact **c.** exact **d.** measured

1.9 **a.** not significant **b.** significant **c.** significant
d. significant **e.** not significant

1.11 **a.** five **b.** two **c.** two **d.** three
e. four **f.** three

1.13 Calculators carry out mathematical computations and display an answer without regard to significant figures. Our task is to round the calculator's answer to the number of significant figures allowed by the precision of the original data.

1.15 **a.** 1.85 **b.** 184 **c.** 0.004 74 (4.74×10^{-3})
d. 8810 (8.81×10^3) **e.** 1.83

1.17 **a.** $45.7 \times 0.034 = 1.6$
b. $0.002\ 78 \times 5 = 0.01$
c. $\frac{34.56}{1.25} = 27.6$
d. $\frac{(0.2465)(25)}{1.78} = 3.5$

1.19 **a.** 45.48 cm + 8.057 cm = 53.54 cm
b. 23.45 g + 104.1 g + 0.025 g = 127.6 g
c. 145.675 mL − 24.2 mL = 121.5 mL
d. 1.08 L − 0.585 L = 0.50 L

1.21 The km/hr markings indicate how many kilometers (how much distance) will be traversed in one hour's time if the speed is held constant. The mph markings indicate the same distance traversed *but measured in miles* during the one hour of travel.

1.23 Because the prefix *kilo* means one thousand times, a *kilo*gram is equal to 1000 grams.

1.25 **a.** mg **b.** dL **c.** km **d.** kg **e.** μL

1.27 **a.** 0.01 **b.** 1000 **c.** 0.001 **d.** 0.1 **e.** 1 000 000

1.29 **a.** 100 cm **b.** 1000 m **c.** 0.001 m **d.** 1000 mL

1.31 **a.** kilogram **b.** milliliter **c.** km **d.** kL

1.33 Because a conversion factor is unchanged when inverted, $\dfrac{1\text{ m}}{100\text{ cm}}$ and $\dfrac{100\text{ cm}}{1\text{ m}}$

1.35 Learning the relationships between the metric prefixes will help you write the following equalities and their resulting conversion factors.

a. 1 m = 100 cm $\quad \dfrac{1\text{ m}}{100\text{ cm}}$ and $\dfrac{100\text{ cm}}{1\text{m}}$

b. 1 g = 1000 mg $\quad \dfrac{1\text{ g}}{1000\text{mg}}$ and $\dfrac{1000\text{ mg}}{1\text{ g}}$

c. 1 L = 1000 mL $\quad \dfrac{1\text{ L}}{1000\text{ mL}}$ and $\dfrac{1000\text{ mL}}{1\text{ L}}$

d. 1 dL = 100 mL $\quad \dfrac{1\text{ dL}}{100\text{ mL}}$ and $\dfrac{100\text{ mL}}{1\text{ dL}}$

1.37 When using a conversion factor you are trying to cancel existing units and arrive at a new (desired) unit. The conversion factor must be properly oriented so that unit cancellation (numerator to denominator) can be accomplished.

1.39 **a.** $175\ \cancel{\text{cm}} \times \dfrac{1\text{ m}}{100\ \cancel{\text{cm}}} = 1.75\text{ m}$

b. $5500\ \cancel{\text{mL}} \times \dfrac{1\text{ L}}{1000\ \cancel{\text{mL}}} = 5.5\text{ L}$

c. $0.0055\ \cancel{\text{kg}} \times \dfrac{1000\text{ g}}{1\ \cancel{\text{kg}}} = 5.5\text{ g}$

1.41 **a.** Unit plan: qt → mL

$$0.500\ \cancel{\text{qt}} \times \frac{946\text{ mL}}{1\ \cancel{\text{qt}}} = 473\text{ mL}$$

b. Unit plan: lb → kg

$$145\ \cancel{\text{lb}} \times \frac{1\text{ kg}}{2.20\ \cancel{\text{lb}}} = 65.9\text{ kg}$$

c. Unit plan: kg → lb body weight → lb fat

$$74\ \cancel{\text{kg}} \times \frac{2.20\ \cancel{\text{lb}}}{1\ \cancel{\text{kg}}} \times \frac{15\text{ lb fat}}{100\ \cancel{\text{lb body weight}}} = 24\text{ lb fat}$$

1.43 **a.** Unit plan: L $\rightarrow$ qt $\rightarrow$ gal

$$250\ \cancel{L} \times \frac{1.06\ \cancel{qt}}{1\ \cancel{L}} \times \frac{1\ gal}{4\ \cancel{qt}} = 66\ gal$$

b. Unit plan: g $\rightarrow$ mg $\rightarrow$ tablet

$$0.024\ \cancel{g} \times \frac{1000\ \cancel{mg}}{1\ \cancel{g}} \times \frac{1\ tablet}{8\ \cancel{mg}} = 3.0\ \text{tablets (add significant zero)}$$

c. Unit plan: lb $\rightarrow$ g $\rightarrow$ kg $\rightarrow$ mg ampicillin

$$34\ \cancel{\text{lb body weight}} \times \frac{454\ \cancel{g}}{1\ \cancel{lb}} \times \frac{1\ \cancel{kg}}{1000\ \cancel{g}} \times \frac{115\ \text{mg ampicillin}}{1\ \cancel{\text{kg body weight}}} = 1.8 \times 10^3\ mg$$

1.45 Density is the mass of a substance divided by its volume. The densities of solids and liquids are usually stated in g/ml or g/cm^3.

$$\text{Density} = \frac{\text{Mass (grams)}}{\text{Volume (mL)}}$$

a. $\frac{24.0\ g}{20.0\ mL} = 1.20\ g/mL$

b. $\frac{1.65\ \cancel{lb}}{170\ mL} \times \frac{454\ g}{1\ \cancel{lb}} = 4.4 g/mL$

c. gem's volume: 34.5 mL total $-$ 20.0 mL water $=$ 14.5 mL

gem's density: $\frac{45.0\ g}{14.5\ mL} = 3.10\ g/mL$

1.47 **a.** $150\ mL \times \frac{1.4\ g}{1\ mL} = 2.1 \times 10^2\ g$

b. Unit plan: L $\rightarrow$ mL $\rightarrow$ g

$$0.500\ \cancel{L} \times \frac{1000\ \cancel{mL}}{1\cancel{L}} \times \frac{1.15 g}{1\cancel{mL}} = 575\ g$$

c. Unit plan: mL $\rightarrow$ g $\rightarrow$ lb $\rightarrow$ oz

$$225\ \cancel{mL} \times \frac{7.8\ \cancel{g}}{1\ \cancel{mL}} \times \frac{1\ \cancel{lb}}{454\ \cancel{g}} \times \frac{16\ oz}{1\ \cancel{lb}} = 62\ oz$$

1.49 **a.** $\frac{1.030\ \cancel{g/mL}}{1.000\ \cancel{g/mL}\ (H_2O)} = 1.030$

b. $\frac{45.0\ g}{40.0\ mL} = \frac{1.13\ \cancel{g/mL}}{1.000\ \cancel{g/mL}\ (H_2O)} = 1.13$

c. 0.85 (sp gr of oil) $\times$ 1.000 g/mL (H_2O density) $=$ 0.85 g/mL density of oil

1.51 This problem requires several conversion factors. Let's take a look first at a possible unit plan. When you write out the unit plan, be sure you know a conversion factor you can use for each step. ft $\rightarrow$ in. $\rightarrow$ cm $\rightarrow$ m $\rightarrow$ min

$$7500\ \cancel{ft} \times \frac{12\ \cancel{in.}}{1\ \cancel{ft}} \times \frac{2.54\ \cancel{cm}}{1\ \cancel{in.}} \times \frac{1\ \cancel{m}}{100\ \cancel{cm}} \times \frac{1\ min}{55.0\ \cancel{m}} = 42\ min$$

1.53 $\frac{1.40\ \cancel{\text{Euro}}}{\cancel{\text{kg}}} \times \frac{1\ \cancel{\text{kg}}}{2.20\ \text{lb}} \times \frac{1.30\ \$}{1\ \cancel{\text{Euro}}} = \frac{0.83\$}{\text{lb}}$

1.55 $4.0\ \cancel{\text{lb}} \times \frac{454\ \cancel{\text{g}}}{1\ \cancel{\text{lb}}} \times \frac{1\ \text{onion}}{115\ \cancel{\text{g}}} = 16\ \text{onions}$

1.57 **a.** $8.0\ \cancel{\text{oz}} \times \frac{6\ \text{crackers}}{0.50\ \cancel{\text{oz}}} = 96\ \text{crackers}$

b. $10\ \cancel{\text{crackers}} \times \frac{1\ \cancel{\text{serving}}}{6\ \cancel{\text{crackers}}} \times \frac{4\ \cancel{\text{g}}\ \text{fat}}{1\ \cancel{\text{serving}}} \times \frac{1\ \cancel{\text{lb}}}{454\ \cancel{\text{g}}} \times \frac{16\ \text{oz}}{1\ \cancel{\text{lb}}} = 0.2\ \text{oz fat}$

c. $50\ \cancel{\text{boxes}} \times \frac{8.0\ \cancel{\text{oz}}}{1\ \cancel{\text{box}}} \times \frac{1\ \cancel{\text{serving}}}{0.50\ \cancel{\text{oz}}} \times \frac{140\ \cancel{\text{mg}}\ \text{sodium}}{1\ \cancel{\text{serving}}} \times \frac{1\ \text{g}}{1000\ \cancel{\text{mg}}} = 110\ \text{g sodium}$

1.59 **b.** $10\ \cancel{\text{days}} \times \frac{4\ \cancel{\text{tablets}}}{1\ \cancel{\text{day}}} \times \frac{250\ \cancel{\text{mg}}\ \text{amoxicillin}}{1\ \cancel{\text{tablet}}} \times \frac{1\ \cancel{\text{g}}}{1000\ \cancel{\text{mg}}} \times \frac{1\ \cancel{\text{lb}}}{454\ \cancel{\text{g}}} \times \frac{16\ \text{oz}}{1\ \cancel{\text{lb}}}$

$= 0.35\ \text{oz amoxicillin}$

1.61 This problem has two units. Convert g to mg, and convert L in the denominator to dL.

$\frac{1.85\ \cancel{\text{g}}}{1\ \cancel{\text{L}}} \times \frac{1000\ \text{mg}}{1\ \cancel{\text{g}}} \times \frac{1\ \cancel{\text{L}}}{10\ \text{dL}} = 185\ \text{mg/dL}$

1.63 The difference between the initial volume of the water and its volume with the lead object will give us the volume of the lead object.

285 mL total − 215 mL water = 70.mL lead

Using the density of lead, we can convert mL to the mass in grams of the lead object.

$7o\ \cancel{\text{mL}} \times \frac{11.3\ \text{g}}{1\ \cancel{\text{mL}}} = 790\ \text{g}$

1.65 Unit plan: L gas → mL gas → g gas → g oil → mL oil → cm^3 oil

$1.00\ \cancel{\text{L gas}} \times \frac{1000\ \cancel{\text{mL gas}}}{1\ \cancel{\text{L gas}}} \times \frac{0.66\ \cancel{\text{g gas}}}{1\ \cancel{\text{mL gas}}} \times \frac{1\ \cancel{\text{g oil}}}{1\ \cancel{\text{g gas}}} \times \frac{1\ \cancel{\text{ml}}\ \text{oil}}{0.92\ \cancel{\text{g oil}}} \times \frac{1\ \text{cm}^3}{1\ \cancel{\text{ml}}} = 720\ \text{cm}^3\ \text{oil}$

1.67 $3.0\ \text{L fat} \times \frac{1000\ \text{mL}}{1\ \text{L}} \times \frac{0.94\ \text{g fat}}{1\ \text{mL fat}} \times \frac{1\ \text{lb}}{454\ \text{g}} = 6.2\text{lb fat}$

1.69 **a.** 1.012 (sp. gr. urine) × 1.000g/mL (H_2O density) = 1.012 g/mL (urine density)

b. 1.022 (sp. gr. urine) × 1.000g/mL (H_2O density) = 1.022 g/mL (urine density)

$5.00\ \cancel{\text{mL urine}} \times \frac{1.022\ \text{g urine}}{1\ \cancel{\text{mL urine}}} = 5.11\ \text{g urine}$

1.71 **a.** The number of legs is a counted number; it is exact.

b. The height is measured with a ruler or tape measure; it is a measured number.

c. The number of chairs is a counted number; it is exact.

d. The area is measured with a ruler or tape measure; it is a measured number.

1.73 **a.** length = 6.96 cm; width = 4.75 cm

b. length = 69.6 mm; width = 47.5 mm

c. There are three significant figures in the length measurement.

d. There are three significant figures in the width measurement.

e. 33.3 cm^2

f. Since there are three significant figures in the width and length measurements, there are three significant figures in the area.

1.75 The volume of the object is 23.1 mL − 18.5 mL = 4.6 mL

The mass is 8.24 g and the density is: $\frac{8.24 \text{ g}}{4.6 \text{ mL}} = 1.8 \text{ g/mL}$

Supplement 2

Answers to the Practice Test

Multiple Choice

1. D

2. C

3. B

4. D

5. D

6. C

7. B

8. C

Fill in the Blanks

1. contrast, resolution

2. better, shorter

3. Nomarski, scanning electron

4. ultrastructure

5. contrast, resolution

Critical Thinking

1. You should always use lowest power (4×). At low magnification you are presented with a larger perceived field of view and smaller specimens which allows you to rapidly scan wide areas of a slide to find what you want to examine more closely. Using a higher power cuts down on the field of view and makes finding specimens very difficult.

Supplement 3

Earth's Surface—Land and Water

Groundwater Flow and Contaminant Transport

The occupants of Houses 1, 2, and 3 wish to drill wells for domestic water supply. Note that the locations of all houses are between Lakes A and B, at different elevations.

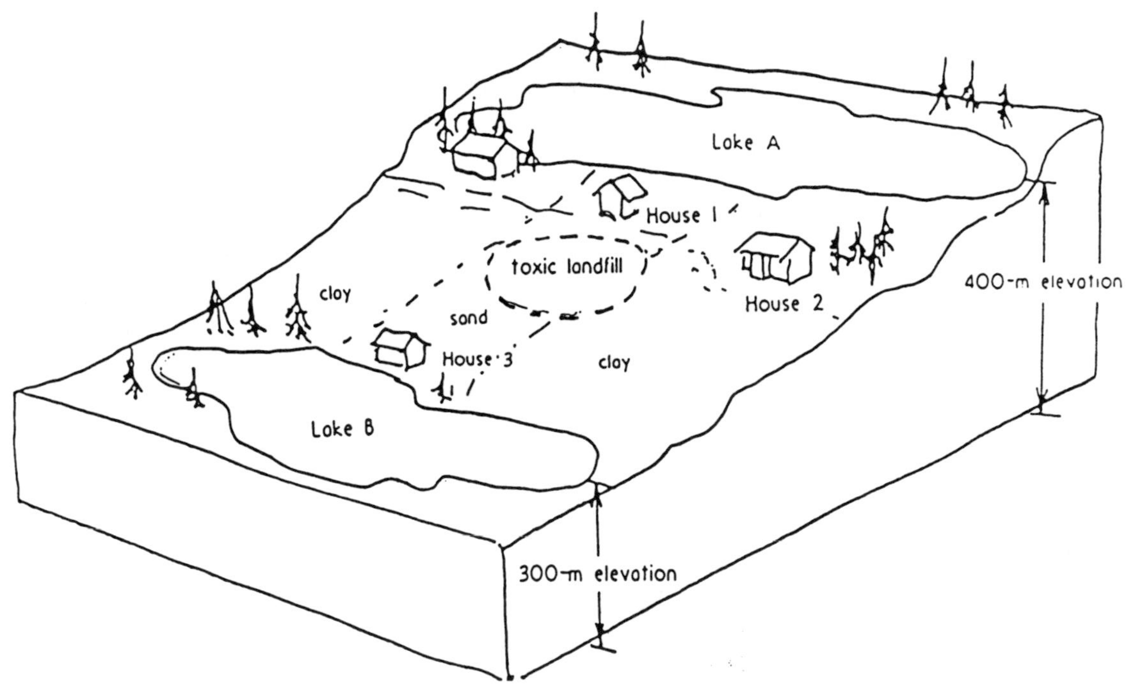

1. Show by sketching dashed lines on the drawing, the likely direction of groundwater flow beneath all the houses.

   SEE DRAWING

2. Which of the wells drilled beside Houses 1, 2, and 3 are likely to yield an abundant water supply?

   WELLS AT HOUSES 1 AND 3 SHOULD YIELD A SUFFICIENT AMOUNT OF WATER BECAUSE SAND IS QUITE PERMEABLE. THE WELL AT HOUSE 2 IS CLAY WHICH HAS A LOW PERMEABILITY AND SO WILL NOT YIELD A SUFFICIENT WATER SUPPLY.

3. Do any of the three need to worry about the toxic landfill contaminating their water supply? Explain.

   HOUSE 2 DOESN'T HAVE A DECENT WATER SUPPLY—NO CONTAMINATION WORRIES. HOUSE 1 IS UPGRADIENT FROM THE LANDFILL SO WILL HAVE NO CONTAMINATION WORRIES UNLESS PUMPING RATE IS HIGH ENOUGH TO DRAW WATER AGAINST THE REGIONAL GRADIENT. HOUSE 3 IS IN BIG TROUBLE.

4. Why don't the homeowners simply take water directly from the lakes?

   SAND ACTS AS A GOOD FILTER FOR BACTERIA AND VIRUSES. ALSO, THE ADDITIONAL RESIDENCE TIME IN GROUNDWATER ALLOWS CHEMICAL REACTIONS TO REMOVE MANY CONTAMINANTS.

Groundwater Flow and Contaminant Transport—continued

5. Suggest a potentially better location for the landfill. Defend your choice.
A BETTER LOCATION WOULD BE IN THE CLAY. CLAY'S LOW PERMEABILITY WOULD HINDER LEACHING OF CONTAMINANTS TO THE GROUNDWATER.

Stream Velocity

Let's explore how the average velocity of streams and rivers can change. The volume of water that flows past a given location over any given length of time depends both on the stream velocity and the cross-sectional area of the stream. We say

$$Q = A \times V$$

where Q is the volumetric flow rate (a measure of the volume passing a point per unit time). Also, A is the cross-sectional area of the stream, and V its average velocity.

Consider the stream shown below, with rectangular cross-sectional areas

$$A = \text{width} \times \text{depth}$$

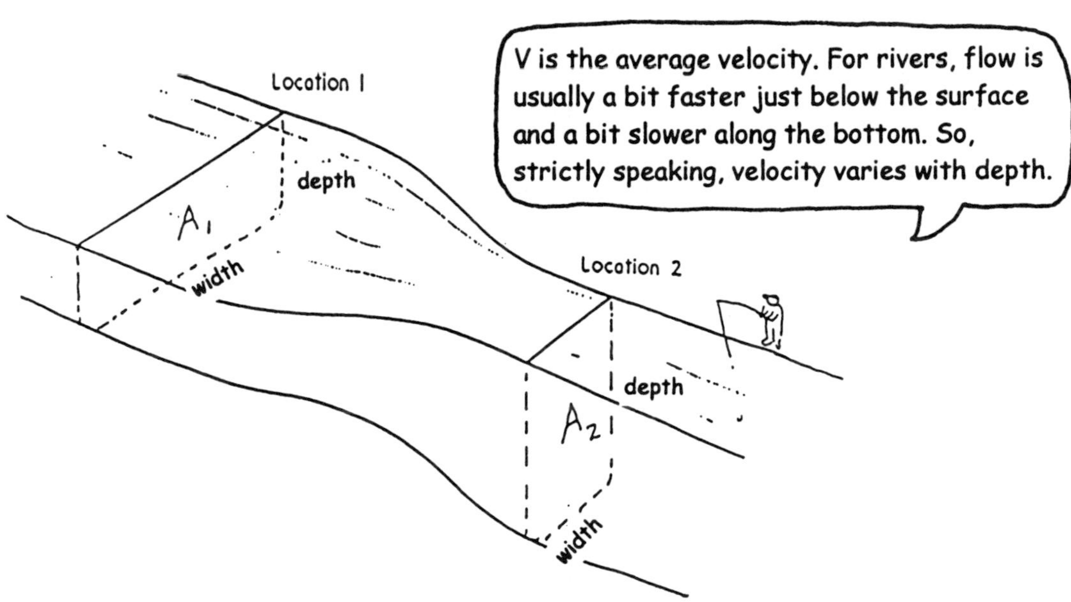
Location 1
depth
A_1
width
V is the average velocity. For rivers, flow is usually a bit faster just below the surface and a bit slower along the bottom. So, strictly speaking, velocity varies with depth.
Location 2
depth
A_2
width

1. The two locations shown have no stream inlets or outlets between them, so Q remains constant. Suppose the cross-sectional areas are also constant ($A_1 = A_2$), with Location 2 deeper but narrower than Location 1. What change, if any, occurs for the stream velocity?
THERE IS NO CHANGE IN AVERAGE VELOCITY

2. If Q remains constant, what happens to stream velocity at Location 2 if A_2 is less than A_1?
AVERAGE VELOCITY INCREASES AT LOCATION 2.

3. If Q remains constant, what happens to stream velocity at Location 2 if A_2 is greater than A_1?
AVERAGE VELOCITY IDECREASES AT LOCATION 2.

4. What happens to stream velocity at Location 2 if area A_2 remains the same, but Q increases (perhaps by an inlet along the way?)
AVERAGE VELOCITY INCREASES AT LOCATION 2.

Stream Velocity—continued

5. What happens to stream velocity at Location 2 if both A_2 and Q increase?

IT DEPENDS. IF Q INCREASES MORE THAN A INCREASES, AVERAGE VELOCITY INCREASES. IF A INCREASES MORE THAN Q INCREASES, AVERAGE VELOCITY DECREASES. IF THEY BOTH INCREASE AT THE SAME PROPORTION, THERE IS NO CHANGE IN AVERAGE VELOCITY.

Answers to Science as a way of Knowing

Ocean Waves

1. They become too tall from the bunching of many waves.
3. Energy.

Ocean Water

1. Only a few elements and compounds are present in abundance.
3. The composition of sea water remains relatively constant.

Groundwater Contamination

1. Sewage, agricultural chemicals such as nitrate fertilizers, and pesticides
3. Gas stations typically store MTBE in underground tanks. If a tank leaks, MTBE can infiltrate to underground and pollute wells.

Supplement 4

Answers to the Practice Test

1. a
2. d
3. b
4. c
5. c
6. b
7. b
8. c
9. a
10. d
11. c
12. a
13. d
14. d
15. c
16. b
17. d
18. a
19. c
20. d
21. h
22. b, i
23. f
24. c
25. i ,g
26. i, k
27. e
28. a
29. d
30. d
31. d
32. b
33. c
34. c
35. c
36. a
37. b
38. c
39. c
40. d
41. b
42. c
43. d
44. a
45. a
46. d
47. b
48. d
49. a
50. a
51. d
52. c
53. b
54. d
55. c
56. d
57. d
58. c
59. c
60. b

Supplement 5

Answers to the Practice Test

Content Quiz

1. red blood cells
2. chromosomes
3. True
4. A
5. False–species
6. False–species
7. True
8. True
9. True
10. True
11. chromatid, telomeres, centromeres, satellite.
12. C
13. centromere
14. histones
15. chromatin
16. heterochromatin, euchromatin
17. B
18. centromeres
19. Metacentric, Submetacenteric, Telocentric. Acrocentric
20. Metacentric
21. Submetacenteric
22. Telocentric
23. Acrocentric
24. C
25. A
26. True
27. True
28. Telomerease
29. B
30. See table below

Term	Its Best Description
Associated proteins ____C.	**A.** Consists of chromatin (a complex of DNA and associated proteins), a centromere, and telomeres.
Centromeres____ D.	**B.** Carries the genetic information (the instructions the cell uses to construct itself, tissue, and the organism of which it is part), and associated proteins.
Telomeres __ E.	**C.** Organize the chromosome physically and regulate the DNA activities.
Chromosome __ A.	**D.** A specialized region along the chromosome to which spindle fibers are attached during cell division.
DNA ___ B	**E.** Involved in the replication and stability of linear DNA molecules.
Klinefelter's syndrome ___ H.	**F.** A species-specific photographic inventory of an individual's (cell's) chromosomes as viewed with light microscope.
Down syndrome ______ G.	**G.** An individual with (Trisomy 21) possesses 3 copies of chromosome 21.
karyotype ___ F.	**H.** A male possesses an extra X chromosome resulting in a genotype of XXY.

31. True

32. True

33. A

34. True

35. Nucleotides

36. Covalent, hydrogen

37. False–Hydrogen

38. False–A-T and C-G

39. True

40. duplicated

41. gametes, gametes

42. Meiosis, homolog

43. True

44. False are responsible?

45. True

46. D

47. D

48. True

49. False–in Mammales, males are XY and females are XX

50. True

51. False–Can

52. True

53. A

54. False–the further

55. True

56. A

57. True

58. True

59. True

60. False–will always change

61. A

62. A

63. A

Supplement 6

Answers to the Practice Test

1. True
2. True
3. True
4. False
5. True
6. True
7. True
8. True
9. True
10. True
11. Reception, Transduction, Response
12. Reception
13. Transduction
14. Response
15. False–causing it to change?
16. True
17. True
18. True
19. True
20. A
21. C
22. Multistep
23. True
24. True
25. A
26. Protein kinase
27. True
28. Protein phosphatases
29. True
30. Cytoplasm, nucleus
31. True
32. *Synthesis*
33. A